THE annual volume of Papers of the Michigan Academy of Science, Arts and Letters is issued under the joint direction of the Council of the Academy and of the Executive Board of the Graduate School of the University of Michigan. The editor for the Academy is Peter Okkelberg; for the University, Eugene S. McCartney.

Previous publications of The Michigan Academy of Science, now known as The Michigan Academy of Science, Arts and Letters, were issued under the title, Annual Report of the Michigan Academy of Science. Twenty-two volumes were published, of which those numbered 1, 21 and 22 are out of print. Copies of the other volumes are still available for distribution and will be sent on exchange so long as the editions last. Applications for copies should be addressed to the Librarian of the University of Michigan.

Annual Reports embracing the proceedings of the Academy will, however, continue to be published. Applications for copies should be addressed to the Librarian of the University of Michigan.

The prices of previous volumes of the Papers and of other University of Michigan publications are listed at the end of this volume.

Volumes may be ordered by addressing the Librarian of the University of Michigan.

MICHIGAN ACADEMY OF SCIENCE ARTS AND LETTERS

VOLUME IX

CONTAINING PAPERS SUBMITTED AT THE ANNUAL MEETING IN 1928

(This volume contains papers in Botany and Forestry only. Volume X will contain papers in Anthropology, Economics and Sociology, Geography, Geology, Language and Literature, Psychology, Sanitary and Medical Science, and Zoölogy.)

PAPERS

OF THE

MICHIGAN ACADEMY OF SCIENCE ARTS AND LETTERS

EDITORS

EUGENE S. McCARTNEY

UNIVERSITY OF MICHIGAN

PETER OKKELBERG

UNIVERSITY OF MICHIGAN

Ann Arbor

UNIVERSITY OF MICHIGAN

1929

Set up and printed,
February, 1929
Published March, 1929

PRINTED IN THE UNITED STATES OF AMERICA

OFFICERS FOR 1928

President

W. B. PILLSBURY
University of Michigan

Vice-President

J. H. HANFORD
University of Michigan

Section Chairmen

ANTHROPOLOGY, W. H. Worrell, University of Michigan

BOTANY, Bradley M. Davis, University of Michigan

ECONOMICS AND SOCIOLOGY, J. V. Van Sickle, University of Michigan

FORESTRY, John C. DeCamp, Michigan State College

GEOGRAPHY, Jerome Thomas, Detroit

GEOLOGY AND MINERALOGY, S. G. Bergquist, Michigan State College

HISTORY AND POLITICAL SCIENCE, Paul Cuncannon, University of Michigan

LANGUAGE AND LITERATURE, Louis I. Bredvold, University of Michigan

MATHEMATICS, A. L. Nelson, College of the City of Detroit

PSYCHOLOGY, C. H. Griffitts, University of Michigan

SANITARY AND MEDICAL SCIENCE, M. H. Soule, University of Michigan

ZOÖLOGY, Carl L. Hubbs, University of Michigan

Secretary

Lee R. Dice, University of Michigan

Treasurer

Robert B. Hall, University of Michigan

Librarian

W. W. Bishop, University of Michigan

Editor

Peter Okkelberg, University of Michigan

DATE OF PUBLICATION
OF VOLUME VIII

February 29, 1928

CONTENTS

BOTANY

FORESTRY

ILLUSTRATIONS

PLATES

FIGURES IN THE TEXT

A SECOND CASE OF SILKLESSNESS IN MAIZE *

ERNEST G. ANDERSON

IN THE summer of 1923 a small culture was grown from selfed seed of a white dent variety of maize, Payne's Dent, obtained from Minnesota. In this culture there were a few plants which were entirely silkless. The silkless character derived from this culture appears to be identical with that described by Jones (1925). Intercrosses have given silkless plants in the first generation showing that the same gene is concerned. The silkless strain described by Jones was derived from a yellow flint variety, Golden Nugget, from Connecticut. The presence of this character in two such widely different varieties of maize is almost certainly due to two independent mutations.

The description given by Jones applies also to the present case. No silks are produced and consequently the ears are completely sterile. The glumes develop larger than in normal ears and stamens are frequently present, especially toward the tip of the ear. There is a strong tendency for the buds in the axils of the husks to develop, giving a branched appearance to the ear shoots. This is most marked on vigorous plants. The tassels are normal and produce an abundance of good pollen.

The gene for silklessness has been shown by Jones to be linked with the *B* factor for plant color. Further data have been obtained on linkage with *B* and with liguleless leaf (*lg*). From crosses of sun red normal (*B Sk*) with dilute sun red silkless

* Paper from the Department of Botany of the University of Michigan, No. 289.

(*b sk*) plants backcrossed with the double recessive, the following plants were obtained:

B Sk	993
B sk	78
b Sk	80
b sk	928
Total	2079

The percentage of recombination is 7.6 ± 0.7, somewhat lower than the percentage reported by Jones from F_2 progenies.

Similar tests were made with liguleless leaf. Here the crosses made were *lg Sk* × *Lg sk*. Backcrosses gave the following progeny:

Lg Sk	187
Lg sk	288
lg Sk	315
lg sk	167
Total	957

The percentage of recombination is 37.0 ± 1.1. As the genes *B* and *lg* usually give about 33 per cent of recombination it is probable that the order is *sk-b-lg*. Two other genes ts_1 (Emerson, 1920) and v_4 (Demerec, 1924) have been located to the left of *B* at somewhat greater distances. A closer determination of the relative order and approximate map distances of the four genes ts_1, v_4, *sk* and *B* must remain for more critical linkage studies.

Table I gives a summary of data obtained on backcrosses of *sk* with the factors *a, c,* and *r* for aleurone color, the *Pl* factor for plant color, and *su,* the gene for sugary endosperm. In all these cases the data conform to the expectation for independent inheritance.

University of Michigan

TABLE 1

MISCELLANEOUS BACKCROSSES INVOLVING SILKLESSNESS

Gene	Total	Recombinations	Percentage of recombination	Deviation from fifty per cent
a	1339	645	48.2	1.8 ± 0.9
c	267	145	54.3	4.3 ± 2.1
r	1298	610	47.0	3.0 ± 0.9
Pl	1399	698	49.9	0.1 ± 0.9
su	354	178	50.3	0.7 ± 1.8

LITERATURE CITED

DEMEREC, M. 1924. Genetic Relations of Five Factor Pairs for Virescent Seedlings in Maize. Cornell Univ. Agric. Exp. Sta. Memoir 84 : 1–38.

EMERSON, R. A. 1920. Heritable Characters of Maize II. Pistillate Flowered Maize Plants. Journ. Hered., 11 : 65–76.

JONES, D. F. 1925. Heritable Characters of Maize XXIII — Silkless. Journ. Hered., 16 : 339–341.

DESCRIPTION OF A MOSAIC PERICARP COLOR IN MAIZE *

ERNEST G. ANDERSON
AND
ADRIAN L. TER LOUW

AMONG variegated pericarp colors in maize, the type best known is the one studied and described by Emerson (1914, 1917). In this type the variegation appears typically as definite red streaks or patches on a white ground color. It may conveniently be considered as an unstable white (colorless), i.e., as a colorless which mutates very readily to colored. The red streaks or patches which appear are uniformly and solidly colored, except for those occurring in the superficial tissues only. When the mutation includes the germ cells, the progeny produced are self-red. Reverse mutations of self-red to white occur, but are relatively rare. The definiteness and constancy of the red streaks have made it possible to use them for studies on mutation frequency (Emerson, 1922; Anderson and Eyster, 1928).

In contrast to the variegated mentioned above, the type which has been called "mosaic" has proved much less definite in the separation of the red and white portions, and consequently less satisfactory for the mutation studies. Mosaic pericarp color has been described by Hayes (1917). A brief description was given by Anderson (1924) in connection with tests for its allelomorphism to the other pericarp colors. Eyster (1925) has since published an extended description. Illustrations are given by both Hayes and Eyster. Mosaic pericarp differs from variegated in that it rarely mutates to solid red. Both darker and lighter mosaics are produced, and extensive colorless areas or whole

* Paper from the Department of Botany of the University of Michigan, No. 290.

ears are often found. When the colored areas are examined, the red, instead of being solid, is usually streaked in appearance. The cobs show comparatively little color. The crown patch at the tip of the grain is usually white.

The type described by Eyster (1924) as orange, better designated as orange variegated, is unlike either of the foregoing types.

MATERIAL

From a sample of maize seed from Cuzco, Peru, there has been derived a type of variegated pericarp color very similar to the mosaic of Hayes, although the crown patches at the tips of the grains appear to be more frequently colored. Perhaps it is identical, but the writers had no material of the mosaic available for careful comparison. This type, like the mosaic of Hayes, behaves as an allelomorph of the red-cob white. Red ears occur rarely if at all as mutations from the mosaic, whereas white or nearly white ears may be very frequent. Changes from mosaic to white are also shown by the presence of large white areas on mosaic ears from mosaic parents (Pl. I, Figs. 1–3). Such freak ears are of frequent occurrence. Smaller white areas are found on practically all ears except the extreme dark types which appear almost like solid reds. Figures 4, 5 and 6, are typical ears. Seed from the colorless areas of such ears as shown in Figures 1, 2 and 3, of Plate I give mostly colorless ears with occasional patches of medium mosaic, together with some ears which are typical mosaic. This shows that the mutational changes occur freely from colorless to mosaic as well as from mosaic to colorless.

An example of the behavior of mosaic pericarp is shown by the progeny of a typical mosaic ear (pedigree No. 4736). The parent plant was a mosaic heterozygous for red-cob white (P^{mo} P^{wr}). It was pollinated by pure white. The grains were sorted into four classes: (1) mosaic; (2) mosaic with a conspicuous part of a grain white; (3) nearly white; and (4) white. The progeny are shown in Table I.

TABLE I

PROGENY OF A HETEROZYGOUS MOSAIC ($P^{mo}P^{wr}$) × WHITE

Description of grain planted	Mosaic ears	Freak ears	Nearly white ears	White ears	Red-cob white ears
Mosaic	64	2	4	2	69
Mosaic, part white	41	4	11	2	40
Nearly white	7	2	3	2	8
White	5	–	–	–	9

The streaked character of the red portions of the mosaic grains is illustrated by the photographs of mosaic grains shown in Plate II, Figures 7–18. The darkest areas do not show any visible streaking, but it is quite prominent in the less dense portions.

Figure 20 is a photomicrograph of mosaic pericarp. It was taken from pericarp softened in water, peeled off and mounted in balsam after dehydration and clearing. The red areas show a fine streaking that is visible only upon magnification. This fine streaking does not appear in many of the darkest stripes but is quite general in the less deeply colored areas.

Figure 19 is a photomicrograph of a cross-section of a mosaic pericarp taken through a Wratten B filter. The marbled appearance of the outer (upper) portion of the pericarp is due to the same streaking that is evident in Figure 19.

INTERPRETATION

Mosaic pericarp is characterized by the streaked nature of the colored portions, the rare occurrence of solid reds, and the frequent occurrence of colorless areas from mosaic and vice versa. This is in marked contrast to the ordinary variegated type which consists of a white ground color with stripes or areas of solid red, and which frequently gives rise to solid red ears and also frequently remains entirely colorless. This variegated may be interpreted as an unstable white which mutates to a relatively stable red. The mosaic type may similarly be interpreted as due to frequent mutations in both directions between an unstable white and an equally unstable red. The instability of the red condition is reflected in the typically much-streaked appearance of the colored areas. The frequent occurrence of sharply delimited white areas indicates that other changes also occur. These appear to be mutations from a less stable to a more stable white. The frequent production of mosaic areas on white ears shows that this change is also a readily reversible one.

There can be but little doubt that these changes which take place in the pericarp are due to changes within a gene. The changes take place in somatic tissue, thus precluding the possibility of any ordinary segregation or recombination. The different altered types of mosaic all behave as allelomorphs of red-cob white. The pericarp series of multiple allelomorphs, including red-cob white, have been shown to belong to one of the established linkage groups, being linked with brachytic culms (*bc*), tassel seed (ts_2), and fine stripe (*f*).

As to the nature of the changes themselves or of the gene which undergoes those changes, nothing is known. Anything which might be said must necessarily be purely speculative. A hypothesis based upon pure speculation would be valuable if it enabled one to calculate reasonably precise predictions which could be put to a reasonably rigid test. The speculations concerning pericarp color which have recently appeared in publication (Eyster, 1924, 1925) are not of this nature. For the present it would seem preferable to put our attention on the accumulation of more information concerning highly unstable genes and the characters they give rise to, rather than on ill-defined or premature interpretations. The work of Demerec (1926 a, 1926 b, 1927) on highly mutable genes of *Drosophila virilis* is giving valuable new information which will probably prove to be the safest ground on which to base interpretations. It is hoped that the cases of pericarp variegation will also furnish valuable information.

University of Michigan

FIGS. 1–6. M

I

ears of maize

PLATE II

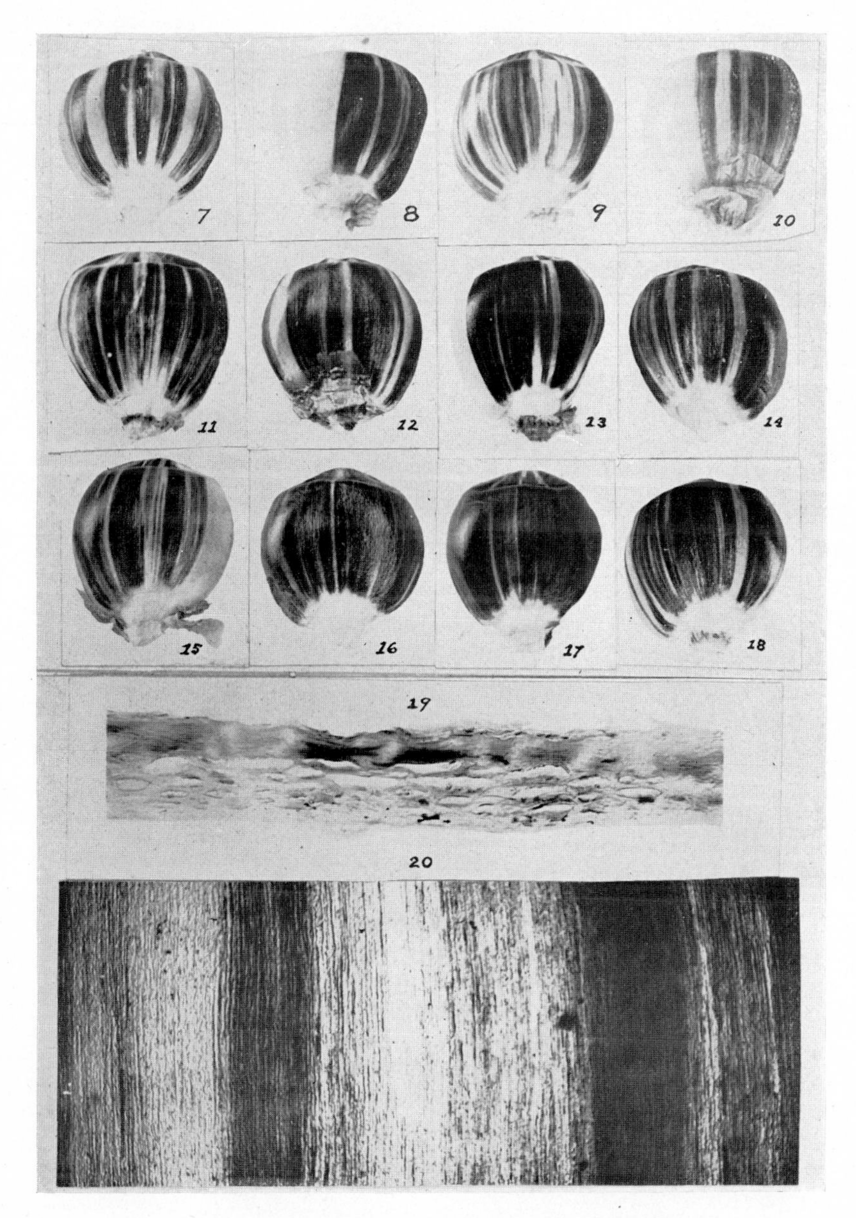

FIGS. 7–18. Typical grains showing mosaic pericarp color
FIG. 19. Photomicrograph of a cross-section of mosaic pericarp
FIG. 20. Photomicrograph of mosaic pericarp by transmitted light

LITERATURE CITED

ANDERSON, E. G. 1924. Pericarp Studies in Maize. II. The Allelomorphism of a Series of Factors for Pericarp Colors. Genetics, 9 : 442–453.

ANDERSON, E. G., AND EYSTER, W. H. 1928. Pericarp Studies in Maize. III. The Frequency of Mutation in Variegated Maize Pericarp. Genetics, 13 : 111–120.

DEMEREC, M. 1926 a. Reddish — a Frequently "Mutating" Character in *Drosophila virilis*. Proc. Nat. Acad. Sci., 12 : 11–16.

—— 1926 b. Miniature-alpha — a Second Frequently Mutating Character in *Drosophila virilis*. Proc. Nat. Acad. Sci., 12 : 687–690.

—— 1927. The Behavior of Mutable Genes (abstract). Zeit. f. ind. Abst. Vererb., 46 : 13.

EMERSON, R. A. 1914. Inheritance of a Somatic Variation in Variegated Ears of Maize. Amer. Nat., 48 : 87–115.

—— 1917. Genetical Studies on Variegated Pericarp in Maize. Genetics, 2 : 1–35.

—— 1922. The Nature of Bud Variations as Indicated by Their Mode of Inheritance. Amer. Nat., 56 : 64–79.

EYSTER, W. H. 1924. A Genetic Analysis of Variegation. Genetics, 9 : 372–404.

—— 1925. Mosaic Pericarp in Maize. Genetics, 10 : 179–196.

HAYES, H. K. 1917. Inheritance of a Mosaic Pericarp Pattern Color of Maize. Genetics, 2 : 260–281.

FOSSILS OF THE CARBONIFEROUS COAL PEBBLES OF THE GLACIAL DRIFT AT ANN ARBOR *

HARLEY HARRIS BARTLETT

THE campus of the University of Michigan is situated on an outwash apron that borders the outer ridge of the Defiance moraine of the Erie-Huron ice lobe. According to Leverett [1] this apron was probably laid down in a lake that bordered the ice lobe from the site of Ann Arbor southwestward to Raisin River, in Bridgewater Township. The elevation of the surface of the lake may have been a little below 875 feet. It was determined by the altitude of the nearest available outlet, near Tecumseh. Back of the outwash basin is a depression or fosse containing several basins, one of which is the " cat hole " just north of the College of Dentistry. This fosse marks the position of the ice border while the lake at the front of the ice was being filled in to a depth of about forty feet to form the outwash plain. The campus is near the edge of the outwash, Angell Hall and the new Physical Laboratory being less than a quarter of a mile from the " cat hole."

The structure of the outwash plain was well shown in the excavations for the two new buildings just mentioned. The coarsest and least assorted bed, containing all grades of material from large boulders to clay, was at the top. It was about six feet deep. Underneath it were cross-bedded deposits of fine,

* Paper from the Department of Botany of the University of Michigan, No. 252. (Read at the 28th Annual Meeting of the Academy, in 1923.)

[1] Russell, I. C., and Leverett, Frank. *Description of the Ann Arbor Quadrangle*. Geol. Atlas U. S., Folio (reprint) No. 155. 1915. (Glacial geology by Leverett.)

washed gravels and sands, in which the material was well sorted, and varied from the finest whitish sand to gravel in which the larger pebbles of crystalline rocks might average half a centimeter to several centimeters in diameter. The lower beds, of washed and sorted material, were sharply set off from the brownish or yellow mixed stratum above them. (See Plate III.)

In the lower beds, conspicuous because of both their size and color, were the coal pebbles which form the subject of this paper. They were first found in the excavation for Angell Hall, and were then looked for and found in abundance at the site of the new Physical Laboratory and in a deep excavation for a heat conduit east of the College of Dentistry.

They were so soft that they were at first thought to be lignite or compact peat, quite like the Lignit-Gerölle of the German Diluvium, figured by Potonié.[2] Some of the first ones collected could readily be moulded into a plastic mass between the fingers, and the writer's first supposition that they were peat, consolidated by pressure and then water worn, was picked up by reporters and published in the daily press. Mr. Leverett's uncanny sagacity in all matters pertaining to the glacial deposits led him to view them as Carboniferous coal from the start, and his diagnosis was shortly confirmed by botanical study, with the use of the maceration method.

The writer has lately had occasion to search through the old accession books of the Museum of the University of Michigan, and was interested to find that coal pebbles from the drift at Ann Arbor were known to Professor Winchell over fifty years ago. Among others were " four specimens of coal obtained from a cistern dug at the corner of the University Campus, and presented by Dr. E. W. Hilgard," May 16, 1874 (accession 579), and " a specimen of coal pebbles obtained from a cistern dug at northwest corner of the University Campus, and presented by Eugene G. M. Hilgard " (accession 581).

That the coal pebbles are more widely distributed has been

[2] Potonié, Henry, *Die Entstehung der Steinkohle und der Kaustobiolithe überhaupt.* 6 Aufl., Berlin, 1920. (See Fig. 49, p. 141.)

shown by Professor W. H. Hobbs, who has recently found them in a gravel pit near Huron Hills, two miles west of Ann Arbor. Material from this locality has not yet been examined, but is doubtless similar to that from the University Campus.

Since the ice planed off the exposed deposits of the Carboniferous throughout the entire Michigan coal field it is of course not at all surprising that coal fragments are found in the drift. It has seemed difficult of explanation to the writer, however, that so much coal should occur east of the supposed easternmost limit of the coal basin, in view of the fact that the material of the drift is considered to have come from the eastward. The literature seems to throw no light upon the precise origin of any of the coal of the drift. Without citing localities, Lane[3] says (p. 8): "The fragments of coal often found in the gravel and till . . . are especially common in Michigan, in the sands and gravels. . . ." Botanical analysis of the coal pebbles of the drift, and a systematic examination of the various beds of Michigan coal to determine the origin of the pebbles, might give data of value in the interpretation of glacial features.

The coal pebbles examined varied in size from a pea to a hen's egg, and were generally flattened, since erosion had taken place much more rapidly in the plane of the bedding than across the bedding. Their occurrence with much finer materials is explained by their low specific gravity, which enabled them to be carried by weak currents into deep water, where they were deposited with the sands and fine gravels. In appearance (see Plate VI) they closely resembled the Lignit-Gerölle figured by Potonié[2] from the German Diluvium. Some were so soft that they could be crushed into a peat-like mass between the fingers. Others were firmer, but could be cut with a knife like fresh lignite. They split readily into thin flat layers in the bedding planes, especially when beginning to dry. Shrinkage was great during drying, and the material fell into small fragments, which broke across with the lustrous fracture of jet. The color of a cut sur-

[3] Lane, A. C., *Coal of Michigan, Its Mode of Occurrence and Quality.* Geol. Surv. Mich., Vol. VIII, Part II. Lansing, 1902.

face of the fresh material was dull brown or black, not lustrous. The pebbles could be preserved only in a moist condition. They appear to keep indefinitely if immersed in water. If buried in moist sand and allowed to dry very slowly, they undergo a disintegration resembling the air-slaking of lime, and are reduced to an impalpable black powder.

The moisture content of the pebbles was determined in four small pebbles, and in one composite sample consisting of pieces of five pebbles. The results showed 48.5 per cent water in a soft pebble; 36.1 per cent, 36.6 per cent, and 37.9 per cent water in three firm pebbles; 37.6 per cent water in the composite sample. Moore [4] gives the water content of lignite from various parts of the world as 0.75 to 43.0 per cent, (average 14.4 per cent); of subbituminous coals from the United States as 1.9 to 40.6 per cent; of bituminous coals from various countries as 0.04 to 34.3 per cent (average 2.5 per cent); of bituminous coals from the United States as 2.0 to 10.0 per cent. It is obvious from these figures that the drift coal contains too much water to be classified as typical bituminous coal. It seems to conform better with the lignites, but even in this category it would be looked upon as a relatively unconsolidated member of the group. One must of course take into consideration the possibility that the long weathering to which the drift lignites have been subjected may have altered them. Centuries of soaking under relatively slight pressure might possibly produce in a soft coal the same degree of softening and swelling that may be attained in a few days by appropriate treatment with alkaline solutions, as, for example, in the procedure used by Jeffrey [5] in the preparation of coals for microtome sectioning. It seems most likely, however, that the coal of the drift is a true lignite from some of the soft, upper strata of the Carboniferous.

[4] Moore, Elwood S., *Coal, Its Properties, Analysis, Classification, Geology, Extraction, Uses, and Distribution.* New York, 1922. (See pp. 84–89.)

[5] Jeffrey, E. C., "The Nature of Some Supposed Algal Coals." *Proc. Amer. Acad. Arts and Sci.*, 46 : 273–290. 1910.

Moore [6] states that there are many examples on record of seams of Carboniferous coal that are still in the lignitic condition. He cites particularly the occurrence in Western Australia of a small area in the Permo-Carboniferous coal measures which was preserved from intense pressure by faulting, and has remained brown coal, although all other Australian coal of the same age is bituminous or anthracite. With regard to the Michigan coals, which are all Carboniferous, Smith [7] says: "According to analyses, the Verne coals appear to be related to the lignite coals. Probably they were never subjected to deep burial, so still resemble the woody end of the coal family." The full series of coal seams in the Michigan field, as recognized by Smith, following Lane,[8] is as follows in order from below upward: Bangor Coal, Bangor Rider, Lower Coal, Lower Rider, Saginaw Coal, Middle Rider, Lower Verne Coal, Lower Verne Rider, Upper Verne Coal, Upper Rider, Salzburg Coal, Salzburg (?) Rider, Unionville Coal (?), Reese Coal (?). Of the higher coals he says: "The Salzburg Coal and its rider are very often removed by erosion. It is only locally that the bed-rock surface is high enough to contain these horizons. . . . The Reese and Unionville coal seams are little represented in drillings. Lying so high in the coal measures, erosion would have removed them in large part if they really ever existed."

No precise correlation of the Michigan coals with those of other regions has been made. David White (quoted by Lane [8]) examined the scanty available plant fossils from the Michigan coal measures and reported that they indicated a very low place in the coal measures. He wrote: "From the characters of the little flora I conclude that it can hardly be later than the Lower Kanawha in West Virginia, of the Brookville coal in Ohio and Pennsylvania. In fact, notwithstanding the small number of species, I am disposed to regard the plants from the Standard

[6] Moore, Elwood S., *op. cit.*, p. 163.

[7] Smith, R. A., "Michigan Coal." Mich. Geol. and Biol. Survey, Publication 8 : 257–303. Lansing, 1912. (See pp. 264–266 and 278.)

[8] Lane, A. C., *op. cit.*

Mine (Saginaw) as Pre-Allegheny, or at least older than the Brookville coal. On the other hand, they are not older than the Sharon coal. . . . Although the material is very fragmentary and the species are few, they indicate for the coals, at whose horizons they occur, a very low place in the coal measures; probably in the Sharon or Mercer groups for the nodules, while the Standard fossils seem to belong below the Homewood sandstone."

The precise origin of the coal pebbles of the drift at Ann Arbor must remain for the present an unsolved problem. The present edge of the Michigan coal basin is roughly fifteen or twenty miles to the westward of Ann Arbor, and the material composing the drift supposedly came from the eastward. If the coal pebbles were derived not from consolidated bituminous coal, but from the upper, lignitic deposits of the Carboniferous, it is unlikely that the material could have been transported far. It may have come, prior to the last glaciation, from west of Ann Arbor, in which case it is present in the deposits of the last glacial period as reworked material, or it may have been derived from an outlying lobe or isolated basin of superficial Carboniferous strata nearer Ann Arbor, perhaps entirely demolished by glacial erosion, and now represented only by pebbles in the drift.

The fossils recovered from the pebbles threw no light upon the matter of origin, for our knowledge of the characteristic floras of different coals is still too slight to enable a coal to be identified by the plant remains in it. As a result of the admirable researches of Jeffrey,[9] White and Thiessen,[10] Thiessen,[11] and Thiessen and Voorhees,[12] progress has recently been made in the study of coal which may result, before many years, in paleobotanical

[9] Jeffrey, Edward C., "On the Composition and Qualities of Coal." *Economic Geology,* 9 : 730–742. 1914.

[10] White, David, and Thiessen, Reinhardt, *The Origin of Coal.* U. S. Bureau of Mines, Bull. 38. Washington, 1913.

[11] Thiessen, Reinhardt, *Structure in Paleozoic Bituminous Coals.* U. S. Bureau of Mines, Bull. 117. Washington, 1920.

[12] Thiessen, R., and Voorhees, Anson W., *A Microscopic Study of the Freeport Coal Bed, Pennsylvania.* Carnegie Institute of Technology, Bull. 2. Pittsburgh, 1922.

criteria for determining the age of such samples as these drift pebbles. Until the plant constituents of the various Michigan coal seams are examined, further speculation as to the origin of the drift coal can hardly prove profitable.

THE MACERATION OF COAL

A scientifically conducted coal maceration is entirely comparable in principle with the determination of humus in soil. That portion of humus which is combined with calcium, magnesium, and similar elements is not directly soluble in sodium or ammonium hydroxide. The complex organic acids must first be liberated by treating the soil with acid. Then a dilute alkaline hydroxide will dissolve out the humus, leaving in the soil undecomposed fragments of plants that are quite comparable with the structural fragments left after a coal maceration.

On account of the remarkable softness of the drift coal, it was readily disintegrated, by the maceration method, for botanical examination. Some of the pebbles consisted practically entirely of cuticles of leaves. Such pebbles yielded relatively little soluble material when macerated, but preserved their shape and became flexible so that they could be bent double. After becoming flexible they could be shaken with water and a vast number of cuticles isolated. The cuticles from such pebbles, however, were far less well preserved than occasional cuticles of similar nature found in pebbles of more mixed composition. The pure leaf coals were apparently laid down under such conditions that decomposition had left little of the leaf but the cuticle by the time that deep enough burial took place to halt decay. The pure leaf coal appears to have been laid down on the very surface of the swamp where aërobic decomposition was active. Subsequently burial took place and decomposition was retarded. Finely laminated leaf coals are of course well known, and are referred to in the standard works on coal. (From a botanical standpoint they were studied by Reinsch, who did much of his work on the Blätterkohle of Central Russia.)

Other pebbles contained more structureless matrix derived from wood, leaf parenchyma, etc., and these gave better fossils. Successive treatment with dilute acid and alkali resulted in the complete solution and removal of the structureless material, leaving a residue of spores, cuticles, a few carbonized particles showing woody structure, and vestiges of siliceous structures interpreted as of Calamite origin. The spores included both microspores and megaspores of Pteridophyta and less distinctive types that might pass for pollen grains. The cuticles were in part of Lepidodendron, and in part unidentified as to origin. The aspect of the material was typically Carboniferous.

Actual charcoal, the so-called mother of coal, hardly occurred at all in most of the pebbles. A few fragments were found which give very strongly the appearance of having been charred before deposition in the swamp floor where the original Carboniferous peat was deposited. It is the writer's very decided opinion that all true charcoal which can be isolated from bituminous coal resulted from forest fires contemporary with the deposition of the beds. Some of the pebbles contained material that was obviously derived from wood, but it dissolved out completely during the maceration of the material. Portions of the coal derived from wood had undergone very great compression. Fragments of charcoal, on the contrary, were of course totally insoluble, and relatively little compressed or distorted by pressure in comparison with the coal derived from wood. Some coals, as, for example, the coal mined at Midland, Michigan, contain a very large component of actual charcoal, almost pure carbon, which can be isolated in fragments and fairly large chunks by dissolving away the other constituents of the coal. Except for charcoal from fires, peat contains no elemental carbon in any form, but only organic compounds that can be dissolved without very drastic chemical treatment. Exactly the same is true of the lignitic coal composing these pebbles in the drift. They consisted almost entirely of material that was soluble in alkali after removal of the ash constituents by acid. The more highly decomposed and structureless portion of soft coal is a mixture of calcium, magnesium, and iron salts of organic acids. These salts are not soluble in water. If they are decomposed by leaching with dilute acid, the acids alone are left, themselves insoluble in water and therefore retaining the structure of untreated coal. The salts of sodium, potassium, and ammonium are soluble in water, and the acid-treated coal therefore dissolves readily in a weak alkaline solution. The portion not dissolved consists (1) of mineral inclusions, such as sand, (2) charcoal, and (3) organic structures which have not been greatly modified, chemically, during the process of coal formation, such as certain spore exines and cuticles.

If we find fragments of charcoal in soil we may be very sure that charring took place by fire or heat, and not by any slow process of decomposition in the soil. We may be equally sure that fragments of charcoal, little consolidated and with well-preserved structure, if found in coal, were likewise originally deposited as charcoal, and not as wood. In holding this view the writer is heartily in accord with Jeffrey, who, commenting upon a Cretaceous coal with wood structure preserved, says: "In all such cases the wood was partially or completely transformed into charcoal before it was incorporated into the accumulation, later transformed into coal. Carbonized wood is in fact the only material derived from the grosser parts of plant bodies which retains its structure in coal. It is generally designated mineral charcoal or mother of coal, and may be present in all categories of coal, from cannels to anthracites." Thiessen has been broader in his definition of mother of coal, including material derived from highly resinous woods which have disintegrated completely, as far as the carbohydrate constituents are concerned, but have left a vestige of structure represented in the undecomposed resin content of the wood.

THE MEGASPORES REFERRED TO TRILETES

Without including dubious specimens which might have been too badly decomposed before burial to display true specific distinctions, the material included three elaborately appendaged types of megaspores which are here described under the convenient inclusive name Triletes. (See the following article, entitled " The Genus Triletes, Reinsch.") These spores probably belong to Lepidodendreae.

Triletes superbus, sp. nov. Body of exine rounded-subtriangular, 1.7 to 2.3 mm. in diameter, the mean being near 2.25 mm.; triradiate clefts extending over half the distance to the periphery; body invested with an indument of cylindriform processes 0.04 to 0.07 mm. long and roughly 0.015 mm. in diameter, blunt or rounded at the apex; equatorial wing often more than 0.8 mm. broad on the radii of the triradiate fissures, and about 0.6 mm. in between, making the total diameter of the spore 3.1 to 3.7 mm.; inner portion or sometimes the whole width of the wing radiately convolute, or the outer portion consisting of more or less completely anastomosed rami extending outward from the convolutions; periphery of wing discontinuous or continuous by the anastomosis of terminal ramuli. — Ann Arbor, Michigan; drift coal. Plates VII and VIII. This spore type was recovered more frequently than any other. When in the finest state of preservation it is indeed a remarkable structure to isolate from coal. Some of the specimens suffered from decay before they were deeply enough buried for perfect preservation, and it is therefore necessary to have considerable material in order to find the short club-like processes with which the body of the spore is invested, and which are quite as interesting and characteristic as the more conspicuous broad equatorial flange. As the specimens are isolated from the coal there is so great a contrast between the very dark mass of the central body and the thin appendage that it was difficult to get photographs showing proper detail in both parts. In Plate VII, Figure 1, the appendage is brought out at the expense of the central body. In Plate VIII, Figure 1, the short cylindriform processes of the body may be made out, but the negative is greatly overexposed for the wing-like appendage, which is nearly lost in the print. The wing was probably an organ which insured the dispersal of the megaspores by wind, doubtless after the triradiate fissures had opened and fertilization had taken place. The Ann Arbor drift coal contains a microspore of similar structure which one is tempted to associate with *Triletes superbus*. The latter is so named because it is unsurpassed in size and beauty of form among all the spores that have been described from coal.

Triletes rotatus, sp. nov. Body of exine practically round, ranging from 0.70 to 0.75 mm. in diameter; triradiate clefts reaching two thirds of the distance to the equatorial appendage; appendage consisting of about fifty long slender sinuate widely spaced processes branched toward the apex and fusing into a marginal rim, the whole spore with the equatorial appendage resembling a wheel with hub, spokes and rim; or processes of the appendage ctenate at apex, either anastomosing or not; average greatest diameter of spore with equatorial appendage 1.7 mm. — Ann Arbor, Michigan; drift coal. Plates IX–XII. A rare and very beautiful type, perhaps actually not as rare as seldom isolated in good condition. A considerable number of spore bodies were recovered which were of the right size to be *T. rotatus,* but lacked the equatorial appendage.

Triletes mamillarius, sp. nov. Roughly globose, with a tendency to be irregular, but not angular; greatest dimension varying from 1.4 to 2.1 mm., mean about 1.5 mm.; equatorial appendage none; triradiate clefts with somewhat thickened margins, short, extending a third to a half of the distance to the periphery; exine covered with mamilliform papillae, the latter hemispheric or taller than broad with the narrowed apical portion generally laterally deflected. — Ann Arbor, Michigan; drift coal. Plates XIII–XVI. Intermediate in abundance between the frequent *T. superbus* and the rare *T. rotatus*. *T. mamillarius* is an extremely characteristic type, and one that would appear from Reinsch's figures to have close relatives in European coals. The supposed genus of parasites named Rhizostaemis by Reinsch (*Micropaleophytologia,* Vol. 2, p. 15) seems to have been based upon just such tubercles as those which invest the exine of *Triletes mamillarius.*

CUTICLES OF LEPIDODENDRON

Hardly less interesting than the spores are the cuticles found in the drift coal, since they give an opportunity to study some details of the superficial anatomy of Lepidodendron that appear not to have been described. The material doubtless includes a number of species. About the coarser kinds, which could not, of course, be adequately represented in a small pebble, it is impossible to say much until additional supplies of coal come to hand. Several smaller sorts, however, are fairly well represented by specimens from the pebbles.

When broken-off branches of Lepidodendron were buried in swamp deposits, the entire structure was transformed into humus except the interareolar cuticle, often very narrow. The stems were pressed practically flat, consequently when a perfect cuticle is recovered from coal by maceration it may be opened out into a tubular net. The open center of the areoles represents the absciss layer of the leaf scar, and the net-work the original cuticle of the stem. Nothing whatever remains of the fibrovascular tissues or the cortex. The interesting specimens represent the few, relatively speaking, which were buried before the stems were subjected to subaërial decay.

Such cuticles are thickest at the center of the ridge between areoles, and are there generally very dark and well preserved. Toward the leaf scar (represented by the opening of the areole) they become thinner, and if well preserved show clearly that the areolar region contained many specialized inflated cells which stood like little domes above the general surface. The function of these, apparently, was to rupture and produce openings into the subepidermal intercellular spaces. The specialized cells frequently had one or more peculiar cuticular outgrowths (of a dark brown color in the recovered cuticles), which for want of a better name may be called cuticular crests. Such a crest may be likened in shape and attachment to a low dorsal fin of a fish, or the keel of a boat. It is an erect plate, not always straight, several times longer than high, adnate by one of its edges, often longitudinally fimbriate or ctenate at the ends, but showing no cellular structure, however large it may be, and therefore apparently a purely cuticular structure. In size it may be so small that several crests occur on a single cell as in the case of the areolar dome cells, or thirty times as long as a single cell. The small ones are so low and rigid that they are seldom seen forced over onto their sides, and without comparison with larger ones would not be recognized for what they are, since they appear on cursory examination as thickenings or wrinkles of cuticle. In general the largest crests, those which are large enough to have been pushed over onto their sides, are found on the thickest cuticle, near the ridge between areoles.

The plates of Lepidodendron cuticles are chosen to illustrate the structural details mentioned, without, for the present, attempting to differentiate the several species, of which there appear to be at least five in the material.

MICROSPORANGIA OF PROBABLE AFFINITY TO LEPIDODENDRON

Many macerations yield very delicate cuticles representing the remains of branches about a millimeter or two in diameter with regularly arranged areoles which resemble those of Lepidodendron, but are more frequently heart-shaped and more distant from one another than in vegetative Lepidodendron.

They do not show any trace of silicification of the cuticle and are, therefore, more like Lepidodendron than Calamites. The state of preservation of the specimens in hand is not altogether satisfactory, but there is no remaining evidence that the areoles represent leaf scars. On the contrary, every specimen contains, tightly adhering to the inner surface of the cuticle, numerous microspores, varying from rounded to subtriangular in outline, with a hyaline margin and darker center. The spores cannot be made out with certainty to have triradiate dehiscence. Similar spores in lenticular masses are found in the coal, each mass representing the content of a whole microsporangium, but too large to belong to the very delicate sporangial branches under consideration, and not yet found associated with any remains of the sporangia by which they were produced. They may represent microsporangia of coarser species than those yielding the delicate fossils under consideration. Although the heart-shaped or oval areolar openings of the slender branches are probably the same as the areoles of the stem of Lepidodendron, namely, leaf scars, the invariable occurrence of microspores in the structure leads to the belief that they also represent openings into cavities in which microsporangia were produced. The areole of Lepidodendron represents more than a leaf scar, of course. The writer suggests that at fertile tips of branches the ligular cavity may in some types of Lepidodendron contain the microsporangium. Although the fossils are distinctly problematic, it seems not unlikely that some of the delicate species of Lepidodendron bore microsporangial branches on which the foliar structures were either much reduced or else quickly caducous, and in which the ligular cavities contained microsporangia. The fact that other types of microsporangia are known for Lepidodendron probably merely demonstrates the heterogeneity of the group. It is greatly hoped that more and better material of these problematic structures may come to light. The writer's suggestion, of course, emphasizes the affinity of Lepidodendron with Isoetes.

MISCELLANEOUS FOSSILS

Numerous fairly well-preserved cuticles have been isolated which are too miscellaneous and uncertain in affinity to make it worth while to discuss them yet. Numerous microscopic pellicles of silica, in shapes suggesting rhizopod shells, are now considered to be the siliceous remains of specialized epidermal cells of Calamites. There are likewise structures with most interesting perforations which are possibly of animal origin. The consideration of much material which now seems hopelessly miscellaneous must be deferred until further accumulations shall have thrown more light upon it.

SUMMARY

The water-worn coal pebbles from the glacial deposits at Ann Arbor, although resembling lignite in softness and high water content, are actually Carboniferous. The coal is almost certainly of local origin. Too soft to have been transported far, it is nevertheless found to the eastward of the supposed edge of the Michigan coal basin.

On account of its extremely soft lignitic nature the drift coal was easily macerated, and yielded three characteristic and beautifully preserved megaspore exines (probably belonging to Lepidodendron), which are described as *Triletes superbus, T. rotatus,* and *T. mamillarius.*

Other fossils include perhaps five species of Lepidodendron, represented by cuticles. These have the surface features in excellent preservation, and show that the epidermis of Lepidodendron had curious cuticular crests which are characteristic and will furnish diagnostic points in discriminating the species. The areolar cuticle shows that there were in this region specialized cells which probably broke down and made openings from the outside to the cortical intercellular air spaces.

Delicate cuticles of branches with areoles arranged as in Lepidodendron may represent fertile microsporangial branch tips of Lepidodendron. They contain numerous microspores, which could not easily have got within the cuticle unless the microsporangia were produced in ligular cavities.

Other fossils of obscure affinity include numerous miscellaneous objects, such as siliceous structures that may represent specialized epidermal cells of Calamites.

University of Michigan

DESCRIPTION OF PLATES

PLATE III

FIG. 1. Vertical section at northeast corner of excavation for Angell Hall, looking east. (The northwest corner of the old building, Mason Hall, shows at the upper right.) Above, coarse, loamy, almost unstratified, brown till containing almost no coal pebbles. Below, more uniform-textured, light-colored washed sands and gravels, variously stratified and cross-bedded, containing numerous coal pebbles. Fig. 2. A few feet from the locality shown in Fig. 1, where a relatively coarse layer, indicated by arrows, consists largely of coal pebbles and smaller fragments of coal.

PLATE IV

Masses of gravel (natural size) from the black stratum shown in Plate III, Fig. 2. FIG. 1 shows six coal pebbles of considerable size. FIG. 2 shows numerous very small pebbles and broken fragments of coal, making up about 25 per cent of the sample, by volume.

PLATE V

At the west side of the same excavation; the coal pebbles here indicated (by arrows) are some of those shown natural size in Plate VI.

PLATE VI

Coal pebbles, from the locality shown in Plate V, natural size. They are all greatly flattened in the plane of the bedding.

PLATE VII

Triletes superbus, sp. nov. Fig. 1, a large specimen with equatorial wing and cylindriform indument in perfect preservation. FIG. 2, a portion of the margin of the wing showing fenestration due to anastomosis of complicated convolutions and branches.

PLATE VIII

Triletes superbus, sp. nov. Fig. 1, a perfect specimen, especially as regards the indument of the central body. FIG. 2, a specimen with narrower and more fenestrated wing.

PLATE IX

Triletes rotatus, sp. nov. Six spores at the same magnification, exposed particularly for the rotate appendage, with loss of detail in the central body.

PLATE X

Triletes rotatus, sp. nov. Fig. 1 shows the usual condition in which the rami of the appendage all fuse into a continuous margin. Fig. 2 shows rami with ctenate ramuli at the apex, in part not anastomosed into a continuous rim. Both figures show the triradiate clefts perfectly.

PLATE XI

Triletes rotatus, sp. nov. Detail of the margin of the appendage of the spore shown in Plate X, Fig. 1.

PLATE XII

Triletes rotatus, sp. nov. Detail of the branches of the equatorial appendage of the spore shown in Plate X, Fig. 2.

PLATE XIII

Triletes mamillarius, sp. nov. Two of the most perfect megaspores, showing investiture with mamilliform tubercles, and the short triradial clefts.

PLATE XIV

Triletes mamillarius, sp. nov. Four spores showing the range of variation in shape and size. The ones in upper left-hand corner and lower right show particularly well the thickened rim of the triradiate clefts. (Both are imperfect specimens viewed from inside the exine.)

PLATE XV

Triletes mamillarius, sp. nov. Tubercles in surface and lateral view, showing the deflection of apical portion.

PLATE XVI

Lepidodendron cuticle. In this species the stem is about 2 cm. in diameter and the areoles are 4 mm. long. It is photographed as the cuticles are usually found, i.e., double, — a cylindrical net pressed flat.

PLATE XVII

Lepidodendron cuticle. A part of the net shown in Plate XVI unfolded (along the line running obliquely through the photograph).

PLATE XVIII

Lepidodendron cuticle. An entire stem width of a species smaller than that shown in Plate XVI, showing the complete loss of everything but the cuticle, which may be opened out as a cylinder over a narrow glass rod. The length of the specimen is 12 mm.

PLATE XIX

Lepidodendron cuticle. The figures both show examples of large and small cuticular crests, the latter appearing as black lines.

PLATE XX

Lepidodendron cuticle. Fragment of a large species, of which Plate XXI is a detail. × ca. 11 diam.

PLATE XXI

Lepidodendron cuticle. Detail of areolar region showing the specialized dome-like cells, with cuticular crests, which appear to have burst and thus to have provided air passages through the epidermis.

PLATE XXII

Supposed microsporangial branches of Lepidodendron. Length of specimens about 10 and 8 mm., respectively.

PLATE XXIII

Supposed microsporangial branch of Lepidodendron. A detail of a similar specimen to that shown in Plate XXII, Fig. 2.

PLATE XXIV

Supposed microsporangial branch of Lepidodendron. High power view of microspores seen through the cuticle.

PLATE XXV

Supposed microsporangial branch of Lepidodendron, a larger species than that shown in Plates XXII–XXIV. Note the distant heart-shaped areoles.

PLATE III

FIG. 1

FIG. 2

Structure of glacial outwash plain at Ann Arbor

PLATE IV

FIG. 1

FIG. 2
Glacial outwash containing coal

PLATE V

Glacial outwash containing coal pebbles

PLATE VI

Coal pebbles from glacial outwash deposits

PLATE VII

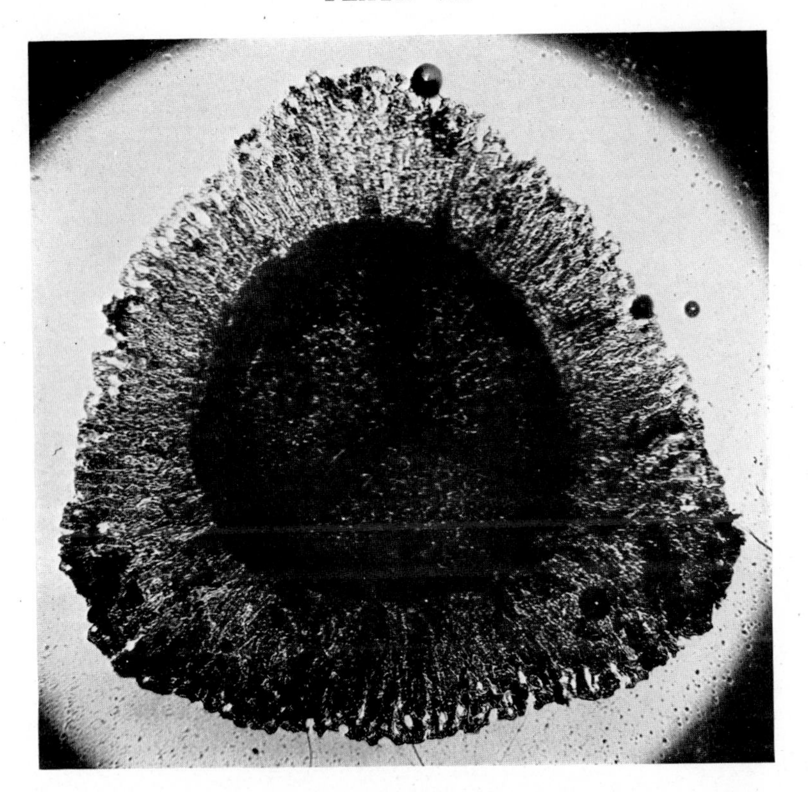

FIG 1

FIG. 2

Triletes superbus, sp. nov.

PLATE VIII

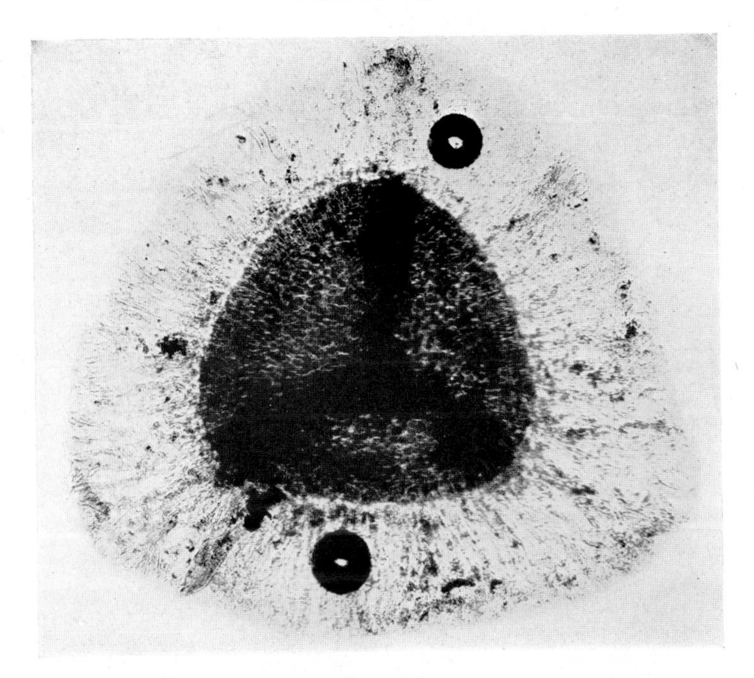

FIG. 1

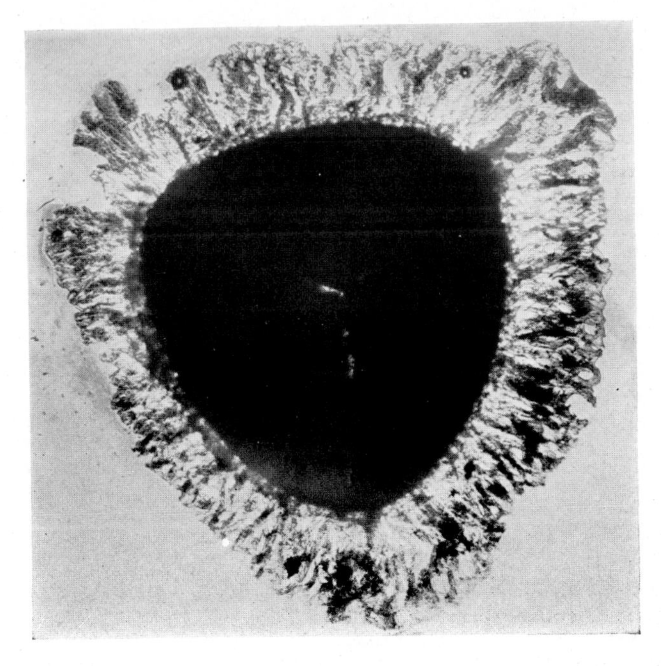

FIG. 2

Triletes superbus, sp. nov.

PLATE IX

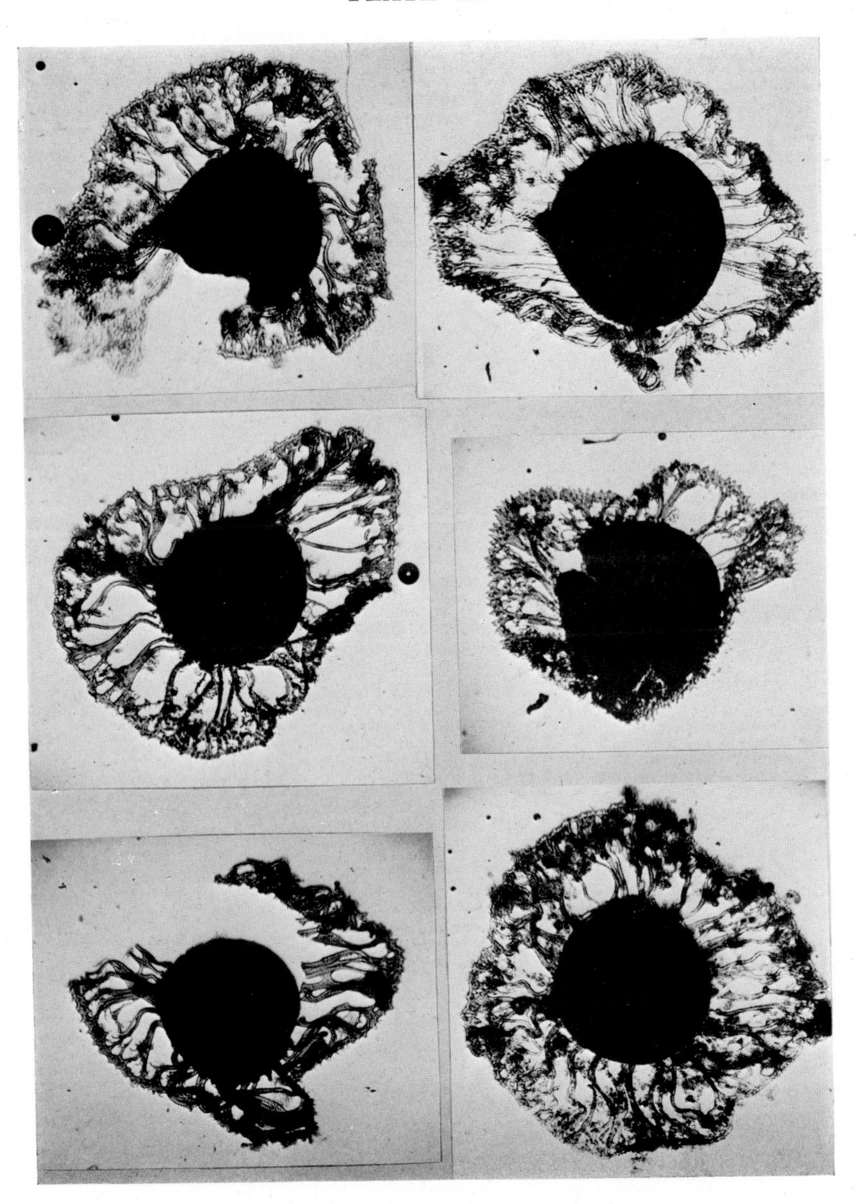

Triletes rotatus, sp. nov.

PLATE X

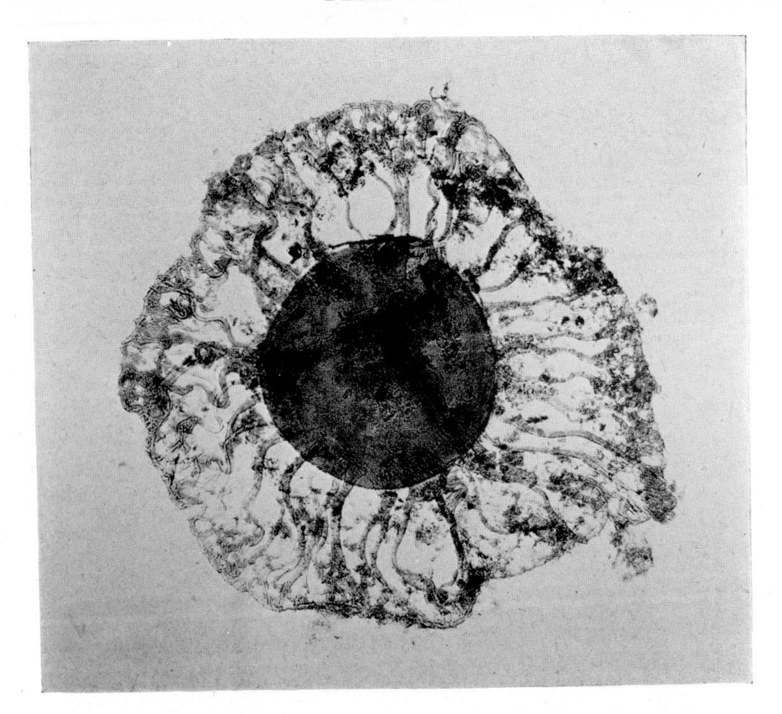

Fig. 1

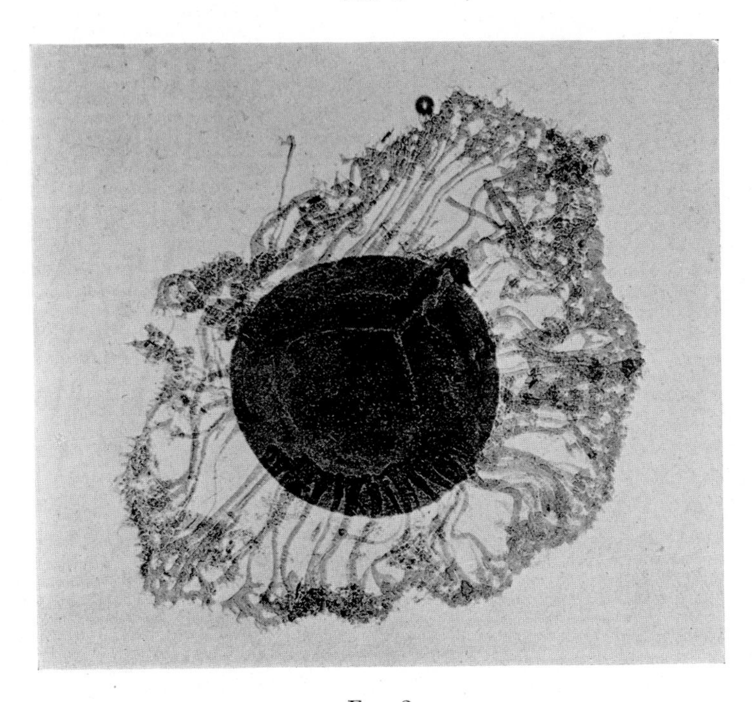

Fig. 2

Triletes rotatus, sp. nov.

PLATE XI

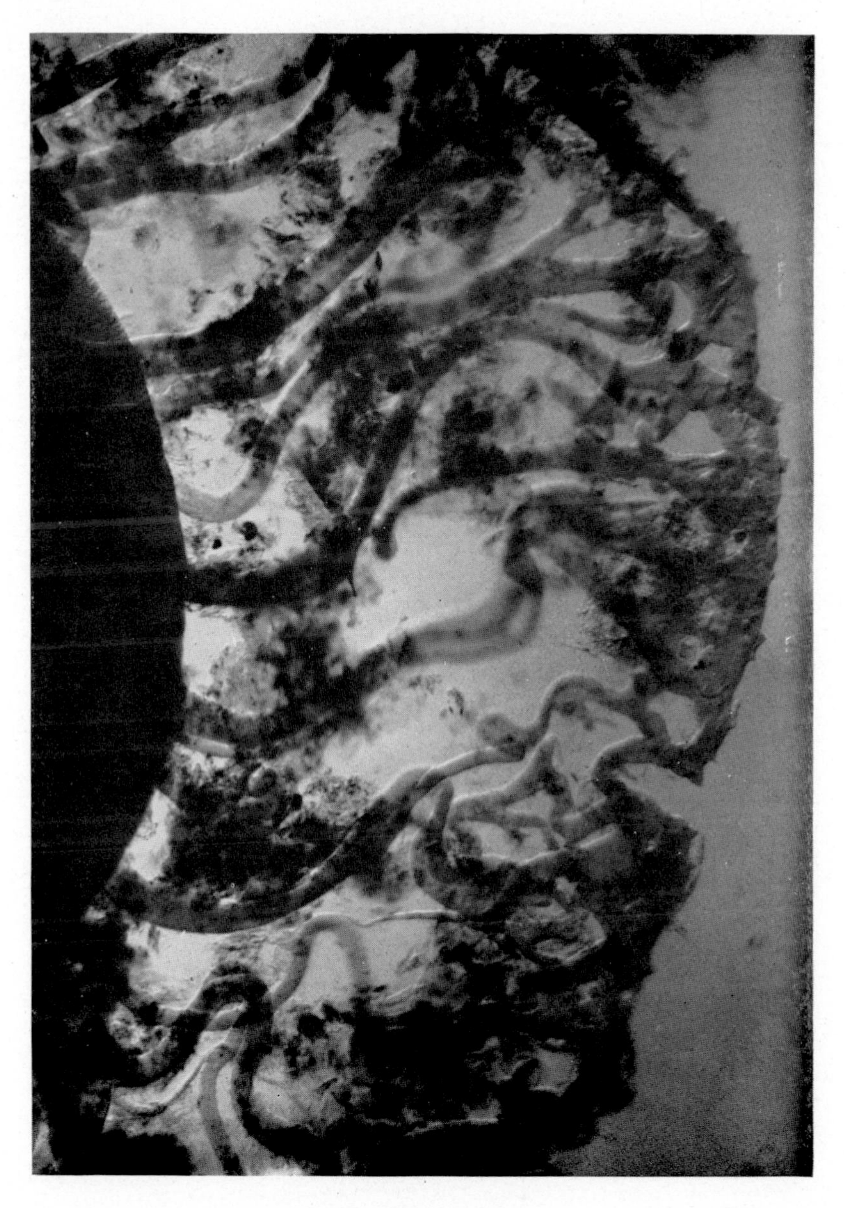

Triletes rotatus, sp. nov.

PLATE XII

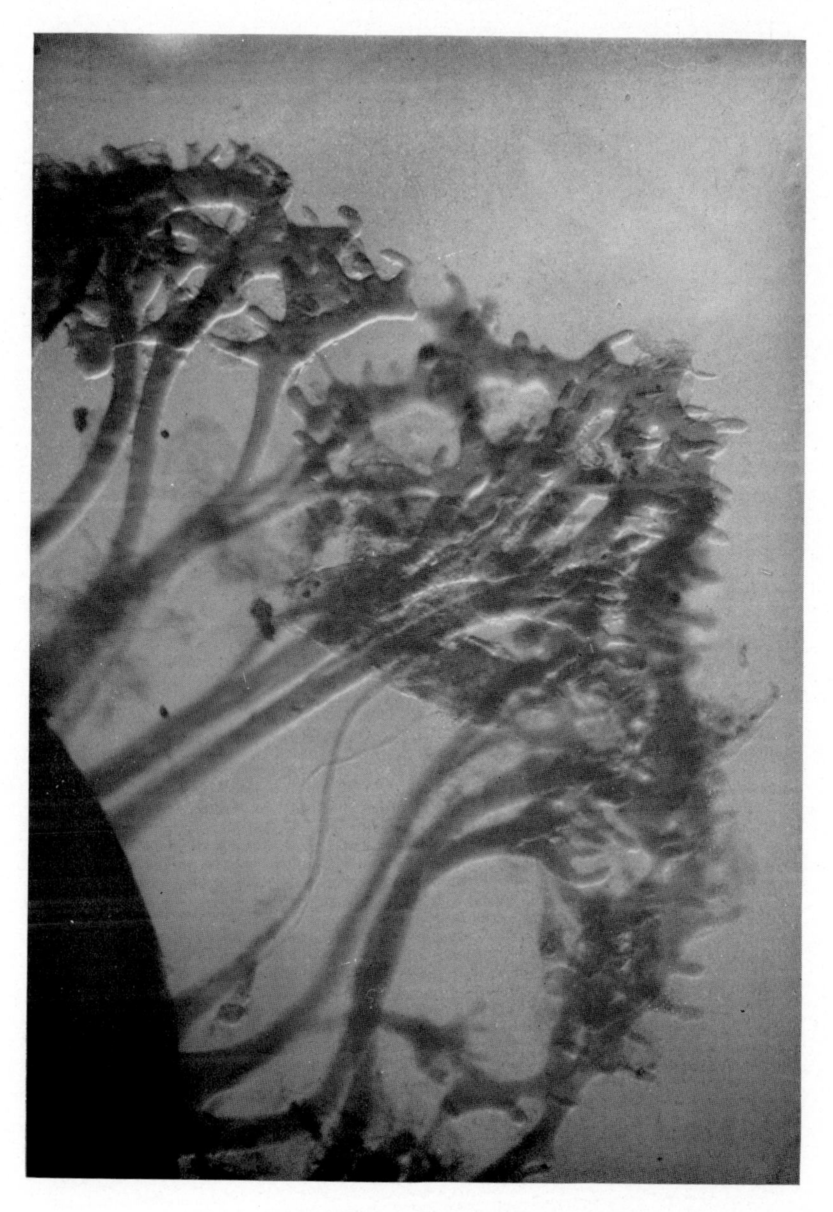

Triletes rotatus, sp. nov.

PLATE XIII

Fig. 1

Fig. 2

Triletes mamillarius, sp. nov.

PLATE XIV

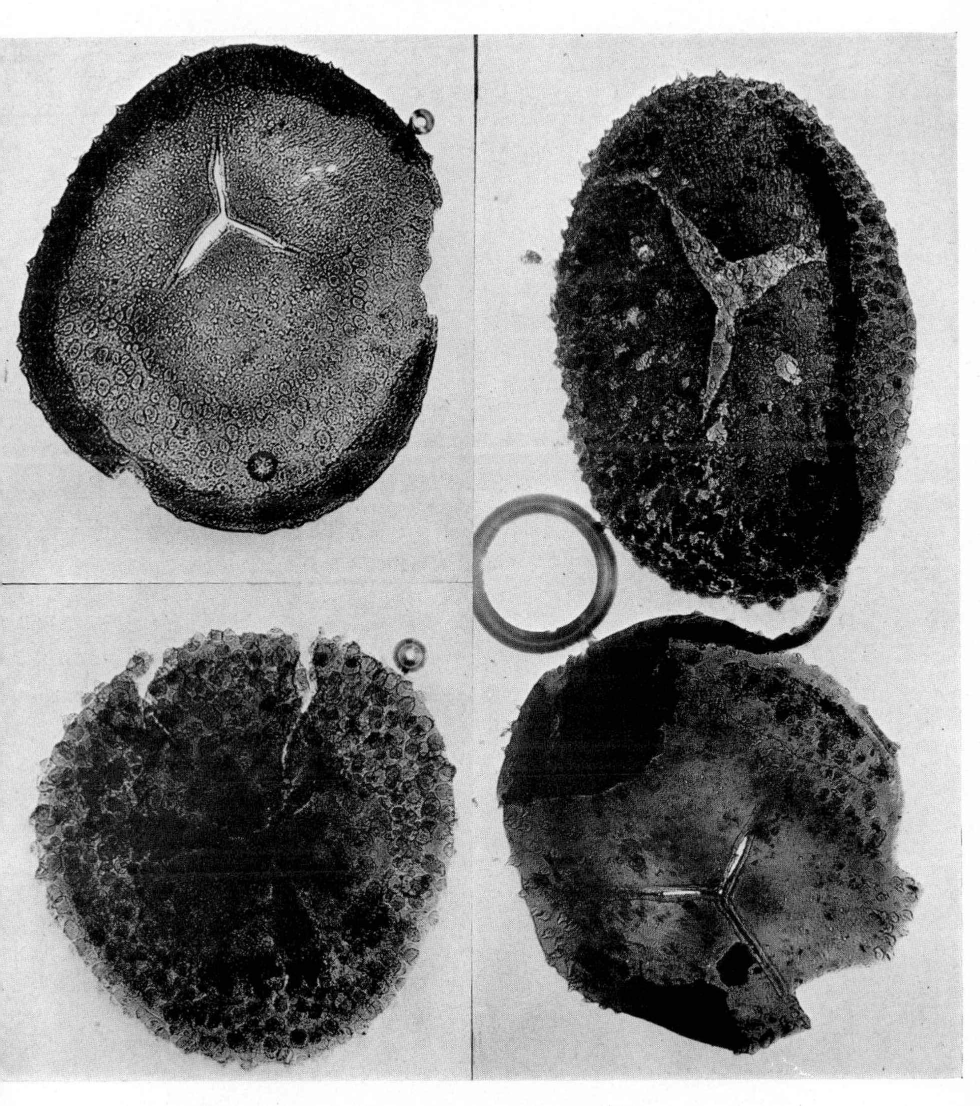

Triletes mamillarius, sp. nov.

PLATE XV

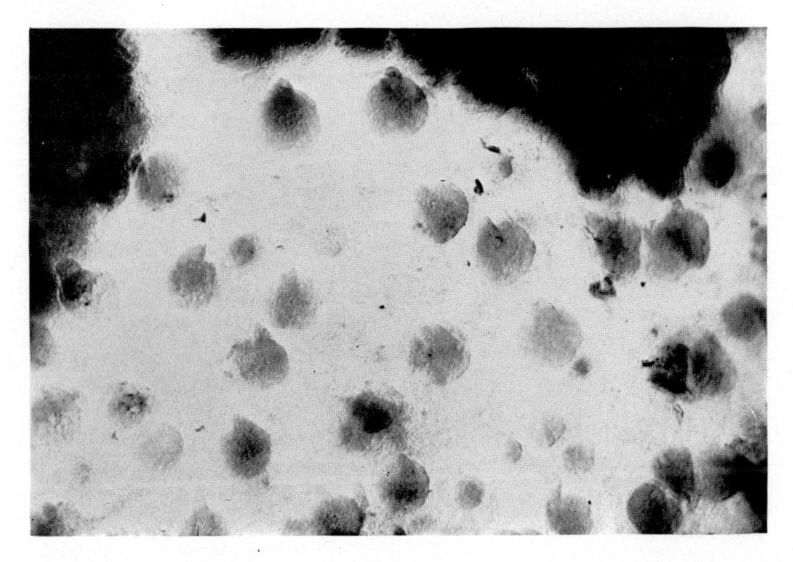

Fig. 1

Fig. 2

Triletes mamillarius, sp. nov.

PLATE XVI

Cuticle of Lepidodendron

PLATE XVII

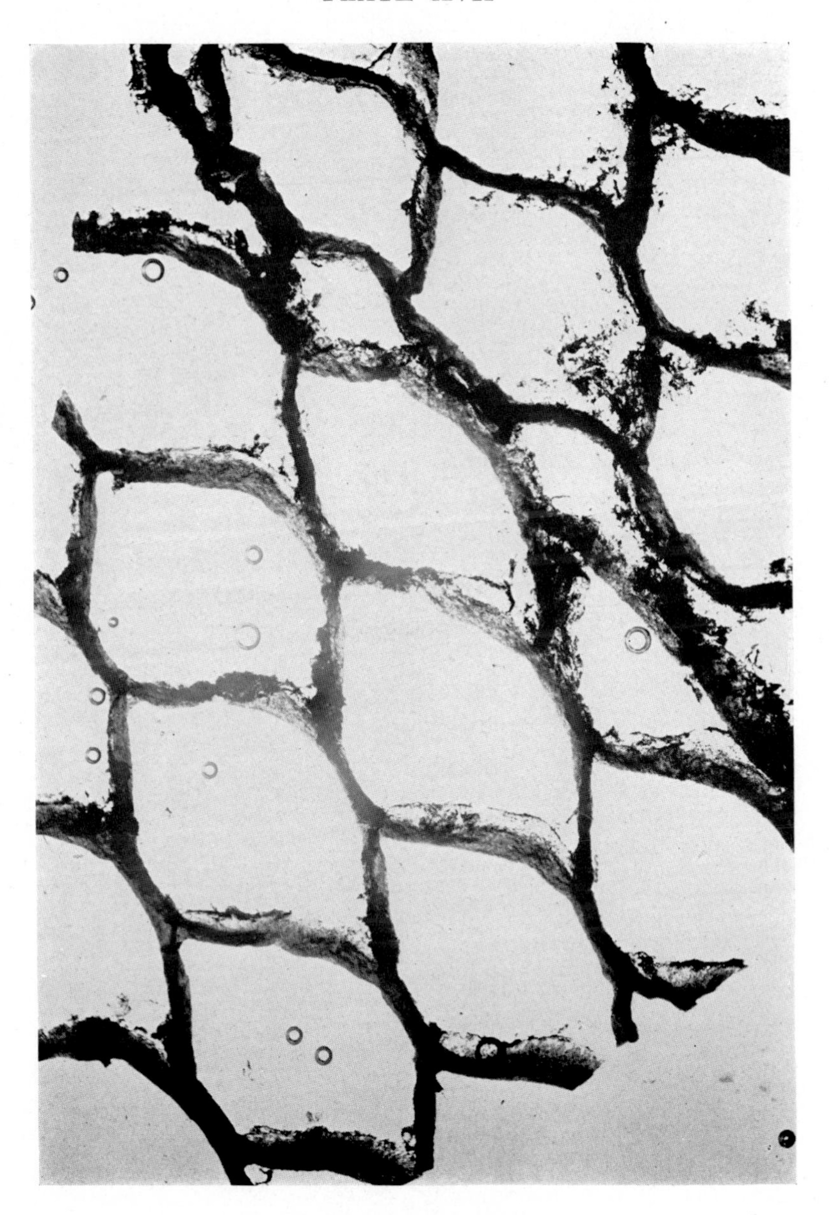

Cuticle of Lepidodendron

PLATE XVIII

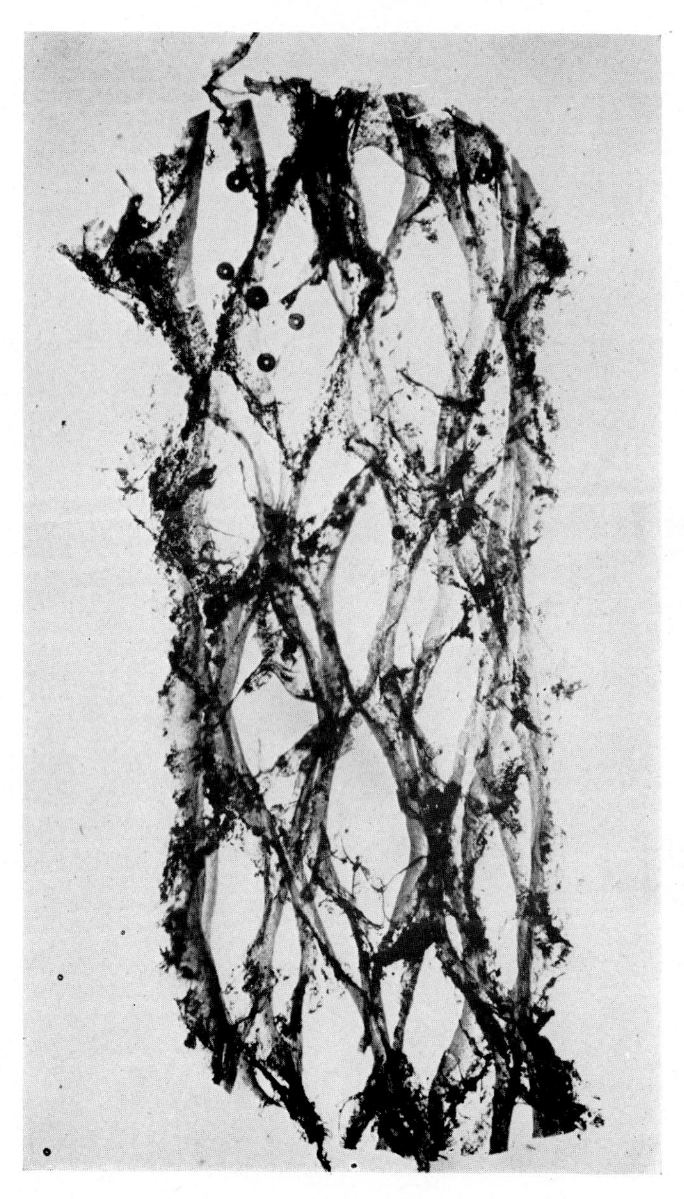

Cuticle of Lepidodendron

PLATE XIX

Fig. 1

Fig. 2
Cuticular crests of Lepidodendron

PLATE XX

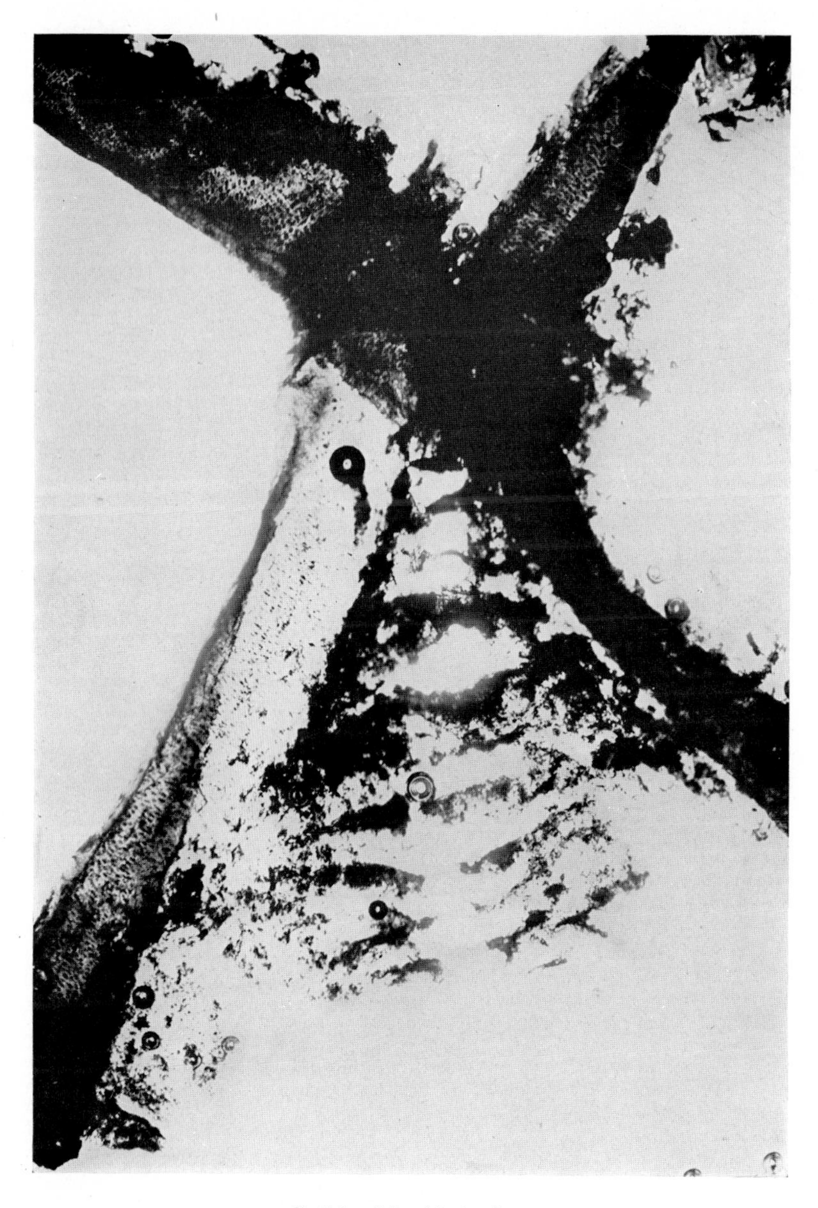

Cuticle of Lepidodendron

PLATE XXI

Dome cells and cuticular crests of Lepidodendron

PLATE XXII

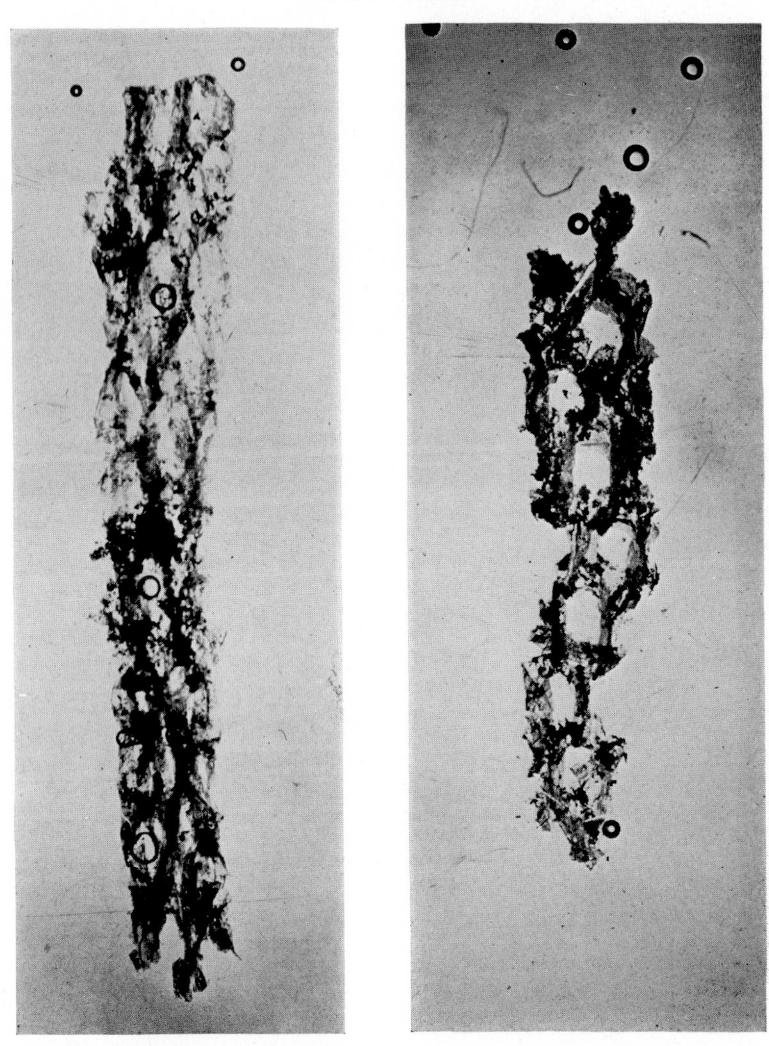

Fig. 1 Fig. 2

Microsporangial branches (of Lepidodendron?)

PLATE XXIII

Microsporangial branch (of Lepidodendron?)

PLATE XXIV

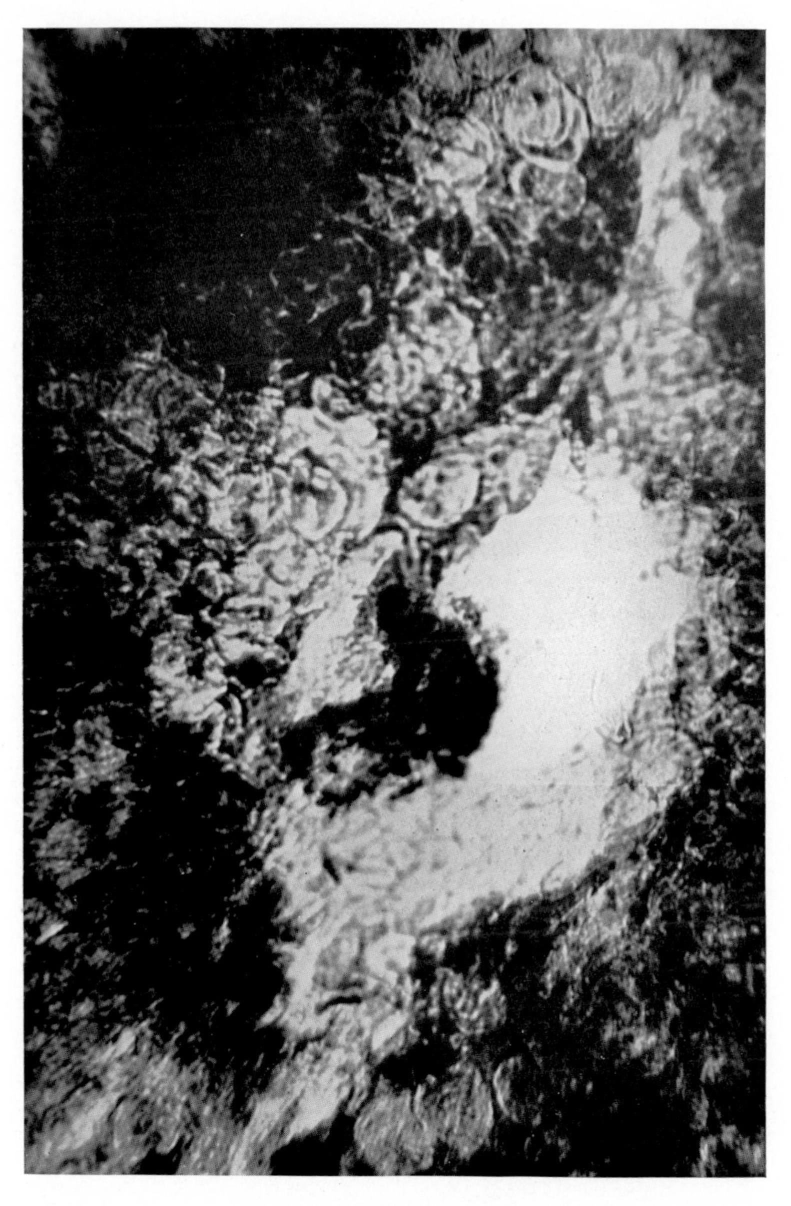

Microspores (of Lepidodendron?)

PLATE XXV

Microsporangial branch (of Lepidodendron?)

THE GENUS TRILETES, REINSCH *

HARLEY HARRIS BARTLETT

INTRODUCTION

THE paleobotanical publications of Paul F. Reinsch [1–7] have suffered general and not altogether deserved neglect. It may seem paradoxical to speak of his work as neglected when as a matter of fact it is not infrequently cited as the basis of the theory of the algal origin of coal — a theory which has had adherents until quite recently. Careful scrutiny of the references to Reinsch by later authors seems to show that most of them are at second or third hand. The overturning of his fantastic interpretation of the plant remains in coal as of algal

* Paper from the Department of Botany of the University of Michigan, No. 253. (Read at the 28th Annual Meeting of the Academy, in 1923.)

[1] Reinsch, P. F., *Neue Untersuchungen über die Mikrostruktur der Steinkohle des Carbon, der Dyas und Trias.* Leipzig, 1881.

[2] Reinsch, P. F., " Über Algen-ähnliche und eigenthümliche einzellige Körper in der Karbonkohle Central Russlands " (mit Tafeln III und IV), *Flora,* 4 : 113–120. 1883.

[3] Reinsch, P. F., " Weitere Beobachtungen über die eigenthümlichen einzelligen Körper in der Carbonkohle," *Flora,* 41 : 187–189. 1883.

[4] Reinsch, P. F., " Über parasitische Algen-ähnliche Pflanzen in der Russischen Blätterkohle und über die Natur der Pflanzen, welche diese Kohle zusammensetzen " (mit Tafeln X, XI und XII), *Flora,* 41 : 323–330, 339–344. 1883.

[5] Reinsch, P. F., " Ein neuer algoider Typus in der Stigmarienkohle von Kurakino (Russland) " (mit Tafel XIII), *Flora,* 41:335–360. 1883.

[6] Reinsch, P. F., *Mikrophotographien der Steinkohle des Carbon.* Leipzig (T. O. Weigel). 1883.

[7] Reinsch, P. F., *Micropalaeophytologia formationis Carboniferae.* Vol. I, continens Triletea s et Stelideas. Vol. II, continens Discieas (Sporangites), Sphaerocladiteas aliasque plantulas algoidicas hucusque incertae sedis in systemate, plantulas Algis proximas, nonullaque animalcula microscopia. Erlangen & London, 1884.

affinity led to the disregard of a vast amount of painstakingly and accurately recorded data, most of which is contained in his latest and least frequently cited work on the coal flora.

It was Reinsch's misfortune to be led astray by erroneous ideas regarding the nature of the plant fossils in coal. It is clear from the introduction to the *Micropalaeophytologia* [7] that Reinsch had never seen a megaspore of Selaginella. He discovered in the coals of Russia and Saxony a beautiful series of microspores and megaspores, many of them elaborately sculptured or provided with ornate appendages of various forms which may have been important in dispersal by wind. He considered the entire series as Algae because of the great range in size, pointing out in his argument that the spores of all groups of living Pteridophyta, however diverse, are of nearly the same size. His measurements, however, in the case of Selaginella, are for microspores only, although he knew of the existence of two types of spores, and possibly thought that the range of size he quoted included both microspores and megaspores. He was equally unfortunate in his ideas of the spore appendages, since he came to the conclusion that they were parasitic organisms growing upon larger plants, the central bodies of the spores. Consequently he frequently figures the appendages with meticulous care, but not the rest of the spore, which he viewed as merely the substratum of the parasites.

Perhaps seldom in the history of science has so much excellent observation and painstaking technique been nullified by bad judgment and prepossession with erroneous hypotheses.

The immediate rejection of Reinsch's ideas by his contemporaries threw discredit upon his entire accomplishment, which stands even today without an equal in the field of coal botany. So completely was Reinsch's work neglected that within a few years even his erroneous theory of the origin of coal from Algae or alga-like plants could be revived by Bertrand and Renault [8-9]

[8] Bertrand, C. E., et Renault, B., *Pila bibractensis et le boghead d'Autun,* Soc. Hist. Nat. Autun, Bull. 5 : 159–253. 1892.

[9] Bertrand, C. E., et Renault, B., *Reinschia australis, et premières re-*

without anyone attempting a new appraisal of his contributions. Bertrand and Renault clearly enough acknowledged their indebtedness to Reinsch for the germ of the algal theory of the origin of coal by giving the name Reinschia to one of the two chief types of supposed Algae, the other being Pila.

Thiessen [10] is inclined to attribute the germ of the algal hypothesis to Von Gümbel,[11] from whom he thinks Bertrand and Renault got it. After a commendatory account of Von Gümbel's work he says: "But Von Gümbel made the seemingly harmless statement that certain bodies looked like certain algae. He was very careful to say that he would not venture the assertion that they actually were such, but, as he was not a botanist, would leave this matter to those who were more familiar with plants. . . . Seemingly acting on the suggestion of Von Gümbel Bertrand interpreted these as gelosic algae, similar to the Volvocineae." The name Reinschia, dating from one of the first papers of Bertrand and Renault (1893) [9] would seem to show that they followed the lead of Reinsch rather than Von Gümbel.

Recent authors, among them Potonié [12] and Thiessen [10] refer to the earlier one of Reinsch's monographs, but strangely enough, not to his final and most significant one, the *Micropalaeophytologia.*[7] Thiessen says (p. 195): [10] "Reinsch developed a technique of his own . . . and prepared numerous samples of coal. He thought the yellowish red and brown, somewhat translucent or transparent figures a very peculiar plant form that he called

---

marques sur le kérosene shale de la Nouvelle-Galles du Sud, Soc. Hist. Nat. Autun, Bull. 6 : 321–425. 1893.

The numerous other papers of these authors are listed by Thiessen. (See following footnote.)

[10] Thiessen, R., *Microscopic Study of Coal,* U. S. Bur. Mines, Bull. 38 : 187–304. 1913.

[11] Von Gümbel, C. W., "Beiträge zur Kenntnis der Texturverhältnisse der Mineralkohlen," *Sitzungsb. Acad. Wiss. München, Math. Phys. Classe,* 13 : 111–216. 1883.

[12] Potonié, H., *Die Entstehung der Steinkohle und der Kaustobiolithe überhaupt.* Sechste Auflage, durchgesehen von Prof. Dr. W. Gothan. Berlin, 1920.

'Protophytae' of which he believed he had recognized seven fossil types not comparable with recent plant forms. Many of his figures show excellent representations of Pteridophytic spore exines; in other cases he allowed his imagination to carry him into the representation of grotesque and odd plant forms." Thiessen goes on to mention the severe criticisms of Reinsch's work that followed the publication, in 1881, of the *Neuere Untersuchungen über die Mikrostruktur der Steinkohle.* Petzholdt[13] in 1882 identified the hypothetical Protophytae with inorganic bodies, fragments of coal, and decomposition products termed bitumen. In 1883 Fischer and Rüst[14] reviewed Reinsch's material. Although they were unable to interpret all the structures figured by Reinsch, they concluded that most of them were amber-like resins, and others leaf cuticles, spores, and wood fibers. They rejected Reinsch's ideas entirely.

It is probable that the unfavorable reception of the *Neuere Untersuchungen* explains the neglect of the *Micropalaeophytologia,*[7] sumptuously published in 1884. In spite of all its defects of interpretation, the latter is a mine of accurate figures of plant structures (mostly spores) recovered from coal in almost incredible perfection.

In addition to other structures, over five hundred spores (referred to as Triletеae) are figured. Although Reinsch interprets them as Algae or algoid plants, his terminology seems to indicate that he may have had some misgivings, since he uses the term exosporium for the sculptured or appendaged outer portion of the structures, stating that he does so for convenience and not because he doubts his own conclusions. The accuracy of the figures as representations of spores affords the strongest possible internal evidence of the accuracy of the figures, since they have not been distorted or modified to bring them more

[13] Petzholdt, A., *Beiträge zur Kenntniss der Steinkohlenbildung.* 1882.

[14] Fischer, H., and Rüst, D., "Über das mikroskopische und optische Verhalten verschiedene Kohlenwasserstoffe, Harze, und Kohlen," *Groth's Zeitschr. Krystall. u. Mineral.,* 7:209–233. 1883.

in accord with their supposed algal affinity. One supposed case of cell-division shows patently two similar spores slightly overlying each other.

Even though they may not be associable with impressions of the vegetative parts of the plants to which they belong, or with structural material, Reinsch's Trileteae are significant both botanically and geologically — botanically because they will give us an idea of the extent of specific diversity in the Carboniferous flora, and geologically because, as Thiessen [15] has discovered, and as Reinsch vaguely appears to have recognized, the different types are characteristic of particular beds, and are sure to come into importance in stratigraphic correlation.

REVIEW OF REINSCH'S "MICROPALAEOPHYTOLOGIA"

The first volume of the *Micropalaeophytologia* [7] is devoted to the Trileteae, of which a single genus, Triletes, is characterized, and to the Stelideae, with the genera Trichostelium and Stichostelium, each comprising a "subtribe." According to present conceptions, the Trileteae are the spores of the Lepidodendraceae and allied plants. Seward [16] retains the name Triletes as a convenient designation for such fossils, with the following comment (p. 192): "The general generic name Triletes, originally used by Reinsch, is a convenient term by which to designate Pteridophytic spores which cannot be referred to definite types." Elsewhere (p. 215) he says: "The designation Triletes is applied to isolated spores of Sigillaria or to those of Lepidodendron."

Recent writers do not appear to have commented upon Trichostelium and Stichostelium. Reinsch himself looked upon them as plants of parasitic nature, and called attention to the fact that they frequently parasitized the larger forms of Triletes. It appears obvious that the majority of them are merely fragments of the elaborately sculptured, complicated zonal ap-

[15] Thiessen, Reinhardt, *Structure in Palaeozoic Bituminous Coals,* U. S. Bureau of Mines, Bull. 117, pp. 296. Washington, 1920.

[16] Seward, A. C., *Fossil Plants,* Vol. 2. Cambridge, 1910.

pendages of the megaspores included under Triletes. References are made elsewhere (see the foregoing paper) to similarities between some of Reinsch's figures and certain spores described by the present writer from the Ann Arbor drift coal. Reinsch's two names will doubtless fall into the synonymy of Triletes, although not all of his figures conform to appendages of known spore types. The coals containing these peculiar structures should by all means be reëxamined in order to bring to light whole spores bearing the elaborate appendages figured by Reinsch as Trichostelium and Stichostelium.

The second volume of the *Micropalaeophytologia* contains descriptions and figures of a congeries of structures — spores, spore appendages, cuticles, etc., from various formations all the way from the Devonian to the Tertiary. Reinsch, of course, considered most of them as autonomous organisms. Some, such as his Discieae, including Sporangites Dawson and Chroococcites Reinsch *ex parte,* seem to fall for the most part under Triletes. Probably the name Sporangites should be reserved for fossil sporangia of dubious association rather than for spores. It was established by Dawson for Devonian shale fossils. The type species of Chroococcites, as indicated by Reinsch (p. 9),[7] is a Triletes of which the exine bears a ramentum designated by Reinsch as an independent parasitic organism, belonging to his group Leptoideae. As to the true nature of Leptoideae there can be no doubt. Reinsch states his unfortunate misconception as follows: "Corpus filiforme, procumbens, substrato viventi (Trileteae, Stelideae et Discieae et a.) dense adpresum et in interna substantia plantularum affectarum expansum; et erectum, substrato parte inferiore affixo." Another group, the Rhizostaemideae, including only the genus Rhizostaemis, is based upon tubercles of a Triletes not very dissimilar to the *Triletes mamillarius* described by the writer from coal in the glacial deposits at Ann Arbor. The Rhizostaemideae are described (p. 15)[7] as "Plantulae parasitice radicantes et nidulantes in Triletum majorum et aliorum corporum organicorum superficie. . . ."

Most of Reinsch's Sphaerocladiteae (another group containing a single genus — Sphaerocladites) must remain dubious pending the reinvestigation of his materials. One, however, is of extraordinary interest because of its striking correspondence to Bertrand and Renault's Reinschia. It is figured from the English torbanite (Torbane Hill) and the Scotch boghead cannel coal, constituting, according to Reinsch, as high as 92–98 per cent of the coal in some sections. It is a megaspore type, a Triletes.

As to Reinsch's remaining groups little need be said. Our author's prevailing error of regarding the appendages of spores as distinct parasitic organisms accounts for some, at least, of the Dictyophiteae, as would be clear from the text even if the plates did not indicate it. He says: "Corpuscula vegetabilica incertae sedis in Systemate, tantummodo reperta parasitica superficiemque aliorum Corpusculorum vegetabilicorum majorum (Trileteae, Discieae, etc.) obducentia. Corpus Plantulae sicut in Stelideis ex Thallo subhomogeneo . . . formatum . . . Dictyophiteas esse corpora propria, nec ad substantiam substrati exhibentia, elucit, 1, ex connexione Dictyophitearum cum substrato, 2, ex facto ut haec corpuscula infecta (Trileteae, etc.) reperiantur partim corpusculis alienis obtectis, partim liberis." His argument that the spore appendages are independent organisms because one kind of spore is found both with and without appendages, and because a simple spore may be partly with and partly without an investiture, is very weak. Prior to burial many spores became more or less completely disintegrated, and in any coal sample containing many spores of a single type, all stages of preservation may be found. Nor can the accidents during isolation by the maceration process be left out of account. The Stolidermieae (type genus Stolidermium) include a variety of cuticles, some of very characteristic aspect. It may be advisable to retain the name Stolidermium for certain Carboniferous cuticles not yet associated with definite genera, just as it will certainly be convenient to retain Triletes for spores.

UTILITY OF THE NAME TRILETES

As already noted, Seward [12] proposes to retain the name Triletes as a convenient designation for fossil spores presumably belonging to Lepidodendraceae and allied families, but not definitely associated as yet with fossils of the vegetative phase of the life-history. Used in this manner, as the writer proposes to do, the name will probably actually cover many genera, belonging to several families.

Thiessen is firmly opposed to the use of names for isolated spores, cuticles, etc., but it seems to the writer that such an attitude cannot fairly be maintained in view of his own conclusion that such fossils are the stratigraphically significant components of the coal. He says (p. 71): [15] "No thorough classification of the spore-exines found in the coals has been made. . . . To try to give a definite name to them, without knowing their affinities and relationships, as has been done by some in the past, would be a waste of time and space. No benefit is gained by naming the exine predominant in and characteristic of the Pittsburgh seam 'Sporangites' Pittsburghensis, as does Dawson, or 'Trilet' Pittsburghensis, as do Bennie and Kidston, or giving some such meaningless name. When their relationships are known proper names will be given them."

Thiessen [15] shows convincingly that coals may be identified as to origin and that correlations may be established through comparison of the characteristic spore exines. How such work is to proceed easily without having a convenient nomenclature for the spores is not evident. Form genera of Fungi Imperfecti with countless named species are maintained in mycology, for present convenience. In the cases of many economically important fungi the perfect forms, which make possible a precise placing in the scheme of classification, may never have been discovered, but who, for that reason, would be willing to get along without names for them? Moreover, it is quite possible that the study of spores, whether or not they are ever connected with vegetative structures, may give us a better idea of the diversification and geographical distribution of the Lepidodendron allies than any other type of fossil. Quite conceivably Lepidodendron stems from America and Europe might appear identical, whereas spores, if known, would demonstrate specific or generic differentiation. To take a concrete case, let us suppose that our knowledge of the species of Selaginella in the group of *S. rupestris* were based only upon vegetative stems, poorly preserved. We could then probably distinguish only one species. If the spores were preserved, however, the existence of several species would become obvious. If the spores only existed, their study would give phytogeographic and floristic information even though we had no information about the kinds of plants that bore them.

The writer is quite convinced of the value of names for the characteristic spore types. If Reinsch had not been content to characterize his coal species under numbers, the inclusion of the specific names in indexes would repeatedly have called attention to his monumental *Micropalaeophytologia* and would have led sooner to a recognition of the importance of his discoveries. Reinsch examined not only Carboniferous coal, but also Devonian material (shale and coal) and coal of later formations. His material came mainly from various localities in Central Russia and from Zwickau in Saxony. The fact that he gives localities for most of the types described would justify the procedure of giving names to the outstanding ones since new specimens may doubtless be isolated as desired from coal from the type localities. If naming a few of his species were to lead interested botanists and geologists to consult his monograph, the writer would gladly be responsible for the iniquity of basing a few names upon his plates and descriptions instead of upon type specimens. Although Reinsch was led astray by consistent adherence to false theories regarding the nature of the structures found in the coal, his work was too good in detail and too extensive to be neglected as it has been. His collections are presumably still preserved and would repay careful examination. It will be obvious to anyone experienced in the study of such material that Reinsch described an excessive number of types. Many of his figures represent the same species over and over again. It is much to be hoped that someone favorably situated to do so will study his type specimens in the light of new isolations from the coals that he investigated, and that the interesting line of investigation opened by Reinsch may lead to many more studies such as those of Jeffrey [17-18] and Thiessen.[10, 15]

UNIVERSITY OF MICHIGAN

[17] Jeffrey, E. C., "On the Composition and Qualities of Coal," *Econ. Geol.*, 9 : 730–742. 1914.

[18] Jeffrey, E. C., "On the Nature of Some Supposed Algal Coals," *Proc. Amer. Acad. Arts and Sci.*, 46 : 273–290. 1914.

SOME PORIAS FROM THE REGION OF THE LAKE STATES II*

DOW V. BAXTER

VERY few studies have been made on the resupinate Polypores which are found throughout the region of the Lake States. Since the appearance of a recent publication by the writer (1) in which twenty species of the genus Poria were listed from this area, additional studies have been made on various species of this group. Some of the porias reported in this paper have been critically studied by Professor Lars Romell and are undoubtedly among the last American plants examined by this student of European mycology. Dr. Romell's interpretation of some of the Friesian plants (listed here in part) has made this collection a valuable one for future comparison.

I also desire to express my appreciation to Dr. D. C. Davies, who permitted the writer to study the Poria collections found in the Field Museum of Natural History, Chicago, Illinois.

Poria albolutescens Romell. — Nos. 526124 and 526116, Herbarium, Field Museum of Natural History. Plant collected by E. J. Harper. Frankfort, Michigan. *Fide* J. R. Weir.

Plant annual, margin fimbriate with chamois-colored rhizomorphic strands of mycelium ramifying throughout the badly decayed wood. Plant dried to "cinnamon-buff" (Ridg.). Tubes less than 0.5–1 mm. long, mouths 2–4 mostly 3 per mm. Hyphae occasionally branched 2–4 microns wide. Clamp connections abundant. Spores 3–4 × 2–2.5 microns. Romell (8) reports this species on rotton wood of Abies. Both specimens from Frankfort, Michigan, are on hardwood. Although badly decayed, the structure of one of the wood specimens shows that the substratum is beech.

Polyporus glomeratus Pk. — This rare plant (usually found in

* Contribution No. 3 from School of Forestry and Conservation, University of Michigan.

the resupinate form) has been collected in both Wisconsin and Michigan. While all of the plants collected in southern Wisconsin have been found on burr oak, this species is reported in the literature (2, 6, 10) on maple, beech, and chestnut.

Plant annual, effused for two or three feet along the logs or on upright trunks. The fungus apparently develops first between the bark and the wood, and later fruits on the wood after the bark has fallen away. Fruiting body "olive brown" to "cinnamon brown," context less than 0.3 mm. and inconspicuous. Tubes 3–8 mm. long, at times breaking up into teeth, mouths angular, becoming cristate, mostly 3 per mm. Spores brown 4–5 (4 × 6) 5–6 microns. Brown projecting setae present 12–22 × 5–7 microns. Dark-colored hyphal strands present in context. Hyphae thick-walled, brown 2–5 microns, occasionally branched.

Weir (10) has called attention to the fact that this fungus seems to be a pronounced wound parasite. Weir states: "Occasionally young smooth-barked trees are found dead in the forest from no apparent cause. On examination it will be found that this fungus has completely girdled the tree." I have attempted to inoculate several logs in southern Wisconsin with this fungus, but at the time of the last examination, seventeen months later, no fruiting bodies had developed from the spores and decayed wood sections. Although this fungus fruits abundantly, the writer was unable to obtain any spore germination in the laboratory. It is believed that the plants found were overmature at the time of collection and that the spores had lost their vitality.

The decayed wood is uniformly bleached to a color much lighter than that of sound oak. The dry decayed wood usually splits along the wood rays and the conspicuous mass of these ray cells in radial section presents a characteristic feature of this decay. Unlike the decay produced by *Polyporus Berkeleyi* Fr., however, there is not a complete absorption of some of the fibers. These bands of rays are, therefore, not interwoven with the long flat strings of the wood as in the case of wood rotted by *Polyporus Berkeleyi*. The irregular brown lines which appear in the decayed oak wood are also characteristic of the rot caused by *Polyporus glomeratus*.

Poria barbaeformis B & C. — No. 526132, Herbarium, Field Museum of Natural History. Plant collected by E. J. Harper. Neebish, Michigan. *Fide* J. R. Weir.

Plant with a very thin white margin, tubes dried "vinaceous-cinnamon" to "clay color." In old plants "sayal brown" (Ridg.). Mouths 3–4, mostly 3 per mm., tubes 0.5–1 mm., mostly 0.5 mm. long, hyphae 2 microns wide, conidia 10–16 (13 × 5) 4–6 microns.

Poria carbonaria B. & C. — On pine and cedar logs, New Richmond, Michigan, and elsewhere in the state. This plant has always been found in this region on charred pine and cedar logs. *Poria carbonaria* is not a common plant in this region and is usually found in a sterile condition. Murrill (4) reports this plant from South Carolina and Florida. I have a rather large collection of this plant on charred logs of *Chamaecyparis Lawsoniana* from Port Orford, Oregon (see Pl. XXVI). The decay usually associated with this fungus is the brown cubical type.

Plant effused with an interrupted or "lobed" type of growth, separable, coriaceous 1–3 mm. thick, margin fertile, brown, tubes brown, somewhat whitish within, mouths hexagonal, 2 per mm., context inconspicuous less than 0.3 mm., hyphae 2–5 microns wide.

Polyporus ferreus Pers. sensu Romell. — On *Acer rubrum, Populus tremuloides,* Rock River, Michigan (3). This Poria is allied to *Poria ferruginosa* (Schrad) Fr. and *Poria contigua* Pers. Identification of this plant is based upon other plants collected in this region which have been determined by Romell. Plant effused, sometimes stratose, margin "ochraceous olive," tubes "tawny olive" (Ridg.), 0.5–3.5 mm. long, mouths 4–5 per mm., cystidia not numerous 24 × 4–7 microns, basidia 11–14 × 4–6 microns, spores 4–6 × 1.6–2 microns, hyphae 2 microns wide.

Poria laevigata Fr. — Parfrey's Glen, Wisconsin. Determined by Romell. On maple; other plants on birch and other hardwoods in the region of the Lake States. Plant effused, inseparable, irregular margin, tomentose when young, becoming glabrous, tubes "buffy brown" to "mummy brown" (Ridg.) when fresh, 2–4 mm. long, some whitish, stuffed, stratose, subiculum 0.5 mm., mouths 6–7 per mm. Spores hyaline 4 × 2.4 microns, cystidia not common 10–17 × 4.5 microns. *Poria laevigata* has been confused with many of the other perennial brown porias such as *Poria prunicola* Murr., and others. It is closely allied, as has been pointed out (7), to *Poria betulina* and has been studied in relation to resupinate forms of *Fomes igniarius*. While the general pore surface resembles that of *Fomes igniarius*, Romell attaches the specific name of *laevigata* to those plants which have smaller pores and spores than those found in *Fomes igniarius*.

Poria mucida Fr. — On oak, Devil's Lake, Wisconsin. *Poria mucida* is one of the most common of all the porias found on oak in southern Wisconsin. It is usually sterile. Although Romell has identified this plant as *Polyporus radula forma cystidius filiformibus*, I am here applying the name which has been more or less established by usage in American mycology. This plant is also found in herbaria under the name of *Irpex deformans* Pers.

Plant effused, forming patches on wood and bark, inseparable, usually 1–2 mm. thick, margin whitish, slightly pubescent, irregular, mostly fertile, tubes "warm buff" (Ridg.), averaging 1 mm. long, mouths lacerate, 2–3 per mm., basidia 12–14 × 5 microns, spores 4–6 (5 × 3) 3 microns, hyphae encrusted, 1–4, mostly 2 microns wide, clamp connections present.

Poria myceliosa Pk. — No. 526164, Herbarium, Field Museum of Natural History. Plant collected by E. T. Harper. Frankfort, Michigan (see Pl. XXVII). Broadly effused; plant at least 17 cm. broad, thin, separable from substratum, margin sterile, dried to "warm buff" to "clay color" (Ridg.), fimbriate margin with radiating strands of mycelium extending outward and through the soft decayed wood. Tubes 0.5–1 mm., mostly 0.5 mm. long, pores 3–4, mostly 3 per mm., sometimes confluent. No cystidia, basidia 4-spored 14 × 4 microns, spores 3–4 × 2–3 microns. Hyphae 2 microns wide, clamp connections present. Mycelial strands abundant in the badly decayed wood. On conifers.

Poria rufa Schroet. — On spruce. McMillan, Michigan. Appears to be most commonly found on spruce in the region of the Lake States. Plant merulioid, effused, ochraceus-salmon when fresh. Context pure white, tubes drying "diamine brown" to "bone brown" (Ridg.). Plant 1 mm. thick, tubes less than

0.5 mm. long, mouths 3–4, mostly 3 per mm. Basidia 4-spored 10–14 × 3–4 microns, spores 4 × 1 microns, hyphae hyaline, thick-walled, branched, septate, 4–6 microns.

Poria subfuscoflavida Fr. sensu Romell. — This plant is reported by Kauffman (3) on *Thuja occidentalis* from Rock River, Michigan. Plant orbicular to widely effused, inseparable. Plant thin, mostly 1 mm. thick, margin white, tomentose narrowly sterile, subiculum less than 0.3 mm. thick, tubes "vinaceous drab" (Ridg.), becoming cinereous, 1 mm. long or less. Mouths 4–6 per mm., basidia 4-spored 8–10 × 4–5 microns, spores hyaline 4 × 2 microns, hyphae slightly encrusted, seldom branched, flexuous, 2–4 microns wide.

The hyphae in badly decayed portions of the coniferous wood characteristically form soft cottony wefts of mycelium which fill the disintegrated and absorbed portions of the wood. The soft nature of these wefts of mycelium remind one somewhat of the soft spongy mycelial nature of *Polyporus leucospongia*. *Poria subfuscoflavida* seems to be confined to conifers. I have collected this plant on logs of *Pinus sabiniana* in the dry situations on the Trinity National Forest in California and have commonly found it on *Tsuga mertensiana* logs in the vicinity of Crater Lake, Oregon (see Pls. XXVIII–XXIX). These western collections represent Romell's opinion regarding the Friesian interpretation of this species. Bresadola's plant, *Poria cinerescens*, is said by Romell to be synonymous with this species. The *Poria subfuscoflavida* Rostk., reported from Crandon and Stone Lake, Wisconsin, by Neuman (5) and identified by Bresadola, is not the *Poria subfuscoflavida* Fr. sensu Romell. My collections are all interpreted in the sense of Romell.

Poria vulgaris var. *calceus* Fr. sensu Romell. — This plant is reported by Kauffman (3) on a pine stump from Rock River, Michigan. *Fide* D. V. Baxter. On pine board, Madison, Wisconsin. Wisconsin Herbarium 173, *fide* Romell. Plant effused, margin fertile, tubes "ivory yellow" to "Naples yellow" (Ridg.), 2–5 mm. long, mouths 4–5 per mm., basidia 12–14 × 4 microns, spores ellipsoidal, minute 4 × 1 microns, hyphae 2–4 microns.

Romell (9) has called attention to the fact that the name

"vulgaris" covers several distinct plants. Romell holds that *P. vulgaris* var. *calceus* is only an oblique form of *P. xantha* Lind.

I have collected *Poria xantha* on Port Orford cedar, Port Orford, Oregon, which has been identified by Romell. Romell comments on this collection as being the *Poria xantha* "as understood in my remarks." The tubes of this plant are distinctly "marguerite yellow" (Ridg.) in color; 4 per mm., and are less than 0.5 to 1 mm. long. The hyphae are flexuous, 2–4 microns wide.

Another collection from this same region is in the writer's herbarium which, according to Romell, might probably be considered the "vitellinous" variety of *Poria xantha* on Port Orford cedar. This variety should have larger pores than the species, but my records show no difference in pore size from the true *Poria xantha* identified by Romell and this possible variety. The color of this last named collection instead of being light yellow is "cream-buff" (Ridg.), and the spores found in the collection are wider, namely 4–5 × 2 microns. Romell suggests that this plant may be held as a distinct species. He further states that Bresadola has referred this plant to *Poria crassa* in his herbarium, but erroneously. Evidently Romell considered *Poria crassa* a rare plant in Sweden, as he stated in a communication to the writer dated March 28, 1927, that he found *Poria crassa* for the first time in Sweden "within the last year."

University of Michigan

LITERATURE CITED

1. Baxter, D. V. 1926. Some Porias from the Region of the Lake States. Papers of the Michigan Academy of Science, Arts and Letters, 6 : 67–76.
2. Kauffman, C. H. 1915. Unreported Michigan Fungi for 1911, 1912, 1913, and 1914. Report of the Michigan Academy of Science, 17 : 194–216.
3. —— 1929. A Study of the Fungous Flora of the Lake Superior Region of Michigan, with Some New Species. Papers of the Michigan Academy of Science, Arts and Letters, 9 : 169–218
4. Murrill, W. A. North American Flora, 9 : 1–72.

5. Neuman, J. J. 1914. The Polyporaceae of Wisconsin. Wisconsin Geological and National History Survey. Bulletin 33, Scientific Series, No. 10 : 1–206.

6. Overholts, L. O. 1917. The Structure of Polyporus Glomeratus Peck. Torreya, 17 : 202–206.

7. —— 1921. Some New Hampshire Fungi. Mycologia, 13 : 24–37.

8. Romell, L. 1911. Hymenomycetes of Lapland. Arkiv für Botanik, 11 : 1–35.

9. —— 1926. Remarks on Some Species of Polyporus. Svensk Botanisk Tidskrift, Bd. 20, H. 1 : 1–24.

10. Weir, James R. 1915. Pathological Observations on the Chestnut in Southern Indiana. 15th Annual Report of the Indiana State Board of Forestry, 156–163.

DESCRIPTION OF PLATES

PLATE XXVI

Poria carbonaria B & C. on *Chamaecyparis Lawsoniana.* Note the interrupted type of growth. This plant has been found in the region of the Lake States on charred pine and cedar logs.

PLATE XXVII

Poria myceliosa Pk. Herbarium, Field Museum of Natural History, No. 526164. Note the strands of mycelium extending through decayed wood.

PLATE XXVIII

Poria subfuscoflavida Fr. *Fide* Romell. Plant on logs of *Pinus sabiniana.* Peanut, California.

PLATE XXIX

Poria subfuscoflavida Fr. *Fide* Romell; on logs of *Tsuga mertensiana.* Crater Lake, Oregon.

PLATE XXVI

PLATE XXVII

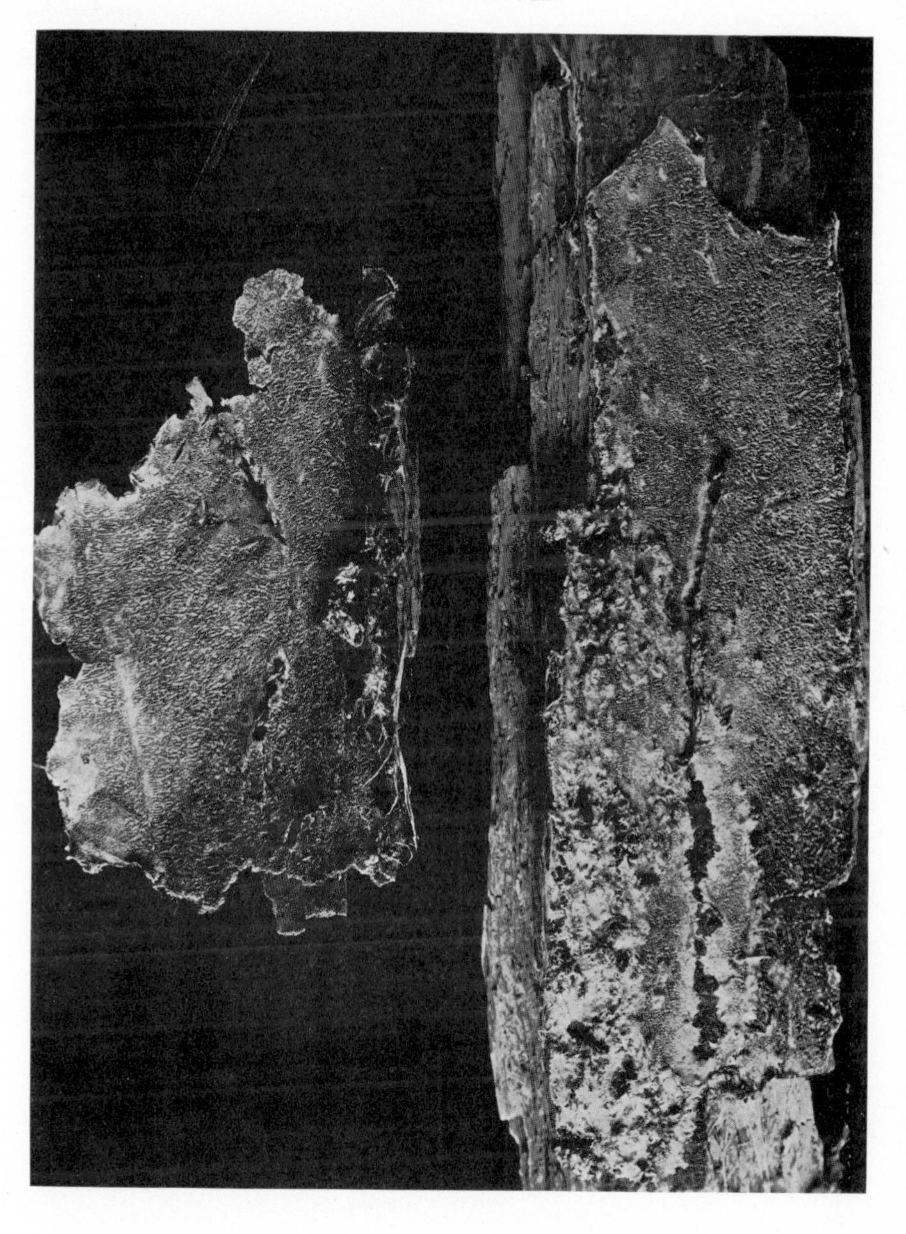

PLATE XXVIII

PLATE XXIX

A GREENHOUSE STUDY OF THE CONIDIAL STROMA OF *EPICHLOE TYPHINA* *

DON M. BENEDICT

THROUGHOUT northern Europe, and especially in Germany, Denmark, and Sweden, during seasons that are more moist than usual, considerable loss is experienced in forage grasses as a result of the attacks of the fungus *Epichloe typhina* (Pers.) Tul. In this country, the fungus, although widely distributed and locally abundant, has received little or no attention because of its apparently lesser economic importance. It attacks a large number of grass species, many of which are inhabitants of moist situations, while others produce their maximum growth and flower during the period of seasonal rains.

The observations of Tulasne (5) and the culture work of Brefeld (1) have hardly touched upon the early development of the fungus or its conidial state on the host. It seemed desirable, therefore, to study the relationship of the conidial stroma of the fungus *Epichloe typhina* to a particular host under controlled greenhouse conditions. *Glyceria nervata* (Willd.) Trin., on which abundant material was found near Ann Arbor, was chosen as the host upon which these studies were made.

This grass is common to both Europe and America. In this country it ranges along the entire eastern part from Newfoundland to Florida, westward to the Pacific Coast and from Alaska to Mexico. It is found in shallow swamps and low, moist places or meadows, situations which allow it to be exposed to full sunlight. When plants are found in partially wooded areas or form a narrow fringe along marshes with partially shaded margins, they are scraggly in appearance, scattered and weak, quite in

* Paper from the Department of Botany of the University of Michigan, No. 285.

contrast to the appearance which they present in the optimum situations mentioned above, where they are the dominant plant over considerable areas; in fact, they occur in practically pure stands in large patches. During the very end of June or early July, the culms have reached a height of from five to seven decimeters when the inflorescence appears. The purple spikelets of the loose panicles are then a conspicuous sight, overhanging the marsh like a faint haze. Seeds mature during the first half of July at this latitude and are mostly shed by the end of the month.

A quantity of seed was gathered with the purpose of raising a large number of plants from them. Many attempts to germinate the seed met with failure during the fall and winter, but finally successful germination was obtained when the seeds were immersed in water in a container and the whole placed in the cold room at a temperature of 4 degrees Centigrade for a month. When the container was removed from the cold room, the seeds, still submerged, germinated within a week. The minimum temperature and the minimum time interval necessary for the stimulus to act were not determined. The submerged condition seems essential. Since the seeds do not germinate immediately, they perhaps must first be submerged in the water of their native habitat during the winter season. Vegetative reproduction seems to be a very extensive means of propagation. Numerous rhizomes form a net or mat at the soil surface or just beneath it, from the nodes of which many culms arise in dense clusters. Any culm, seemingly, may act as a rhizome if it is forced into a horizontal position and surrounded by sufficient moisture. Culms frequently become top-heavy and recline as a result of their own weight or are blown over. Wherever the nodes touch the water or moist soil, they take root and produce a number of young sprouts. These young sprouts are particularly numerous during the fall and measure from five to thirteen centimeters as winter approaches, the smaller ones being entirely submerged beneath the water. It is these sprouts which develop into culms the following spring. It is also important to emphasize the fact that in this species the leaf-sheaths are closed nearly to the summit and those in the lower part of the culm overlap the sheaths above them, even when fully developed (4).

The material studied was secured during the latter part of October, 1927, from a marsh north of Manchester, Washtenaw County, Michigan. At this time the fall sprouts were seven to ten centimeters high. Certain healthy areas of practically pure stands of the grass were selected, from which clumps of the grass were removed with considerable care, so as not to disturb the root system; large blocks of muck were included along with the plant portions, so as to bring in as much soil as possible. These were placed in large pans and removed to the laboratory greenhouse. At first an attempt was made to keep the temperature of the plant room fairly low, between 50 to 60 degrees F., but later this temperature increased to 70 degrees F. and fluctuated between 70 and 80 degrees. Every effort was made to maintain the relative humidity of the room high by keeping the benches and floor wet. Good growth seems to be more closely associated with a high humidity factor than with a narrowly limited range of temperature. Although the plants were standing in three or four inches of water at the time that they were collected, no effort was made to keep water standing in the pans in the plant room. The dead culms, which had produced flowers and seed during the previous summer, were cut away so as to allow as much light to reach the young growth as possible. The growth of the plants seemed not to have been checked and there was no evidence that they suffered in any way by their removal from the swamp to the greenhouse. The young culms soon began to grow slowly and probably at any time grew as rapidly as the subdued light of the partially cloudy and shortened days of the winter season would permit. The plants developed normally in every respect; the culms stretched up to their full size and developed inflorescences which were at anthesis during the end of January and the first of February. The seeds ripened and were being shed during the middle of March. In all respects, then, the greenhouse plants grew and matured seed just as if they were under summer conditions in their natural habitat. The fact that growth was slower can be explained by the reduced amount of light.

Another area from the same swamp was selected because the almost pure stand of *Glyceria nervata* was known to have been heavily infested with the fungus *Epichloe typhina* during the previous summer. At intervals during the latter part of October and during November, clumps of the grass were removed from these areas where the fungus was known to occur and likewise transferred to the greenhouse. These plants had produced fall sprouts similar to those described for the plants previously selected, and the same care was exercised in cutting out the clumps so as to bring in plenty of the marsh soil in order not to disturb the roots. These plants were also placed in large pans in the plant room and under the same conditions of moisture, temperature and light as the controls. They continued to grow normally and certain of the culms produced inflorescences.

We come now to a consideration of the fungus. Numerous stromata appeared on the culms of the group last described. The greatest number of culms which had stromata developed upon them were produced from a collection brought in on November 25, after there had been considerable rather cold weather. This fact, however, may have no significance upon the conditions favorable to the development of the stromata. The first stromata appeared during the first week of January, 1928, and continued to appear for about three weeks. At this time, no difference could be seen between the culms which did not produce stromata and those upon which the stromata appeared within a few days. It was not possible to foretell with certainty that a culm would bear a stroma until about two days before the appearance of the stroma. At that time, the outline of the stroma can be clearly seen beneath the leaf-sheath which covers it, although there is no hypertrophy which accompanies its formation. Once the stroma becomes evident, the subsequent development of the infected culm becomes very different from the normal. The elongation of the internode, which finally frees the stroma from the leaf-sheath, marks the end of growth in length of that culm. Whatever undeveloped internodes there are which exist in the bud hidden within this terminal leaf-sheath, cease to develop; consequently, culms which are infected with this fungus never produce any inflorescence. Also, the stroma which appears on infected culms is always located on the uppermost internode.

In respect to their general appearance and position on the culm, two general types of stromata are produced, although morphologically this grouping is superficial, and is justified only by the very striking difference in appearance. The type which I shall describe first is by far the more abundant, occurring probably in 75 to 80 per cent of the stromata produced. The stromata of this type (Text Fig. 1 *a*, *s*) are large, extending for a distance of 1–2 cm. along the culm, and usually for a greater length on one side than upon the other, as if an oval disk had been rolled around it. As has been pointed out, the stroma can be seen outlined through the leaf-sheath a day or two before it is freed by the lengthening of the internode which bears it. It is always located in the lower part of the internode within two or three millimeters of the node and often reaching it. The second type of stroma is much smaller, being only three to six millimeters in length and located on a dwarfed inflorescence. It frequently appears as a blunt projection just protruding beyond the leaf-sheath (Text Fig. 1 *a*); however, its true nature is more clearly shown by a greater lengthening of the rachis, thus exhibiting its characteristic zigzag appearance, and bearing the stroma in its upper part (Text Fig. 1 *b*, *c*). On some occasions, a single rachilla is also partially developed and likewise contains a tiny stroma. Since the attachment of the spikelet to the main axis, or the attachment

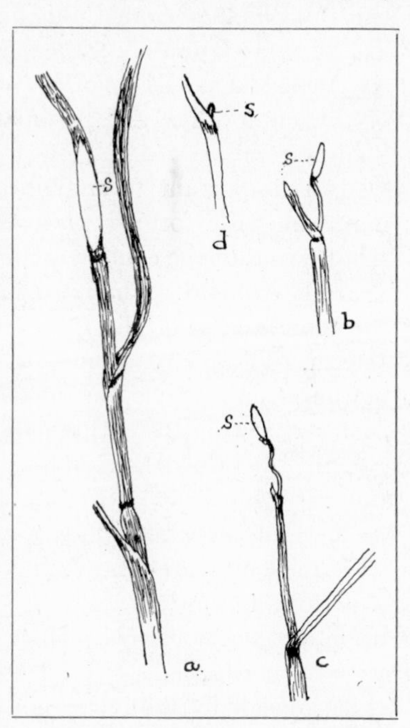

FIG. 1. Forms of conidial stromata of *Epichloe typhina* (Pers.) Tul.

of a single inflorescence on a spikelet, is indicative of a morphological node, it is apparent that the two types of stromata are in the same morphological position in respect to each other. From these two types, it would seem that the ultimate position of the stroma on the culm might be associated with the extent to which the mycelium occupied the bud during the incubation period. The only real difference, then, between the two stromata is one of size, which depends upon the difference of diameter of the parts of the culm where the stroma appears and upon the available food material.

It is important to emphasize the fact that the conidial stromata are fully formed while they are still covered by the leaf-sheath, so that the conidia are ready for functioning as soon as they are fully exposed. This, as was pointed out, is brought about by the lengthening of the internode in its growth out of the leaf-sheath. The color is glistening white, due in part to the mycelium of the stroma itself, and in part to the conidia which cover its surface. Owing to its thinness, the stroma adds very little to the general thickness of the culm. The stroma consists of a compact but very thin layer of mycelial hyphae bearing club-shaped conidiophores upon which the conidia are produced. Viable conidia were present on the individual stromata in the greenhouse during a period of from ten days to two weeks. They are borne singly upon the conidiophores. The conidial stromata contrast markedly with the perithecial stromata as seen outdoors; the latter are rather thick, decidedly fleshy, papillate and orange-yellow in color.

The conidia are ovoid to bluntly ellipsoidal, averaging about five microns in length and three in width. The wall, through which three or four small vacuoles may be seen, is thin and hyaline. They are fully formed before the stroma is freed from the leaf-sheath and are capable of germinating immediately. In fact, I have germinated conidia which have been removed from the stroma while they were yet covered by the leaf-sheath. They germinate readily in either distilled water or "tap water"; no other medium was tried. All germination tests were made by placing the conidia in a drop of water on a glass slide and then placing the slide on glass supports in a petri dish having the bottom covered with water or a moistened piece of filter paper. At ordinary room temperature of 18–21 degrees Centigrade, the spores germinate in approximately 15–18 hours. An attempt was made to get an idea of the lower temperature limits at which germination would occur. To determine this, spores in germinators were placed in two different cold-rooms, with temperatures of 10 degrees and 4 degrees Centigrade, respectively. After 24–30 hours, the spores at the higher temperature had germinated. None of the spores germinated at the lower temperature of 4 degrees. Therefore the lower temperature limit for germination lies between 4 and 10 degrees Centigrade and probably nearer the higher value since germination at that temperature was weak and took place several hours after the normal time period had elapsed. Light has a very definitely retarding effect upon the germination of the conidia. Spores exposed to sunlight for varying periods of time after being placed in germinators have their germination retarded or inhibited according to length of exposure. One extreme case might be cited. Spores in a moist chamber were exposed to direct sunlight during a period of seven hours, after which they were placed in a dark chamber. A control set was placed in the dark. The temperature of the two sets could not have varied more than one degree at any one time during the experiment. The spores exposed to light showed no germination after twenty-four hours, while those in the control had produced germ-tubes many times the length of the spore at the end of 18 hours. When a conidiospore germinates, a germ-tube is first produced at one end of the spore; when this has reached a length of 40–50 times that of the length of the spore, a tube develops at the opposite end of the spore. The first branching is always uniform and occurs a short distance from the spore in both tubes in succession.

The fact that *Epichloe typhina* can be made to appear in its conidial form in mid-winter under greenhouse conditions throws light on the relation of this fungus to its host, for, provided that the culms have reached a certain stage of development and that they have been infected by the fungus, the stroma appears regardless of the season. The time of appearance of the stroma is dependent, then, upon the stage of development of the host rather than upon a seasonal condition. Besides the relationship of parasite and host, there are probably other contributing factors, physiological or other, which determine the conidial phase, and which need further investigation.

Grateful acknowledgment is due to Professor C. H. Kauffman under whose direction and interest this study was made.

UNIVERSITY OF MICHIGAN

LITERATURE CITED

1. BREFELD, OSCAR. 1891. Mykologie, Vol. X.
2. DE BARY, ANTON. 1887. Comparative Morphology and Biology of the Fungi, Mycetozoa and Bacteria (English translation).
3. ERIKSSON, JACOB. 1904. Kolvsjuka a timotej. Lantbruksbotanisk Berattelse av ar 1904 : C.
4. ROBINSON, B. L., AND FERNALD, M. L. 1908. Gray's New Manual of Botany (Seventh edition).
5. TULASNE, L. R. AND C. 1865. Selecta Fungorum Carpologia III.

A STUDY OF THE DIGESTIVE SECRETION OF *SARRACENIA PURPUREA**

EPHRAIM B. BOLDYREFF

THE majority of chlorophyll-bearing plants derive the substances necessary for the maintenance of life from mineral sources of air and soil. A much smaller group of plants, in addition to this means of getting nutriment, are also capable of obtaining nourishment through consumption of food in the same manner as animals. The ability of this group of plants to digest and assimilate the animal protein has attracted considerable attention, and owing to this striking characteristic they have received the name "carnivorous plants."

The so-called carnivorous plants do not, however, subsist solely on animal food; therefore the name "carnivorous" does not convey the right idea; these plants are capable of digesting their food only in the way typical to the animals, and this is their distinctive feature.

In North America are found the following representatives of this group: Dionaea, Drosera, Sarracenia and Utricularia. The Dionaea, Drosera and Utricularia are generally recognized as capable of digesting and assimilating food, while the Sarracenia is usually placed in this group but tentatively. Some investigators (1; 4) either state that: "Nothing is yet known positively as to the manner in which the products of decomposition are utilized by the plant, if, indeed, they are at all serviceable to it"; or they call Sarracenia an example of "maladaptation between plants and animals, for while they [plants] serve as traps for insects they are neither harmed nor benefited by them."

* Paper from the Pavlov Physiological Institute, Battle Creek Sanitarium, and from the Biology Department, Battle Creek College, Battle Creek, Michigan.

Hepburn, St. John and Jones (3) give a brief review of the literature devoted to this subject and mention the works of Batalin, Zipperer and Lambert, who reported the proteolytic property of pitcher liquid of *Sarracenia purpurea* and other species. These authors offer an interesting study of the processes of digestion and absorption of nutrients which take place in the pitchers of Sarraceniaceae and apparently consider that pitchers secrete a proteolytic enzyme. But they also mention the presence of proteolytic bacteria in the pitchers. Suessenguth (5), on the other hand, states that there is no conclusive evidence of either the presence of digestive enzymes or of putrefaction-inhibitive substances in the secretion of the pitchers of Sarraceniaceae. Hegner (2) likewise questions "whether these enzymes are produced by the plant or by bacteria." (See Pl. XXX.)

EXPERIMENTAL

The object of the present work is: (1) to study the secretion of pitchers of *Sarracenia purpurea* on different substances; (2) to throw some light on the question of whether the secretion of pitchers or bacterial activity is responsible for the presence of enzymes; (3) to examine the pitcher liquid for proteolytic, amylolytic and lipolytic enzymes; (4) to study the temperature variations in the pitchers as the possible source of evidence of the metabolic heat.

SECRETION OF PITCHERS ON FOODSTUFFS

The contents of many pitchers of *Sarracenia purpurea* were examined in the field. Usually pitchers were half-filled with colorless or sometimes, owing to decomposition of organic matter, pinkish liquid. The organic material found in the pitchers consisted of abundant animal and plant débris. The remains and dead bodies of the following animals were found in the pitchers: snails, spiders, millipedes, bees, flies, beetles, moths, etc., as well as tamarack leaves.

The diversity of food material found in the pitchers suggests the possibility of the difference in the secretory response to different foods. The secretion on albuminous substances is men-

PLATE XXX

Sarracenia purpurea

tioned in the literature (3). The systematic study of the secretory processes of the pitchers of *Sarracenia purpurea*, however, was never undertaken and the information found in the literature on this subject is of a casual and fragmentary character. The occurrence of plant débris in the pitchers as well as the contention of Robinson (4) that pitchers of *Sarracenia purpurea* secrete enzyme which converts starch into reducing substance, may be considered as indications of the possibility of adaptation of the plant to food source other than animal proteins. With this in mind the secretory response of pitchers to the following foodstuffs was studied: raw meat, white of egg, beef broth, beef extract, peptone, beef tallow, milk, cornstarch, dextrin, sucrose, lactose, glucose and yeast extract.

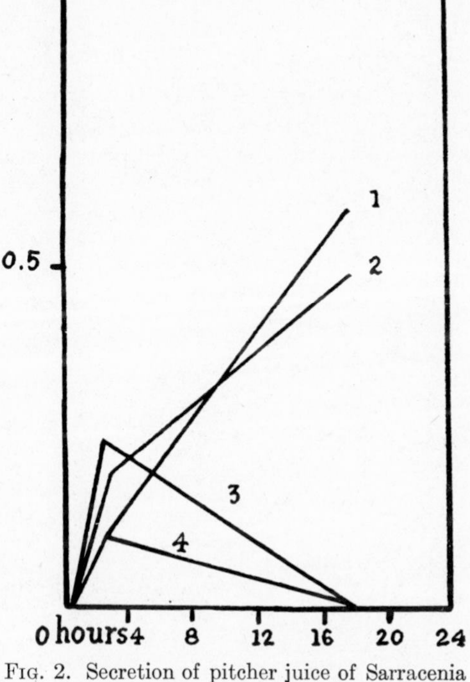

FIG. 2. Secretion of pitcher juice of Sarracenia on various food substances

1. Secretion on Armour's Extract of Beef, 8 c. c., 6 per cent solution
2. Secretion on peptone (Digestive Ferments Co.), 8 c. c., 10 per cent solution
3. Secretion on cornstarch, 10 c. c., 2 per cent solution
4. Secretion on sucrose, 10 c. c., 10 per cent solution

It was found that albuminous substances generally have a stronger secretagogue action than that of the carbohydrates. The lactose and dextrine, however, produced a copious secretion. The beef broth containing fat had, it seems, a stronger effect than broth made of lean beef. The yeast extract caused abundant secretion of pitcher juice. The types of the secretion of pitchers on various food substances are demonstrated in Figure 2 and in the protocols of the experiments given below.

PROTOCOL I

SECRETION OF PITCHER JUICE ON BEEF BROTH

Into empty pitcher washed with distilled water the broth was pipetted; 3 hours and 30 minutes later the contents of pitchers were measured with pipette.

July 25, 1927

Pitcher No.	No. of c. c. of beef broth	No. of c. c. of liquid 3 h., 30 m. later	No. of c. c. of juice secreted
1	10	10.4	0.4
2	10	10.1	0.1
3	10	10.3	0.3
4	10	10.6	0.6
Average	10	10.35	0.35

Control Experiment with Water

5	10	10	0
6	10	9.8	0
7	10	10	0
8	10	10	0
9	10	10	0
		Average Secretion....	0

Secretion of Pitcher Juice on Beef Broth

July 31, 1927

10	10	10.2	0.2
11	10	10.4	0.4
12	10	10.4	0.4
13	10	10.3	0.3
14	10	10.3	0.3
		Average Secretion	0.32

PROTOCOL II

SECRETION OF PITCHER JUICE ON LACTOSE AND DEXTRIN: MIXTURE 10 PER CENT

Into empty pitcher washed with distilled water aqueous 10 per cent solution of mixture of lactose and dextrin was pipetted; 12 hours later the contents of pitchers were measured with a pipette.

July 9, 1927

Pitcher No.	No. of c. c. of mixture	No. of c. c. of liquid 12 h. later	No. of c. c. of juice secreted
15	10	11.0	1.0
16	10	11.1	1.1
17	10	11.5	1.5
18	10	11.4	1.4
Average	10	11.33	1.33

THE EFFECT OF ACIDS AND ALKALIES UPON SECRETION OF PITCHERS

The pitchers respond very readily to administration of acids and alkalies. The introduction of acids is followed by a strong

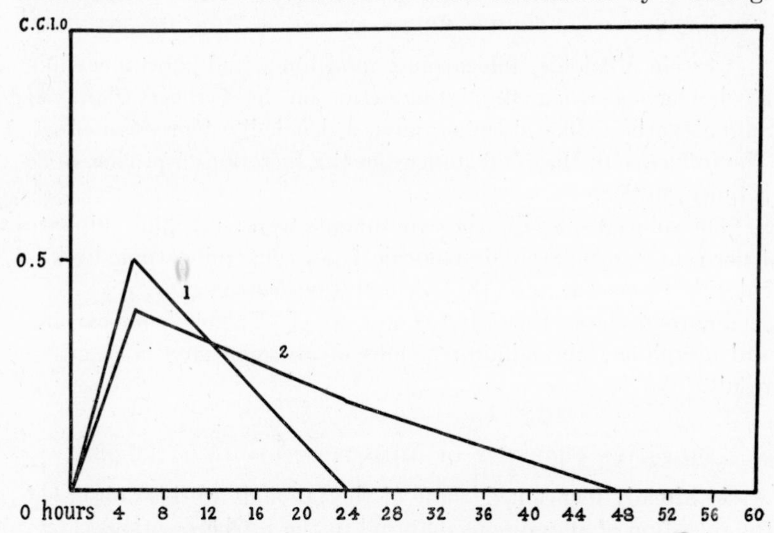

Fig. 3. Effect of acids on secretion of pitcher juice in Sarracenia

1. Secretion on 10 c. c. of 0.5 per cent solution of hydrochloric acid
2. Secretion on 10 c.c. of 1.25 per cent solution of lactic acid

secretion, which is possibly an effort to dilute or neutralize the artificially increased acidity of the pitcher content. The pitcher liquid, when free from decaying organic matter, has a slightly alkaline reaction, and, as the experiments showed, the action of acids is detrimental to the plant. Normally, in spite of the presence of acid-producing bacteria, the alkalinity of the liquid found in the pitchers is maintained fairly constant.

The effect of alkalies on the secretory process is somewhat obscured because of increased absorption caused by administration of alkalies. The zone of the pitcher cavity where the absorption takes place becomes distinctly darker after the administration of the alkalies. There was also observed a slight decrease of the alkalinity of Na_2CO_3 solution introduced into empty pitchers.

The following solutions were used: 0.5 per cent hydrochloric acid, 1.25 per cent lactic acid and 2 per cent solution of sodium bicarbonate. The effect of acids on the secretion of pitchers is shown in Figure 3.

THE EFFECT OF VARIOUS DRUGS ON SECRETION OF PITCHERS

Certain alkaloids (pilocarpine, morphine) and substances like alcohol have a strong stimulating action on the secretory glands of animals; others, like atropine, have a decidedly depressive effect. The influence of these substances on the secretion of pitcher juice is quite similar.

The solutions used in the experiments were: atropine sulphate 1 per cent, morphine hydrochloride 1 per cent, pilocarpine hydrochloride 1 per cent and ethyl alcohol 2 per cent.

Figure 4 shows the secretagogue effect of alcohol, pilocarpine and morphine; the administrations of atropine gave a negative result.

DIGESTIVE PROPERTY OF THE SECRETION OF PITCHERS

As already mentioned, some of the previous workers observed the digestion of albuminous material in the pitchers; others, however, either denied that the digestion took place or attributed it to the action of bacterial fermentation. The strong secretagogue

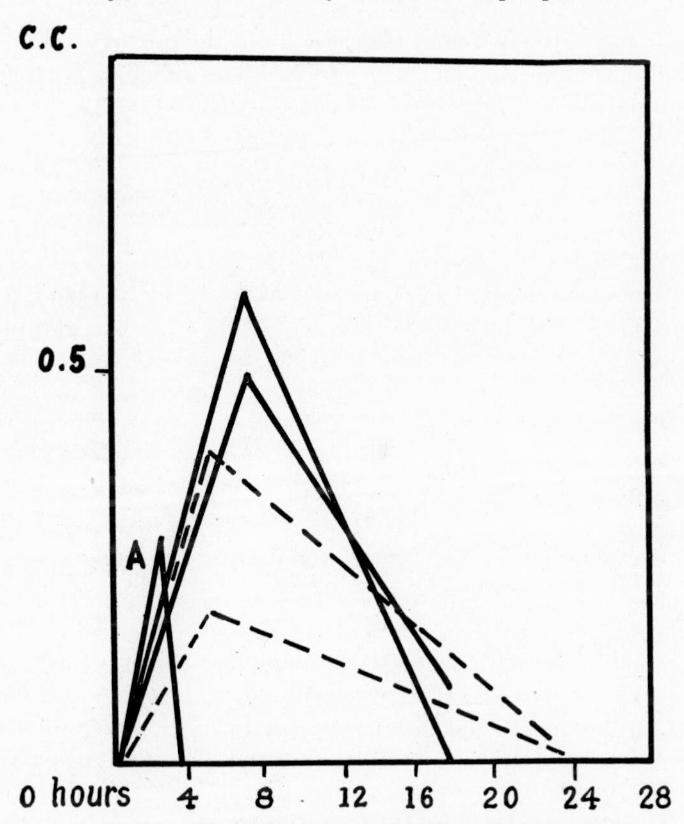

Fig. 4. Effect of various drugs on secretion of pitcher juice

A. Secretion on 5 c.c. ethyl alcohol, 2 per cent

Solid line curves — secretion on 5 c. c., 1 per cent solution, of pilocarpine hydrochloride

Interrupted line curves — secretion on: (1) 1 c. c. solution of 1 per cent of morphine hydrochloride; (2) 15 c. c. solution of 0.3 per cent of the same solution

action of pilocarpine suggests that, if secretion of the pitchers contains digestive enzymes, the more juice secreted the greater will be the concentration of enzymes and consequently the greater will be the digestive power.

The proteolytic strength of the pitcher liquid was estimated by Mett's method generally employed in the medical routine gastric test. It was found that usually in the pitchers which received pilocarpine the digestion of egg white was more complete. Figures given in Table I may serve as an illustration.

TABLE I

PROTEOLYTIC ENZYME OF THE PITCHER JUICE

Habitat of the plant	Kind of secretion	Proteolytic activity
St. Mary's Lake marsh	Liquid originally found in the pitcher in the field	3.6 mm.
Brigham Lake marsh	Same as above	1.2 mm.
Brigham Lake marsh	Secreted on pilocarpine, 1 c. c. 1 per cent	6.3 mm.

The proteolytic activity was estimated by Mett's method; duration 48 hours.

OCCURRENCE OF DIGESTIVE ENZYMES IN THE PITCHERS

The following enzymes were detected in the pitcher liquid of *Sarracenia purpurea:* proteolytic, lipolytic and amylolytic. The lipolytic strength of the pitcher liquid in some cases was considerable. It is probable that secretion of the pitchers contains all the three mentioned enzymes. But in order to obtain convincing evidence further investigation in this direction is necessary.

TEMPERATURE OBSERVATIONS

The leaves of *Sarracenia purpurea* resist the action of frost and usually survive through the winter. The observation of the temperature of the pitcher contents made in the laboratory as well as in the field shows that the temperature of the pitchers has a tendency to be nearly constant at the given time and to differ from the temperature of the surrounding air and soil approximately by 1.0° C. In this respect *Sarracenia purpurea* may be compared with cold-blooded animals, which within 1.0° C. variation (due to metabolic processes) have the temperature of their surroundings. On the following page are tabulated the results of one of the series of observations made in the field.

PROTOCOL III

TEMPERATURES IN DEGREES OF CENTIGRADE SCALE

March 26, 1927, 4:20–4:30 P.M., Brigham Lake

Plant No. 1	Temperature of Pitchers	Temperature of Air	Temperature of Soil
	4.2		
	4.3		
	4.3		
	4.3		
	4.2		
	4.5		
	4.5		
Average.....	4.33	3.6	3.5
Plant No. 2	4.0		
	4.3		
	4.5		
	4.7		
	4.3		
Average.....	4.36		

CONCLUSIONS

1. The pitchers of *Sarracenia purpurea* possess the secretory function.

2. The secretion of pitchers may be caused by protein, carbohydrate or other food substances.

3. Alkaloids and other substances known as stimulants for secretory glands of animals have also a stimulating effect on the secretion of the pitchers of *Sarracenia purpurea*.

4. Proteolytic, lipolytic and amylolytic enzymes are found in the pitcher liquid of *Sarracenia purpurea*.

5. Secretion of the pitchers of *Sarracenia purpurea* is slightly alkaline in reaction.

6. The phenomena of temperature variations in the pitcher plant resemble the variation of the temperature in the cold-blooded animals.

Pavlov Physiological Institute
Battle Creek Sanitarium
Battle Creek Michigan

LITERATURE CITED

1. Gray, Asa. 1885. Botanical Text-Book. Vol. II, Chap. X, pp. 338–349.

2. Hegner, R. W. 1926. The Protozoa of the Pitcher Plant — Sarracenia purpurea. Biol. Bull., 50 : 271.

3. Hepburn, J. S., St. John, E. Q., and Jones, F. M. 1920. The Absorption of Nutrients and Allied Phenomena in the Pitchers of Sarraceniaceae. Journ. Franklin Institute, 189 : 147–184.

4. Robinson, W. J. 1907–9. Study of Digestive Power of Sarracenia purpurea. Contributions from the New York Bot. Garden, Vol. V, No. 109.

5. Suessenguth, Karl. 1927. Handbuch d. normalen und pathologischen Physiologie. Vol. III. Verdauung und Verdauungsapparat, pp. 102–109. Berlin.

NEW METHODS FOR THE DIAGNOSIS OF SPECIES OF THE GENUS FUSARIUM

GEORGE H. COONS AND MIRIAM CARPENTER STRONG

IN THE beginnings of the science of plant pathology the study of the causation of plant disease was apparently a simple matter. One had merely to swear allegiance to the rules of Koch and turn to the handmaiden sciences, mycology and bacteriology, for methods and a solution. As a result of further research, the apparently simple etiological situations have been found in reality to be extremely complicated. As precision of diagnosis increased, the large catch-all groups of fungi have been subdivided and have undergone drastic reclassification. Certain large groups of fungi, which by their "pleomorphism" had almost defied classification under the standard methods of the mycologist, still remain to vex us. The genus Fusarium has been noteworthy among these groups as presenting difficulties of classification for the taxonomist and of species-diagnosis for the worker. The obstacles in the way of determination of the species of these fungi have hampered investigation in this line more than one who has not worked in the group can easily recognize.

The old mycologist, Link, erected the genus Fusarium in 1809 for those members of the Fungi Imperfecti possessing fusiform spores (18). Since that time the description of species has gone on, for the most part inadequately, until much of the literature in this group presents almost undecipherable confusion. When a summary of our progress was made, it was found that plant diseases attributable to the various members of the genus Fusarium were among the most serious known and they were frequently characterized by the fact that the capacity of the fungus for persistence in the soil rendered infested soils permanently unfit for the culture of the susceptible crop. We must pass over the mass of plant pathological work which has been done with the various fusarial forms with the mere comment that the listing of the susceptible plants from which Fusaria have been more or less adequately reported would be practically a listing of all economic hosts, so widespread are the fungi of this genus, so versatile the attack, and so important are they as pathogens. Workers must arrive at some concordance of opinion as to the organism involved in this or that disease complex. This has more in it than mere agreement as to name of the causal organism, since it involves a recognition of the true situation as regards the Fusaria concerned. Each contribution which represents a reworking of old disease complexes brings to light the inadequacy of our knowledge of the etiological factor involved in pathological conditions which we believed at one time completely explained. For example, Goss (10), working on the wilt disease of potato, which, for years, had been assigned to *Fusarium oxysporum*, finds that the wilt disease in Nebraska is largely due to another species with quite different parasitic habit.

The reason for this constant overturning of our presumably settled convictions is to be found in the difficulties inherent in determination of the species of Fusarium. As has been said, this fungus group seems to be characterized by its variability. Every laboratory has its isolations of Fusaria, all awaiting some specialist to determine them. The problem of physiological forms within the species, once the species themselves are determined, remains as yet largely untouched and its relative importance with this group of fungi can only be surmised from the significance found in other groups.

The basis for classification of the Fusaria was laid in 1910 by Appel and Wollenweber in their important contribution, *Grundlagen einer Monographie der Gattung Fusarium* (Link) (1). These workers brought order out of the chaos of inadequate descriptions and inaccurate diagnoses. They were the first to show clearly that in spite of irregularities of spore forms, spore shapes and spore sizes and vagaries in their appearance in culture, it was possible to obtain enough constancy to permit a classification if a definite technique was utilized.

This paper made possible a classification of Fusaria because of one feature, the recognition that there is for each Fusarium, as it is grown in pure culture, a period of normality, and a fungus to be recognized must be in this condition of "Normkultur." This feature, which is the basic thing in their work, is also its weakness, for the norm is often difficult of definition and often attainable only with great difficulty after months of culture, and naturally is variously interpreted by different workers. Appel and Wollenweber conceived that Fusarium cultures showed three phases of development — "Ankultur," "Normkultur," and "Abkultur" — types characterized by the kinds of spores produced and the relative activity of the culture in the vegetative and fruiting phases. The "Ankultur" was believed unsuitable for diagnostic purposes, since in this stage of development microconidia and mycelial growth predominate. In the stage of "Normkultur," which too has its subdivisions, young, high, and old, the fungus produces relatively a large mass of spores, prevailingly macrospores, and at time of "Hochkultur" these spores may be conceived as representing the normal for the species. Spores taken from such a suitable culture, by their morphology, were believed to be decisive for classification purposes. They placed the species studied into sections and these sections have in Wollenweber's treatment of the subject been named and more and more amplified, each section being built up around a type species (28). Appel and Wollenweber used other characters in differentiating Fusaria, such as the color of spores in mass, the character of the mycelium and the stroma, the nature of the spore heaps, the presence or absence of sclerotia, the nature and position of chlamydospores — all these and many other manifestations on certain culture media, mostly vegetable plugs or stems of plants. They outlined a technique whereby it was possible to describe a species of Fusarium so that it could be recognized by someone else expert in this technique.

Then, during the five or six years after the publication of this paper, there began intensive studies on the etiology of Fusarium diseases of plants and an attempt to delineate the species. The contributions of Sherbakoff (24), Wollenweber (27), Lewis (15), Harter and Field (12), Carpenter (3), Link (16), and Pratt (22) fall into this early group of papers in which the usability of the Appel and Wollenweber methods was given rigorous tests. The soundness of the method is evidenced by the fact that these workers were able to identify organisms by using it, and organisms described with attention to the characteristics necessary for definition under this code have been recognizable by workers applying the same technique.

Since that time hundreds of species have been proposed and for some of these there are varieties as well. There is still lacking a monograph of the genus, the nearest approach being Wollenweber's contributions.

The Fusaria associated with the potato plant in disease have been the most fully charted. Appel and Wollenweber (1) in their work dealt with thirteen species, mostly secured from the potato plant. Sherbakoff (24) in his memoir, *Fusaria of Potatoes*, listed twenty previously described species and forty-one new species and varieties. Morris and Nutting (20) turned to these published accounts and, using single spore cultures isolated from rotting potatoes in Montana, attempted to diagnose a series of one hundred cultures. They arrived after some years of work at a more or less definite diagnosis of ninety-seven of the cultures, some of their determinations being provisional and others made with reservations. They noted discrepancies in the descriptions. The organisms dealt with were put in seventeen of the described species. Their comments are pertinent to the present situation of Fusarium studies (20, p. 355):

"The greatest obstacle in the way of accurate determination of species of Fusarium is the lack of a good monograph of the genus, and this lack is due in part to the non-standardization of the methods used in identification work, especially as regards kinds of media, environmental conditions, and the relative value ascribed to various characteristics of the fungus when grown in pure culture under laboratory conditions. The species and varieties intergrade and the differential characters used in the keys are not sufficiently distinct to permit any but an experienced investigator to use the key. To become an authority one must work long enough and with large enough numbers of species so that he can create within himself a concept of the species. In other words, he judges to what species the fungus in question belongs rather than actually identifying it."

A second worker has published his conclusions after attempting work on this complicated genus. Hansford (11), working with Fusaria isolated from suspected banana wilt material, has criticized the minute limits set up by the specialists for the wilt-producing species of Fusaria belonging to the section Elegans. He has dealt with three hundred and fifteen isolations from soils, from diseased banana plants, and from débris from banana plants. The species encountered in this study number thirty-five, but the greatest attention was placed upon the Fusaria of the Elegans group. He was able, using the accepted technique, to divide the organisms isolated from the vascular system of diseased bananas into five morphologically distinct divisions, and representatives of these when inoculated into banana plants produced the banana wilt disease. From soils he also obtained organisms, which he could put into groups paralleling the pathogenic forms, but representatives of these forms did not prove to be pathogenic to banana. He states: "From the present work, it becomes evident that the only possible test for this organism (banana wilt) is that of inoculation into healthy banana plants. In other words *Fusarium cubense* is a purely biological species, as distinct from the purely morphological species such as *Fusarium oxysporum*, etc., and cannot be diagnosed from its morphological characters, as shown in artificial culture." And further:

"During the course of the present work the writer has been struck with the defects of the present system of classification of this genus, as given by previous workers. Up to the present it seems that the conception of a single species in this group of fungi has been kept too rigid, and does not allow a sufficient range of variability within the species. Especially is this the case in the sections Elegans and Martiella. The organisms of the former include many parasites of crop plants, and the workers on this group have endeavored by a minutely detailed examination of the characters of these fungi grown in culture under as far as possible closely specified conditions, to separate these organisms from each other on morphological characters, which necessarily show extremely minute differences, if indeed, any at all, between the various strains of the group. Not only are these differences between the so-called 'species' so minute, but at the same time each organism shows such a great range of variability in its morphological characters that the differences used to separate the various 'species' are almost negligible by comparison. . . . It appears to me that much would be gained, and much labour spared, were the various sections of the genus which have been erected by Wollenweber and his colleagues to be considered as species rather than sections of the genus, and then the various species at present included in these sections could be regarded as forms of these large species which show a slight variation from a central type."

Whether the suggestions of Hansford would simplify the complex problem the writers cannot say, but Hansford's experience is cited as evidence of the baffling conditions that meet the worker in this field. We have demanded precision in diagnosis and now that we have it, its very complexity overwhelms us.

Recently the results of a conference of the leading specialists on the taxonomy of Fusarium have been published. (Wollenweber, Sherbakoff, Reinking, Johann, and Bailey, 28). In this article there is recognition of the variations in methods employed in the different laboratories and attempt is made to standardize procedure. The difficulties involved with this genus are admitted and recommendations are made which should be helpful. The methods outlined do not differ essentially from those already in vogue in these studies. Distinct advantage will arise from the descriptions (in the form of a key) of the fifteen sections now recognized within the genus.

Workers in plant pathology are confronted with grave problems in the diagnosis, separation and control of Fusarium diseases and the enormous accumulation of species and the elaborate technique necessary in making determination of species has brought us to an *impasse.* We have no desire to disparage in any way the value of the taxonomic work which has been done on this genus. It has been of such a nature that we are forced to admire it. We must frankly face the fact that the whole Fusarium problem is held up until methods can be devised which will help the worker who is engaged in the study of Fusaria as pathogens to make dependable diagnoses. The isolated worker needs some ready method of identifying an organism and of separating in his work related forms which, though interesting of themselves taxonomically, are a hindrance in the solution of a problem where a specific pathogen is involved. To those whose work leads them to apparently new forms, the question arises whether it is better to master a difficult technique and attempt to describe the fungus or to name it provisionally a form of some old species, thus confusing the situation rather than helping it.

It is not exaggerating the situation to say that probably only a half-dozen specialists in the world at present are qualified to determine species of Fusarium, and it is obvious that these workers, many of them not devoting their full time to studies of this sort, cannot be called upon for solution of the problems of identification which arise so often in the laboratory. Every laboratory has its stock of undetermined Fusaria and anyone bold enough to offer to determine Fusaria would be flooded.

We seem to have reached a point where progress in studies in which this group is involved hinges upon the development of methods which give some promise of relief. The situation seems analogous to that of the bacteriologist who has had to develop methods of ready diagnosis for the various important animal pathogens. In this paper there are presented two methods which have been adapted from the methods of bacteriology which have promise of workability within the limits for which they are suitable of application.

SEROLOGICAL TESTS WITH FUSARIA

In the first method we have sought to apply serological technique to this problem. In spite of the conspicuous success of serological methods of diagnosis in the field of animal pathology, the literature of plant pathology contains but few reports of utilization of these methods in the diagnosis of bacterial and fungous pathogens. Fred and his associates (8) have applied serological technique in their studies of *Bacillus radicicola*. Brooks and his associates (2) have used the technique with a few bacterial pathogens. Riker (23) reports immunization of rabbits with the crown gall organism and the utilization of the sera with suspected cultures. Goldsworthy (9) has utilized a high titre anti-serum to identify *Bact. maculicolum* suspects plated from soils. Recently Link and Sharp (17) have extended the possibilities of the methods for the working plant pathologist.

It is evident that for the bacterial pathogens agglutination tests offer wide possibilities for quick determination of suspects and for deciding relationships, subject of course to the limitations of the method.

For the fungi, if we exclude the fungi pathogenic to animals, we find only casual attempts to use serological reactions. The conspicuous advance made by Mez and his students (cf. Mez, *Botanisches Arkiv*, Konigsberg, 1915 to date) in the utilization of precipitation and conglutination reactions as an index to plant relationships has now become fairly well known in the United States and we may expect increased interest in the subject. This work has been pretty largely confined to the higher plants, or at least to those forms which yield sufficient quantity of material to make the tests feasible. Work of this sort seems to stand upon safe ground as evidenced by the classic work of Wells and Osborne (26) on the specificity of serum reactions when pure plant proteins were used as antigens. The interesting relationships brought out by serum reactions are in the future to be more and more taken into account in phylogenetic studies.

Application of serological technique to fungous studies were made by Schütze in 1902 (25) in his precipitin tests to determine the relations of various types of yeasts. He compared the reactions obtained with sera from animals sensitized with upper and lower brewery yeasts and with the yeasts from bread and potato, and he stated that even with the application of the "most beautiful and most sure biological" technique often repeated, he could not obtain differences. In later work, using the complement fixation reaction, this worker was able to separate the yeasts of the upper and lower fermentation, but he was not able to differentiate the bread and potato yeasts by this test. Citron (6) showed that the fungi causing favus formed a similar precipitin, since a serum produced by infections of *Trichophyton microsporon* gave precipitation with the Trichophyton from cats and with extracts from favus material from mice and from human beings. Magnus and Friedenthal (19), in order to test the genetic relationship of the higher fungi yeasts and the truffle, *Tuber brumale*, injected animals with expressed sap with the following results: Although the reaction with yeast, truffle and *Agaricus campestris* is throughout specific, and although the serum from an animal immunized with truffle material gives a precipitate only with its homologous antigen, the serum of the animal sensitized with the yeast antigen gives a precipitate with the juice from truffle as well, and therefore, they concluded, the yeasts are more closely related to the truffle than to the higher fungi.

In the early work with fungi as antigens, the writers tested the sensitization of guinea pigs by observing if anaphylaxis occurred with subsequent delayed injections of the homologous antigen in comparison with the results of crossed injections with a heterologous antigen. Guinea pigs when injected with material from fungous cultures were sensitized by these injections as evidenced by their behavior and in most cases by death on the second injection with the homologous antigen. Guinea pigs sensitized with small injections of *Phoma sp.* were killed by a second injection of this material, while companion animals similarly sensitized tolerated injections of different species only to be killed by injections of the homologous antigen on the succeeding day. We carried on enough of these trials to convince us that specific sensitization was being built up by the extremely small amounts of protein we were able to inject using fungous mycelium, but gave up the method as not being usable for our purpose. We were not able to secure results using the elevations of temperature as an index of anaphylactic reaction, as has been done by some workers.

We then cast about for other methods which could be made to serve. Preliminary work with the precipitin test was not promising since we were not able to produce a high titre serum because of the scantiness of our injection material and the comparatively high dilution of our antigens. For it must be remarked that this factor, the obtaining of sufficient suitable antigen and its standardization, is the great obstacle in experimental work of this type.

We then turned to the complement fixation test as a method fine enough to detect the very small amount of reacting substance possible of production considering the nature of our material. The methods employed in our work have been dictated by the type of growth with which we have had to deal. The members of this genus produce an abundant growth on all laboratory media, but in the aggregate this represents only a small dry weight of substance, especially since we wished to work with young cultures (ten-day). The fungous mats which are obtainable after growth on a liquid culture medium — and we have always used a synthetic medium with potassium nitrate as a source of nitrogen — consist of cottony wefts of mycelium with more or less spore material included. The walls of the fungus are extremely refractory to dissolution and the protein content is locked up within these walls, so that extraction is extremely difficult. Antigens have commonly been prepared by drying the mycelial mats and grinding them in a mortar with an aliquot amount of salt, so that on subsequent dilution the material was suspended in a physiological salt solution. This method is tedious and fraught with the dangers associated with large particles which escape grinding. It has been found possible to sensitize rabbits with antigens prepared in this manner.

The usual methods employed have consisted of a series of intravenous injections at two-day intervals, and in general five injections of 5 c.c. are given. The antigens were made, as has been indicated, from washed mycelial mats grown on synthetic solution. The dried antigen was weighed and ground to fineness in a mortar with salt. At the time of use water was added, so that 0.1 gram of mycelium was used in 5 c.c. of distilled water. After about ten days the animals are then bled from the heart and the serum obtained, inactivated and preserved in the usual manner. Sera thus obtained have been tested against the homologous antigen and against some related forms. A typical test with sera prepared in this manner is shown in Table I.

TABLE I

COMPLEMENT FIXATION TEST WITH FUSARIA

Reaction against a homologous antigen compared with the reaction against heterologous antigens

SCHEDULE:								
Complement........	.1	.1	.1	.1	.1	.1	.1	.0
Serum 1/100........	.05	.04	.03	.02	.05	.0	.05	.05
Antigen 1/200*......	.05	.05	.05	.05	.03	.05	.0	.05
RESULTS:								
Serum 301 with F. 313	+	+	+	±	−	−	−	+ homologous
F. 156	−	−	−	−	−	−	−	+
F. 348	−	−	−	−	−	−	−	+
Serum 303 with F. 348	+	+	+	+	+	−	−	+ homologous
F. 156	±	−	−	−	−	−	−	+
F. 313	−	−	−	−	−	−	−	+

* For the tests the supernatant liquid over the ground mycelium which had been used for sensitizing animals was used.

F. 313 = *Fusarium radicicola*
F. 156 = *Fusarium conglutinans*
F. 348 = *Fusarium martii phaseoli*

Rabbit 301 was sensitized with *Fusarium radicicola* (313) [1] and Rabbit 303 was sensitized with *Fusarium martii phaseoli* (348). Sera from these animals diluted one hundred times were tested against their own antigens and cross-tested. They were also tested against *Fusarium conglutinans* (156). For antigens in the fixation test, the supernatant liquid of the material such as was used for injection purposes was diluted two hundred times in physiological salt solution. It should be mentioned that preliminary to injection each rabbit was tested for natural fixing bodies and was found negative. So far it has not been necessary to reject any rabbits on this score. Tests to determine the anticomplementary dose for both the sera and the antigens were made

[1] The names used in this paper for the most part follow the determinations made by the various workers furnishing the original cultures and no attempt has been made to revise the original determinations except in cases of obvious error.

at each test and quantities chosen well below the limits. In this test it will be noted that the sensitized sera have fixed 2 units of complement when in the presence of the homologous antigen and have been effective in fairly low dilution.

An important and, for a time, a vexing factor has arisen in our tests, and that is the variability of complements. We have lost much time and had many tests which were not consistent, which we now attribute to the variation in the fixability of the various complements. Bearing in mind the picture shown by the last test, make the comparison with the results shown in Table II.

TABLE II

COMPLEMENT FIXATION TEST WITH FUSARIA

Comparison of reactions when different complements were used. Animals sensitized with ground mycelium

SCHEDULE:												
Complement	.08	.08	.08	.08	.08	.08	.1	.1	.1	.1	.1	.0
Serum 1/100	.1	.08	.06	.05	.05	.02	.1	.06	.04	.0	.1	.1
Antigen 1/200	.05	.05	.05	.05	.05	.05	.05	.05	.05	.05	.0	.05
	COMPLEMENT A											
RESULTS:												
Serum 301												
with F. 313	+	+	±		±	±	±	−	−	−	−	+
with F. 348	±	−	−	−	−	−	−	−	−	−	−	+
Serum 303												
with F. 348	±	±	−	−	−	−	−	−	−	−	−	+
with F. 313	±	−	−	−	−	−	−	−	−	−	−	+
	COMPLEMENT B											
Serum 301												
with F. 313	+	+	+	+	+	+	+	+	−	−	−	+
with F. 348	±	−	−	−	−	−	−	−	−	−	−	+
Serum 303												
with F. 348	+	+	+	+	+	+	+	−	−	−	−	+
with F. 313	+	±	±	−	−	−	−	−	−	−	−	+

F. 313 = *Fusarium radicicola*
F. 348 = *Fusarium martii phaseoli.*

In this test the complement was used in $1\frac{1}{2}$ and 2 unit quantities. It must be noted that in these tests we are dealing with an antigen which does not produce any diseased condition in the animal and we probably cannot expect to find a large amount of antibody in the blood. It will be seen that complement *B* showed a far greater fixability than complement *A* and would permit of far more delicate differentiation. Neither of these complements was as suitable for the test as the complement used in the first test. We have found some animals which gave complements which showed no fixability, although normal in their reactions in the hemolytic system. It is, therefore, necessary to test each complement separately and to eliminate animals which give refractory complement.

We have also used a method developed in a study of the legume organism by Dr. R. M. Snyder of Michigan State College whereby he has been able to disperse dry plant tissue with selenium oxychloride. Dr. Snyder has used peptized leaves of plants to incorporate in bacteriological culture media and has some evidence that aside from the adsorbed selenium proteins of the material are unchanged in the peptization process. We have applied Dr. Snyder's method to the dry mycelium and our work with the peptized mycelial mats of Fusarium seems to give strong corroborative evidence of the correctness of Dr. Snyder's interpretation.

We have found that animals tolerate this peptized material with its adsorbed selenium if the material is well washed and the colloid resuspended after centrifugalization. The method of preparation of this antigen in a typical test was as follows: 0.87 gram of dry mycelium was dissolved in selenium oxychloride and poured into 100 c.c. of distilled water. Fifteen c.c. of this solution was centrifugalized and washed six times and then resuspended in 10 c.c. of salt solution. There was, therefore, in an injection quantity of 5 c.c. approximately 0.06 gram of dried mycelium given at each injection. Animals will tolerate at least 8 c.c. of such a suspension, and probably much more without ill effects.

The results of a series of immunizations using the selenium

method of antigen preparation are given in Table III. The antigen used in this test was made from ground fresh mycelium extracted in salt solution so as to give approximately a one-twentieth dilution. The table, while not so decisive as other tests we have made with

TABLE III

COMPLEMENT FIXATION TESTS WITH FUSARIA

Sera from rabbits sensitized by use of dried mycelium peptized with selenium oxychloride and tested against ordinary ground mycelium extracts

SCHEDULE:									
	Complement		.15	.1	.15	.1	.1	.1	.0
	Serum 1/10		.1	.1	.05	.05	.1	.0	.1
	Antigen		.05	.05	.05	.05	.0	.05	.05
RESULTS: Serum	Antigen								
199	F. radicicola	homol.	±	+	−	±	−	−	+
	F. of Aster wilt	heterol.	−	−	−	−	−	−	+
	F. martii I	heterol.			−	−	−	−	+
198	F. radicicola	homol.	−	±	−	±	−	−	+
	F. oxysporum	heterol.	−	±	−	±	−	−	+
190	F. martii I	homol.	−	+	−	+	−	−	+
	F. oxysporum	heterol.	−	−	−	−	−	−	+
191	F. martii I	homol.	±	+	−	−	−	−	+
	F. oxysporum	heterol.	−	−	−	−	−	−	+
195	a-F. of Aster wilt	homol.	±	+	−	±	−	−	+
	b-F. of Aster wilt	homol.	−	±	−	−	−	−	+
	a-F. oxysporum	heterol.	−	±	−	±	−	−	+
	b-F. oxysporum	heterol.	−	−	−	−	−	−	+
194	F. of Aster wilt	homol.	−	+	−	−	−	−	+
	F. oxysporum	heterol.	−	−	−	−	−	−	+
186	F. orthoceras	homol.	+	+	+	+	−	−	+
	F. oxysporum	heterol.	+	+	−	−	−	−	+

the ground type of antigen, shows a strong general trend in favor of the homologous antigens but there are some exceptions. Certain animals are more suitable for building up antibodies than others. We are mentioning this utilization of selenium oxychloride because of its wide applicability.

Since we have been spending much time on this phase of the work, it is perhaps fitting to give our impressions of the possible utilization of the method in Fusarium research by phytopathologists. We have been successful in demonstrating by means of the complement fixation reaction differences between closely related organisms and between a species and its variety. The reactions are extremely specific. This test is exceedingly delicate and the many factors involved make it a test whose manipulation is not easy. We believe it will be possible to develop sera of far greater potency than any we have so far obtained, and sharper and sharper distinctions can be made. As a tool for research where close differentiation of species and variety is required, we feel that the complement fixation test has great possibilities. For the general worker we feel that, unless precipitation and simple agglutination methods can be devised, the serological tests will not be of great service.

It cannot be gainsaid that there are now facing us enormous problems in relationship, and, for the many reasons outlined, the morphological approach cannot completely answer the questions which arise. For the solution of these problems in relationship we may confidently expect that the serological methods will be of service.

TESTS WITH ANILINE DYE MEDIA

As the work with the complement fixation tests progressed, we began to feel the limitations of the serological methods and other biological methods were sought to help in the attack on this problem of differentiating pathogens. The first attempts concerned themselves with a search for differentiating media. The early work represented a trial of a variety of synthetic media with and without various indicators and other chemicals utilized in bacteriological research for a similar purpose. Without going into detail as to these, suffice it to say that none of the common indicators and none of the various carbon and nitrogen sources tried in connection with a base nutrient solution seemed to give great promise. We were then led to the use of aniline dyes as toxic agents with the hope that the various species would exhibit different orders of tolerance to the toxic substances.

The use of dyes in selective media has become a definite part of bacteriological technique in the last decade. One has merely to refer to Endo's (7) fuchsin-sulphite agar or to Holt-Harris and Teague's (13) eosin-methylene blue agar used for differentiating *B. typhosus* colonies from *B. coli* as examples of this technique. Krumweide, Pratt and McWilliams (14) used two concentrations of brilliant green for typhoid differentiation, while in 1915, Petrof (21) used gentian violet as a differential dye in media for the isolation of the tubercle bacillus.

The basic work along this line is found in the contributions of Churchman (4) on the behavior of bacteria to gentian violet. Churchman demonstrated the parallelism between the Gram reaction and the gentian violet reaction taking place on his plates and his observations have had wide application not only in cultural work but in clinical medicine as well. Churchman (28) has found that this selective bacteriostasis is not limited to gentian violet, but is shown by other members of the triphenylmethane series.

In the development of the work on fungi with the aniline dyes twenty-one water-soluble dyes selected from the several classes of dyes were used:

Monazo..............	chrysoidine yellow, orange green, and Ponceau blue
Diazo................	diamine blue, benzopurpurin, Congo red, Biebrich scarlet
Diphenylmethane.....	auromine orange
Triphenylmethane.....	rosaniline, malachite green, isamine blue, crystal violet, brilliant green
Xanthane............	eosin (yellow), rhodamine blue
Acridine.............	acridine yellow
Hydrazone...........	tartrazine
Quinone-imide........	Nile blue A, Magdala red, methylene blue (bact.)

The results with these dyes in various concentrations when used with three species of Fusarium in a synthetic medium are given in Table IV. It will be noted from the table that the greatest checking of growth took place in malachite green, brilliant green, and crystal violet, all of them dyes of the triphenyl-

TABLE IV

RESULTS OF TESTS WITH REPRESENTATIVE DYES AT VARYING CONCENTRATIONS, USING THREE SPECIES OF FUSARIUM

Period, 20 days. Dye added to Coons' synthetic agar

	F. radicicola						F. conglutinans callistephi						F. oxysporum					
	Growth in medium						Growth in medium						Growth in medium					
	1–40,000	1–20,000	1–13,200	1–10,000	1–4,000	Decolorized	1–40,000	1–20,000	1–13,200	1–10,000	1–4,000	Decolorized	1–40,000	1–20,000	1–13,200	1–10,000	1–4,000	Decolorized
Rosaniline	+	+	+	+	+	−	+	+	+	+	+	−	+	+	+	+	+	−
Isamine blue	+	+	+	+	+	−	+	+	+	+	+	+	+	+	+	+	+	−
Malachite green	−	−	−	−	−	−	+	+	+	−	−	+	+	+	−	−	−	+
Brilliant green	−	−	−	−	−	−	+	−	−	−	−	+	+	−	−	−	−	+
Crystal violet	+	+	+	−	−	+	+	−	−	−	−	+	+	+	+	−	−	−
Chrysoidine	+	+	+	−	−	+	+	+	+	+	+	+	+	+	+	+	+	−
Orange G	+	+	+	+	+	−	+	+	+	+	+	−	+	+	+	+	+	−
Ponceau	+	+	+	+	+	+	+	+	+	+	+	−	+	+	+	+	+	+
Diamine blue	+	+	+	+	+	−	+	+	+	+	+	+	+	+	+	+	+	−
Congo red	+	+	+	+	+	−	+	+	+	+	+	−	+	+	+	+	+	−
Biebrich scarlet	+	+	+	+	+	−	+	+	+	+	+	−	+	+	+	+	+	−
Rhodamine	+	+	+	+	+	−	+	+	+	+	+	−	+	+	+	+	+	−
Eosine	+	+	+	+	+	−	+	+	+	+	+	−	+	+	+	+	+	−
Acridine	+	+	+	+	+	−	+	+	+	+	+	−	+	+	+	+	+	−
Tartrazine	+	+	+	+	+	−	+	+	+	+	+	−	+	+	+	+	+	−
Nile blue	+	+	+	+	+	−	+	+	+	+	+	−	+	+	+	+	+	+
Magdala red	+	+	+	+	+	+	+	+	+	+	+	−	+	+	+	+	+	−
Methylene blue	+	+	+	+	+	−	+	+	+	+	+	−	+	+	+	+	+	−
Checks	+	+	+	+	+	−	+	+	+	+	+	−	+	+	+	+	+	−

methane series. In a series of tests using these dyes on synthetic media [2] containing agar it was found that gentian violet was less

[2] The synthetic medium used throughout these tests is one devised so as to give strong mycelium growth and contains:

	Grams
Sucrose	7.2
Dextrose	3.6
Magnesium sulphate	1.23
Potassium acid phosphate	2.72
Potassium nitrate	2.02
Water	1000.

12 grams of agar added per liter.

toxic than malachite green, and malachite green less toxic than brilliant green, so far as one can judge from percentage relationships.

TABLE V

Reactions of Fusaria Obtained with a Synthetic Medium Containing Malachite Green, 1–40,000

Period, 10 days

Name of Organism	No. of Organism	Growth	Size of growth		Type of growth			Type of Mycelium		
			Diameter							
			More than 2 cm.	Less than 2 cm.	Submerged	Aërial growth in center	Abundant aër.al growth	Cottony	Villous	Sericeous-tomentose
Fusarium orthoceras.		+		+	+					
F. orthoceras var. longius...........		+		+			+	+		
F. conglutinans....	156	+	+				+	+		
F. conglutinans....	165	+	+				+	+		
F. conglutinans var. callistephi........		+	+			+		+		
F. redolens........		+	+				+			+
F. sclerotioides.....		+		+		+				+
F. oxysporum......	209	+	+		+					
Do.	211	+	+		+					
Do.	204	+	+				+			+
Do.	160	+	+				+			+
Do.	212	+	+				+			+
Do.	208	+	+				+			+
F. euoxysporum....		+	+				+	+		
F. vasinfectum.....		+	+				+	+		
F. batatis.........		+		+	+					
F. trichothecioides .		0								
F. discolor.........		0								
F. discolor var. sulphureum.......		+	+				+		+	
F. culmorum.......		0								
F. eumartii........	206	0								
F. eumartii........	171	0								
F. radicicola.......	157	+	+				+	+		
Do.	202	+	+				+	+		
Do.	203	+	+				+	+		
Do.	207	+	+				+	+		
F. solani..........		+	+				+			+
F. coeruleum.......		0								
F. zonatum........		+	+				+	+		
F. bulbigenum.....		0								
F. aurantiacum....		+	+				+	+		
F. malli...........		+		+			+	+		
F. asclerotium.....	56	+	+				+			+
Do.	213	+	+				+			+
Do.	207	+	+				+			+
F. lycopersici......	170	+		+		+				+
Do.	153	+		+		+				+

TABLE VI

REACTIONS OF FUSARIA OBTAINED WITH A SYNTHETIC MEDIUM CONTAINING GENTIAN VIOLET, 1–26,000

Period, 10 days

NAME OF ORGANISM	No. of organism	Size of growth		Type of growth			Type of mycelium			Medium	
		Diameter									
		More than 2 cm.	Less than 2 cm.	Submerged	Aërial growth in center	Abundant aërial growth	Cottony	Villous	Sericeous-tomentose	Decolorized	Deep purple zone below
F. orthoceras.....		+			+				+		
F. orthoceras var. longius.........		+				+			+		
F. conglutinans...	156	+				+			+		
F. conglutinans...	165	+				+			+		
F. conglutinans var. callistephi......		+				+			+		
F. redolens.......			+			+	+				
F. sclerotioides...		+							+		+
F. oxysporum....	209	+				+	+				+
Do.	211	+				+	+				+
Do.	204	+				+			+		
Do.	160	+				+			+		
Do.	212	+				+			+		
Do.	208	+				+			+		
F. euoxysporum..		+				+	+				
F. vasinfectum ..		+				+	+				
F. batatis........		+				+			+		
F. trichothecioides			+			+	+				
F. discolor.......		+				+			+		
F. discolor var. sulphureum.....		+				+			+		
F. culmorum.....		+				+	+				
F. eumartii......	206		+			+	+				
Do.	171		+			+	+				
F. radicicola.....	157	+				+	+			+	
Do.	202	+				+	+				
Do.	203	+				+	+				
Do.	207	+				+	+			+	
F. solani.........		+				+	+			+	
F. coeruleum.....			+	+							
F. zonatum......		+			+		+				
F. bulbigenum....			+			+			+		
F. aurantiacum...		+				+	+			+	
F. malli.........		+				+	+				
F. asclerotium....	56	+				+			+		
Do.	213	+				+			+		
Do.	174	+				+			+		
F. lycopersici.....	170	+				+			+		+
Do.	153	+				+			+		+

The results of preliminary work with plate cultures of various species of Fusarium are shown in Tables V and VI, and these results form the basis of our later work. The malachite green was used in 1/40,000 concentration and the gentian violet in 1/26,000.

The presence or absence of growth is, of course, the most distinctive thing with any toxic medium. In the lower concentrations more or less growth takes place and this has certain characteristics. Some species of the Fusaria show a natural tendency to produce colored threads, and these colors may be red, blue, or brown, but the majority of the forms are white. The mycelium may grow entirely within the medium "submerged," or it may show considerable aërial mycelium. The type of aërial mycelium under controlled environmental conditions seems constant for the species. The growth may be cottony, showing mycelial threads intermingled to make a cottony pad or felt. A colony with soft, short, hairlike growth has been termed "villous," while those mats showing long silky threads which have a tendency to clump together to form distinct wisps have been termed "sericeous-tomentose." Very marked differences occur with certain species in their effects upon the substratum. Certain species such as *radicicola* decolorize the medium, so that not the slightest trace of color remains near the colony. Other organisms produce a range of color changes. Zonation frequently occurs in some species, while the great majority do not affect the color to any extent. (See Pl. XXXI, Figs. 1–2).

The variation in response of the forms tested is great and it seems that in this difference in response we have a means of differentiating forms rather easily.

We have grown many of these species several times and recorded their reactions. With extremely few exceptions, each species has shown a distinct reaction to the toxic media. Age and past history of the culture do not seem to affect the response, since progenies of the same parent cultures received from different laboratories show identical reactions, and where they have been correctly determined show the characters of the species.

We have not found any correlation of response in the organisms of related groups, since it seems that the reactions are individual species and variety reactions and not group reactions. We feel that the results are but another form of expression of the specificity of living things to the external factors of the environment, and the utilization must be for convenience in diagnosis of the organisms rather than for taxonomic purposes.

The second method described seems to have great possibilities as means of quick and accurate diagnosis, especially when it is possible to compare a suspect with a known form. Attempt is now being made to catalog the reactions of a great many species of Fusarium which have been authentically determined, so that determination of unknown Fusaria met with by the worker can be attempted.

SUMMARY

The genus Fusarium consists of hundreds of species and varieties more or less completely described. The host plants attacked are numerous and include practically all economic plants. The species of this genus, because of their variety of growth forms, have presented grave difficulties to the general worker seeking to determine them. The basis for classification was given by Appel and Wollenweber and work of subsequent investigators has followed the general features of this fundamental contribution. Workers have found determination of the species in this genus extremely difficult and tedious, and the results of work with these forms have not been wholly satisfactory.

Attempt has been made by the writers to employ serological technique which previously has been used in a few cases to diagnose bacterial species causing plant disease and also with some fungi. It was found possible to secure anaphylactic reactions with sensitized guinea pigs, but the method was not found applicable to the problem at hand. Complement fixation technique permitted the differentiation between closely related Fusaria. With either ground mycelial mats or mats peptized by selenium oxychloride reacting sera were obtained. The method is believed to be too exacting to allow it to have any general applicability, but it may be of value in special investigations.

The triphenylmethane dyes in a synthetic medium have given

promise of affording a degree of differentiation among the species tested which will enable ready recognition of the species. Some species will not grow at concentrations at which others produce growth. The growth form produced is characteristic for the species and distinct enough to afford a characteristic description. The effect of the growth upon the substratum varies with the species, a few members of the genus producing strong decolorization of the medium containing the dye. The reactions to the toxic dye seem to be specific rather than group reactions and the method has value for diagnostic rather than taxonomic purposes.

MICHIGAN STATE COLLEGE
EAST LANSING, MICHIGAN

LITERATURE CITED

1. APPEL, O., AND WOLLENWEBER, H. W. 1910. Grundlagen einer Monographie der Gattung Fusarium (Link). Arb. K. Biol. Anst. f. Land. u. Forstw., 8 : 1–198.

2. BROOKS, R. ST. J., NAIN, K., AND RHODES, MABEL. 1925. The Investigation of Phytopathogenic Bacteria by Serological and Biochemical Methods. Journ. Path. and Bact., 28 : 203–209.

3. CARPENTER, C. W. 1915. Some Potato Tuber Rots Caused by Species of Fusarium. Journ. Agr. Res., 5 : 183–209.

4. CHURCHMAN, J. W. 1912. The Selective Bacteriocidal Action of Gentian Violet. Journ. Exp. Med., 16 : 221.

5. —— 1923. Bacteriostasis by Mixture of Dyes. Journ. Exp. Med., 38 : 1.

6. CITRON, JULIUS. 1905. Über das Verhalten der Favus- und Trichophyton-pilze im Organismus. Zeitschr. f. Hyg., 49 : 120–134.

7. ENDO, S. 1904. Über ein Verfahren zum Nachweis der Typhus Bacillen. Cent. f. Bakt. I, 35 : 109.

8. FRED, E. B., WHITING, A.L., AND HASTINGS, E. B. 1926. Root Nodule Bacteria of Leguminosae. Wis. Agr. Exp. Sta. Res. Bull., 72 : 1–43.

9. GOLDSWORTHY, M. C. 1926. Studies on the Spot Disease of Cauliflower; a Use of Serum Diagnosis. Phytopathology, 16 : 877–884.

10. GOSS, R. W. 1924. Potato Wilt and Stem End Rot Caused by *Fusarium eumartii*. Neb. Agr. Exp. Sta. Bull., 27 : 1–83.

11. HANSFORD, C. G. 1926. The Fusaria of Jamaica. Kew Bull. Misc. Inf., 1926 : 257–288.

12. Harter, L. L., and Field, E. C. 1914. The Stem Rot of Sweet Potato. Phytopathology, 4 : 279–304.

13. Holt-Harris, J. E., and Teague, Oscar. 1916. A New Medium for the Isolation of *B. typhosus* from Stools. Journ. Inf. Dis., 18 : 596.

14. Krumweide, C., Jr., Pratt, J. S., and McWilliams, H. I. 1916. Brilliant Green for the Isolation of Typhoid Bacilli. Journ. Inf. Dis., 18 : 1.

15. Lewis, Chas. E. 1913. Comparative Studies of Certain Disease Producing Species of Fusarium. Me. Agr. Exp. Sta. Bull., 219 : 1–55.

16. Link, George K. K. 1916. A Physiological Study of Two Strains of Fusarium in Their Causal Relation to Tuber Rot and Wilt of Potato. Bot. Gaz., 62 : 169–209.

17. Link, George K. K., and Sharp, C. G. 1927. Correlation of Host and Serological Specificity of *Bact. campestre, Bact. flaccumfaciens, Bact. phaseoli*, and *Bact. phaseoli sojense*. Bot. Gaz., 84 : 145–160.

18. Link, H. F. 1809. Observationes in Ordines Plantarum naturales. Dissertatio I. Magaz. d. Ges. naturf. Freunde, 3 : 3–42.

19. Magnus, Werner, and Friedenthal, H. 1906. Ein experimentaler Nachweis natürlicher Verwandschaft bei Pflanzen. Ber. d. Deutschen bot. Gesellsch., 24 : 601–607.

20. Morris, H. E., and Nutting, Grace B. 1923. Identification of Certain Species of Fusarium Isolated from Potato Tubers in Montana. Journ. Agr. Res., 24 : 339–364.

21. Petrof, S. A. 1915. A New and Rapid Method for the Isolation and Cultivation of the Tubercle Bacilli Directly from Sputum and Feces. Journ. Exp. Med., 21 : 38.

22. Pratt, O. A. 1916. A Western Field Rot of the Irish Potato Tuber Caused by *Fusarium radicicola*. Journ. Agr. Res., 6 : 297–310.

23. Riker, A. J. 1926. Studies on the Influence of Some Environmental Factors on the Development of Crown Gall. Journ. Agr. Res., 32 : 83–96.

24. Sherbakoff, C. D. 1915. Fusaria of Potatoes. N. Y. (Cornell) Agr. Exp. Sta. Mem., 6 : 1–270.

25. Schütze, Alb. 1911. Zur Frage der Differenzierung einzelner Hefearten auf dem Wege der Komplementbindung. Zeitschr. f. Immunitätsforsch., 8 : 611–615.

26. Wells, H. G., and Osborne, T. B. 1913. I. Is the Specificity of the Anaphylactic Reaction Dependent upon the Chemical Constitution of the Proteins or on Their Biological Relations? II. The Biological Reactions of the Vegetable Proteins. Journ. Inf. Dis., 12 : 341–358.

27. Wollenweber, H. W. 1913. Studies on the Fusarium Problem. Phytopathology, 3 : 24–50.

28. Wollenweber, H. W., Sherbakoff, C. D., Reinking, O. A., Johann, Helen, and Bailey, Alice A. 1925. Fundamentals for Taxonomic Studies of Fusarium. Journ. Agr. Res., 30 : 833–843.

EXPLANATION OF PLATE

PLATE XXXI

Various types of reactions shown by species of Fusarium to synthetic media containing triphenylmethane dyes.

Fig. 1 A. Cottony growth of *F. orthoceras longius* (gentian violet, 1–26,000)

B. Retarded growth of *F. heterosporum* (gentian violet, 1–26,000)

C. Sericeous-tomentose growth of *F. lycopersici* (gentian violet, 1–26,000)

Fig. 2 A. Sericeous-tomentose growth of *F. solani* (malachite green, 1–40,000)

B. Cottony growth of *F. vasinfectum* (malachite green, 1–40,000)

C. Cottony growth of *F. zonatum* (malachite green, 1–40,000)

D. Villous growth of *F. discolor* var. *sulphureum* (malachite green, 1–40,000)

PLATE XXXI

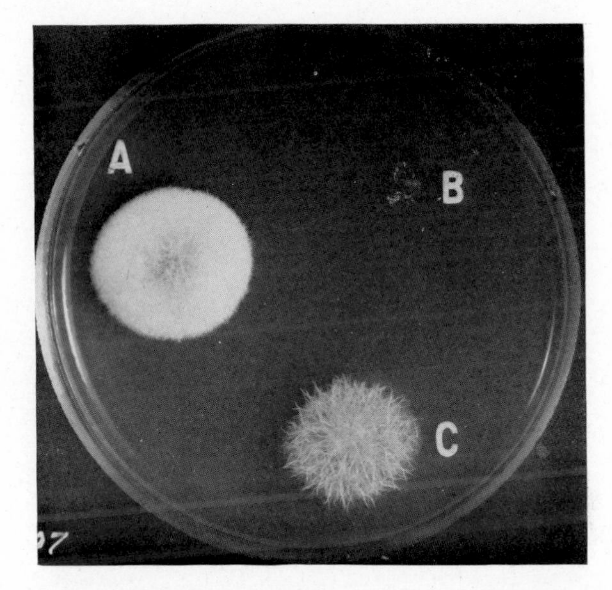

Fig. 1

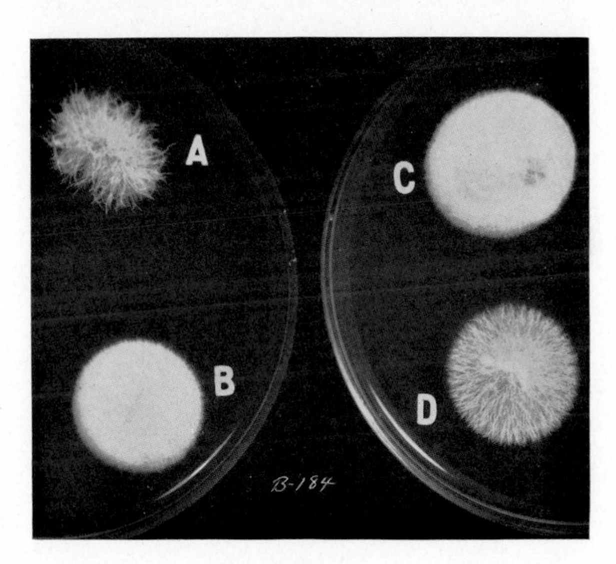

Fig. 2

INHERITANCE OF FRUIT-LENGTH IN CAPSICUM *

ERNEST E. DALE

CONTENTS

INTRODUCTION

THE work of Halsted (1914, 1915 and 1916) indicates that quantitative characters in Capsicum follow the multiple-factor rule for size inheritance. Halsted figures F_2 progenies of the cross Golden Queen × Red Cluster showing continuous variation in the size and shape of the fruits. He found that an F_2 progeny of nearly a thousand individuals did not fully reproduce either parent.

* Paper from the Department of Botany of the University of Michigan, No. 292.

MATERIALS AND METHODS

The present study was limited to a single character, the length of the fruit, and for this purpose two varieties of hot peppers, Coral Gem Bouquet and Anaheim, were used. The differences between these types are shown in the accompanying illustrations (Pl. XXXII). Both varieties have elongate slender fruits, although the Anaheim is much the larger in all respects. The mean length of Coral Gem was 23.2 mm. while that of Anaheim was 156.9 mm. By the use of such types it was hoped that complicating factors due to extreme differences in the shape of the

TABLE I

VARIATION IN FRUIT–LENGTH OF CORAL GEM PEPPER GROWN IN DIFFERENT YEARS

Class value in mm.	1923	1926	Total
14	2		2
15	1	4	5
16	3	4	7
17	3	11	14
18	11	14	25
19	11	40	51
20	23	44	67
21	23	64	87
22	50	72	122
23	67	77	144
24	69	67	136
25	85	46	131
26	52	25	77
27	59	23	82
28	21	5	26
29	13	4	17
30	5		5
31	1		1
32	0		0
33	1		1
Total	500	500	1000
Mean	24.1	22.4	23.2

PLATE XXXII

FIG. 1. The Coral Gem parent

FIG. 2. The Anaheim parent

fruits could be eliminated and, as the peppers were easy to grow, the production of large progenies offered ample material for a study of the inheritance of the factors for length. All measurements were to the nearest mm.

The seed used were from commercial sources. Both the original parent generations and the later self-pollinated generations of the parents bred true.

EXPERIMENTAL WORK

Variation in the parents

Table I shows the variation in the length of the Coral Gem pepper grown in two different years. Five hundred fruits were measured in each year. The mean length for the two years differed by 1.7 mm. The mean length of the Coral Gem parent is taken as the mean of both years. Table II gives like data for the Anaheim parent grown in four different years. There is considerable variation in the length of the Anaheim from year to

TABLE II

VARIATION IN FRUIT-LENGTH OF ANAHEIM PEPPER GROWN IN DIFFERENT YEARS

Class value in mm.	1923	1924	1925	1927	Total
100–109	1				1
110–119	5		2		7
120–129	0		3	2	5
130–139	1	3	8	33	45
140–149	6	8	8	89	111
150–159	18	18	17	109	162
160–169	33	4	28	27	92
170–179	17	8	42	5	72
180–189	7	2	18		27
190–199	2		3		5
200–209	1		1		2
Total	91	43	130	265	529
Mean	162.5	157.8	165.7	150.3	156.9

year. In 1925, for example, 139 fruits had a mean length of 165.7 mm. while in 1927 the mean length of 265 fruits was 150.3 mm. The records show, however, that the fruits measured in 1925 came from 52 plants, an average of 2.7 fruits per plant, while the fruits measured in 1927 came from 53 plants, an average of 5 fruits per plant. The plants grown in 1927 probably averaged at least 6 fruits each although only 5 were measured. In 1925 all the available fruits were measured. It seems probable that the normal seasonal variation plus the heavier set of fruits for 1927 accounts for the difference in the mean length of the Anaheim for these years. It should also be observed that the number of fruits measured in any one year was not large. The heavier set of fruit in the last year was presumably due to the weather conditions which prevailed at the time of pollination. If the mean of the Anaheim parent be taken by combining the data for the four years, it is 156.9 mm.

TABLE III

VARIATION IN FRUIT-LENGTH OF F_1 HYBRIDS BETWEEN CORAL GEM AND ANAHEIM

Class value in mm.	1923		1925		Total
	Anaheim × Coral Gem	Coral Gem × Anaheim	Anaheim × Coral Gem	Coral Gem × Anaheim	
33–37			4	4	8
38–42		1	14	6	21
43–47	6	5	54	29	94
48–52	18	19	107	106	250
53–57	49	42	177	172	440
58–62	125	109	101	116	451
63–67	172	172	35	53	432
68–72	104	111	7	14	236
73–77	24	31	1		56
78–82	2	9			11
83–87		1			1
Total	500	500	500	500	2000
Mean	63.6	64.3	54.2	55.7	59.4

The F_1 generation

Table III shows the variation in the F_1 hybrids of Coral Gem and Anaheim. The difference between the F_1 generations grown in 1923 and 1925 amounts to 9.0 mm. or 16 per cent of the F_1 mean for 1925. The reciprocal crosses are, however, consistent, the differences between them being 0.7 mm. in 1923 and 1.5 mm. in 1925, and the variation, though rather extreme, appears to have been due to seasonal conditions alone. By combining the F_1 data for the two years the mean is found to be 59.4 mm.

TABLE IV

VARIATION IN MEAN FRUIT-LENGTH OF F_2 PLANTS (10 FRUITS PER PLANT) OF CROSSES BETWEEN CORAL GEM AND ANAHEIM

Class Value in mm.	1924		1925		Total
	(Coral Gem × Anaheim) Selfed	(Anaheim × Coral Gem) Selfed	(Coral Gem × Anaheim) Selfed	(Anaheim × Coral Gem) Selfed	
23–27		1			1
28–32		2	4	6	12
33–37	4	2	9	9	24
38–42	11	10	13	10	44
43–47	17	18	27	16	78
48–52	24	19	20	9	72
53–57	34	16	31	13	94
58–62	34	18	27	13	92
63–67	27	13	15	7	62
68–72	20	14	15	6	55
73–77	19	14	4	2	39
78–82	13	5	7	3	28
83–87	9	5	3	1	18
88–92	3	4	1	4	12
93–97	1	3		0	4
98–102	3	2		0	5
103–107		1		1	2
108–112		2			2
Total	219	149	176	100	644

Mean = 58.6 Skewness = 0.53

The F_2 generation

Table IV gives the variation in the F_2 generation for two successive years. In the parent and F_1 generations data were obtained by measuring mass collections from each family. This procedure could not be followed in the generations involving segregation, since the segregating units were not individual fruits but plants. It was necessary in such cases to determine a mean length of fruit for each plant. In the F_2 generation 10 fruits per plant were measured. Thus the 644 individuals of the F_2 generation represent a total of 6440 measured fruits. The mean of F_2 was 58.6 mm.

Discussion of variation in F_1 and F_2

The means of the Coral Gem and Anaheim parents were respectively 23.2 and 156.9 mm. and the arithmetic mean of the two was 90.0 mm. The mean of the F_1 was 59.4 mm. or 30.6 mm. less than the mean of the parents. As a rule, divergence of the F_1 from the mean of the parents is attributed to dominance and in the present case it would seem that the smaller parent was to a considerable extent dominant over the larger. A very different explanation is that in the inheritance of quantitative characters the hereditary factors have a proportionate rather than an absolute effect. This hypothesis of the proportionate effect of quantitative factors is given in detail by Zeleny (1922) in his studies of eye facet number in Drosophila. Earlier studies, Seyster (1919) and Krafka (1920), showed that in both bar and ultra-bar the eye facet number decreased with increase in the temperature at which the larvae were grown. On an average a decrease in temperature of one degree Centigrade gave an increase of 10 per cent in facet number. The effect of a change in temperature was thus proportional to the mean of the stock, those with low mean values giving smaller effects while those with high mean values gave greater effects. Zeleny reasoned that germinal factors would produce an effect similar to that produced by temperature. He says: "It is a common principle of embryology that a changed condition does not act by accretion, i.e. by the addition or subtraction of individual parts without affecting the rest. On the contrary, the action is upon all the pre-existing parts of the organ. The result then depends not only upon the strength of the new agent, but also upon the reaction capacity of these pre-existing parts. Since a new factor, f, acts upon the whole complex, the value of the pre-existing mechanism, m, is a factor in the result as well as f. This general statement applies to both germinal and environmental factors."

An important consequence of the theory of proportionate effect of the factors is that a population which has a normal distribution of the factors will usually give a skewed curve if the data are arranged in the customary equal-size classes. In other words, a skewed curve is the normal expectation for such a distribution. The analysis of such data should, as Zeleny has pointed out, be based upon the logarithmic mean and the dispersion of the logarithms of the measurements. Inasmuch as the factors are assumed to have a proportionate effect, it becomes necessary to vary the class ranges accordingly. If throughout the entire range of variation the size of each class is made a certain fixed per cent of its own mean, all the classes will then have the same logarithmic range. They will be factorially equal and a population having a normal distribution of the factors should, when treated in this way, give a normal curve. Zeleny's analysis of variation in facet number is based upon logarithmic distributions.

There seems to be no question but that the type of distribution based upon logarithmic classes gives a more suitable means of representing the effects of temperature upon eye facet number in bar-eye stocks of Drosophila, than does a distribution based upon equal-size classes. There is a very strong a priori presumption that the same thing holds true of genetic factors. The fact that growth phenomena are of a geometric order makes it probable that the changes produced by genetic factors would also be proportionate effects and thus conform to a logarithmic distribution.

It has been pointed out in discussing the pepper data that the wide departure of the F_1 mean from the arithmetic mean of the parents might be explained in two very different ways: (1) on the theory of partial dominance on the part of the small parent; and (2) on the theory that the factors for length have a proportionate effect. If the latter theory is correct we should expect the F_1 mean to approximate not the arithmetic mean of the parents but their logarithmic mean. Since the F_1 mean was 59.4 mm. and the logarithmic mean of the parents was 60.3 mm. the expectation is verified. If, however, it were assumed that dominance accounted for the difference between the F_1 and the arithmetic mean of the parents, it would be a remarkable coincidence that the degree of dominance should have been such as to give an F_1 mean so nearly identical with the logarithmic mean of the parents.

If the effects of the factors are proportionate, the mean of the F_2 generation, as well as that of the F_1, would be expected to conform to the logarithmic mean of the Coral Gem and Anaheim parents. The F_2 mean was 58.6 mm., a difference of only 1.7 mm. from the logarithmic mean of the parents and again the expectation is realized. The variation in F_2 was continuous, with no indication of bi- or multi-modal distribution. Theoretically the F_2 generation should reproduce the parent types. There were 644 progeny in the F_2 with a range of 85 mm. The inter-parental range was 133 mm. Thus the range of F_2 was only 64 per cent of the parent range.

It was pointed out earlier that, if the factors have a proportionate effect, the logarithmic distribution of a population segregating for length factors should give a normal curve, or at all events, a more nearly normal curve than the same population when arranged in equal-size classes. Table VII gives the F_2 data arranged in logarithmic classes. It is clear that the distribution here is much more nearly normal than when the same data are grouped in equal-size classes (Table IV). Calculating the skewness of the two distributions by the formula $\alpha_3 = \frac{\mu_3}{\sigma^3}$ we have

	Equal-size classes	Logarithmic classes
$\alpha_3 F_2$	0.53 ± 0.07	-0.08 ± 0.07

The skewness of the logarithmic distribution is only slightly greater than the probable error, while the skewness of the arith-

TABLE V

VARIATION IN MEAN FRUIT-LENGTH OF BACK-CROSS PLANTS (20 FRUITS PER PLANT) IN BACK-CROSSES BETWEEN CORAL GEM AND F_1

Class value in mm.	Coral Gem × F_1	F_1 × Coral Gem	Total
23–27	7	20	27
28–32	31	57	88
33–37	51	62	113
38–42	48	56	104
43–47	39	23	62
48–52	25	6	31
53–57	11	1	12
58–62	1		1
Total	213	225	438

Mean = 37.6 Skewness = 0.37

TABLE VI

VARIATION IN MEAN FRUIT-LENGTH OF BACK-CROSS PLANTS (5 FRUITS PER PLANT) IN BACK-CROSSES BETWEEN ANAHEIM AND F_1

Class value in mm.	Anaheim × F_1	F_1 × Anaheim	Total
50–59	1		1
60–69	2	1	3
70–79	9	1	10
80–89	26	15	41
90–99	28	14	42
100–109	27	12	39
110–119	23	11	34
120–129	12	11	23
130–139	3	3	6
140–149	1	2	3
150–159	0		0
160–169	1		1
170–179	1		1
Total	134	70	204

Mean = 102.6 Skewness = 0.53

metic distribution is more than seven times the probable error. It can scarcely be doubted that the difference is significant and that the absence of skewness in the logarithmic curve indicates that the factors have a proportionate effect.

The Back-crosses

In the back-cross between the F_1 and the Coral Gem parent (Table V) the gametes produced by the Coral Gem would all be identical. The gametes produced by the F_1 would, on the other hand, vary from pure Coral Gem to pure Anaheim. Thus the back-cross progeny would be expected to range from the F_1 to the Coral Gem in size and the mean of the progeny should agree with the logarithmic mean of the F_1 and Coral Gem. As the mean of the back-cross was 37.6 mm. and the logarithmic mean of the parents was 37.1 mm., the agreement is extremely close, the difference being 0.5 mm.

In the same way the back-cross between the F_1 and Anaheim (Table VI) should give a progeny whose mean would conform to the logarithmic mean of the parents. The mean of the back-cross was 102.6 mm. while the logarithmic mean of the parents was 96.5 mm. The difference amounts to 6.1 mm. or 6 per cent of the mean of the back-cross. While this difference is greater than might have been expected, it could well be the result of seasonal variation.

The variation in the back-crosses like that of the F_2 was continuous and gave no indication of a bi- or multi-modal character. And also, as in the case of the F_2, the back-cross data in logarithmic classes (Tables VIII and IX) showed much less skewness than when grouped in equal-size classes (Tables V and VI). The data on skewness are summarized below:

Back-cross	Type of distribution	Skewness
$F_1 \times$ Coral Gem	arithmetic	0.37 ± 0.08
$F_1 \times$ Anaheim	"	0.53 ± 0.12
$F_1 \times$ Coral Gem	logarithmic	0.05 ± 0.08
$F_1 \times$ Anaheim	"	0.11 ± 0.12

TABLE VII

LOGARITHMIC DISTRIBUTIONS OF MEAN FRUIT-LENGTHS OF F_2 PLANTS (10 FRUITS PER PLANT) OF CROSSES BETWEEN CORAL GEM AND ANAHEIM

Width of logarithmic classes 0.05

Class value in mm.	1924		1925		Tota
	(Coral Gem × Anaheim) Selfed	(Anaheim × Coral Gem) Selfed	(Anaheim × Coral Gem) Selfed	(Coral Gem × Anaheim) Selfed	
25.1–28.1		1			1
28.2–31.5		1	2	4	7
31.6–35.4	2	2	5	5	14
35.5–39.7	9	7	14	10	40
39.8–44.6	6	11	19	11	47
44.7–50.0	32	27	25	16	100
50.1–56.1	37	14	31	12	94
56.2–63.0	42	27	39	21	129
63.1–70.7	37	14	21	9	81
70.8–79.3	31	24	13	6	74
79.4–89.0	17	11	7	2	37
89.1–99.9	4	5		3	12
100.0–112.2	2	5		1	8
Total	219	149	176	100	644

Skewness = – 0.08

The arithmetic distribution of the data from the back-cross to Coral Gem gives a value for skewness amounting to more than four times the probable error, while the skewness of the logarithmic distribution for the same data is less than the probable error. The skewness of the arithmetic distribution of the data from the back-cross to Anaheim is again more than four times the probable error, whereas the skewness of the logarithmic distribution is, as before, less than the probable error. Thus the back-cross generations and the F_2 behave alike with respect to skewness, and it becomes increasingly probable that the theory of proportionate effects is the correct one.

The mean fruit-length of the back-cross progenies was based upon 20 measurements per plant in the back-crosses with Coral

TABLE VIII

LOGARITHMIC DISTRIBUTIONS OF MEAN FRUIT-LENGTHS OF BACK-CROSS PLANTS (20 FRUITS PER PLANT) IN BACK-CROSSES BETWEEN CORAL GEM AND F_1

Width of logarithmic classes 0.05

Class value in mm.	Coral Gem × F_1	F_1 × Coral Gem	Total
22.4–25.0	1	7	8
25.1–28.1	9	22	31
28.2–31.5	18	37	55
31.6–35.4	41	51	92
35.5–39.7	42	50	92
39.8–44.6	50	41	91
44.7–50.0	31	15	46
50.1–56.1	18	2	20
56.2–63.0	3		3
Total	213	225	438

Skewness = − 0.05

TABLE IX

LOGARITHMIC DISTRIBUTIONS OF MEAN FRUIT-LENGTHS OF BACK-CROSS PLANTS (5 FRUITS PER PLANT) IN BACK-CROSSES BETWEEN ANAHEIM AND F_1

Width of logarithmic classes 0.05

Class value in mm.	Anaheim × F_1	F_1 × Anaheim	Total
50.1–56.1	1		1
56.2–63.0	1		1
63.1–70.7	1	1	2
70.8–79.3	9	1	10
79.4–89.0	26	15	41
89.1–99.9	28	14	42
100.0–112.2	37	17	54
112.3–125.8	23	13	36
125.9–141.2	5	8	13
141.3–158.4	1	1	2
158.5–177.8	2		2
Total	134	70	204

Skewness = − 0.11

Gem and upon 5 measurements per plant in the back-crosses with Anaheim. The reason for this difference was that in the latter case the fruits were much larger and fewer were produced upon a single plant.

The Second Generation after the Back-crosses

Tables X and XI give the distributions in arithmetic and logarithmic classes for the various families of the second generation after back-crossing. The 28 families of these tables were derived from selfed plants of the back-cross generation whose mean length of fruits ranged from types as small as the Coral Gem to others as large as the F_1. Each individual represents the mean of 20 measured fruits from a single plant. The outstanding feature of the tables is the unimodal character of the distributions, there being scarcely a suggestion of discontinuous variation. In this respect the distributions agree with the F_2 and back-cross generations. When, however, we compare skewnesses (Table XII), large discrepancies appear. In the first place many families in Table XII show a very low value for the skewness of the arithmetic distributions. In only six families is the skewness as large as three times the probable error. As might be expected, the families with very low skewness in arithmetic distribution show a higher value for skewness in logarithmic distributions. Such are the distributions in families number 25.21, 25.22, 25.32, 25.40, 25.45, and 25.58. Of these 25.32 and 25.40 exceed three times their probable errors and are presumably significant, i.e. not due to errors in sampling.

Interpretation of the Data

The regularity with which the pepper data give unimodal distributions in the F_2, the back-crosses and the second generation after the back-crosses, indicates that the length of the fruit is determined by a large number of genetic factors. The skewness of the arithmetic distributions of the F_2 and back-crosses is found to be greater than three times the probable errors, while the logarithmic distributions of these generations give normal curves. This is the expected behavior for quantitative factors

TABLE X

VARIATION IN MEAN FRUIT–LENGTHS (20 FRUITS PER PLANT) IN FAMILIES OF SECOND SELFED GENERATION AFTER BACK–CROSS BETWEEN CORAL GEM AND F_1

Family number	Class values in mm.													
	13–17	18–22	23–27	28–32	33–37	38–42	43–47	48–52	53–57	58–62	63–67	68–72	73–77	78–82
25.5		8	21	18	6	3								
25.8		10	20	21	10	3	2							
25.18			4	1	21	16	17	12	7	3	1			
25.20		1	1	10	22	20	12	4						
25.21		1	5	6	12	17	16	12	6	4	1			
25.22		1	10	13	29	15	7	4						
25.24		1	4	6	11	10	4	4	0	0	1			
25.25	1	7	17	38	31	12	6	3						
25.26		2	21	16	6	1								
25.30			1	6	12	24	28	29	14	9	7	2	1	1
25.31		1	6	9	7	13	5	1	0	1				
25.32		1	1	10	9	12	21	19	9	4	4	1		
25.33		7	50	51	2	1								
25.34	1	12	31	16	2	1								
25.40			6	7	25	14	25	14	5	3	1			
25.42			12	19	41	36	40	27	24	11	6	0	4	1
25.43		4	12	25	28	26	13	9	4	2				
25.44		3	19	30	19	14	9	1						
25.45		9	27	40	43	15	1							
25.46		3	27	22	20	5								
25.48			7	12	19	15	6	0	2					
25.51		5	12	26	31	22	6	1	1	3				
25.52		2	14	14	13	9	5	3	3					
25.58		1	5	13	22	11	11	5						
25.64			3	13	17	12	10	7	4					
25.71			7	21	28	22	8	3	2	1	1			
25.83II		4	30	47	24	6								
25.84		4	23	21	9	2								

TABLE XI

LOGARITHMIC DISTRIBUTIONS OF MEAN FRUIT-LENGTHS (20 FRUITS PER PLANT) IN FAMILIES OF SECOND SELFED GENERATION AFTER BACK-CROSS BETWEEN CORAL GEM AND F_1

Width of logarithmic classes 0.05

Family number	Class value in mm.														
	15.8–17.7	17.8–19.8	19.9–22.3	22.4–25.0	25.1–28.1	28.2–31.5	31.6–35.4	35.5–39.7	39.8–44.6	44.7–50.0	50.1–56.1	56.2–63.0	63.1–70.7	70.8–79.3	79.4–89.0
25.5		1	7	12	13	11	7	4	1						
25.8		1	9	16	13	9	9	5	3	1					
25.18				2	2	1	10	20	14	19	9	4	1		
25.20			1	1	0	7	16	22	10	11	2				
25.21			1	1	4	4	9	15	13	17	10	6			
25.22			1	5	8	5	21	20	9	10					
25.24				1	5	4	3	11	9	7	0	1			
25.25		1	1	6	11	14	29	22	15	10	4	2			
25.26			2	6	17	13	5	3							
25.30					2	4	8	17	21	37	23	15	5	1	1
25.31			1	4	3	6	8	8	7	5	0	1			
25.32			1	0	3	5	9	7	20	24	11	8	3		
25.33			7	26	37	34	6	0	1						
25.34	1	1	11	20	19	7	2	2							
25.40				3	5	4	12	22	18	23	9	3	1		
25.42				2	11	12	28	30	42	38	33	15	5	5	
25.43		1	3	2	14	16	25	23	18	12	7	2			
25.44			3	7	18	17	20	12	13	5					
25.45			9	12	26	20	38	21	7						
25.46			3	14	20	11	15	11	3						
25.48				3	7	7	11	20	8	3	2				
25.51			5	6	11	13	27	21	16	4	1	3			
25.52			2	5	12	11	6	13	5	5	4				
25.58			1	1	5	6	20	15	10	8	2				
25.64				1	4	5	17	10	13	9	6	1			
25.71				1	9	15	19	22	17	6	2	1	1		
25.83II			4	16	24	30	24	12	1						
25.84			4	10	19	12	10	2	2						

TABLE XII

SKEWNESS OF ARITHMETIC AND LOGARITHMIC DISTRIBUTIONS IN FAMILIES OF SECOND SELFED GENERATION AFTER BACK-CROSS BETWEEN CORAL GEM AND F_1

Family number	Number of individuals	Skewness		
		Equal-size classes	Logarithmic classes	Probable error *
25.5	56	.49	.26	± .22
25.8	66	.59	.51	± .20
25.18	82	.21	– .37	± .18
25.20	70	– .17	– .43	± .20
25.21	80	.00	– .51	± .18
25.22	79	.17	– .39	± .19
25.24	41	.61	– .32	± .26
25.25	115	.32	– .05	± .15
25.26	46	.57	.21	± .24
25.30	134	.54	– .17	± .14
25.31	43	.40	– .14	± .25
25.32	91	.03	– .55	± .17
25.33	111	.15	.22	± .16
25.34	63	.44	.35	± .21
25.40	100	.18	– .57	± .17
25.42	221	.58	– .06	± .11
25.43	123	.40	– .12	± .15
25.44	95	.38	.05	± .17
25.45	135	– .14	– .29	± .14
25.46	77	.23	.18	± .19
25.48	61	.51	– .15	± .21
25.51	107	.83	– .01	± .16
25.52	63	.65	.22	± .21
25.58	68	.11	– .23	± .20
25.64	66	.36	– .03	± .20
25.71	93	1.07	.39	± .17
25.83 II	111	.17	– .07	± .16
25.84	59	.38	.39	± .22

* The formula $E\alpha_3 = 0.6745 \sqrt{\frac{6}{n}}$ was used in the calculation of probable error.

if the factors have proportionate effects and if there is no dominance, or if any dominance of factors in one direction is offset by equal dominance of other factors in the opposite direction. Since the F_2 and back-crosses represent random distributions of the factors, it is assumed that there would be no disturbing effect of dominance. The statistical analysis thus agrees with the theory of proportionate effects of the factors.

The irregularity of skewness in the second generation after back-crossing contrasts strongly with the skewness of the F_2 and back-cross generations. The difference appears to be due to dominance resulting from the fact that there is not a random distribution of the factors in the second generation after the back-crosses. The skewnesses of Table XII are, however, not all equally significant because of the smallness of some of the families and the limited range of others. Nevertheless, the fact that all but 2 of the arithmetic distributions show positive skewness, while the logarithmic distributions show 10 positive and 18 negative, is compatible with the theory of proportionate effects.

GENERAL DISCUSSION

Factorial Interactions and Quantitative Inheritance

Examination of the literature shows various types of factorial interactions which bear on the inheritance of quantitative characters.

Bridges (1919), in a study of eosin eye color in Drosophila, found eight recessive modifying factors each of which in a double homozygous combination with eosin produced a specific modification of the eosin character. The types of modification resulting from the interaction of these modifiers and the eosin factor were as follows: (1) general modifications in which the combination of eosin and a modifier had a cumulative effect, each factor having a more or less proportionate influence; (2) specific modifications (the most common type) in which the modifier had no visible effect except in the presence of eosin, the combination giving a much lighter type than eosin; (3) disproportionate modifications in which the modifier alone had only a slight effect, but in combination with eosin had a very pronounced effect; and (4) reversed modification in which the modifier alone produced a darker eye color than wild-type, but in combination with eosin produced an eye color lighter than the eosin.

Emerson (1918) shows that three dominant factors, *A*, *C*, and *R*, are necessary to the production of aleurone color in maize. The fact that all three dominant factors must be present made it possible to segregate out "aleurone testers" in which one factor was kept in a recessive condition and the other two in the dominant condition. Such a type furnished a simple means of testing for the presence of the third dominant in an unknown stock.

Emerson and Emerson (1922) describe two dwarf types of maize, anther ear and dwarf, of which the double recessive dwarf anther ear was disproportionately small. Anther ear was about three fourths of the normal in height while dwarf was approximately one fourth of normal. The double recessive dwarf anther ear was about one sixteenth as tall as the normal.

Equality of the Factors

Nilsson-Ehle (1908) found that red color in wheat (*Triticum vulgare*) was due to three apparently equal dominant factors which were cumulative in their effects. Such factors are known as duplicate factors. Subsequently to Nilsson-Ehle's work several cases involving two duplicate factors were worked out. Of these the inheritance of capsule form in Capsella (Shull, 1914) is perhaps best known. A number of additional cases of duplicate factors have been found in wheat and oats and, as recent cytological work has shown, polyploid series occur in both these forms. For example, Sax (1921) has shown that common wheat is a hexaploid (42-chromosome) form and it seems very probable that the three-factor series for red color represents a threefold replication of a single pair of chromosomes, each carrying a factor for red color. There are, however, a few cases which cannot be explained in this way.

In spite of the rare occurrence of duplicate factors which was pointed out by Shull (1914), the impression grew up that quantitative characters were in the main determined by factors which were equal and independent in their effects. Castle's formula

(1921) for the determination of the number of factors in blending inheritance is an example of this. It is to be expected that duplicate factors would be found chiefly in forms belonging to polyploid series. They play only a minor part in the simpler types of inheritance and there is no reason to suppose they play a more important part in complex types of quantitative inheritance.

Dominance

Crosses involving quantitative characters usually give an F_1 which is intermediate between the parents. Dominance is either incomplete or not apparent and the result is often called blending inheritance. But it occasionally happens, as in the case of crossing inbred races of corn, that such a cross gives very greatly increased size and vigor in the F_1. Such an effect has been called vigor of heterozygosis, or "heterosis." Jones (1917) suggested that this increased growth is due to the number of dominant factors brought together in the F_1 and this explanation is now generally accepted.

Proportional versus Additive Effects

Both Zeleny's data and the pepper data furnish strong presumption in favor of the theory of proportionate effects of the factors. It is clearly impossible to explain the pepper data on the theory of absolute or additive effects. There is, furthermore, a priori support for the theory of proportionate effects in that (1) growth phenomena tend to be of a geometric order and (2), as Zeleny (1922) pointed out, quantitative data very commonly show positive skewness.

Multiple-factor Expectations from Simple Cases

There is no obvious difference between the genetic behavior of quantitative characters and a synthetic multiple-factor situation such as could be built up from a combination of non-allelomorphic factors all affecting a single character. In Drosophila, for example, the color of the eye is affected by a large number of factors. The F_2 generation of a cross between a normal red-eyed fly and one homozygous for the six factors, eosin, vermilion, purple, purploid, peach and claret, would almost certainly baffle any attempt at genetic analysis. It could, in fact, be used as a typical case of quantitative inheritance.

Manglesdorf (1926) gives a list of eighteen factors affecting the development of endosperm in maize. Some of the factors affect primarily the texture of the endosperm, while others affect the amount of endosperm produced. There does not appear, however, to be any fundamental difference between these characters. The amount of deficiency varies with the different factors and Manglesdorf has calculated the percentage in each case. All the factors behave as simple recessives. A cross between normal starchy endosperm and an individual homozygous for any six or more of the defective endosperm factors taken at random would be expected to give an F_2 distribution typical in all respects of quantitative inheritance.

Behavior of the Factors in Quantitative Inheritance

As a rule the data of quantitative inheritance are, in a critical sense, unanalyzable. Any conclusions as to the factors for quantitative characters must be based upon the known facts of normal genetic behavior. We might expect dominance (partial or complete), recessiveness, equality or inequality of the factors, modifying factors, linkage and crossing-over. It is an interesting fact that a most improbable assumption, that of the equality of factors, has played a large part in the study of quantitative inheritance. The demonstrated cases of duplicate factors indicate that they are so rare as to be negligible, except in polyploids. There is no warrant for supposing that, aside from the cases of duplicate factors, equality of the factors occurs except as a result of coincidence.

It can hardly be doubted that in the inheritance of quantitative characters all degrees of dominance and recessiveness occur. So thoroughgoing a demonstration of modifying factors as Bridges (1919) has given in the case of modifiers of eosin eye-color in Drosophila indicates that factors of this type may be widespread, and that they may explain, as Bridges believes, the results of selection experiments. Moreover, the whole bulk of the Drosophila work points to the fact that all characters, if sufficiently analyzed, show the effect of many genetic factors.

SUMMARY

Inheritance of fruit-length was studied in a cross between Coral Gem pepper with a mean fruit-length of 23.2 mm. and Anaheim with a mean length of 156.9 mm.

The data of the F_2 and back-cross generations in logarithmic classes gave normal curves and in arithmetic classes gave skewed curves. This indicates that the factors for length have proportionate rather than additive effects.

Skewness was irregular in the second generation after the back-crosses.

A general discussion of the interpretation of quantitative inheritance is given.

The work here reported was carried on from 1921 to 1927 under Professor H. H. Bartlett, to whom my thanks are due for the use of the facilities of the University of Michigan Botanical Garden. I wish to thank also Dr. E. G. Anderson and Dr. C. C. Craig, both of the University of Michigan, for assistance in the interpretation of the data.

University of Michigan

LITERATURE CITED

BRIDGES, C. B. 1919. Specific Modifiers of Eosin Eye Color in Drosophila melanogaster. Journ. Exp. Zoöl., 28 : 337–384.

CASTLE, W. E. 1921. An Improved Method of Estimating the Number of Genetic Factors Concerned in Cases of Blending Inheritance. Science, 54 : 223.

EMERSON, R. A. 1918. A Fifth Pair of Factors, Aa, for Aleurone Color in Maize and Its Relation to the Cc and Rr Pairs. Cornell Univ. Agr. Exp. Sta. Mem., 16 : 231–289.

EMERSON, R. A., AND EMERSON, S. H. 1922. Genetic Interrelations of Two Andromonoecious Types of Maize, Dwarf and Anther Ear. Genetics, 7 : 203–236.

HALSTED, B. D. 1914, 1915 and 1916. Rep. Bot. Dept. New Jersey Agr. Exp. Sta.

JONES, D. F. 1917. Dominance of Linked Factors as a Means of Accounting for Heterosis. Genetics, 2 : 466–479.

KRAFKA, JOSEPH, JR. 1920. The Effect of Temperature upon Facet Number in the Bar-eyed Mutant of Drosophila. Journ. Gen. Physiol., 2 : 409–464.

MANGLESDORF, P. C. 1926. The Genetics and Morphology of Some Endosperm Characters in Maize. Conn. Agr. Exp. Sta. Bull., 279 : 513–614.

NILSSON-EHLE, H. 1909. Kreuzungsuntersuchungen an Hafer und Weizen. Lunds Univ. Arsskrift. N. F. Afd. 2. Bd. 5 Nr. 2, 1–22.

SAX, K. 1921. Chromosome Relationships in Wheat. Science, 54 : 413–415.

SEYSTER, E. W. 1919. Eye Facet Number as Influenced by Temperature in the Bar-eyed Mutant of Drosophila melanogaster (ampelophila). Biol. Bull., 37 : 168–182.

SHULL, G. H. 1914. Duplicate Genes for Capsule Form in Bursa bursa-pastoris. Zeitschr. Abstamm. u. Vererb., 12 : 97–149.

ZELENY, CHAS. 1920. The Tabulation of Factorial Values. Am. Nat., 54 : 358–362.

—— 1921. The Effect of Selection for Eye Facet Number in the White Bar-eye Race of Drosophila melanogaster. Genetics, 7 : 1–115.

THE ANATOMY OF THE OVERGROWTH ON SUGAR BEETS CAUSED BY *BACTERIUM BETICOLA*

HARRY A. ELCOCK

THERE are two distinct types of overgrowths occurring on sugar beets. One of these has been called "tumors," the other "tuberculosis" (Smith, 1911, pp. 105, 194). It is very difficult to distinguish between these two macroscopically, especially the young gall-like overgrowths. However, the older galls caused by *Bacterium beticola* Smith, Townsend, and Brown, are characteristic in that they are irregular. These irregularities are for the most part due to large fissures, a very rough outward appearance, and more or less decay of the outer cells of the overgrowth. In contrast to this, the tumorous type of gall caused by *Bacterium tumefaciens* Smith shows very little tendency toward deterioration or roughness. The irregularities which do occur are much less marked in outline, and the contours are smooth as compared with the other type of gall. The fact that the galls caused by *Bacterium tumefaciens* are white and free from surface decay offers still furthur means of distinction between the exterior symptoms of tumor and tuberculosis types.

Before the Société de Pathologie Végétale et d'Entomologie Agricole de France, Smith stated that he believed that there were structures in plants which are analogous to the tuberculosis of animals. He furthur stated that *B. savastanoi* EFS., causing "olive knot," and *Bacterium beticola*, causing tuberculosis of sugar beet, furnished additional proof of the truth of this statement. There are three distinctly different organisms causing plant tubercles. In addition to the two already mentioned, there is also *Bacterium leguminosarum* (Frank) EFS., which causes the tubercles on plants of the Leguminosae. All three produce symptoms in plants that are closely analogous to those caused by organisms which produce tubercles in animals. The organisms in both plants and animals are confined within localized areas by the host tissue.

Examination of a cross-section of the tuberculosis type of overgrowth in sugar beet will reveal small, yellowish, watery spots surrounded by greatly contorted tissue. Upon microscopic examination it is noticed that these spots are bacterial pockets. The tumorous type of proliferation presents no such appearance.

A study was made of the overgrowths and also of the cells surrounding tubercle tissue. The material selected for this study was fixed, and imbedded in paraffin; sectioned, and stained with Haidenhain's iron alum haematoxylin.

The organism causing the neoplasm was found in a wide range of tissue, including phloëm, xylem, cambium, and cortex. The resultant overgrowths are the direct cause of a stimulus produced by materials secreted by the bacteria. These overgrowths show typical tuberculoma type of neoplasm, in that the host tissue involved holds the parasite within localized areas. The organism causes no decay of the tissues with which they come in contact, but new host cells or enlarged old cells restrict the bacteria to small pockets. This condition is closely analogous to granulomatous tissue of animals.

When the bacteria are found located in the vicinity of the meristematic cells, hyperplasia is the most characteristic type of proliferation. When the bacterial cavities are surrounded by parenchyma cells, hypertrophic type is the most abundant form of overgrowth. Studies of cross-sections of diseased material revealed the origin of bacterial pockets. The organisms in early stages of infection are intercellular, and they collect and multiply at certain advantageous points (Fig. 2). Such points are in the cortex where the intercellular spaces are very prevalent, and at almost any point in between the cells of the cambium. As the bacteria collect and reproduce at these points, the pressure and byproducts caused by their activities crush the immediate cells, thus forming the disorganized cavities (Fig. 1). Immediately surrounding these pockets are contorted strands of parenchyma cells.

In Figures 3 and 4 the characteristic growths resulting from both hyperplasia and hypertrophic reactions to the stimulus are shown.

In a large number of sections the pockets are found to be located within the cambium layer; this is especially true in petiole infection (Fig. 5). The cells of the cambium are in rapid division, but with the stimulus produced by the organisms these cells divide even more rapidly; thus large amounts of the hyperplasia tissue appear. This internal cell production takes place faster than the cells can differentiate into tissues, and hence this excess of cells causes the cracking and splitting of the proliferated tissue. This accounts for the formation of the deep fissures over the surface.

When the organisms are located in the parenchyma tissue of the cortex, the effects of the stimulus are mostly hypertrophic in nature (Fig. 4). The cells are of various shapes; cylindrical, polyhedral, and spherical with large intercellular spaces. There is no evidence of an epidermis in later stages of gall development. As the proliferation develops, the epidermis is ruptured so that the large hypertrophic cells, with the large intercellular spaces, are left exposed, which allows soil organisms to enter. This causes the very rough and decayed surface spoken of earlier as a distinguishing characteristic under the external symptoms.

The parenchyma cells next to the xylem are thick-walled, and are spoken of as the "sugar sheath." It is at this point that cells attacked by *Bacterium beticola* lose their turgidity, and suffer partial or complete collapse, producing the bacterial pockets. The bacteria are able to break down the "sugar sheath" cells much more easily than the tracheae and the tracheids. The organisms penetrate, however, into the tubes and travel along in them only to collect in masses again, break out, and form new pockets (Fig. 6). Certain pockets have been observed in the beet root which have extended over a distance of two inches. These pockets extend in the direction from root to tip, and are more or less parallel to the vascular system.

SUMMARY AND CONCLUSIONS

The galls formed by *Bacterium beticola* and spoken of by Erwin F. Smith as "tuberculosis of the sugar beet," show a resemblance to animal tubercles. They may be classed as forming a tuberculous tissue in plants.

The tissues entering into the formation of galls are of both a hyperplasia and hypertrophic type. This causes the distinctive external appearances.

No structures of what Smith termed "tumor strands" are produced in this type of gall, which is a marked distinction from crown gall.

The bacterial organisms in living tissues are distinctly intercellular, and form pockets. These pockets may occur in all types of beet tissues. It has been determined, however, that the organism may enter the tracheids and tracheae from colonies in pockets. They may move for a considerable distance in these water-conducting cells, possibly carried in the transpiration stream, and cause gall formation in areas remote from the point of entrance.

Michigan State College
East Lansing, Michigan

LITERATURE CITED

1. Smith, Erwin F. 1911. Crown-Gall of Plants: Its Cause and Remedy, pp. 105, 194.

2. Smith, Erwin F. 1924. Le Crown-Gall. Extrait de la Revue de Pathologie végétale et d'Entomologie agricole, t. XI, fasc. 4.

3. Schiff-Giorgini, Dr. Ruggero. 1906. Untersuchungen über die Tuberkelkrankheit des Ölbaumes. Centralblatt für Bakteriologie, Parasitenkunde und Infektionskrankheiten, II. Abt., Bd. XV, No. 1, pp. 200–209.

PLATE XXXIII

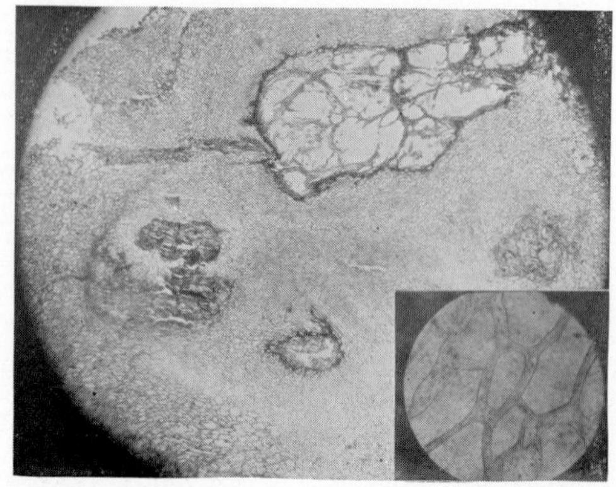

Fig. 1 Fig. 2

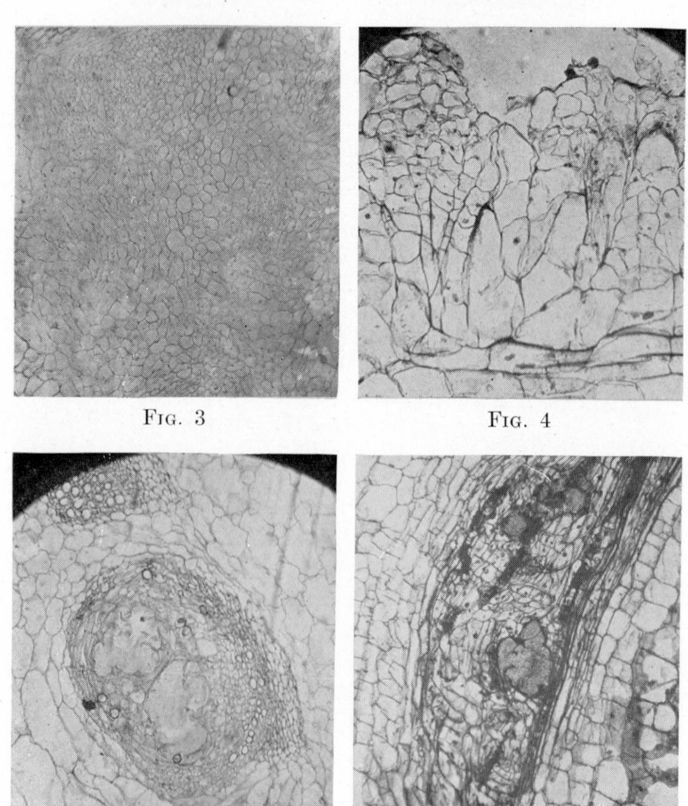

Fig. 3 Fig. 4

Fig. 5 Fig. 6

EXPLANATION OF PLATE XXXIII

Fig. 1. Cross-section through gall showing bacterial cavities

Fig. 2. Bacteria gathering at intercellular spaces, and starting to form cavities

Fig. 3. Hyperplasia taking place

Fig. 4. Result of hypertrophy on the surface of gall

Fig. 5. Cavities formed within cambium. Vessels withstand the pressure

Fig. 6. Bacteria in cavities within bundles

CHROMOSOME CONFIGURATION IN A DWARF SEGREGATE FROM *OENOTHERA "FRANCISCANA SULFUREA"**

STERLING H. EMERSON

CONTENTS

INTRODUCTION

THE *Oenothera* known as hybrid *"franciscana sulfurea"* arose in 1914 as a single light-flowered plant in the second generation of the cross *Oe. biennis* × *Oe. franciscana,* which had been made by Professor Davis in 1912 (Cleland, 1924). Aside from the difference in flower color (which in the hybrid is identical with the sulphur flower color of *Oe. biennis sulfurea*), hybrid *"franciscana sulfurea"* resembles *Oe. franciscana* in most characteristics. It differs in having the green buds of *Oe. biennis,* in its heterozygous character, and in chromosome configuration.

Cleland (1923, 1924) has described the configuration of chromosomes at meiosis in this hybrid, finding, in the late prophase, a ring of twelve chromosomes and a single pair. At metaphase, the paired chromosomes separated normally, while the chromosomes constituting the ring separated in the characteristic zigzag manner typical of oenotheras with non-pairing chromosomes. I have since observed the same arrangement and separation of chromosomes in later generations of the same material.

* Paper from the Department of Botany of the University of Michigan, No. 288.

When inbred, hybrid "*franciscana sulfurea*" regularly gives segregating progenies, consisting chiefly of the parental form with about one third of the plants of a new dwarf type. The dwarf segregate differs from the parent not only in stature but in bud color (being red-budded as is *Oe. franciscana*), and in being apparently homozygous for all characters.

MATERIAL AND METHODS

The plants used in this investigation were inbred descendants from a dwarf plant isolated from a culture of hybrid "*franciscana sulfurea*" by Professor B. M. Davis.

Anthers were fixed for fifteen minutes in a solution consisting of 1 gram picric acid and 5 ml. dichloracetic acid in 100 ml. of absolute alcohol. A volume of absolute alcohol equal to the volume of killing solution used was then added and after fifteen minutes the solution was decanted off and the anthers placed in absolute alcohol. A mixture of one half xylol and one half cedar oil was then added in a layer under the alcohol and the buds were allowed to settle into this mixture. The anthers were then placed in fresh xylol-cedar oil mixture, and melted paraffin was added. The anthers were imbedded directly in hard paraffin with only two changes of paraffin. The entire process of fixing and imbedding required considerably less than 24 hours.

Sections were cut at 15 microns to insure entire nuclei and stained by the iodine-crystal violet method described by Clausen (1926).

In some pollen sacs the microsporocytes were badly shrunken, but, for the most part, very good preparations were obtained by this short method.

DESCRIPTION OF CHROMOSOMES

In the late prophase, the chromosomes appear as seven pairs, the members of any pair usually forming a small ring (Pl. XXXIV, Figs. 1–5). Some of the chromosomes often appear to be clumped, in which cases the seven pairs cannot be seen distinctly. In those nuclei in which all fourteen chromosomes can be recognized with certainty, they appear as seven pairs completely unassociated.

Metaphase is extremely regular in all respects. Ordinarily

the chromosomes lie too close together for recognition of all seven pairs (Pl. XXXIV, Fig. 6). It is only when the plane of the section is slightly oblique to the spindle that the seven pairs may be seen distinctly (Pl. XXXIV, Figs. 7–8).

In some prophase nuclei, a small deeply staining body was seen (Pl. XXXIV, Figs. 2, 4, 5). This body was completely absent in some nuclei and was never seen at metaphase. It resembled a chromosome fragment, but was more probably formed by the degeneration of the nucleolus.

DISCUSSION

The case described in this paper makes the third in which a heterozygous form of Oenothera is known to have many non-pairing chromosomes and to give rise to a homozygous form with chromosomes all normally pairing.

Cleland (1925) has described the cytological situation in the case of mut. *rubrinervis* and its segregate mut. *deserens*. Mut. *rubrinervis* was found to have a circle of six chromosomes and four pairs, while mut. *deserens* had seven pairs of chromosomes. The genetics of these forms is briefly as follows: Mut. *rubrinervis* is heterozygous; when self-pollinated it produces two types of offspring, the parent type and mut. *deserens* (De Vries, 1916). Mut. *rubrinervis* is also heterogametic as shown by the twin hybrids in crosses with *Oe. muricata* (*Auct. non* L.) (De Vries, 1913), and with *Oe. biennis* (Renner, 1917, 1918, 1919). Mut. *deserens* seems to be completely homozygous and produces but one type of gamete.

The situation for mut. *rubricalyx* and its segregate mut. *latifrons* is much the same. Mut. *rubricalyx* has been found by Cleland (1925) to have a circle of eight chromosomes and three chromosome pairs. Mut. *latifrons* has all pairing chromosomes.

The case described in this paper is in some respects more striking than the two just mentioned. The heterozygous form, hybrid "*franciscana sulfurea*," has but one pair of chromosomes. It is known to produce two types of gametes, only one of which functions as pollen. It is also known to be heterozygous for three independent characters. The dwarf segregate is known to produce but one type of gamete and is completely homozygous for all characters that can be tested. The experiments on which these statements are based will be published shortly.

The relation shown to exist between the chromosome configuration and the relatively homozygous or heterozygous condition in the forms contrasted above helps to substantiate the general contention that the genetic behavior of the oenotheras is in some way dependent on the chromosome arrangement at the reduction division.

University of Michigan

LITERATURE CITED

Clausen, J. 1926. Genetic and Cytological Investigations on *Viola tricolor* L. and *V. arvensis* Murr. Hereditas, 8 : 1–156. (See p. 9.)

Cleland, Ralph E. 1923. Chromosome Arrangements during Meiosis in Certain Oenotheras. Am. Nat., 57 : 562–566.

—— 1924. Meiosis in Pollen Mother Cells of *Oenothera franciscana sulfurea.* Bot. Gaz., 77 : 149–170.

—— 1925. Chromosome Behavior during Meiosis in the Pollen Mother Cells of Certain Oenotheras. Am. Nat., 59 : 475–479.

Renner, O. 1917. Versuche über die gametische Konstitution der Oenotheren. Zeitschr. ind. Abst. Vererb., 18 : 121–294.

—— 1918. Weitere Vererbungsstudien an Önotheren. Flora, 111–112 (Stahl-Festschrift): 641–667.

—— 1919. Zur Biologie und Morphologie der männlichen Haplonten einiger Oenotheren. Zeitschr. f. Bot., 11 : 305–380.

De Vries, Hugo. 1913. Gruppenweise Artbildung. Berlin.

—— 1916. Gute, harte und leere Samen von Oenothera. Zeitschr. ind. Abst. Vererb., 16 : 239–292.

EXPLANATION OF PLATE XXXIV

All figures were drawn with the aid of a camera lucida. A Spencer compound binocular microscope and a Zeiss 90–1.4 apochromatic objective and 20× compensating ocular were used.

Fig. 1. Prophase, after second contraction, showing seven pairs of chromosomes.

Figs. 2–5. Slightly later than Figure 1. All show seven pairs of chromosomes.

Fig. 6. Typical metaphase showing regular pairing of chromosomes. Not all pairs can be definitely recognized.

Figs. 7 and 8. Metaphase. The sections are cut somewhat oblique to the spindle, allowing all seven pairs to be seen.

PLATE XXXIV

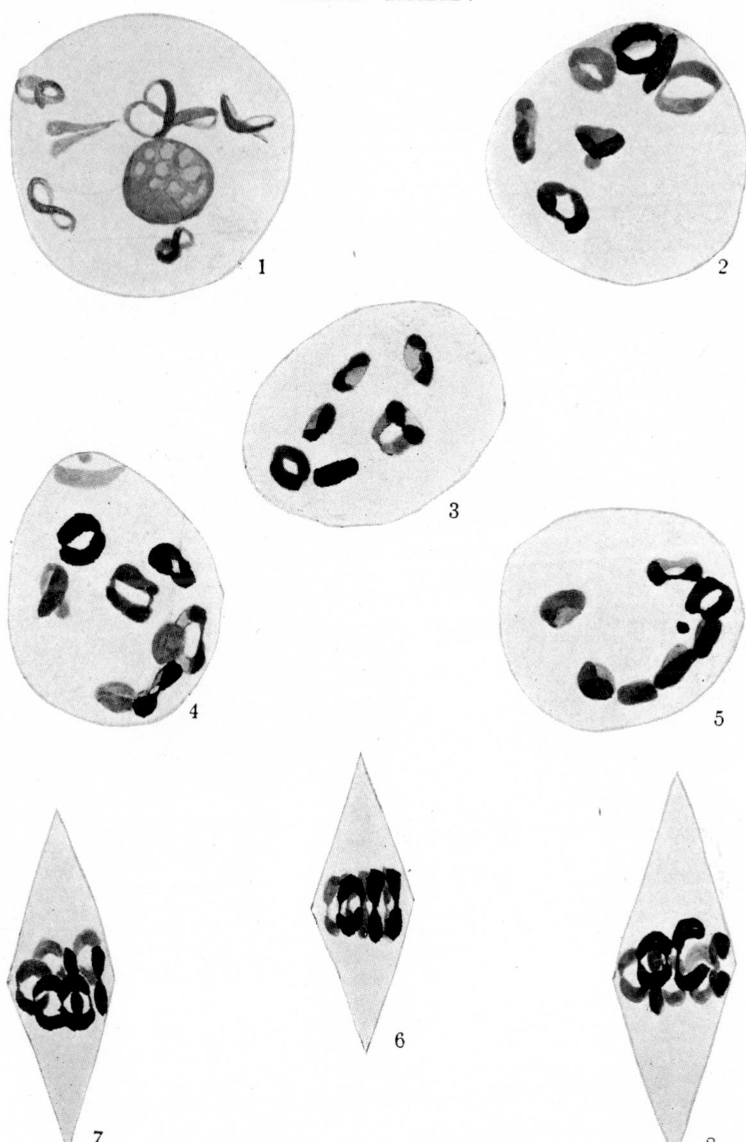

MULTIPLE-FACTOR INHERITANCE IN CROSSES BETWEEN *OENOTHERA GRANDIFLORA* AND *OENOTHERA FRANCISCANA* *

STERLING H. EMERSON

CONTENTS

INTRODUCTION

Material

THE original crosses between *Oenothera franciscana* and *Oenothera grandiflora* were made by Professor Davis in the summer of 1921 and the first generations were grown at Ann Arbor in the summer of 1923, at which time Professor Davis kindly turned over

* Paper from the Department of Botany of the University of Michigan, No. 287.

to me all the material of these crosses, including seed from pollinations made by him that summer. Succeeding generations were grown at Ann Arbor in 1924 and 1925.

The strain of *Oe. grandiflora* used in these crosses was one that had been grown by Professor Davis since 1909 in an inbred line, coming originally from seed collected for him at Dixie Landing, near Tensaw, Alabama (Davis, 1911). This is the strain of *Oe. grandiflora* that was used in the early cytological studies (Davis, 1909).

The plants of *Oe. franciscana* used were the descendants in an inbred line from the original collection by Dr. Charles Piper Smith (Davis, 1916; Bartlett, 1914). This strain has also been analyzed cytologically (Cleland, 1922).

Scope of Experiments

At the time these experiments were planned, it was hoped that crosses between these two species would prove more simple in their genetic behavior than most oenotheras because of the large number of normally pairing chromosomes in both parents. The studies of Davis (1919) showed that *Oe. grandiflora* had seven pairs of chromosomes. Cleland has reëxamined this species with the same result. *Oe. franciscana* has been found by Cleland (1922) to have five pairs and a ring of four chromosomes. Apparently the plants of the first generations of crosses between these two species may have the chromosome configuration of either parent. Only one plant (the parent of culture 30) was examined by me; this had seven pairs of chromosomes. Cleland has examined several plants of the first generations of reciprocal crosses and found a ring of four and five pairs of chromosomes in each.

The genetic behavior to be reviewed in this paper shows certain peculiarities doubtless due to the paired condition of the chromosomes. The material did not prove well adapted to genetic analysis, however, because of the absence of sharply segregating characters. For this reason the experiments were not pushed to a definite conclusion, but since the behavior noted is unusual for the oenotheras, it seems well to publish the findings of these crosses in their incomplete form.

I wish to take this opportunity to thank Professor Davis for the original material and for his kind permission to utilize his notes on the lines before they were taken over by me.

GENETIC ANALYSIS

The two species used in the crosses described in this paper differ from each other in a great many characteristics, the inheritance of several of which was studied. No attempt will be made to give a detailed description of either of the parental forms or of the hybrid generations, but each will be contrasted separately for each characteristic studied.

Not all plants in the second generation cultures were classified for each character studied. The number of individuals listed for a given culture indicates only the number that have been classified for the particular character under discussion.

Time of Flowering

Oe. franciscana is ordinarily one of the first species in our collection to flower, while *Oe. grandiflora* is about the latest. Under our ordinary methods of culture, sowing the seeds in the greenhouse in January or February and transplanting to the field in May, *Oe. franciscana* will begin to flower as early as the first week in July. *Oe. grandiflora* under similar conditions rarely flowers before the last week in August, at which time *Oe. franciscana* is nearly past its flowering season. Most plants of *Oe. grandiflora* fail to ripen seeds before frost at Ann Arbor.

The first generation plants were intermediate between the two parents for time of flowering. The reciprocal F_1 cultures were uniform in this respect, all coming into flower about the end of July. The only exceptions were the weaker chlorotic plants of the cross *franciscana* × *grandiflora*, which were later in flowering, a few failing entirely.

In the second generation there was extreme variation in the time of flowering of different individuals, some approximating the season of the early-flowering parent, and some failing to flower before frost. This great variability in the season of flowering made it difficult to classify the plants for characteristics that change with the maturing of the individual. For this reason many plants were not noted at all. No records were kept of the exact flowering date of individuals in the second generation cultures.

Growth Habit

In most oenothera crosses, the individuals in the first and second generations fall into a comparatively few definite classes with respect to growth habit. Such was not the case in the crosses here described.

The first generation of the cross *grandiflora* × *franciscana* was remarkably uniform in every respect. In growth habit it was denser than *Oe. franciscana*, but definitely intermediate. The reciprocal cross, *franciscana* × *grandiflora*, differed chiefly in the development of green pigmentation. The plants were smaller and more open than in the former F_1, but otherwise resembled it closely. The plants with relatively dark green leaves were indistinguishable from plants of the reciprocal cross.

Second generations were grown from each of the F_1 cultures. These, including double reciprocal F_2 cultures, totaled more than three hundred plants,[1] but it would have been practically impossible to find any two plants of strikingly similar growth habit. All intermediate types between the parental forms were present as well as many that were more extreme than either parent, the dwarfed plants being especially noticeable. No method was devised for recording the different habits of growth.

Bud Color

Oe. franciscana has brilliant red buds (Text Fig. 5 *a*); *Oe. grandiflora* has buds entirely green except for slight red markings on

[1] Most of the F_2 population came from the cross *grandiflora* × *franciscana:* culture 30, grown in 1924, had 77 individuals, and culture 262, grown the following year, had 136 individuals. Only 7 plants of the second generation of the reciprocal cross lived to flower; these belonged to culture 263, grown in 1925. Culture 37, with 36 individuals recorded, was the double reciprocal cross (*grandiflora* × *franciscana*) × (*franciscana* × *grandiflora*), a chlorotic plant being used as pollen parent. Culture 38, with 54 individuals recorded, was the same double reciprocal cross except that a dark green plant was used as pollen parent.

the most brightly illuminated side, and these are often lacking (Text Fig. 5 *e*).

All first generation plants had red buds, but of lighter color than the red-budded parent. F_1 culture 169 had 6 plants with

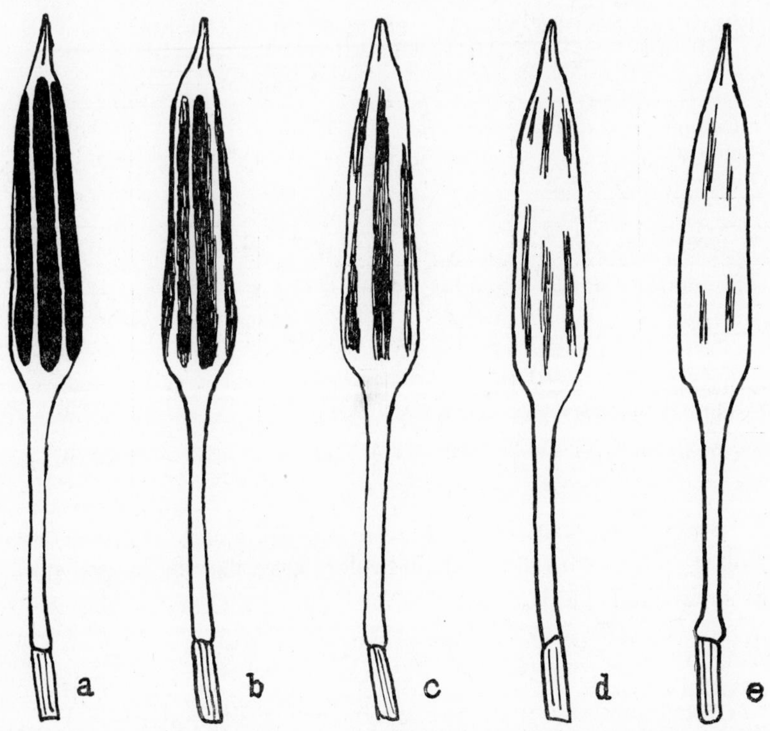

FIG. 5. Extent of red pigmentation on the buds of plants from the second generation of the cross *Oe. grandiflora* × *Oe. franciscana*. The red color is indicated by the black shading.

light red (*b*) buds and 3 with splashed (*c*) buds (compare Text Fig. 5).

Many of the plants in the second generation had buds intermediate in appearance between the red and green of the parents. In order to record the approximate color of the buds in the F_2 cultures, five "types" were selected with which the buds of any plant might be compared. These types are illustrated in Figure 5 in the text. The F_2 frequencies for these five classes are given in Table I.

TABLE I

FREQUENCIES OF FIVE CLASSES OF BUDS IN THE SECOND AND DOUBLE RECIPROCAL F_2 GENERATIONS OF THE CROSS *GRANDIFLORA* × *FRANCISCANA*

Culture number 2	Red a	Light Red b	Splashed c	Light Splashed d	Green e
30	28	12	9	5	9
262	26	24	8	8	12
F_2 subtotal	(54)	(36)	(17)	(13)	(21)
37	11	11	5	7	2
38	16	15	9	7	7
double recip. subtotal	(27)	(26)	(14)	(14)	(9)
Total	81	62	31	27	30

Five F_2 plants of culture 30 were self-pollinated. F_3 progenies from F_2 plants with different bud colors gave varying frequencies, as shown in Table II.

TABLE II

FREQUENCIES OF FIVE CLASSES OF BUDS IN THE THIRD GENERATIONS FROM F_2 PLANTS WITH DIFFERENT BUD COLORS

Culture number	Bud color of parent	Red buds a	Light Red b	Splashed c	Light Splashed d	Green e
171	a red	15	12			
172	a red	20	4			
174	b lt. red	2				
170	e green (?)	3	5	13		9
173	e green	1	1	4		5

A back-cross, (*grandiflora* × *franciscana*) × *franciscana*, consisting of 14 plants, had 6 plants with red (*a*) buds, 2 with light red (*b*), 4 with splashed (*c*) and 1 with light splashed (*d*).

Sepal Tip Length

Oe. grandiflora has long sepal tips while those of *Oe. franciscana* are relatively very short (Pl. XXXV, Figs. 2 and 1). The

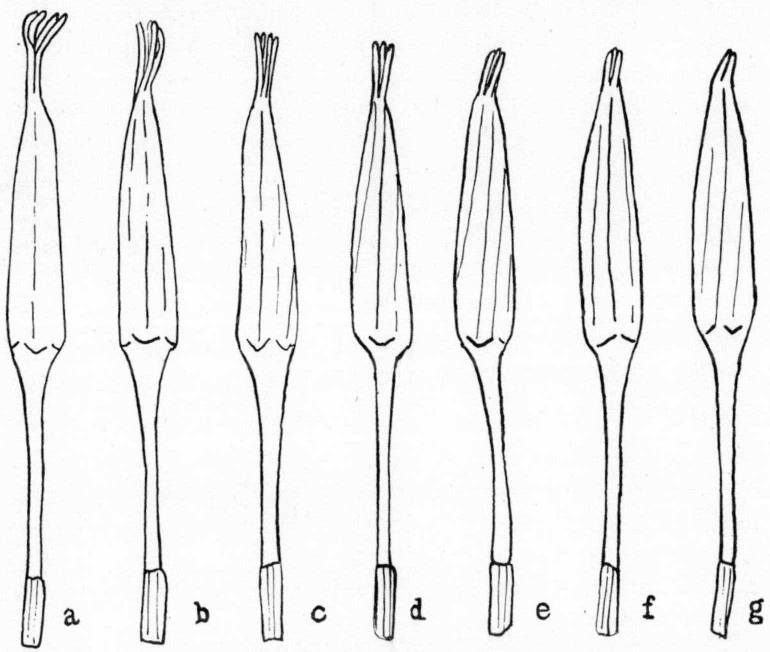

Fig. 6. Length of sepal tips on buds of second generation plants of the cross *Oe. grandiflora* × *Oe. franciscana*

first generation plants had buds of an intermediate nature, but with sepal tips much longer than the mean length of the F_2 population (Pl. XXXV, Fig. 3, and Text Fig. 6 *b*). F_1 culture 169 had 5 plants with rather long (*b*) sepal tips and 4 with very long (*a*) tips. In the F_2 there was great variation in the expression of this character. It proved difficult to make measurements with accuracy as there is no definite point at which the "tip" arises, and there were great differences in total bud length. The general appearance of the tip of the bud seemed a better criterion for classifying the various types. Buds with short sepal tips are more sharply shouldered near the tip, while those with longer sepal tips are more tapering and have a stronger tendency to twist. There is also a difference in the firmness of the sepal tips, the short ones being tightly appressed and the longer ones more spreading (compare Pl. XXXV and Text Fig. 6). Seven arbitrary classes were chosen for convenience in classification. These are illustrated in Figure 6 in the text. The frequencies for the seven classes are given in Table III for the F_2 generations and in Table IV for the F_3.

TABLE III

FREQUENCIES OF SEVEN CLASSES OF SEPAL TIPS IN THE SECOND, AND DOUBLE RECIPROCAL F_2, GENERATIONS OF THE CROSS *GRANDIFLORA* × *FRANCISCANA*

Culture number	a (long)	b	c	d	e	f	g (short)
30	5	13	13	17	10	3	2
262	3	16	32	45	22	5	
F_2 subtotal	(8)	(29)	(45)	(62)	(32)	(8)	(2)
37	3	6	13	7	5	2	
38	3	12	14	9	11	5	
double reciprocal subtotal	(6)	(18)	(27)	(16)	(16)	(7)	
Total	14	47	72	78	48	15	2

TABLE IV

FREQUENCIES OF FOUR CLASSES OF SEPAL TIPS IN THE THIRD GENERATIONS FROM F_2 PLANTS WITH DIFFERENT LENGTHS OF SEPAL TIPS

Culture number	Sepal tips of parent	a	b	c	d
170	a	23	5	1	
171	b	19	8		
173	b	8	2		1
174	c				2
175	d	3	9	7	5

The back-cross (*grandiflora* × *franciscana*) × *franciscana* had 6 plants with *d* sepal tips, 4 with *e* sepal tips, 3 with *f* sepal tips, and 1 with *g* sepal tips.

Stem Tip Color

The young growing parts of the stem in the inflorescence of *Oe. franciscana* are marked with purple, the color disappearing on the older parts of the stem. The color is especially prominent in stripes just below the points of attachment of the youngest floral bracts, but in some cases the entire stem tip is uniformly colored. The coloring is more pronounced as the plant nears the end of its flowering season; late-flowering plants might be difficult to determine. *Oe. grandiflora* has green stem tips.

Plants of the first generation of crosses between these two species had stem tips intermediate in color between those of the parents. F_1 culture 169 had 2 plants classed as light purple and 6 as very light purple (compare with F_2 distribution).

The second generation did not segregate clearly into plants with green and purple stem tips, but many plants appeared intermediate. Some of the differences in color may have been due to differences in growth habit (the coloring is more noticeable on plants with a relatively open habit) and difference in season of flowering. Five arbitrary classes for degree of coloring were selected as an aid in classifying this character. These classes, together with the frequencies in F_2 culture 262, were as follows: 4 "strong purple"; 26 "purple"; 17 "light purple"; 11 "very light purple"; and 17 "green"; totaling 75 plants recorded for this character.

Coloring of Stems at Base of Plant

The stems of *Oe. grandiflora* develop a diffused red color on all the older regions, especially near the base of the plant. This coloring varies in intensity with the exposure of the stems to sunlight and with the maturing of the plant. *Oe. franciscana* has green stems, often turning brown or slightly red late in the season. Plants of the first generations of crosses between these two species had the red stems like those of *Oe. grandiflora*. In culture 169, 7 plants were recorded with "red" stems and 2 with "light red" stems (compare with F_2 frequencies). Plants of the second generation gave every appearance of forming an intergrading series between red and green, though the extent of the variation due to density of foliage and season of flowering could not be determined.

Six classes were used in comparing the plants of the second generation for stem color. These classes with their frequencies in F_2 culture 262 were as follows: 6 "intense red"; 26 "red"; 16 "light red"; 6 "green with some red"; 28 "green with almost no red"; and 9 "green"; making a total of 91 plants recorded for this character.

Length of Floral Bracts

In the inflorescence of *Oe. franciscana* (Pl. XXXVI, Fig. 1) the young buds are shorter than the floral bracts subtending them. The buds elongate more rapidly than the bracts, until, on the day before opening, the buds are about one fourth longer than the subtending bracts. When the flower is open, the hypanthium is about equal to the bract in length. In *Oe. grandiflora* the buds are always longer than the floral bracts (Pl. XXXVI, Fig. 2). At first only the tips of the buds project beyond the bracts, but by the time of opening the bud is three or four times as long as the bract.

The first hybrid generation was intermediate for length of bracts (Pl. XXXVI, Fig. 3). Buds and bracts were of about equal length at first, and by the time of opening, the buds were about twice as long as the bracts.

Variation of the floral bracts in the second generation was nearly as great as the variation in growth habit (Pl. XXXVI, Figs. 3–5; Pl. XXXVII, Figs. 6–12). Some plants had bracts at first equaling or surpassing the buds, but which were not much greater than one fourth of the bud length at anthesis (Fig. 4). Some had bracts at first shorter than the buds, but growing longer than the hypanthia of the open flowers (Fig. 11). Some resembled *Oe. franciscana,* but were more extreme (Figs. 10 and 12), while others were more extreme in the opposite direction than the *Oe. grandiflora* parent (Fig. 6). The great majority of the F_2 plants were intermediate between these four extremes. In the field the floral bracts were classified in nine groups, based chiefly on the relative lengths of the youngest bracts and buds. These classes with the number of individuals in each in culture 262 were as follows: 4 "very long"; 26 "long"; 5 "rather long"; 23 "more than medium"; 8 "medium"; 5 "less than medium"; 6 "somewhat short"; 10 "short"; and 4 "very short"; making 91 individuals noted for this character.

Length of Buds

Oe. grandiflora and *Oe. franciscana* are fairly uniform for size of flowers and length of buds, but the second generations of crosses between the two were quite variable in both respects (Pls. XXXV–XXXVII). No measurements were made of flower size, but the bud cone of F_2 plants was measured, giving actually an indication of flower size. All measurements were made from herbarium specimens collected late in the summer of 1925, and only culture 262 was measured. The bud cone varied from 12 to 35 millimeters in length. Grouped in somewhat larger classes, the frequencies were as follows: 17 mm. or less, 21 plants; 18 to 20 mm., 20 plants; 21 to 23 mm., 29 plants; 24 to 26 mm., 30 plants; 27 to 29 mm., 18 plants; 30 to 32 mm., 2 plants; and 33 mm. or over, 3 plants; making a total of 123 plants measured.

Pubescence (Thick-walled)

The entire plant of *Oe. franciscana* is clothed with long thick-walled hairs. These are especially striking on the buds (Pl. XXXV, Fig. 1). *Oe. grandiflora* is almost entirely free from pubescence of this type. I failed to note carefully the pubescence of the plants of the first generation. Buds of F_2 culture 30 were examined under the microscope and the number of hairs per unit area were counted. The following is a summary of these counts: 1 hair per 10 units, 9 plants; 1 hair per 2 units, 2 plants; 1 hair per unit, 10 plants; 2 hairs per unit, 7 plants; 3 hairs per unit, 14 plants; 4 hairs per unit, 9 plants; 6 hairs per unit, 7 plants; and 8 hairs per unit, 5 plants; totaling 63 plants measured.

Pubescence (Thin-walled)

Both *Oe. franciscana* and *Oe. grandiflora* have another type of pubescence composed of numerous thin-walled secretory hairs. This type is also more numerous in *Oe. franciscana,* though the difference is not nearly as great as in the amount of thick-walled pubescence. The same buds used in the counts of thick-walled hairs were counted for thin-walled hairs, and the same unit of measure was used both times. Sixty-two plants were recorded for thin-walled pubescence; a summary of the counts follows: 4 hairs per unit area, 2 plants; 6 hairs per unit, 19 plants; 8 hairs per unit, 14 plants; 10 hairs per unit, 10 plants; 12 hairs per unit, 4 plants; 18 hairs per unit, 1 plant; 20 hairs per unit, 5 plants; and 25 hairs per unit, 7 plants.

EVIDENCE OF CORRELATION

Correlation between Five Characters

A group of five characters showed marked correlation in their inheritance. These were bud color, sepal tip length, stem tip color, basal stem coloring, and length of floral bracts. The characters coming into the cross from the *Oe. franciscana* parent were red buds, short sepal tips, purple stem tips, green stems, and long floral bracts. In all the following cases, the coefficients of correlation have been calculated in terms of the characters coming from this parent.

Red buds and short sepal tips: the coefficient of correlation, based on 63 individuals of F_2 culture 30, was $.314 \pm .076$.

The coefficient of correlation, based on 78 individuals of F_2 culture 262, was .027 ± .076.

The coefficient of correlation, based on 36 individuals of the double reciprocal culture 37, was .533 ± .080.

The coefficient of correlation, based on 54 individuals of the double reciprocal culture 38, was .349 ± .084.

The coefficient of correlation, based on 231 individuals of all F_2 cultures, was .244 ± .042.

Red buds and purple stem tips: the coefficient of correlation, based on 72 individuals of F_2 culture 262, was .598 ± .051.

Short sepal tips and purple stem tips: the coefficient of correlation, based on 75 individuals of F_2 culture 262, was .334 ± .069.

Red buds and green stems: the coefficient of correlation, based on 76 individuals of F_2 culture 262, was .547 ± .054.

Short sepal tips and green stems: the coefficient of correlation, based on 89 individuals of F_2 culture 262, was .377 ± .054.

Purple stem tips and green stems: the coefficient of correlation, based on 75 individuals of F_2 culture 262, was .358 ± .068.

Red buds and long floral bracts: the coefficient of correlation, based on 75 individuals of F_2 culture 262, was − .398 ± .066.

Short sepal tips and long floral bracts: the coefficient of correlation, based on 93 individuals of F_2 culture 262, was − .071 ± .069.

Purple stem tips and long floral bracts: the coefficient of correlation, based on 72 individuals of F_2 culture 262, was − .556 ± .055.

Green stems and long floral bracts: the coefficient of correlation, based on 87 individuals of F_2 culture 262, was − .235 ± .068.

A summary of the relations of these five characters is given in Table V.

TABLE V

SUMMARY OF COEFFICIENTS OF CORRELATION FOR FIVE CHARACTERS

	Bud color	Sepal tip length	Stem tip color	Stem color
Length of floral bracts....	− .394	(− .071)	− .556	− .235
Stem color..............	.547	.377	.358	
Stem tip color...........	.598	.334		
Sepal tip length..........	.244			

Characters Independently Inherited

Red bud color and thick-walled pubescence: the coefficient of correlation, based on 62 individuals of F_2 culture 30, was .044 ± .085.

Short sepal tips and thick-walled pubescence: the coefficient of correlation, based on 62 individuals of F_2 culture 30, was .192 ± .082.

Red bud color and thin-walled pubescence: the coefficient of correlation, based on 61 individuals of F_2 culture 30, was − .163 ± .083.

Short sepal tips and thin-walled pubescence: the coefficient of correlation, based on 61 individuals of F_2 culture 30, was .252 ± .079.

Thick-walled and thin-walled pubescence: the coefficient of correlation, based on 62 individuals of F_2 culture 30, was .356 ± .075.

Red bud color and long buds: the coefficient of correlation, based on 78 individuals of F_2 culture 262, was − .095 ± .075.

Short sepal tips and long buds: the coefficient of correlation, based on 123 individuals of F_2 culture 262, was .003 ± .061.

Purple stem tips and long buds: the coefficient of correlation, based on 75 individuals of F_2 culture 262, was − .099 ± .077.

Green stems and long buds: the coefficient of correlation, based on 89 individuals of F_2 culture 262, was − .217 ± .068.

Long floral bracts and long buds: the coefficient of correlation, based on 91 individuals of F_2 culture 262, was .127 ± .071.

DISCUSSION

Multiple-Factor Interpretation

For the crosses reviewed in this paper, a multiple-factor interpretation is suggested in two distinct ways. In the first place, the F_2 distributions for certain characters resemble typical examples of multiple-factor inheritance. In the second place, when the inheritance of all the characteristics studied is considered collectively, it is evident that a great many factors must be involved.

The most striking multiple-factor distribution for the second generation of these crosses is noticed in the inheritance of growth habit; but for this character the inheritance was only described, with no attempt at analysis. An almost parallel case appears in the inheritance of size of floral bracts, and here we know a little more about the inheritance. Both parents seem to contribute factors tending to increase the size of floral bracts, as shown by the segregates with extremely large bracts. *Oe. franciscana* has larger bracts than *Oe. grandiflora*, but largeness of bracts seems to be associated with other characters coming from *Oe. grandiflora* (Table V). The plausible explanation is that *Oe. grandiflora* carried dominant factors for small bract size (shown by the intermediate F_1) and also factors for large bract size, the latter associated in their inheritance with factors for green buds, green stem tips, and red stems. It is at least evident that the inheritance in this cross is not simple, and not due to one factor pair.

The inheritance of time of flowering, to judge from the F_2 distribution, would also seem to involve multiple factors. Here, again, the exact times were not recorded, but it was noted that both red- and green-budded plants, differing in sepal tip length, were among the first to flower. This is an indication of independence in inheritance between flowering season and the group of correlated characters shown in Table V.

The second generation, classified for bud color, gives a curve with the mode at the red end of the series. This is very different from the normal curve for multiple-factor inheritance, and it might be believed that a single factor pair was concerned in this cross if it were not for the frequencies in the back-cross to the red-budded parent (see p. 126). The presence of a large number of plants with intermediate bud colors in this back-cross suggests a difference of more than one factor pair between red and green bud colors.

The inheritance of bud cone length must also be due to several different factors. Both parents are somewhat similar for bud size, but it was noted that the second generation showed great variability for this character. It must be supposed that both parents contributed factors for both long and short buds.

Only two of the characters studied gave in F_2 definitely bimodal curves suggestive of single-factor differences with dominance. These were stem color and thin-walled pubescence. In the former case there is a mode in the red region and another in the green, with approximately three fourths of the individuals having stems distinctly showing red. The case for thin-walled pubescence is more striking because of the break in the curve between the two modes. The frequencies of the classes having 4 to 12 hairs per unit area form a smooth curve. No individuals occur in the region between 12 and 18 hairs per unit. After this break, there is another group of individuals with its mean slightly above 20 hairs per unit area. The frequencies for these two groups are 49 and 13, respectively, a difference of but 2.5 from the theoretical 3 : 1.

The coefficients of correlation for the various character combinations may indicate very little when considered singly because of the uneven range of the arbitrarily chosen classes, but collectively they must be of some significance. It has been noted earlier that a group of five characters were correlated in their inheritance. With one exception (length of sepal tips and floral bracts), noticeable correlation is shown between every pair of the characters. These characters must either have certain factors in common or have factors that are closely associated in their inheritance.

All other characters studied seem to be independent in their inheritance, except that there seem to be correlation between the two types of pubescence and a possible indication of correlation between thin-walled pubescence and short sepal tips.

Since most of the characters studied seem to be the expression of several factors, and since many of the characters are independent in their inheritance and the others never completely associated, it is evident that a large number of factors have been segregating in the crosses described above.

Relation of Multiple Factors to the Paired Condition of Chromosomes

In a cross between two species differing in as many respects as the two discussed in this paper, it might well be expected that segregation for a great many factors would be shown in the second generation. Such, however, is not ordinarily the case in the oenotheras. A cross between two oenothera species usually gives in F_2 comparatively few types of plants, each type differing from the others in a great many characteristics.

Unfortunately, the chromosome configuration in most crosses of species is not known. For *Oe. biennis*, *Oe. Lamarckiana*, and *Oe. muricata* (*Auct. non* L.), however, we do know the configuration of chromosomes, and in each of these there is little or no pairing of chromosomes at the reduction division. *Oe. Lamarckiana* has but one set of normally pairing chromosomes; the other two species have no pairing chromosomes (Cleland, 1923, 1925). Crosses between these three species show a large number of characteristics being inherited in blocs, the type of inheritance that is considered typical for the oenotheras. The crosses *Oe. muricata* × *Oe. Lamarckiana*, and *Oe. biennis* × *Oe. Lamarckiana* give in the first generation the twin hybrids *laeta* and *velutina*, both of which breed true when self-pollinated (De Vries, 1907; 1913, p. 126). Reciprocal crosses between *Oe. biennis* and *Oe. muricata* give first generations showing patroclinic inheritance for all characteristics except sepal tip length, which is matroclinic (Davis, 1914). None of the characters segregate in the following generation. The inheritance of sepal tip length is especially noteworthy, as there is no intergrading between the parental forms as seen in crosses between *Oe. franciscana* and *Oe. grandiflora*.

The crosses between *Oe. franciscana* and *Oe. grandiflora* appear to be the first between species which have been proved to have pairing chromosomes. Since this cross shows segregation for a great many factors, multiple-factor inheritance in the oenotheras may be concluded to be a function of pairing chromosomes.

University of Michigan

LITERATURE CITED

Bartlett, Harley Harris. 1914. Systematic Studies on Oenothera, — IV. Oe. franciscana and Oe. venusta, spp. novv. Rhodora, 16 : 33–37.

Cleland, Ralph E. 1922. The Reduction Divisions in the Pollen Mother Cells of Oenothera franciscana. Am. Journ. Bot., 9 : 391–413.

—— 1923. Chromosome Arrangements during Meiosis in Certain Oenotheras. Am. Nat., 57 : 562–566.

—— 1925. Chromosome Behavior during Meiosis in the Pollen Mother Cells of Certain Oenotheras. Am. Nat., 59 : 475–479.

DAVIS, B. M. 1909. Cytological Studies on Oenothera. I. Pollen Development of Oenothera grandiflora. Annals Bot., 23 : 551–571.

—— 1911. Genetical Studies on Œnothera. II. Some Hybrids of *Œnothera biennis* and *O. grandiflora* That Resemble *O. Lamarckiana*. Am. Nat., 45 : 193–233.

—— 1914. Genetical Studies on *Oenothera*. V. Some Reciprocal Crosses of *Oenothera*. Zeitschr. ind. Abst. Vererb., 12 : 169–205.

—— 1916. Hybrids of *Oenothera biennis* and *Oenothera franciscana* in the First and Second Generations. Genetics, 1 : 197–251.

DE VRIES, HUGO. 1907. On Twin Hybrids. Bot. Gaz., 44 : 401–407.

—— 1913. Gruppenweise Artbildung. Berlin.

EXPLANATION OF PLATES

PLATE XXXV

Photograph of buds taken from herbarium specimens

FIG. 1. Buds of *Oe. franciscana*

FIG. 2. Bud of *Oe. grandiflora*

FIG. 3. Buds of *Oe. franciscana* × *grandiflora* F_1

FIG. 4. Buds of *Oe. grandiflora* × *franciscana* F_2

FIG. 5. Bud of F_2 plant with semi-cruciate flowers

PLATES XXXVI–XXXVII

Tracings of buds and floral bracts made from herbarium specimens and reduced one half

FIG. 1. *Oe. franciscana*

FIG. 2. *Oe. grandiflora*

FIG. 3. *Oe. franciscana* × *grandiflora* F_1

FIGS. 4–12. *Oe. grandiflora* × *franciscana* F_2

PLATE XXXV

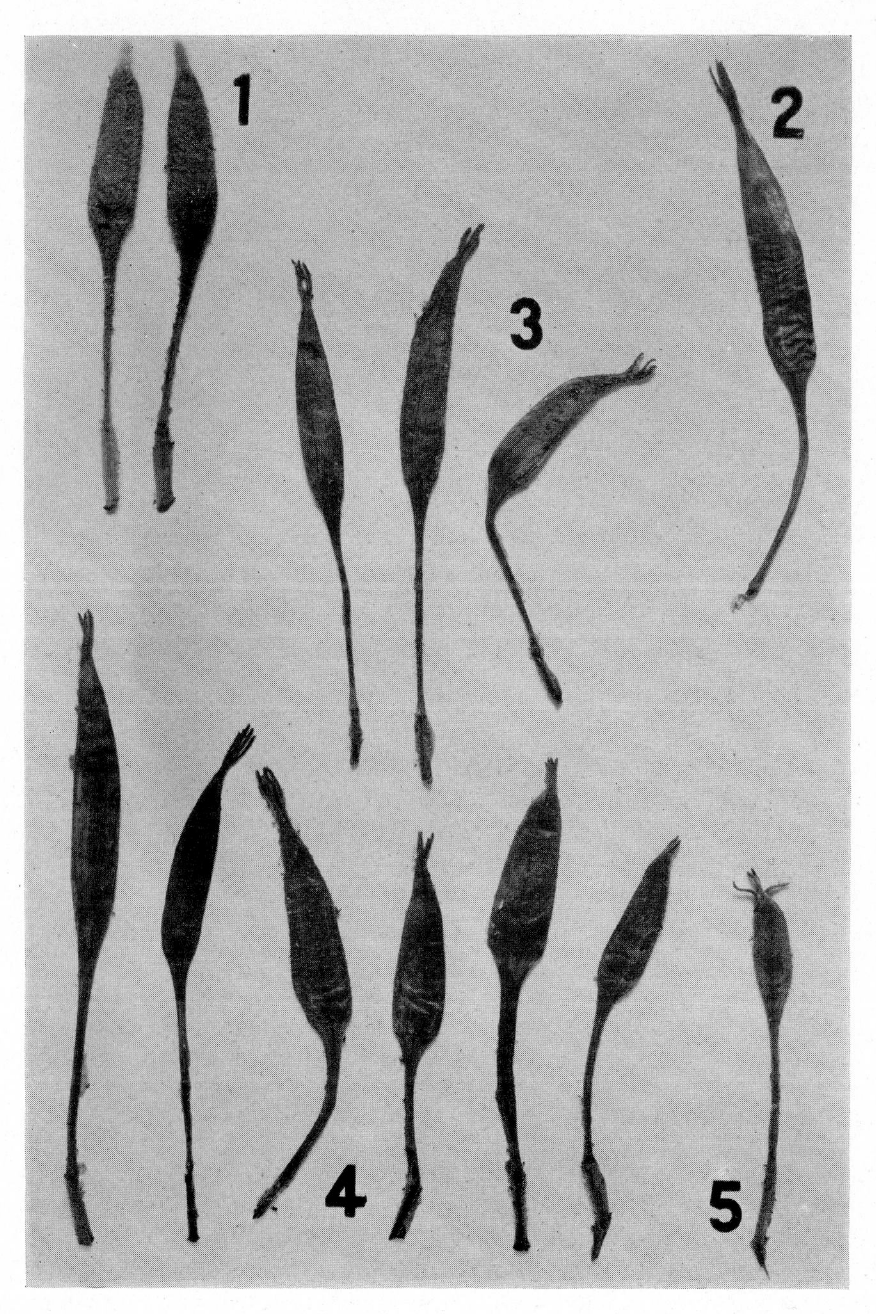

PLATE XXXVI

PLATE XXXVII

BIOCHEMICAL STUDIES ON SEED VIABILITY

II. CHEMICAL CONSTITUENTS OPERATING IN REDUCTION

R. PERCIVAL HIBBARD AND ORMAN E. STREET

INTRODUCTION

THE present study was planned as a continuation of the work on the permanganate reduction method of measuring seed viability, as reported by Hibbard and Miller (10). In that report, mention is made of the numerous papers that have appeared on the subject of the determination of viability. The conclusion reached by most of the investigators is that their method is applicable to measurements of high, medium and low germinating power, but a statement is frequently added that with further study and refinement, narrower ranges could probably be delimited. The most striking correlation is reported by Nemec and Duchoň (19), working on oats and peas. In their study of the relation between catalase activity and viability, they report consistent differences between seeds varying not more than two or three per cent in germination. In the same year, de Vilmorin and Caquabon (30) repeated the test with different varieties of peas, and later Marotta and Kaminka (16) tried the test with wheat, but in neither case was it possible to obtain concordant results.

In spite of the wide divergence in the chemical and physical composition of different seeds within a class or group, it was hoped that with the present method there might be some simple relation that would operate as a function of the germinating power of the seed, and would serve with sufficient refinement to measure that power within limits of two or three per cent. Considered from that viewpoint, the results are rather conclusively negative, but with further studies it has been possible to demonstrate some of the factors responsible for the results obtained.

HISTORICAL

Of the long list of reagents used in oxidation-reduction reactions, potassium permanganate is undoubtedly the most favored, both for inorganic and organic reductions. Its ability to react in acid, alkaline or neutral solutions, combined with its intense coloration, which serves as its own indicator, lends to its adoption in a wide range of situations.

Within the more restricted range of plant materials, it is often used. Reichert (26) lists a number of methods for its use in the preparation of soluble starch. Lasser-Cohn (14) in his *Manual of Organic Chemistry*, gives the reactions of potassium permanganate with a number of aromatic compounds, including a quantitative estimation of glycerol. Reed (25) reported a reduction of concentrated potassium permanganate by horse-radish extract, in which the peroxidases were held to be the reducing agents. Bunzel and Hasselbring (2) refuted the evidence of Reed, so far as the peroxidase was concerned, as they listed ten organic compounds that reduce permanganate.

Hibbard and Miller (10) introduced the use of this reagent in a time-rate reaction for measuring seed viability. The general relation established was that less viable seeds reduced permanganate more rapidly than did those of higher germinating power.

RECENT DEVELOPMENTS OF OTHER METHODS

Among the late methods is an application of thermal relations by Munerati (18), who finds that seeds of wheat, as they age, germinate better at temperatures above their normal. This could be taken as an approximation of the age of the seeds, within a relatively narrow range. This work is similar to that reported by Pierce, Darsie and Elliott (24) in 1914.

Wilmer Davis (6) found that the meal from dead and live seeds of lettuce often showed an equal catalase activity, but that, after soaking in water overnight, that from the dead seeds showed a marked decrease. This he interpreted as a chemical decomposition of the catalase. It would be more reasonable to say that the dead cells were more permeable, and allowed a more rapid exosmosis of the enzyme.

The general relation of catalase activity to viability of seeds has been verified by Gračanin (7), in that new seeds gave greater evolution of oxygen than old seeds. Killing seeds by chemicals did not stop enzyme activity, but often retarded it.

Hottes and Huelson (11) have very recently demonstrated that a relation exists between the colloidal properties of a seed extract of sweet corn and the viability of the seeds.

EXPERIMENTAL WORK

At the point where work on this problem was terminated by Hibbard and Miller, the procedure in the potassium permanganate method was as follows. The seeds were soaked overnight in water and 1 c.c. aliquots withdrawn for the test. To this was added one drop of N/2 $KMnO_4$ and the time required for reduction noted. In order to obtain a clear end point, a few drops of N/10 oxalic acid was added when the reaction was nearly complete.

In the present work, it was deemed advisable to germinate the seeds after soaking, as the irregularities within a sample were often greater than the difference ascribed to different samples. The differences of vigor of seedlings were noted and a system of rating arbitrarily set up, in order that there might be a basis for sharper distinctions.

Preliminary tests, with varying amounts of aqueous extract, and varying amounts and concentrations of potassium permanganate as the agents, failed to yield any consistent relation between time of reduction and viability. The technique was gradually changed, introducing one variant for a series of tests, and then another, until the method closely approximated the conditions for a standard permanganate-oxalate reaction. The procedure then was as follows: Permanganate in excess (1 c.c. of N/2 $KMnO_4$) was added to 10 c.c. of solution (acidified to two per cent H_2SO_4 and kept at 70° C. in a water bath), and at the end of exactly ten minutes the unreduced permanganate was titrated back with sodium oxalate. The results are shown in Table I.

In this and subsequent experiments, several concentrations of $KMnO_4$ were used as work on the method progressed. These will all be reduced, however, to a basis of N/10 $KMnO_4$, computed on the pentavalent reactivity of the reagent in an acid medium.

TABLE I

Application of Standard Oxidation Reduction Reaction to Aqueous Extracts of Corn

Sample	Percentage of germination	Net c.c. $KMnO_4$	Sample	Percentage of germination	Net c.c. $KMnO_4$
12	96	1.25	4	69	2.00
11	95	3.00	6	67	3.90
10	95	3.15	7	60	2.65
8	93	3.15	5	51	1.15
17	88	2.30	1	50	4.30
3	81	2.75	14	42	1.75
13	74	4.67	16	21	4.51
2	73	2.95	15	0	4.25

The fact that an end point of a clear solution was not always attainable would indicate that in those cases the reaction was not reaching a point of equilibrium. If, however, there is a relation between reducing power and viability, it does not appear to be a direct function.

An attempt was made to apply the reagent in alkaline state to aqueous extracts of beans, but no consistent results were obtained, although wide differences in reducing power of the extracts were noted. As it took several days to obtain differences in reduction, it would be disqualified as a quick method.

As permanganate absorption, within definite time limits, closely parallels methods used for iodine absorption, it was thought feasible to try the latter method. In this case, the reagents were of the normality recommended in the handbook of the Association of Official Agricultural Chemists (1), but the net iodine absorption is computed on the basis of decinormality. The solution was left in contact for 15 minutes, and the excess iodine titrated back with sodium thiosulphate, using starch as an indicator. The results are shown in Table II.

TABLE II

ABSORPTION OF IODINE BY AQUEOUS EXTRACTS OF CORN

Sample	Percentage of germination	Net Iodine	Sample	Percentage of germination	Net Iodine
12	96	.16	4	69	.20
11	95	.24	6	67	.10
10	95	.11	7	60	.11
8	93	.17	5	51	.17
17	88	.13	1	50	.20
3	81	.17	14	42	.19
13	74	.16	16	21	.20
2	73	.14	15	0	.28

The low reactivity of the extracts with this reagent would indicate that there was not a definite reaction. This observation is fortified by the inconsistencies in amount of net iodine absorbed.

At this point it was decided to substitute an electrometric titration method for the colorimetric permanganate technique. The potentiometer set-up which was used is described by Sherrill (28). A mechanical stirrer was connected with a Cenco motor, as a means of insuring a uniform solution. The reference electrode was not the conventional calomel electrode, as it was desired to avoid the presence of the Cl ion. Instead, the half-cell, Hg (metal), Hg_2SO_4, H_2SO_4 (1N), technically known as the mercurous sulphate cell, was used.[1] A platinum foil, carefully cleaned and not platinized, was used as the other electrode. This was later changed for a platinum wire because the latter did not collect bubbles, which cause incorrect voltage readings.

[1] Credit for the suggestion to use this electrode is due to Mr. A. M. Malloy, of the Chemistry Department, Michigan State College.

Although diffusion proceeds from the greater to the lesser concentration and the liquid electrode was one normal, which was greater at all times than the titration mixture, the electrode yet suffered contamination from the permanganate in the solution. Other salts might also have proceeded up the arm of the electrode, but, being colorless, could not be detected. To overcome this error it was necessary to allow a small amount of the fluid in the electrode to drain into the beaker at frequent intervals during the titration.

An optimum temperature of 70° C. was maintained by means of a "micro-burner" regulated to give the minimum flame.

It was necessary to subject the method to a period of trial variations. Direct titration of the solution was not possible because it possessed an apparently endless ability partly to reduce permanganate. Addition of a set amount of permanganate, as in the colorimetric technique, was also discontinued. The formation of colloidal brown MnO_2 was often a deterring factor in these cases, as it was characterized by a sharp drop in voltage at a time when none was justified. It was necessary, therefore, to add as much as 1 c. c. of oxalate in excess of the end point, when the colloid would be broken down, and the excess could be run back with permanganate.

The acid concentration was raised to 5 per cent by weight, in order to keep the cell in a highly acid state, and to obtain sharp voltage changes.

The standard solutions used in this phase of the work were more carefully prepared than those formerly used. The potassium permanganate was standardized repeatedly, and the sodium oxalate was electrometrically titrated against the permanganate.

These trials led to the development of a technique wherein the permanganate was added at the rate of 1–1.5 c. c. per minute, enough being added to keep the solution faintly purple at all times. At the end of ten minutes, the beaker was placed in the apparatus, and oxalate solution added drop by drop, until the fall in voltage indicated the end point. By these discrete additions of permanganate, the colloid was eliminated.

While it would be possible to show titration curves for all the

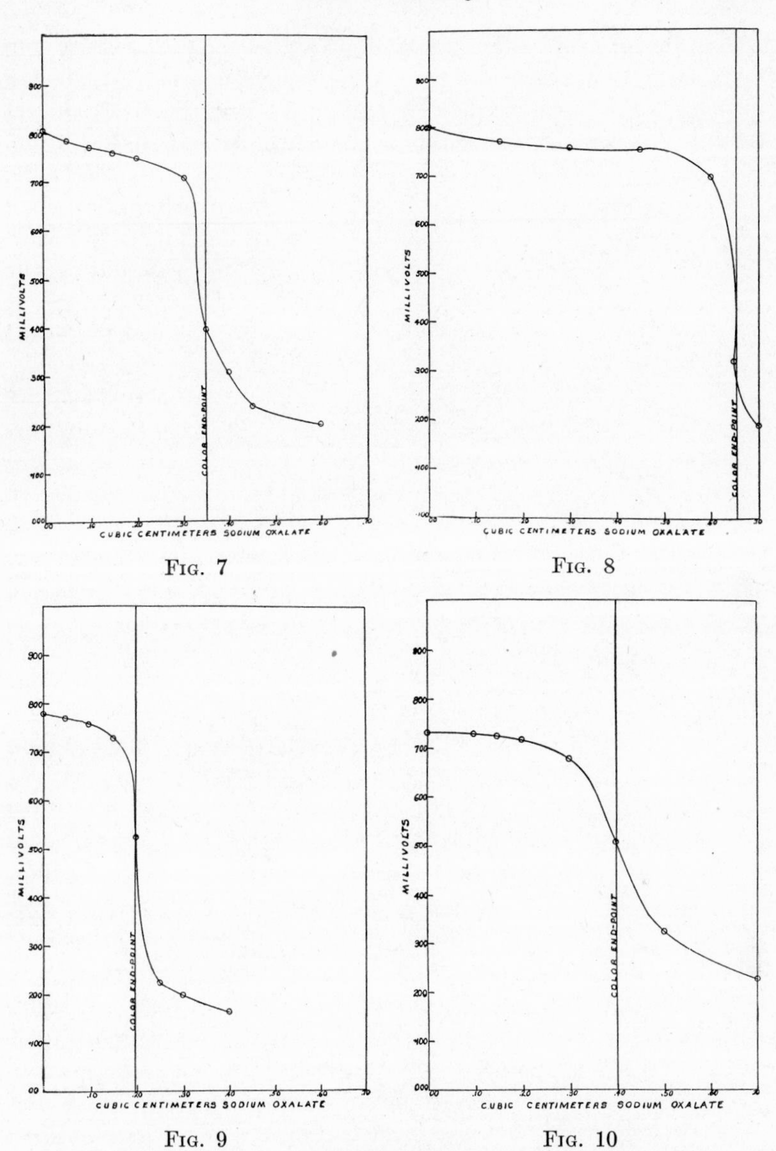

FIG. 7

FIG. 8

FIG. 9

FIG. 10

FIGS. 7–10. Permanganate-sodium oxalate electrometric titration curves

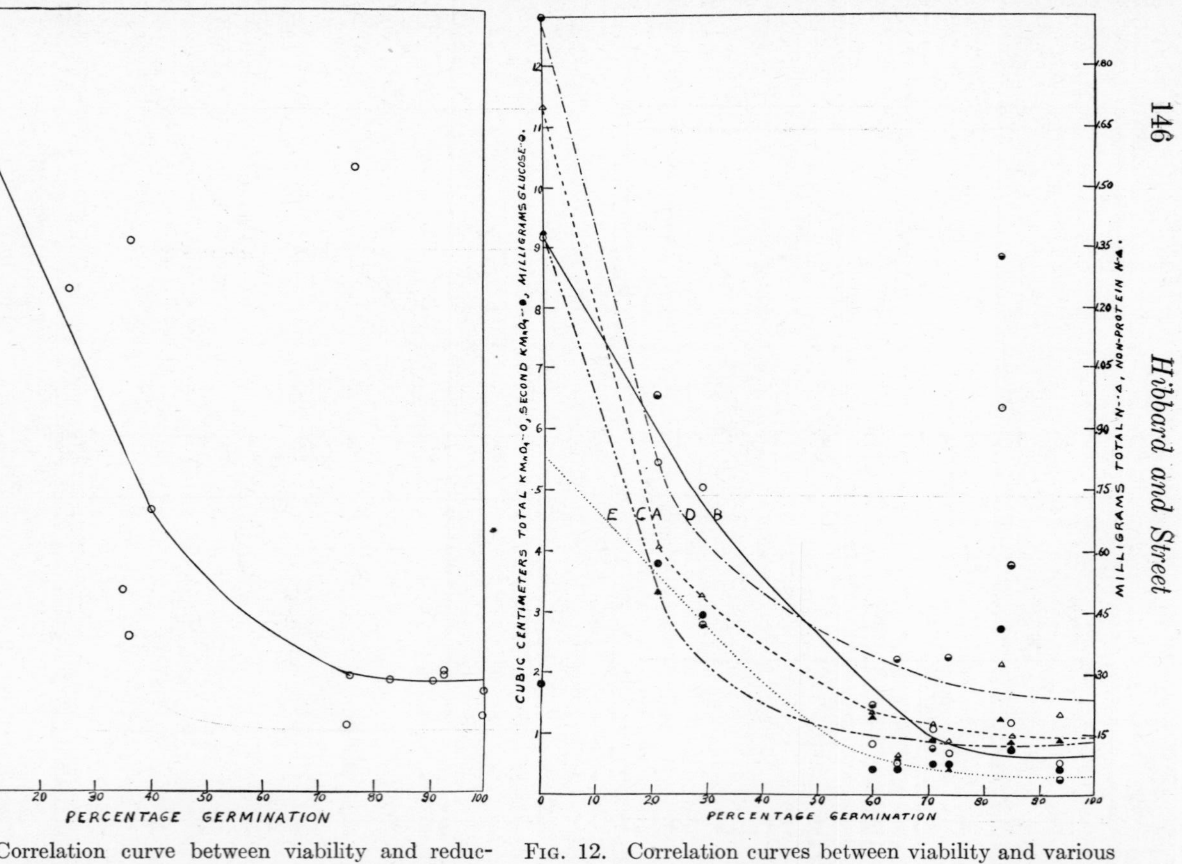

FIG. 11. Correlation curve between viability and reduction of permanganate as measured by electrometric titration

FIG. 12. Correlation curves between viability and various chemical components as follows: *A*, total nitrogen; *B*, total $KMnO_4$; *C*, non-protein nitrogen; *D*, glucose; *E*, second $KMnO_4$ (reduction of protein-free extract)

reactions studied by this method, there would be no particular justification for the inclusion of such a mass of data. Instead, a few charts chosen from widely separated titrations are shown (Figs. 7–10). It is to be noted that the color end point coincides very closely with the point of maximum change in voltage. Because of this, no stress is laid on the fact that certain titrations are electrometric and others colorimetric. Table III will suffice to give the type of result obtained.

TABLE III

ELECTROMETRIC TITRATION AS A MEASURE OF VIABILITY

Sample	Percentage of germination	Net c.c. $KMnO_4$	Sample	Percentage of germination	Net c.c. $KMnO_4$
11	100	1.25	13	74	1.10
7	100	1.61	2	40	4.54
10	93	1.90	5	36	2.48
17	93	1.89	1	36	8.78
12	91	1.80	3	35	3.20
6	83	1.82	16	25	7.96
8	76	9.96	15	0	12.38
14	75	1.88			

The titrations reported here are of a degree of accuracy which would be worthy of better ends. There is every reason to believe that the technique is such that the maximum reduction of permanganate occurs, and the ease with which checks are obtained is noteworthy.

Yet the results indicate that there is no simple relation between viability and reduction of permanganate. From the graph (Fig. 11) there is possible evidence that the total reduction is due to a number of components in the extract, and these may be present in such a multiplicity of proportions as to render it impossible to establish a correlation.

The general inconclusiveness of the results precluded the hope of a direct solution of the problem, and it was only the appearance of some secondary developments which justified the continuance of the work.

The first of these was the result of an attempt to preserve the solutions of an incompleted series by adding a few drops of 5 per cent phenol. The extremely high reactions shown subsequently by most of the samples led to the testing of the reactivity of permanganate with phenol. It was found to reduce the permanganate in large amount, and this evidence led to a study of the reactivity of permanganate with organic compounds associated with seed extracts.

Another point of interest was the fact that the ability of the solutions to reduce permanganate was diminished quite rapidly by exposure to room conditions. Half of the reducing power would be lost within three or four days, and within two or three weeks there would be a total absence of reducing power.

These reactions, involving probably the oxidation of unstable organic compounds, may thus go on with atmospheric oxygen at room temperatures. Where fungi appeared on the extracts, the loss was hastened. Coons and Klotz (4) report the lowering of the content of certain classes of nitrogenous compounds in the diseased leaves of celery. The loss of reducing power in seed extracts may be due to a progressive breakdown of protein compounds into α-amino acids.

If the reducing power was resident in the proteins, there should be a possibility of separation by dialysis. Collodion sacks formed on the inside of large test tubes were used for this test. The results obtained indicated that both portions possessed ability to reduce permanganate, although the larger part of that ability lay with the material found in the colloidal state.

The question then arose whether the reducing power of the colloidal fraction might not serve as a measure of viability. The preliminary tests indicated that the dialysate did not vary greatly in its reducing power, while the colloidal material showed considerable variation. A complete series was attempted, in which the extracts were placed in uniform collodion sacks, which were then placed in an apparatus for continuous dialysis. Distilled water was siphoned through the beakers from an overhead supply at the rate of one liter per hour. At the end of the week, the contents of the bags were tested for reducing power. A check series, consisting of aliquots of the same solutions kept in stoppered flasks, was tested similarly at the end of an equal time period.

The only evidence from the two series was that the loss of reducing power was more rapid when the products of oxidation were removed by dialysis and hydrolysis. The reaction proceeded in one direction until nothing remained to be oxidized or broken down. There was no applicability to measurements of viability.

On the evidence of these tests, the only clue seemed to lie in an attempt to isolate the compound or compounds which were responsible for the reduction of permanganate. The loss of reducing power, on prolonged standing or as a result of dialysis, would indicate unstable organic compounds. But such an assumption is not the basis for any conclusions, because of the number and complexity of organic compounds which might diffuse out of the seed. It becomes necessary to examine further as to the nature of the compounds in question. Empirical considerations would indicate that proteins have no monopoly on the property of reduction, yet they would seem to occupy a commanding position in this study.

Hawk (9) lists lead acetate and ammonium sulphate among the common precipitants for proteins. Saturation with these reagents is supposed to bring down all the proteins. In the case of the former salt the excess lead in solution is removed by anhydrous sodium carbonate. Table IV gives the result of tests with these reagents.

TABLE IV

REDUCING POWER OF FRACTIONS OF EXTRACT OF CORNMEAL

Description of fraction	Net $KMnO_4$	Description of fraction	Net $KMnO_4$
Original extract.........	37.29	Original extract.........	7.40
Filtrate of lead acetate...	4.53	Filtrate of $(NH_4)_2SO_4$....	2.62
Precipitate of lead acetate	0.00	Redissolved precipitate $(NH_4)_2SO_4$............	2.46

In the ammonium sulphate precipitation, the failure of the two portions to equal the original in reducing power may be attributed to the fact that some of the proteins were denaturalized and failed to redissolve in the dilute solution of ammonium sulphate which resulted. The lead precipitate was entirely insoluble in the concentration of acid employed in these tests.

Osborne and his associates (20, 21, 22, 23) devoted a lifetime to the study of vegetable proteins. Their classifications, nomenclature and methods of isolation are standard; hence any procedure dealing with these compounds will be borrowed *en tout* from their works. In relation to the proteins of corn, their amounts and properties, the following classification is valuable.

CLASSIFICATION OF THE PROTEINS OF CORN, *ZEA MAYS*

		Percentage
1. Proteins soluble in pure water	Proteose	0.06
2. Protein soluble in aqueous extract (Very dilute salt and acid solution)		
A. Reprecipitated by dialysis	Maysin	0.25
B. Coagulable by heat in presence of NaCl	Maize globulin	0.04
3. Protein soluble in 10 per cent NaCl	Maize edestin	0.10
4. Protein soluble in 60–90 per cent alcohol	Zein	5.00
5. Protein soluble in dilute acids and alkalies	Glutelin	3.15

In our work, it is not claimed that the proteins were obtained in even an approximately pure state, but they were nevertheless recognized as entities, and it was possible to measure their reducing power. Because of the fact that precipitation of the globulins and albumins is likely to cause the formation of irreversible gels, the tests were conducted directly upon these solutions. In the case of maysin, which is coagulated by removal of the protective ions, it was impossible entirely to redissolve it, only a small fraction being amenable to boiling with 5 per cent H_2SO_4. The results of the tests are shown in Table V.

Thus instead of finding a single protein capable of reducing permanganate, all were found to possess the ability. Osborne (21) reports the reduction by zein of ferric chloride in an alcoholic solution, but the failure of that protein to reduce potassium ferricyanide. We were not able to secure reduction of potassium dichromate, using aqueous extracts which reduced permanganate strongly.

TABLE V

REDUCING POWER OF PROTEINS OF CORN

Material	Amount in grams	Net $KMnO_4$
Proteose	.001	0.09
Maize globulin plus proteose	.004	0.80
Maysin	.020	1.98
Edestin	.006	0.65
Zein	.020	4.24

If the proteins reduce permanganate, might it not be that they do so by being themselves broken down by the rigorous treatment of the test? If such an assumption is sound, then amino acids should be able to reduce permanganate as well. Osborne and Clapp (22) give the products of the hydrolysis of the proteins of maize. It was not possible to obtain all the amino acids desired, but several were available. In this connection it might be noted that non-protein compounds of nitrogenous nature were reported in corn. Jodidi (12), in addition to finding polypeptides, free amino acids and acid amides, reports previous investigators who found lecithin. An indication of the reducing power of some of these compounds is found in Table VI.

TABLE VI

REDUCING POWER OF PRIMARY NITROGENOUS COMPOUNDS

Material used (20 mg. of each)	Net c. c. $KMnO_4$	Material used (20 mg. of each)	Net c. c. $KMnO_4$
Leucine	2.31	Nucleic acid (yeast)	2.49
Aspartic acid	0.05	Sodium glycocholate	0.57
Asparagine	0.00	Brucine	13.12
Tyrosine	24.36	Xanthine	0.19
Tryptophane	17.84	Creatine	0.00
Lecithin	1.44		

The first half of Table VI deals with amino acids found as products of the hydrolysis of the proteins of corn. Included in this group is the phospho-protein, lecithin. The latter half of the table is not directly applicable to this study, but had general interest in demonstrating the wide range of reactivity of permanganate.

It is interesting to note that all the high reacting compounds contained a ring structure. According to the classification of Haas and Hill (8, p. 324) these are as follows: tyrosine, an aromatic compound, β-parahydroxyphenyl α-amino propionic acid; tryptophane, a heterocyclic compound, β-indole α-amino propionic acid; brucine, a complex alkaloid of the quinoline group, characterized by two six-membered rings condensed together. Lasser-Cohn (14) mentions also that permanganate reactivity is a means of distinguishing between unsaturated acids and saturated acids containing open or closed chains, and carboxylic acids of benzene and similar bodies.

The rôle of this group of compounds was thus sufficiently established, but there had also been indications that the simple sugars were not lacking in reducing ability. Qualitative tests on glucose confirmed the suspicion, so the tests tabulated below were performed.

TABLE VII

Permanganate Reduction by Common Sugar

Sugar used (20 mg. of each)	Net c. c. $KMnO_4$	Sugar used (20 mg. of each)	Net c. c. $KMnO_4$
Arabinose	9.13	Galactose	9.37
Xylose	8.80	Sucrose	9.96
Dextrose	8.38	Maltose	5.13
Mannose	8.01	Lactose	3.24
Levulose	8.36	Raffinose	4.43
Sorbose	8.68		

While the data on the reducing power of sugars in no way constitute a scientific novelty, the direct application of permanganate is not mentioned in the literature. The nearest approach is the indirect method wherein the reduced copper is measured by permanganate titration. In this connection mention might again be made of the action of permanganate on starch, noted by Reichert

(26). The significance of sugar in the aqueous extract is differently interpreted by Miller and Hibbard (17). They consider it as a stabilizing agent in the formation of silver sols by reductions of silver nitrate, while proteins were given the power of reduction.

The actual presence of sugar in the aqueous extracts was positively determined by a standard method. Clarification of the extract was made by use of Horne's anhydrous lead sub-acetate, which would remove proteins, but not the nitrogenous compounds of non-protein character, or the sugars. The excess lead was then removed with Na_2HPO_4. The test for sugar was based on the Schaffer-Hartmann iodometric titration of copper (24). The only modification was that 9.3N H_2SO_4 to the amount of 17 c.c. was used, instead of 5 N to the same amount.[2] Fading of the end point was overcome by this change.

With proteins and sugars aligned in respect to their property of reducing permanganate, the only remaining group of water-soluble compounds of any importance was the non-protein nitrogenous derivatives. A rather devious method of proof was employed for them. The clarified extract, prepared as described above, was submitted to both the standard sugar test and the permanganate reduction test. By means of the data of Table VII, the permanganate reduction for that quantity of glucose was computed. The difference in permanganate reduction might then be attributed to the non-proteins. Extracts of cornmeal were used for this test, in order that larger differences might be obtained and thus give a firmer basis for comparison. The scheme is shown in the following table.

TABLE VIII

NON-PROTEINS AS AGENTS IN THE REDUCTION OF PERMANGANATE

Description of test or procedure	Net $KMnO_4$
Permanganate on clarified meal extract	34.46 c.c.
Standard sugar on same in mg. of glucose	24.4
Computed $KMnO_4$ for 24.4 mg. glucose	11.66 c.c.
Difference attributable to non-proteins	22.80 c.c.

[2] Credit for the change is due to Mr. H. F. Clements of the Botany Department of Michigan State College.

It is not possible, in the light of later findings, to give much weight to the results of Table VIII, except in conceding that it would certainly show that the non-proteins are not immune to the action of permanganate.

With only a few tests, it is not possible to attempt the establishment of a correlation between the amounts of these components and the total reduction of permanganate. The various constituents are all influential in the reduction, yet not in equal measure, or even in intensity of reaction. The fact that the reducing power is quite rapidly diminished upon standing may be in part a matter of actual decrease of the materials, or it may be an oxidation without any other quantitative differences.

A test of the correlation of the content of proteins, non-proteins and sugars, with the reduction of permanganate, was next attempted. It was hoped that some clue to the unusual reactivity of several samples of good germination might be obtained.

The methods were conventional. The sugar test was as given in the preceding pages of this paper. Total nitrogen was run by the Kjeldahl method, using $CuSO_4$ as the catalyst. The acid used to absorb the evolved ammonia was found to be exactly N/10 by gravimetric determination.

On the first few samples an attempt was made to run the non-protein nitrogen from the clarified sugar-test extract. This proved impossible because the lead sub-acetate contained considerable nitrogen as a contamination. Precipitation by phospho-tungstic acid provided more consistent results. The test was as follows: 5 per cent phospho-tungstic acid in 5 per cent H_2SO_4 was added to a seed extract made acid to 5 per cent with H_2SO_4, and heated to boiling. Fortunately, a sufficient amount of the samples remained to repeat the test with the latter reagent. The protein nitrogen was obtained by difference. Direct determination was unaccountably inconsistent, and it was not considered germane to this study to spend time on that problem.

Permanganate reduction was run on the original extract and the sugar-test extract. The reacting power of the latter to permanganate exactly equaled that property in the phospho-tungstate extract, so that the results in their bearing on the reducing power of the non-proteins are entirely applicable. The results of the complete tests are shown in Table IX.

TABLE IX

TEST OF CORRELATION OF CONTENT OF PROTEINS, NON-PROTEINS AND SUGARS, WITH REDUCING POWER IN TERMS OF PERMANGANATE

Sample	Percentage of germination	Total $KMnO_4$	Total N in mg.	Non-proteins N in mg.	Glucose in mg.	Second $KMnO_4$
10	94	0.53	.195	.130	0.29	0.42
3	85	1.16	.146	.122	3.80	0.91
8	83	6.32	.326	.204	8.83	2.73
7	73	0.71	.130	.082	2.28	0.49
2	71	1.08	.163	.130	0.80	0.48
6	64	0.52	.114	.082	2.24	0.42
5	60	0.77	.212	.203	1.52	0.42
1	29	5.05	.489	.185	2.72	2.95
16	21	5.49	.619	.521	6.53	3.82
15	0	9.15	1.695	1.385	12.77	1.82

In this series 100 seeds of each sample were placed in a flask with 200 c.c. of distilled water and allowed to soak for 24 hours at room temperature. The extract was decanted, filtered through a coarse filter paper, and made up to 200 c.c. Of this, 50 c.c. was precipitated with lead for sugar and permanganate tests, 50 c.c. with phospho-tungstic acid for non-protein nitrogen, 50 c.c. used for duplicate determinations of total nitrogen, and the remainder devoted to total permanganate reduction tests.

As the data in previous tables are all on the basis of 10 c.c. of extract, the amount obtained from five seeds, these results are similarly reduced. In that proportion the amount of some of the constituents would be too small for detection, but as the results were obtained on samples averaging five or ten times the minimum amount, checks were very consistent.

From Table IX it may be computed that the amount of sugar

in the extract varied from 0.02 per cent to 0.80 per cent of the average weight of the corn, while the amounts of nitrogen were of a lower order.

As far as the possibility of establishing a close correlation between the components and their total reduction is concerned, a study of the graph (Fig. 12) will show that it is not to be expected. It is clear that proteins, non-proteins, and sugars are all partners in the enterprise of reducing permanganate. But just how active each one may be is difficult to determine by this data. For instance, if only samples No. 5 and No. 6 in Table IX were considered, it would be seen that the protein-free extract of each reduced permanganate equally. But No. 6 had a lesser amount of non-protein nitrogen and No. 5 a lesser amount of sugars, and the differences were compensating. Beyond these two samples, the correlation in this part of the table was very haphazard.

A more important correlation, and one that seems to have a sound basis, is the relation of the total permanganate to the total nitrogen plus the glucose. If it is remembered that the amounts of elemental nitrogen may be multiplied by 6.25 and the proteins thus estimated, the comparative amounts of nitrogenous and carbohydrate extract would seem more reasonable. Interesting results are obtained by disregarding the viability, and rearranging the samples with regard primarily to their total permanganate reduction, thereby comparing this reduction with the combined amounts of nitrogen and sugars. Only one sample, No. 2, is radical in its departure from the type, as shown in Table X.

Even granting the fact that the nitrogenous compounds are present as proteins or similar compounds, they are nevertheless more active, gram for gram, than the sugars. A difference of 0.08 mg. of nitrogen or 0.50 mg. of protein between samples No. 6 and No. 10 is compensated by 1.95 mg. of sugar to give an equal permanganate reduction. But between samples No. 7 and No. 5 an equally great difference in nitrogen is compensated by 0.76 mg. of sugar, so it is hardly wise to draw any hard and fast conclusions.

With only general reactions under consideration, it is convenient to consider the samples in pairs of nearly equal reducing power.

In all cases of this sort, an excess of sugars in one is compensated by an excess of nitrogen-bearing compounds in the other. In the latter part of the table, samples of markedly greater reducing power are found to surpass those of lesser activity in content of both sugars and nitrogenous compounds. That the reducing power of aqueous extracts rests on the sugars and nitrogenous compounds is clearly demonstrated.

TABLE X

COMPARATIVE REDUCING POWER OF SUGARS AND NITROGENOUS COMPOUNDS

Sample	Total $KMnO_4$	Total N in mg.	Glucose in mg.
6	0.52	.114	2.24
10	0.53	.195	0.29
7	0.71	.130	2.28
5	0.77	.212	1.52
2	1.08	.163	0.80
3	1.16	.146	3.80
1	5.05	.489	2.72
16	5.49	.619	6.53
8	6.32	.326	8.83
15	9.15	1.695	12.77

The variations in germinability of a sample of seed upon successive trials by the conventional method of growing the seeds may amount to as much as five or ten per cent. If there was any correlation between viability and reducing power, it might be expected to stay within the same limits. But when the variation in reducing power is much greater, as was shown in Table IX, it is sound to conclude that a positive correlation is lacking.

DISCUSSION ON EXPERIMENTAL DATA

On the basis of results presented in this paper, it cannot be assumed that there is any correlation between the viability of seeds and the reducing power of their aqueous extracts. As far as the relative position of samples in a series was concerned, there was a fair consistency in the reaction as tested from time to time. But it was only infrequently possible to find a group of samples which would give graduations in reactivity at all comparable to viability.

Why are the results inconsistent? A number of reasons might be advanced and no one alone suffice to interpret the situation. For the first line of approach let us consider the chemical phases of the question. A great amount of work on the chemical composition of corn has been published, and a large portion is summarized by Keith (13).

The content of all the important constituents may be varied by a host of circumstances. The state of maturity enters very strongly in influencing the composition. Bushey (3) found that corn killed by frost had a high percentage of non-proteins in the form of polypeptides and amino-acids. Immature corn is also known to have more sugars and less starch than riper samples. Genetic differences are the bases of great differences in composition, as has been shown, among others, by Lindstrom and Gerhardt (15). Lack of chemical uniformity is so conclusive that no further mention need be made of it.

Added to these differences, the fact that in permanganate reduction several groups of compounds were active makes the task of establishing a correlation on chemical grounds well-nigh impossible. The various possible combinations in amount of these components, combined with the differential reactivity of the groups, makes the relation still more complex.

The physical state of plant membranes is not the least important factor in establishing differences. Shull (29) in his study of the semipermeability of seed coats, found that even dead plant membranes might be semipermeable. The entirely impermeable nature of the coats of many seeds and the deterrent effect of this on germination have been the subject of investigation.

The effect of the colloidal state on the permeability is none too clearly defined. Whether or not changes in permeability are due to the coagulation of the proteins, a view advanced by Crocker (5), the fact remains that it has never been definitely established.

The recent findings of Hottes and Huelson (11) on sweet corn constitute an interesting study of physico-chemical state. The relation of the colloidal properties of the extract to viability was indicated. Between samples of zero germination and those of 95 to 100 per cent germination, the colloidal index, as measured with a Leitz nephelometer, varied considerably. The results show that the denser suspensions were found in extracts from seeds of low viability, but as far as the applicability of these findings to measurements of lesser differences in germinating power is concerned, the method shows little promise.

In consideration of the data presented in Table IX, it would seem that the most important change accompanying loss of germinating power is an increase in permeability. Yet even this rule is violated in at least two cases out of ten, and it is necessary to assume some uncommon occurrences in the history of samples like No. 8 and No. 3 in order to explain their high rate of exosmosis. Subject to these deviations, the differences in permeability seem to bear a fundamental relation to the phenomenon of death.

SUMMARY

1. The permanganate reduction method as a measure of viability was made the subject of a process of refinement.

2. Electrometric titrations were substituted for colorimetric titrations with a view toward development of a more discriminating technique.

3. The method was perfected sufficiently to be considered chemically reliable.

4. No correlation between differences of viability of ten per cent, and permanganate reducing power of extract, was established in any case. Differences of viability of two and three per cent cannot be obtained by this method.

5. Colorimetric titrations under the conditions established were proved to be as accurate as electrometric.

6. In a supplementary experiment, iodine absorption of aqueous extracts was measured, but even less promise was shown by this method.

7. The reducing power of dialyzed extracts was found to have no correlation with viability.

8. Isolation of compounds causing reduction of permanganate was attempted.

9. The following classes of compounds were found to have reducing power: (1) proteins found in corn; (2) some amino-acids found in corn, and other primary nitrogenous compounds; (3) common sugars; (4) nitrogenous compounds of non-protein character found in corn.

10. A correlation between content of proteins, non-proteins and sugars of extract and permanganate reducing power of extract was attempted on basis of standard analyses.

11. Positive correlation between permanganate reducing power of solution and total nitrogen plus sugar content was indicated.

12. No correlation between viability and amounts of any of the constituents was found.

13. A word of caution is suggested to the effect that one should not be overoptimistic in regard to any method proposed.

MICHIGAN STATE COLLEGE
EAST LANSING, MICHIGAN

LITERATURE CITED

1. ASSOCIATION OF OFFICIAL AGRICULTURAL CHEMISTS. 1925. Official and Tentative Methods of Analysis, Second edition.

2. BUNZELL, H. H., AND HASSELBRING, H. 1917. The Supposed Action of Potassium Permanganate with Plant Peroxidases. Bot. Gaz., 63: 225–228.

3. BUSHEY, A. 1924. Some Chemical Characteristics of Soft Corn. South Dakota Agr. Expt. Sta. Bull. 210.

4. COONS, G. H., AND KLOTZ, L. J. 1925. The Nitrogen Constituents of Celery Plants in Health and Disease. Journ. Agr. Research, 31 (No. 3): 287–300.

5. CROCKER, WM. 1906. The Rôle of Seed Coats in Delayed Germination. Bot. Gaz., 42: 265–291.

6. DAVIS, WILMER E. 1925. The Use of Catalase As a Means of Determining the Viability of Seeds. Proc. Assoc. Off. Seed Anal.

7. GRAČANIN, M. 1926. Sur la question de la catalase comme un indicateur de la faculté vitale des semences. Ann. Sci. Agron. (Paris), 43 (6): 430–438.

8. HAAS, P., AND HILL, T. G. 1921. An Introduction to the Chemistry of Plant Products, Third edition. Vol. 1. London.

9. HAWK, P. B. 1916. Practical Physiological Chemistry, Fifth edition. Philadelphia.

10. Hibbard, R. P., and Miller, E. V. Biochemical Studies on Seed Viability. I. Measurements of Conductance and Reduction. Plant Physiol., 3 (No. 3) : 335–353.

11. Hottes, C. F., and Huelson, W. A. 1927. The Determination of Quality in Sweet Corn Seed by Means of the Optical Measurement of Leached Materials. Journ. Agr. Research, 35 (No. 2) : 147–166.

12. Jodidi, S. L. 1925. The Occurrence of Polypeptides and Amino Acids in the Ungerminated Maize Kernel. Journ. Agr. Research, 30 (No. 6) : 587–592.

13. Keith, M. H. 1921. A Bibliography of Investigations Bearing on the Composition and Nutritive Value of Corn and Corn Products. Issued by Nat. Res. Council, Washington, D. C.

14. Lasser-Cohn, A. 1895. Manual of Organic Chemistry. Translated by Alex Smith. Macmillan and Co., New York.

15. Lindstrom, E. W., and Gerhardt, F. 1926. Inheritance of Carbohydrates and Fat in Crosses of a Dent and Sweet Corn. Iowa State Res. Bull. No. 98.

16. Marotta, D., and Kaminka, R. 1924. Valutazione della vitalità del frumento per via biochimica. Annali di Chimica applicata, 14 : 207–208.

17. Miller, E. V., and Hibbard, R. P. 1926. Aqueous Extracts of Seeds as Agents in the Preparation of Silver Sols. Plant Physiol., 1 : 409–413.

18. Munerati, O. 1926. Possibilité de déterminer l'âge des graines de blé par la température de leur germination. Compt. Rend. Acad. Sci. (Paris), 182 (8) : 533–537.

19. Němec, A., et Duchoň, F. 1922. Sur une méthode indicatrice permettant d'évaluer la vitalité des semences par voie biochimique. Compt. Rend. Acad. Sci. (Paris), 174 (9) : 632–634.

20. Osborne, T. B. 1912. The Vegetable Proteins. Longmans, Green and Co. London.

21. —— 1897. The Amount and Properties of the Proteids of the Maize Kernel. Journ. Am. Chem. Soc., 19 : 525–532.

22. ——, and Clapp, S. H. 1908. Hydrolysis of the Proteins of Maize, "Zea mays." Am. Journ. Physiol., 20 : 477–493.

23. ——, and Harris, I. F. 1903. The Precipitation Limits with Ammonium Sulphate of Some Vegetable Proteins. Journ. Am. Chem. Soc., 25 : 837–842.

24. Pierce, G. J., Darsie, M. L., and Elliott, C. 1914. A Study of the Germination Power of Seeds. Bot. Gaz., 58 : 101–136.

25. Reed, G. B. 1916. The Mode of Action of Plant Peroxidases. Bot. Gaz., 62 : 233–238.

26. Reichert, E. T. 1913. The Differentiation and Specificity of Starches in Relation to Genera, Species, etc. Carnegie Inst. of Wash. Publ. No. 173, Part I.

27. Schaffer, P. A., and Hartmann, A. E. 1920. The Iodometric Determination of Copper and Its Use in Sugar Analysis. Journ. Biol. Chem., 45 : 349–390.

28. Sherrill, M. S. 1924. Laboratory Experiments on Physico-Chemical Principles. Macmillan and Co., New York.

29. Shull, C. A. 1913. Semipermeability of Seed Coats. Bot. Gaz., 56 : 169–199.

30. Vilmorin, J. de, et Caquabon. 1922. Sur la catalase des graines. Compt. Rend. Acad. Sci. (Paris), 175 (1) : 50–51.

THE FLORAL DEVELOPMENT OF THE STAMINATE FLOWER OF THE CUCUMBER

JAMES E. JUDSON

SOME contradictory discussion occurs in the literature concerning the developmental succession of the floral parts of the staminate flower of the cucumber. This investigation has been made to determine the order in which the floral parts appear, by a study of the early stages in the development of the flower.

Heimlich (3) has reported the developmental succession of the floral organs in the staminate flowers of the cucumbers as follows: perianth tube, stamens, pistillodium, calyx lobes and corolla lobes. Payer has shown in his studies on the staminate flowers of various members of the Cucurbitaceae, including *Cucurbita Pepo*, that the first parts to appear are the sepals. He further shows the receptacle at first to be flat, later becoming hollow, and bearing five sepals on its upper edge. The petal lobes appear soon afterward slightly below and alternate with the sepals on the internal side of the hollowed receptacle. The stamen lobes appear next, followed closely by the pistillodium lobes which appear in the bottom of the cup-shaped receptacle. In many species of the Cucurbitaceae five distinct "mamelons" appear alternating with the sepals. In other genera, as Cucurbita and Bryonia, four of the "mamelons" group themselves two by two and the fifth one stays isolated. This results in two double stamens and one single stamen.

Müller (6), Eichler (2) and Kirkwood (5) find, in the pistillate flowers of the Cucurbitaceae, the floral parts in the following order: sepal lobes, petal lobes, staminodium lobes and pistil lobes.

METHODS AND OBSERVATIONS

The young flowers were drawn from observations with a Spencer binocular microscope equipped with 32, 48, and 55 mm.

objectives and 6 × and 10 × oculars. Flowers in the earliest stages were placed in a watch glass containing a saturated solution of iodine in 70 per cent alcohol. They were examined with the binocular microscope, light being thrown on them from above. All light was cut off from underneath. An ordinary table lamp equipped with a 75-volt electric bulb supplied the illumination.

The first staminate flowers are found in the first or second leaf axis of the seedling. A single flower appears first as a blunt protuberance upon the stem in the axil of a leaf (Pl. XXXVIII, Fig. 1). It has much the same shape as a Mazda electric light bulb. As development takes place, this blunt protuberance becomes flattened on its terminal end. Cell division and elongation take place in the outer margin more rapidly than in the center, which results in a terminal depression surrounded by a slightly elevated ridge. Soon growth takes place at five points on this elevated ridge more rapidly than in other places on the ridge, forming five sepal lobes (Pl. XXXVIII, Fig. 2). Division and growth of the cells within the terminal ridge as well as just below the sepal lobes, especially at the outer margin of the ridge, cause an elevation of the outer border of the receptacle as well as an upward extension of the sepal lobes. The apex of the stem, which is at the center of the terminal depression, grows very slowly, while the outer margin grows to form a cup-shaped receptacle about and above the apex (Pl. XXXVIII, Figs. 3–4). The cup-shaped receptacle tends to be roofed over by the sepal lobes, which curve upward over its center in a tentlike arrangement (Pl. XXXIX, Figs. 6–10). Many hairs coat the inner and outer surfaces of the sepals.

The primordia of the petal lobes appear soon after those of the sepals in a cycle within and alternate with them (Pl. XXXVIII, Fig. 2). They first appear as blunt, more or less rounded protuberances (Pl. XXXVIII, Figs. 2–5). As cell division and growth take place in the petal lobes, they likewise assume a tentlike arrangement over the center of the cup-shaped receptacle, immediately underneath the sepal lobes (Pl. XXXIX, Figs. 8–10).

Growth takes place in the tissues just beneath the bases of the sepal and petal lobes, which increases the depth of the cavity within which the stamens and carpels develop (Pl. XXXIX, Figs. 6–8). This tissue formed beneath the sepal and petal lobes makes the perianth tube. Further cell division and growth occur at the base of the petal lobes, just within the bases of the sepal lobes. This growth forms a corolla tube. The tissues at the base of the petal lobes do not divide into five separate petals, and the result is the formation of a corolla tube with five lobes, which is attached to the upper extremity of the perianth tube at the level of the attachment of the separate sepal lobes (Pl. XL, Fig. 11). The tissues of the perianth tube fail to become differentiated into two separate structures at their bases; therefore a common tube is formed, which is separated at the upper surface into a corolla tube and five sepal lobes (Pl. XL, Fig. 11). There is no evidence of a separate corolla tube whose basal portion unites or coalesces with a calyx tube.

The primordia of the stamens are laid down directly after, or in some cases simultaneously with, those of the petal lobes. There are three stamens, one of them smaller than either of the other two. The stamens are arranged equidistant from each other, in the cup-shaped receptacle below the insertions of the petal lobes. Each of the larger stamens stands opposite petal lobes, and the smaller stamen is mid-way between sepal and petal lobes.

As the primordium of each stamen develops, a broad filament is formed, which supports a broader mass of tissue called the connective (Pl. XXXIX, Fig. 9). Growth takes place in the filaments, and the stamens bend over toward the center of the perianth tube, where their connectives fit closely together (Pl. XL, Fig. 11). Each of the two larger stamens has two S-shaped thecae or "pollen sacs." The small stamen has just one. The upper extremity of the perianth tube is almost completely filled with the stamens (Pl. XL, Fig. 11). As growth takes place in the perianth tube, cell division and elongation become evident below the bases of the stamens, until in the mature flower the stamens appear to branch off from the perianth tube near the median level.

Immediately after the primordia of the stamens appear, three small lobes may be recognized equidistant from one another, near the bottom of the receptacle and below and within the stamen lobes (Pl. XXXIX, Figs. 8–9). These lobes are alternate with those of the stamens. They grow toward each other and form a small three-lobed pistillodium in the base of the perianth tube.

DISCUSSION AND SUMMARY

The floral parts of the staminate flowers of many of the Cucurbitaceae were found by Payer (7) to appear in the following order: sepal lobes, petal lobes, stamen lobes and pistillodium lobes. Kirkwood (5) shows that, in the pistillate flowers of various Cucurbitaceae, among them Bryonopsis which belongs to the same tribe as the cucumber, the developmental succession of floral parts agrees with the contentions of Payer. The writer (4) has investigated the development of the floral parts of the pistillate flower of the cucumber and has found the developmental succession of the floral parts to be in the same order as reported by Payer and Kirkwood in the other Cucurbitaceae.

Heimlich (3) found the floral parts in the staminate flower to appear in the following order: perianth tube, stamens, pistillodium, sepal lobes and petal lobes. These statements are contradictory to those of Payer and Kirkwood. He further points out that the calyx and corolla tube exhibit both cohesion and adnation.

The present investigation shows that the flower parts of the staminate flower of the cucumber appear in the same order as reported among the Cucurbitaceae by Payer and Kirkwood. The sepal lobes appear first, the petal lobes next, followed closely by the stamen lobes and finally the pistillodium lobes. The perianth tube is formed by the growth of the whole zone at the base of the sepal and petal lobes. There is no evidence of a so-called calyx tube fusing with a corolla tube. The tissues of the perianth tube fail to become differentiated into separate structures at their bases, resulting in the formation of a single tube.

Albion College
Albion, Michigan

LITERATURE CITED

1. Baillon, M. H. 1878. Sur la constitution de l'androcée des Cucurbitaceae. Compt. Rend. Assoc. Franc. Av. Sci. 7e Session, 676–685. Paris.

2. Eichler, A. W. 1875. Blüthendiagramme, 1 : 302–321. Leipzig.

3. Heimlich, L. F. 1927. The Development and Anatomy of the Staminate Flower of the Cucumber. Am. Journ. Bot., 14 : 227–237.

4. Judson, J. E. The Morphology and Vascular Anatomy of the Pistillate Flower of the Cucumber. Doctor's Thesis, University of Wisconsin. (Unpublished.)

5. Kirkwood, J. E. 1905. The Comparative Embryology of the Cucurbitaceae. Bull. N. Y. Bot. Gard., 3 : 313–402.

6. Müller, E. G. O., and Pax, F. 1894. Cucurbitaceae. In Engler and Prantl, Die natürlichen Pflanzenfamilien, III, 5 : 1–19. Leipzig.

7. Payer, J. B. 1857. Traité d'organogénie comparée de la fleur. Ordre des Cucurbitacées, 440–449. Paris.

DESCRIPTION OF PLATES

PLATE XXXVIII

FIG. 1. Two blunt protuberances, which are the primordia of two staminate flowers

FIG. 2. A young staminate flower, showing the primordia of the sepal lobes (*S*), and the first appearance of the five petal lobes (*P*)

FIG. 3. A later stage showing the sepal lobes (*S*), the petal lobes (*P*), and the beginning of the formation of the cup-shaped receptacle

FIG. 4. Two young staminate flowers, one of them a very young stage and the other a later stage showing the sepal lobes (*S*), the petal lobes (*P*), and the cup-shaped receptacle

FIG. 5. A later stage showing the sepal lobes (*S*), the petal lobes (*P*), and the first appearance of a stamen lobe (*St*)

FIG. 6. A still later stage with a portion of the flower shaved off, showing the location of the sepal lobes (*S*), the petal lobes (*P*), and the stamen lobes (*St*)

PLATE XXXIX

FIG. 7. Showing the arrangement of the sepal lobes (*S*), petal lobes (*P*), and the stamen lobes (*St*) upon and within the cup-shaped receptacle

FIG. 8. The sepal lobes (*S*) and the petal lobes (*P*) bend inward and assume a tentlike arrangement. One large stamen lobe (*St*) and a portion of the small stamen are shown, as well as the first appearance of the pistillodium lobes (*C*)

FIG. 9. The sepal lobes (*S*) bend outward, the petal lobes (*P*) retain their tentlike arrangement. Also a portion of two stamens (*St*) and a part of the pistillodium (*C*) are shown

FIG. 10. A later stage showing the sepals (*S*), the five-lobed corolla tube (*P*), the stamens (*St*), and the pistillodium (*Pl*)

PLATE XL

FIG. 11. A half of a mature staminate flower, showing the petal lobes (*P*), the corolla tube (*Ct*), the sepals (*S*), the stamens (*St*), the perianth tube (*Pt*), and the pistillodium (*Pl*)

PLATE XXXVIII

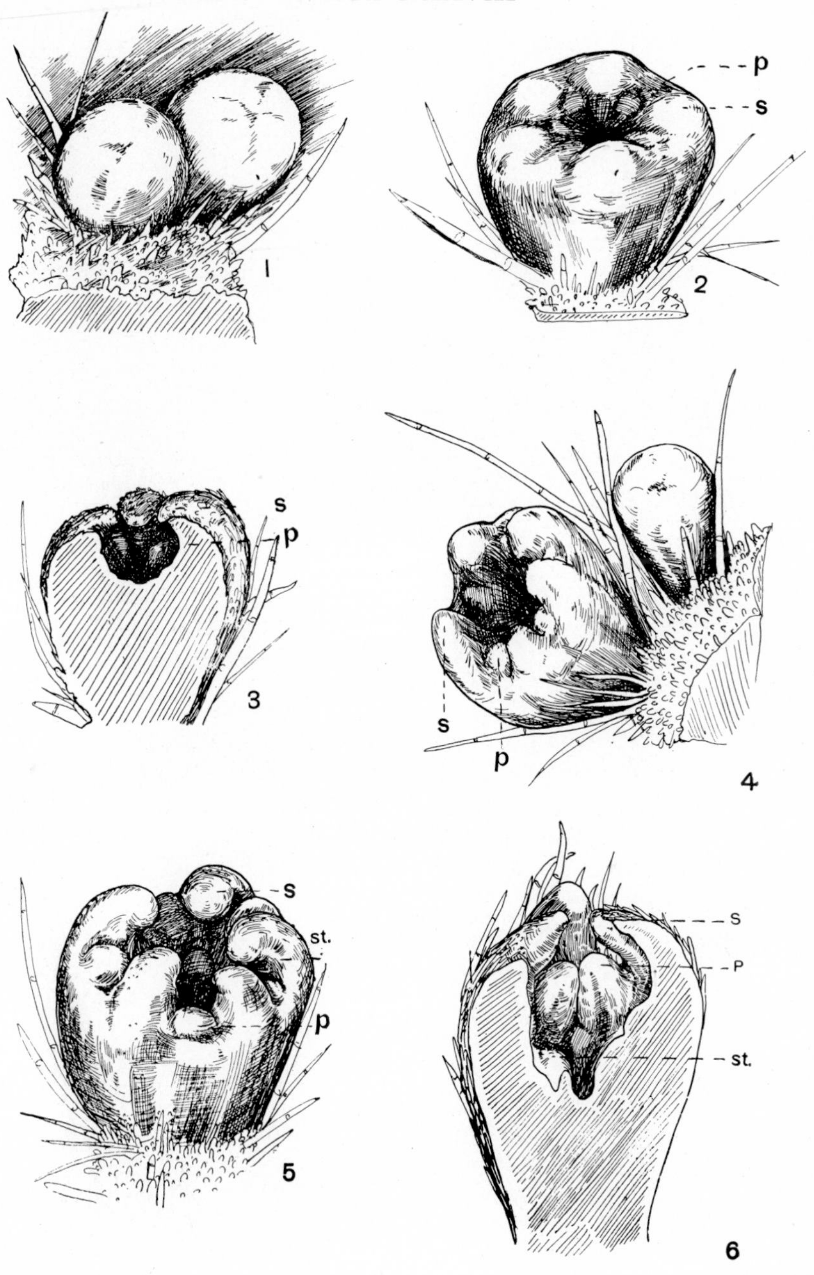

PLATE XXXIX

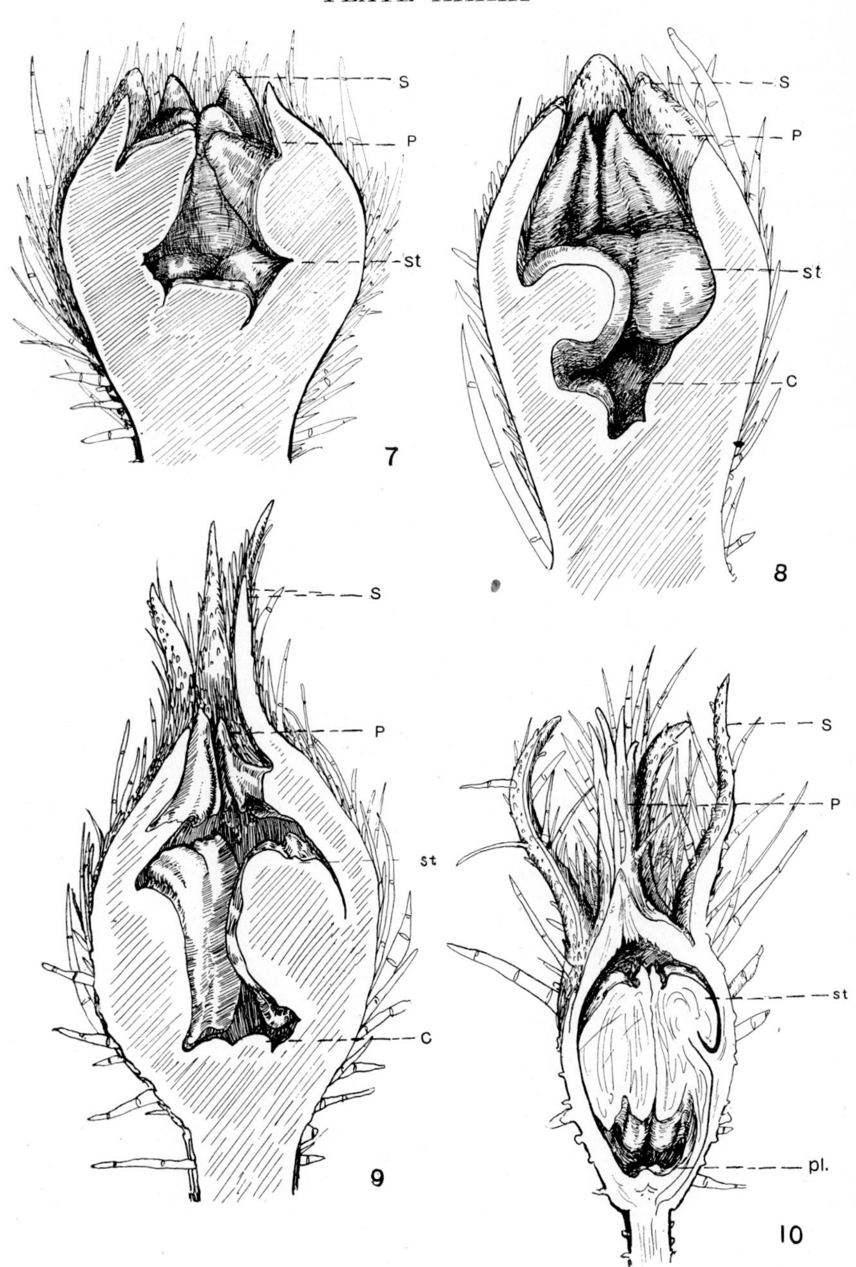

PLATE XL

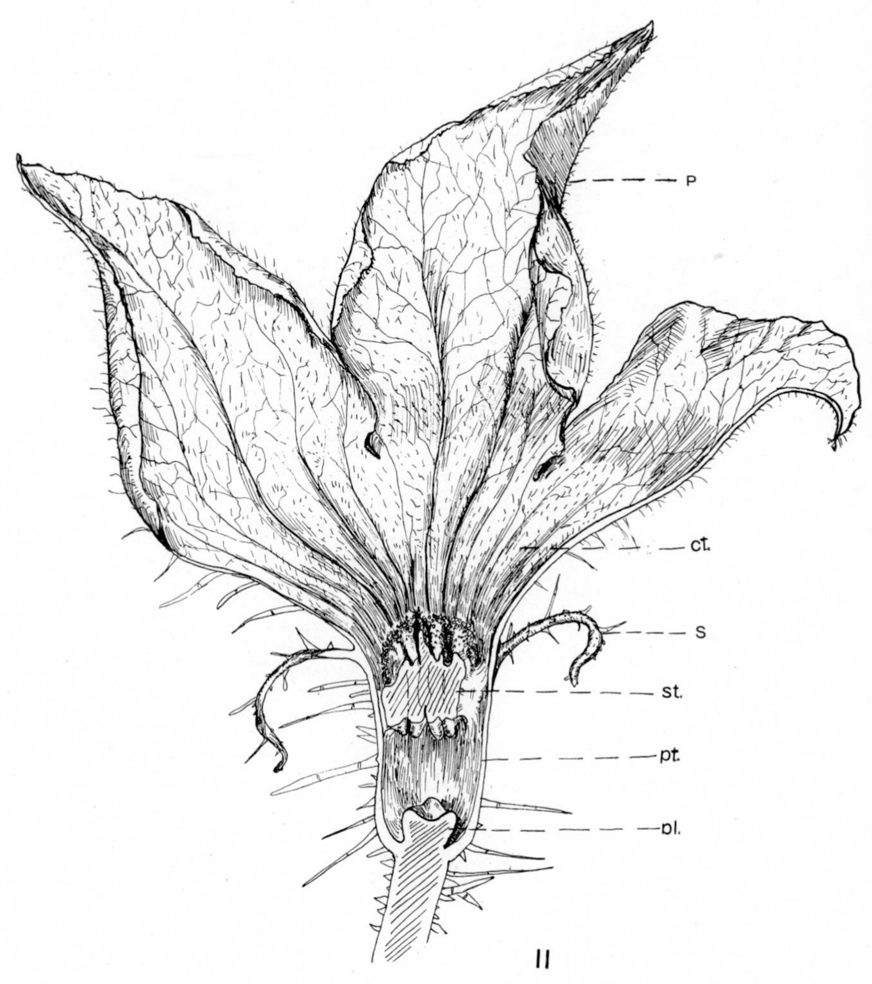

A STUDY OF THE FUNGOUS FLORA OF THE LAKE SUPERIOR REGION OF MICHIGAN, WITH SOME NEW SPECIES *

CALVIN H. KAUFFMAN

DURING the late summer of 1927, a short expedition, under the auspices of the University of Michigan Herbarium, was made to the southern shore of Lake Superior. The expedition was under the direct supervision of the Director of the Herbarium, who was accompanied by Dr. A. H. W. Povah of Northwestern University, Dr. Bessie B. Kanouse of the Herbarium, and Delbert Swartz, a graduate student at the University. The station selected was in a rather isolated "camp" situated at the mouth of Rock River, on Shelter Bay, owned by Mr. C. C. Brown and consisting of about a dozen cottages; it was surrounded by the lake shore on the north side and elsewhere by extensive swamps of cedar, alder, balsam, spruce, tamarack, etc., in the lower areas, with birch, poplar, maple, pitch pine, etc., on the slightly higher ground. Small areas of virgin timber were to be found here and there at some distance from camp.

The work of collecting and studying extended over a little more than three weeks, viz. from August 20 to September 15. Warm and dry weather prevailed during our stay. As a result of the lack of rain both preceding and during this time, relatively very few species of ground-inhabiting fungi appeared. This gave us an opportunity to make a more exhaustive study of those fungi which fruit on wood, bark and various forest substrata, and resulted in an unusually fine collection of such forms. The sphagnum swamps, in which sufficient moisture persisted in and about the mosses, gave additional yields of what may be called the dry-

* Paper from the Department of Botany of the University of Michigan, No. 281, and from the University Herbarium, No. 10.

weather species of these areas, although very many species characteristic of sphagnum areas did not fruit, especially the agarics.

The most intensive work was done on the Ascomycetes growing on trees and wood. A large number of unusual species were gathered and most of them were in good condition for study. It is to be pointed out that the lack of rain throughout the summer had prevented many species from expelling their spores, so that not only those species which mature normally in late spring but also those maturing in early autumn were in stages of maturity that made it possible to identify them. If the summer had been interspersed with soaking rains, it is believed that a large number gathered during these few weeks would have been weathered or too overmature for identification. The advantage of this was realized almost at once, and every effort was made, therefore, to get exhaustive collections of Ascomycetes on as many of the local hosts as possible. As a result about sixty species of Ascomycetes are reported for the first time as occurring in Michigan.

The collections made by Dr. Povah can unfortunately not be included, on account of his illness during the preparation of the paper. The Myxomycetes and certain of the Discomycetes have been identified by Dr. Kanouse. The species of Poria were worked over by Dr. Dow V. Baxter of our School of Forestry and Conservation. Dr. L. E. Wehmeyer gave most valuable assistance in the proper placing of the Valsaceae. The others were identified by the writer and any errors occurring throughout the paper are to be laid at his door.

Thankful acknowledgement is made to Miss Kanouse, who prepared the drawings accompanying some of the new species and varieties.

The reader's attention is called to the list of fungi reported by Dr. Povah (17) in the present volume of the Academy, also collected in the Lake Superior region.

MYXOMYCETES

Arcyria incarnata Pers. — On very rotten wood.
Arcyria nutans (Bull.) Grev. — On wood.
Badhamia macrocarpa (Ces.) Rost. — On living *Sphagnum sp.*

DIDYMIUM MELANOSPERUM (Pers.) Macbride. — On bark of *Betula sp.*

FULIGO MUSCORUM A. & S. — This seems to be a rare species and variable as to habitat. Macbride (13) gives the range of the size of the aethalium as 1 cm. or less in diameter. Lister, however, says it may reach a diameter of 5 cm. Our specimen measures 2.5 cm. It developed on a rotten log. The spores are subglobose, up to 13 μ in diameter and coarsely warted.

FULIGO SPETICA (L.) Gmel. — Common. On birch and other bark and wood.

HEMITRICHIA VESPARUM (Batsch.) Macbride. — On decayed wood.

LAMPRODERMA ARCYRIONEMA Rost. — On wood.

LAMPRODERMA ROBUSTUM E. & E. — On dead twigs of *Picea sp.*

LINDBLADIA EFFUSA (Ehr.) Rost. — On decayed wood.

OLIGONEMA NITENS (Lib.) Rost. — On wood.

PHYSARUM LEUCOPHAEUM Fr. — On pore surface of *Fomes applanatus.*

RETICULARIA LYCOPERDON (Bull.) Rost. — On standing birch trunk.

STEMONITIS AXIFERA (Bull.) Macbride. — On rotten stump; also on mosses.

STEMONITIS SPLENDENS Rost. — On a log of some hardwood tree.

STEMONITIS UVIFERA Macbride. — On bark of birch.

STEMONITIS WEBBERI Rex. — On rotten wood of *Thuja occidentalis.*

TRICHIA PERSIMILIS Karst. — On birch bark.

TRICHIA VARIA (Pers.) Rost. — On rotten log.

TUBIFERA FERRUGINOSA (Batsch.) Macbride. — On old stumps, logs and leafy débris.

MYXOBACTERIA

MICROCOCCUS RUBESCENS Thaxter. — On porcupine dung. Cultured in the laboratory.

PHYCOMYCETES

ENDOGONE SPHAGNOPHILA Atk. — On living Sphagnum.

MUCOR CORTICOLUS Hagem. — On porcupine dung. Cultured in the laboratory.

MUCOR GRISEO-LILACINUS Povah. — On porcupine dung. Cultured in the laboratory.

PYTHIOMORPHA GONAPODIOIDES Petersen. — In the river.

RHIPIDIUM AMERICANUM Thaxter. — In the river.

SPORODINIA GRANDIS Lk. — On decaying mushrooms.

SYNCHYTRIUM VACCINII Halsted (*auth. nov.*). — On living leaves of *Gaultheria procumbens* growing in the woods along the beech. This species was first collected apparently by B. C. Halsted in 1889 on species of Vaccinium, of Kalmia and of Chamaedaphne; his material was distributed by Ellis (N. A. Fungi No. 2432) and by Seymour and Earle (Economic Fungi No. 43). The identity of "Thomas" who has been the accredited author of the species seems to have been lost; at least the name of the fungus was merely suggested in a letter from him to Halsted. An account of the collection on the cranberry by Halsted seems to be the only study of it, and he seems to be the bona fide author of the species. An examination of our fresh plant showed it to be a true Synchytrium, so far as free-hand sections can be used to determine this point.

ASCOMYCETES

DISCOMYCETES

GEOGLOSSACEAE

HELVELLA LACUNOSA Afz. — Along very wet bank of a stream.

GEOGLOSSUM NIGRITUM Cke. — Frequent; among Sphagnum or hummocks of decayed wood, humus, etc., in cedar and mixed conifer swamps. The absence of other species, under the dry weather conditions, indicates that this species has a wider moisture range for fruiting than the others. Its geographic range seems to be throughout the northern United States and Canada, as far south as South Carolina and Tennessee in the East and California in the West. I have obtained it in northern Idaho, Lake Superior, Pennsylvania and Tennessee, localities not mentioned by Durand (7). It occurs also in Europe. It has been surprising not to find more geoglossums (including Gleeoglossum and Trichoglossum) in Oregon and Washington. Only a few specimens of this group, although carefully looked for, have been obtained by the author, during a total of twenty weeks' intense collecting on four different expeditions into these states, and during very favorable weather conditions. Durand (7 p. 391) comments on their absence in this region, but is inclined to consider it due to lack of exploration in these regions. Zeller (24, 25) does not include any in his two Oregon lists.

SPATHULARIA VELUTIPES Cke. & Farlow. — On top of a rotten conifer stump and on disintegrated wood-humus.

PEZIZACEAE

LACHNEA ERINACEA (Schw.) Sacc. — On mossy log. This is the second collection in northern Michigan of this curious Lachnea, having been obtained at Bay View near Little Traverse Bay in 1905, also on rotten wood. One would like to refer it to *L. Hystrix* (Saut.) Sacc., were it not for Rehm's remarks (*Discom.*, p. 1054) that the setae of that species are supposed to be non-septate. Otherwise, it certainly agrees well with that description. It approaches two other European species, *L. livida* (Schum.) Gill. with "broadly elliptical, rough spores," and *L. fuscoatra* (Rebent.) Sacc. which, however, has larger apothecia and occurs on the ground.

The main features of our plant are as follows: Apothecia 1–3 mm. diam. when mature; disk pallid or becoming pale livid; externally and on the incurved margin provided with dense, stiff, shiny and rich "chestnut brown" (R.) setae, which are at first twice the height of young apothecia, straight or curved slightly inward; under the microscope the setae appear deep brown throughout, are many-septate, taper rather regularly from the base to a subacute or blunt apex, 200 to 400 μ long, 10–12 (14) μ thick near base; asci cylindrical, 200–230 $\times$ 10–13 μ, 8-spored, not colored blue by iodine; paraphyses filamentose, not or scarcely enlarged at apex, abundant; spores ventricose-ellipsoid, obtuse at ends, with one large oil-globule, hyaline, granular within, smooth or very minutely rough under the immersion lens, colored yellowish-brown by iodine, more so than the hyaline paraphyses, 18–22 (24) × 9–10 μ.

The fresh plant may have an ochraceous tint in the disk, as given by Schweinitz, but no such tint was noted.

LACHNEA LEUCOTRICHA (A. & S.) Quél. — On black soil in Sphagnum swamp. This is one of the very few white species of Lachnea.

LACHNEA SCUTELLATA (F'k'l.) Gill. — On old bark of *Betula alba*. Frequent.

LAMPROSPORA CREC'HQUERAULTII (Cr.) Boud. — On moist sand near river bank. This is more commonly known as *Barlaea asperella* (Rehm) Sacc. and is found under this name in Rehm's *Discomycetes*. According to Seaver (21), *Peziza echinosperma* Pk. is also identical. Since the genus Barlaea is antedated by an orchid genus of that name, Rehm later placed the species of Barlaea under Detonia. Seaver (*l.c.*) and Boudier (2) use the older genus Lamprospora. Its habitat on sandy soil, instead of clay as given by Seaver (*l.c.*), seems to show that this factor is not constant.

Three other species of this genus have been found in Michigan by the author: *Lamprospora miniata* (Cr.) De Not., *Lamprospora polytrichina* (Rehm) Seaver and *Lamprospora dictydiola* Boud., all in the southern part of the state. *L. miniata* is not infrequent, and usually nestles among mosses. The other species seem to be rare. Dodge (5) reports five additional species as occurring in Wisconsin, so that the region of the Great Lakes seems to be fairly rich in members of this genus. Three of our four species are beautifully illustrated by Boudier (*Icones II*, Pls. 402, 403 and 404).

MACROPODIUM MACROPUS (Pers.) F'k'l.

HELOTIACEAE

CHLOROSPLENIUM AERUGINASCENS (Nyl.) Karst. — On decayed branches of Alnus, etc. Common.

CIBORIA FUSCOCINEREA Rehm (*Ann. Myc.*, 7: 525, 1909). — On

decayed wood in conifer swamp. See remarks on this by Dodge (5). Our plant deviates only in showing no tawny color on base of stem. It has the colors and somewhat the habit of *Rutstroemia nebulosa,* discussed below, but the microscopic characters are different. The ascospores are ovate.

CIBORIA SULPHURELLA (E. & E.) Rehm. — On petioles of Fraxinus leaves in swamp. Apparently *C. tabacina* Ell. & Holw.

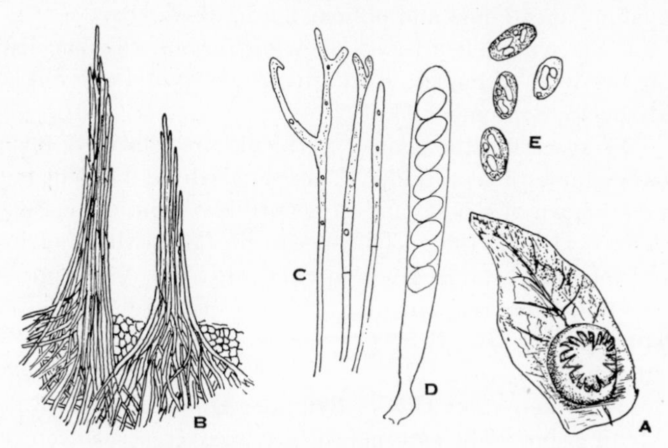

FIG. 13. CYATHICULA ALNI Kauff. & Kanouse, sp. nov. *a,* habit sketch of sessile apothecium on portion of a leaf; *b,* radiating teeth composed of bundles of narrow hyphae; *c,* paraphyses; *d,* an ascus; *e,* ascospores

(*Syll.*, VIII, p. 206) is a synonym. Durand (6) refers to the characteristic loss of the yellow color which the apothecia undergo when dried. The ascospores measure 9–12 × 3–4 (5) μ. The filiform stems are attenuated at base. This species is reported by Durand (*l.c.*) in New York and by Seaver (20) in Iowa and North Dakota, and is generally distributed.

CORYNE URNALIS Sacc. — On rotten wood, logs, sticks, etc., of Thuja, Populus and other trees. Frequent. The large ascospores separate this from *C. sarcoides.*

Cyathicula alni Kauff. & Kanouse, sp. nov. (see Text Fig. 13). — ASCOMATA loosely gregarious, turbinate, sessile or with obscure thick stipe, fleshy-waxy, thin, grayish-pallid when fresh, becoming subincarnate on drying, 0.5–2 mm. broad, cupulate, margin crenate-serrulate from the wedge-shaped radiating teeth which are 0.25 to 0.5 mm. long, and composed of bundles of narrow hyphae. ASCI cylindrical, 8-spored, 100–110 × 10–12 μ. SPORES elliptic-oblong, smooth, hyaline, rounded at ends, 10–12 × 4–4.5 μ. PARAPHYSES filiform, branched, hyaline, apex equal and obtuse, 2 μ in diam.

On decaying fallen leaves of *Alnus incana*. Type collected by Bessie B. Kanouse, Rock River, shore of Lake Superior, Michigan, September 11, 1927.

The species of the genus Cyathicula are relatively few and rather rare. The stipitate *C. coronata* (Bull.) De Not is perhaps known the best, and is beautifully figured by Boudier (*Icones*, III, pl. 499). The species on fallen leaves of beech and related hosts, as given in Saccardo (Vol. VIII, pp. 305–306), all differ from our plant in color or spore size.

DASYSCYPHA AGASIZII (B. & C.) Sacc. — On dead branches and fallen trees of *Abies balsamea*.

DASYSCYPHA ALBOLUTEA (Pers.) Rehm. — On conifer wood, probably of cedar. The external surface is covered with conspicuous sulphur-yellow to citron-yellow hairs, making it a striking object under the lens. This color disappears on drying, so that the herbarium specimens are wholly pale silvery-gray. Asci 50–55 × 5–6 μ. Ascospores 9–11 × 3–3.5 μ. Paraphyses filiform, blunt.

DASYSCYPHA CERINA (Pers.) F'k'l. — On a decorticated, weathered log. This is another beautiful species, the apothecia retaining their original color well after drying. The surface of the wood seems to be black-gray from the presence of the fungus. The preceding crop of apothecia had persisted and frequently the fruiting occurred at the same point; these old and weathered apothecia give the impression that a minute gray lichen is scattered over the wood. Boudier (*Icones,* III, Pl. 509) gives figures of it.

HELOTIUM CITRINUM (Hedw.) Fr. — On decayed wood. Frequent.

HYMENOSCYPHA EPIPHYLLUM (Pers.) Rehm. — Common on decaying leaf-mats, especially of Alnus.

HYMENOSCYPHA SUBLENTICULARE var. CONSCRIPTUM Karst. — On wood of *Alnus incana*.

LACHNUM NIVEUM Karst. (sense of Rehm). — On dead stems of *Rubus sp.* The hymenium is beset with very conspicuous, stout and lance-pointed spicules (paraphyses), reminding one of the cystidia in certain Basidiomycetes, and this, of course, distinguishes it from the *Dasyscypha nivea* (Fr.) Sacc. and that of Phillips, as pointed out by Rehm (*Discomycetes*, p. 880). In addition to normal asci and the "paraphyses" mentioned above, there are present in the hymenium ordinary filamentous paraphyses, equal and blunt at the apex and scarcely if at all longer than the asci. The ascospores measure 5–8 × .8–1 μ, straight and hyaline. The apothecia are snow-white, with slender stem, hairy on the stem and on the external surface of the cup.

Lachnum thujinum Kauff. sp. nov. — ASCOMATA gregarious to subcespitose, sometimes confluent in pairs, cupulate, stipitate; cup fleshy-waxy, thin, disk "empire yellow" (R.), margin and exterior densely covered, as is the stipe, with cream-yellow or paler, slender, subcapitate hairs, 0.5–1.5 (2) mm. in diam., retaining the yellow color when dried; stipe 0.5–1 mm. long, concolorous, scarcely slender, hairy. ASCI clavate, 30–45 × 4 μ, 8-spored. SPORES 5–7 × 0.5–0.8 μ, subfusiform, hyaline, smooth. PARAPHYSES filamentose, lance-pointed above.

On dead decorticated wood at base of a tree of *Thuja occidentalis*. Type collected by C. H. Kauffman, at Rock River, shore of Lake Superior, Michigan, September 5, 1927.

There seems to be no record of any similar Lachnum. *Helotium limonicolor* Bres. and *Helotium thujinum* Pk. occur on the fallen leaves of Thuja, but the apothecia lack the conspicuous hairiness of our plant.

LACHNUM VIRGINEUM (Batsch.) Karst. (sense of Rehm). — On bark of old fallen branchlets in moist places. This is another species with white, stipitate and hairy apothecia. The tips of the hairs are markedly clavate or knobby. The ascospores measure 7–9 (10) × 1.5–2 (2.5) μ. The paraphyses, as in the preceding, are prominent and lance-pointed above. The asci are similar in size in both species.

OMBROPHILA ENTEROCHROMA (Pk.) Sacc. — On Thuja branchlets buried among Sphagnum.

This species will be looked for in non-gelatinous genera, especially in herbaria. When fresh, however, it has a stiff habit due to a tremelloid texture in part at least. Through the kindness of Dr. House, I was able to examine Peck's plant. The cups of our specimens are 0.5–1.25 mm. in diam., pale yellowish when fresh, naked, and borne on a stipe which is 2–2.5 mm. long, equal, subrigid and concolorous. On drying the plants turn dark. The asci measure 140–160 × 16 μ, and are 8-spored. The paraphyses are abundant, tending to form a slight epithecium, filamentous and slightly branched, with clavate tips. The spores are fusiform, smooth, hyaline, one-celled, 22–26 × 7–9 μ. Iodine slowly stains the pores of the asci blue. This species is evidently distributed, on its proper hosts, across the continent, as I have it also from southern Oregon on *Librocedrus decurrens*.

OMBROPHILA LIMOSELLA (Karst.) Rehm. — On decaying fallen alder leaves and soil in swamp.

The short-turbinate apothecia taper down to scarcely a stalk, 4–6 mm. broad across disk, colored "cinnamon drab" (R.). Asci 70–80 × 9–10 μ. Spores 8–12 × 5–6 μ.

Rutstroemia nebulosa (Cke.) Kauff. & Kanouse, comb. nov.

Peziza nebulosa Cke.

Geopyxis nebulosa (Cke.) Sacc.

Pilocratera abnormis Pk.

This species is widely distributed in the United States and appears to be quite variable. It occurs scattered and not many apothecia are found at a time. We have it from New York, Kentucky, Michigan and Ohio. Dodge (5) reports it from Wisconsin and Seaver (20) from North Dakota. Cooke originally received it from South Carolina. In most collections the large, fusiform, hyaline ascospores are one-celled, but in some the spores have become two- or four-celled, in which stage of maturity germinated spores have been seen by us; the germ tubes may arise from several cells at the same time. The spores mature slowly. The size of the spores varies in length, measuring 20–24 (30, 36) or even 40 μ long, by 8–10 μ wide; occasionally, the spores, which ordinarily taper to a point at the ends, have the points drawn out into thread-like appendages. This, however, may be abnormal. It is not a characteristic Geopyxis, by reason of its spore-characters and toughish texture, even though it may have the pseudoparenchymatous structure of the Pezizaceae rather than of the Helotiaceae. In 1908, one of us sent a collection from Michigan to Dr. Peck at Albany. This material was made the type of a new species by Peck. Some of this material, still in our Herbarium, is found to agree with the Ellis specimen (*N. A. F.*, No. 437) as well as with our other collections, except for deviations noted above. Peck named it *Pilocratera abnormis* (see *N. Y. State Mus. Bull.* 150, p. 37. 1911). Cooke illustrates his plant in *Monographia*, Pl. 73, Fig. 281. P. Hennings' genus Pilocratera seems to be too poorly limited to be retained. *Rustroemia nebulosa* is recognizable by its tapering stem, usually widest at the cup, its nebulous-ashy color and its tendency to break off at its insertion on the wood.

If the principle of types is made to apply, then a new genus must be erected for Rutstroemia (see Honey *Mycologia*, 22:127–136. 1928).

Mollisiaceae

Mollisia benesuada (Tul.) Phill. var. **borealis** Kauff., var. nov. (see Text Fig. 14). — On decorticated, weathered wood of Pinus, Betula, etc. Three collections. This is perhaps an Eriopeziza, sense of Rehm (*Discomycetes*); no connection, however, could be established between the blackish-brown subiculum which is more or less associated with the areas where apothecia occur, and which is composed of large dark brown hyphae penetrating the wood and forming Helminthosporium-like spores and conidiophores. The lower portion of the apothecia are provided with manifest, whitish-gray radiating hairs which spread to the wood, while upwards toward the margin they are pubescent-granular. This ornamentation is not characteristic of *M. benesuada,* as far as I can find. It does not appear to belong to any described species of Tapesia. Our plants have the color and habit

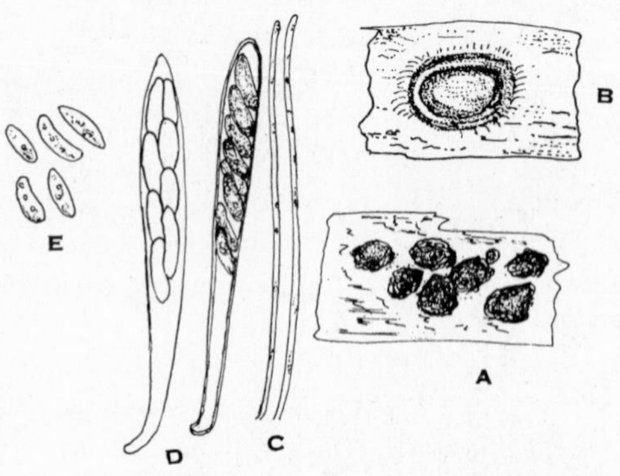

FIG 14. MOLLISIA BENESUADA (Tul.) Phill. var. BOREALIS Kauff., var. nov. *a,* habit sketch showing a cluster of mature apothecia; *b,* a young apothecium enlarged showing the inrolled margin with the prominent hairs; *c,* filiform paraphyses; *d,* asci; *e,* ascospores

shown for *Tapesia Rosae* by Boudier (*Icones,* III, Pl. 539), but are twice as large and occur on a different substratum; also the apothecia of that and related species are glabrous exteriorly. A description follows:

ASCOMATA 0.5–2 mm. broad, gregarious or subconfluent, associated with a blackish-brown thin subiculum, which is shot through here and there by grayish-white hyphae, and where the latter are most evident, the young apothecia arise. Under a lens the apothecia are "storm gray" (R.), paler, grayish-white and granular-pubescent toward the inflexed margin, below with long, silvery-gray radiating hairs; disk at first gray, then "dark olive-buff" (R.); shape of apothecia varies from orbicular to elliptical, but on drying they become angular or irregular, with incurved margins; the disk remains exposed. ASCI subclavate, 40–55 × 5–6 μ, 8-spored. Ascospores sublanceolate-subfusiform, pointed at one end, smooth, hyaline 8–10 × 1.5–2.5 μ. PARAPHYSES filamentous, equal, apex obtuse, relatively few.

Type collected by Delbert Swartz, August 29, 1927, at Rock River, Michigan.

MOLLISIA BENESUADA (Tul.) Phill. var. **polyspora** Kauff., var. nov. (see Text Fig. 15). — On wet and rotten pine wood. This remarkable plant has many-spored asci, which may be the result of conidium-formation within the ascus from the original 8 ascospores as in Diatrypella, but this point could not be established. The fact is that one can occasionally find an ascus with 8 ascospores, and the scanty occurrence of such spores is further revealed in a good mount because of the relatively few and scattered ascospores which are seen among the thousands of asco-conidia in the mount, the latter appearing in clouds when the ascus-layer is pressed down by pressure on the cover-glass. These conidia are definitely in the asci, not on conidiophores in the manner figured by Tulasne (*Ann. Sci. Nat.*, 3, Pl. 20, Fig. 9) for *Mollisia benesuada*. The asci measure 45–55 × 5–7 μ, subventricose-clavate with rounded tips, polyspored. The ascospores measure about 5–8 × 2–2.5 μ or are often smaller and narrower, in which case they are doubtless immature. The asco-conidia are short-oblong, somewhat curved, hyaline, and about 3 × 1 μ in size, very many per ascus. The apothecia are scattered-gregarious, mostly occur-

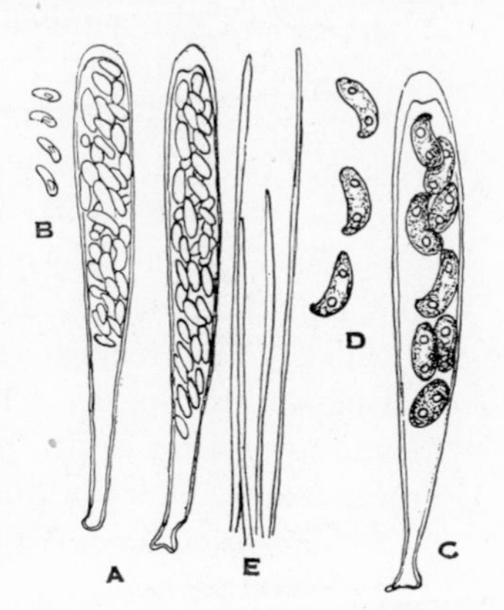

FIG. 15. MOLLISIA BENESUADA (Tul.) Phill. var. POLYSPORA Kauff., var. nov. *a*, polysporous asci; *b*, small spores from a polysporous ascus; *c*, an eight-spored ascus; *d*, spores from an eight-spored ascus; *e*, filiform paraphyses

ring on a thin, whitish, pulverulent-arachnoid, basidiomycetous fungus, whose mycelium has abundant clamp-connections and has no relation, e.g. as a subiculum, to our plant. Although the apothecia are somewhat darker than in the typical species, the detailed characters are very similar.

Type collected by C. H. Kauffman, September 7, 1927, at Rock River, Michigan.

MOLLISIA UDA (F'k'l.) Sacc. — On decayed wood of Alnus (?)

ORBILIA EPIPORA Karst. — On pore surface of *Fomes igniarius* on poplar. This is also reported from Wisconsin by Dodge (5).

ORBILIA LUTEORUBELLA (Nyl.) Rehm. — On rotten, decorticated wood. The reddish-yellow apothecia and the spores distinguish this species. The ascospores measure 6–10 × 1–1.5 μ and are fusiform with pointed ends.

PYRENOPEZIZA PHACIDIOIDES (Fr.) Rehm. — On old stalks of *Eupatorium purpureum*. Associated with it is *Leptosphaeria Doliolum*.

TAPESIA ATROSANGUINEA F'k'l. — On old wood of *Thuja occidentalis*.

TAPESIA UNDULATA Bomm. — On bark of a fallen branch, probably of Thuja. Asci are 8-spored, 45–50 × 4–5 μ. Ascospores 6–7 × 1.5 μ, straight, hyaline. The apothecia are quite black, in both the young and old condition scutelliform to irregular-undulate.

CENANGIACEAE

CENANGIUM ABIETIS (Pers.) Rehm. — On twigs of *Pinus resinosa*.

GODRONIA NEMAPANTHES (Pk.) Sacc. — On dead stems and branches of *Nemapanthus mucronata*.

TYMPANIS AUCUPARIAE (Fr.) Wallr. — On dead branches of *Pyrus americana*.

URNULA CRATERIUM (Schw.) Fr. — This common species is found in Rehm (*Discomycetes*) under the genus Geopyxis. A detailed study by Miss Kupfer (11) has made it clear that this species cannot be placed in the Pezizaceae.

STICTIDACEAE

OCELLARIA AUREA Tul. — On dead branches of *Salix sp.* The ascospores, as usual, measure 20–25 (rarely 30) × 9–11 (12) μ. This occurs on willows throughout the northern part of North America, from coast to coast. The writer has collected it in the Pacific Coast states as well as in the East.

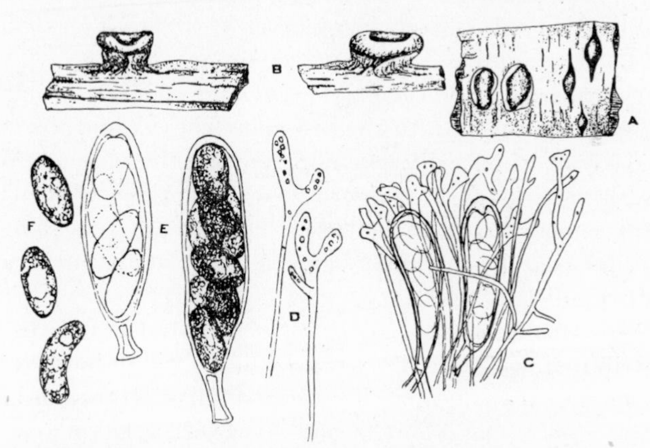

FIG. 16. OCELLARIA AUREA Tul. var. CORNICOLA Kauff. & Kanouse, var. nov. *a,* habit sketch showing both young and old apothecia; *b,* side views showing the exserted apothecia; *c,* a cluster of asci and paraphyses which form an epithecium; *d,* paraphyses enlarged, showing the enlarged bifurcated apices; *e,* asci with ascospores, showing the short stalks and thick-walled apices; *f,* thin-walled ascospores

OCELLARIA AUREA Tul. var. **cornicola** Kauff. & Kanouse, var. nov. (see Text Fig. 16). — APOTHECIA solitary or erumpent in pairs, splitting the periderm transversely, sessile, at first closed, later exposing the circular, flat or semiconvex disk, which is "ochraceous-orange" (R.), 0.5 to 1 mm. broad, exserted, waxy, fragile when dry, pulverulent, hypothecium "ochraceous-orange." ASCI elongated subellipsoid, thick-walled, apex rounded, tapering abruptly to a narrow short stalk, 110–150 × 25–30 μ, 8-spored. SPORES elliptical or slightly curved, rounded at ends, 30–35 × 12–14 μ, unicellular, hyaline, thin-walled, densely filled with granular protoplasm and many small highly refractive oil droplets evenly distributed, partly biseriate, apex turning blue with iodine. PARAPHYSES abundant, slender, septate, branched irregularly, often bifurcate with the enlarged ends intertwining to form an epithecium, brownish-orange upwards, 5–7 μ at apices.

On dead branches of *Cornus alternifolia*, near Lake Superior, Rock River, Michigan. September 4, 1927. Type collected by C. H. Kauffman.

Differs from *Ocellaria aurea* in its large spores, the markedly exserted apothecia with the disk more convex and the margin of the disk at maturity extending beyond the raised periderm; the asci are distinctly short-stalked, while those of the typical form scarcely taper at the base. These characters along with the different host seem to give it at least distinct varietal rank.

This may be Peck's *Dermatea inclusa*, but is not the plant distributed in Ellis and Everhart Fungi Columbiana No. 1918 under that name. *Dermatea Corni* Phill. & Hark. also seems to be close. Our plant is not, however, a Dermatea, since the apothecia are not leathery or horny; nor are they stalked or cespitose. On the other hand, specimens of typical *O. aurea* from Europe and of a number of American collections examined fall well into the description given by Rehm (19).

PROPOLIS FAGINEA (Schrad.) Karst. — On a decorticated log of Abies, and also on hardwood logs. This species is not infrequent in coniferous regions. We have it from Oregon on Pseudotsuga. The plants on conifers do not seem to differ from those found commonly on beech and other hardwoods.

Schizoxylon bipartitum Kauff., sp. nov. (see Text Fig. 17). — APOTHECIA gregarious or subconfluent, at first imbedded in the surface of the wood which is blackened in elongated areas around them, breaking through and exposing the subcircular, elliptical or narrowly elongated, pallid-gray disk which becomes lead-colored or at length black, 1–2.5 mm. in diam., flattened-discoid, with thin erect margin, waxy. ASCI cylindrical-subclavate, apex subacutish and thin-walled, about $210 \times 14\ \mu$. Ascospores filiform, many-septate, in parallel bundles of 8, breaking into two segments of equal length, each half needle-shaped with a slightly larger and rounded cell at the separated end and measuring $75–85 \times 1.5\ \mu$. Paraphyses filiform, branched above with short, hyaline, curved or curled branchlets which form an epithecium.

On decorticated logs of *Picea* (probably *nigra*). Type collected by C. H. Kauffman, September 3 and 6, 1927, Rock River, shore of Lake Superior, Michigan.

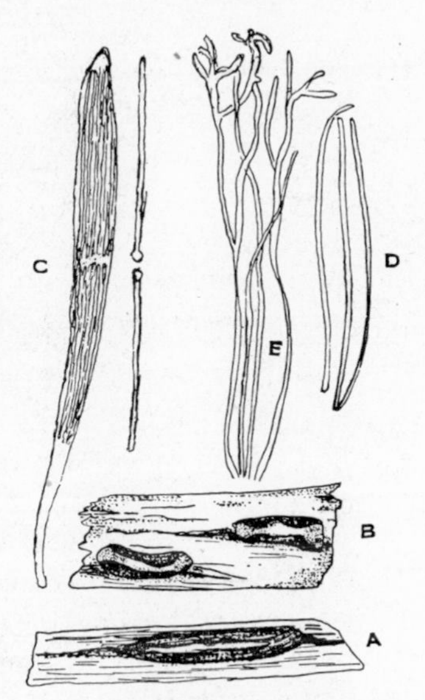

Fig. 17. Schizoxylon bipartitum Kauff., sp. nov. *a*, view of an elongated apothecium with opening appearing as a slit; *b*, subcircular elliptical apothecia, showing the erect margins; *c*, ascus with ascospores; *d*, needle-shaped ascospores; *e*, paraphyses

This interesting species of Schizoxylon was fairly frequent on spruce wood in this region, and even when there was scarcely a sign of the apothecia, the blackened surface of the wood was almost a sure indication of its presence. When the ascospores are immature they each have the appearance of a row of granular beads; at maturity they lie in two superposed bundles with a hyaline cross-area between them showing where bipartition has taken place. On drying, the apothecia tend to become narrowed from the tensions of the wood fibers.

Phacidiaceae

Rhytisma ilicis-canadensis Schw. — On leaves of *Nemapanthus mucronata*.

Hypodermataceae

Hypoderma Osmundae (Schw.) Sacc. — On dead stalks of *Osmunda regalis*. Common.

Hysteriaceae

Hysterographium mori (Schw.) Rehm. — On decayed wood of Alnus, etc. Not rare.

PYRENOMYCETES

Erysibaceae

Erysiphe communis (Wallr.) Schlecht. — On living and fallen leaves of *Thalictrum polygamum*.

Hypocreaceae

Claviceps purpurea (Fr.) Tul. — Very frequent on *Phleum pratense* wherever this host was found in the region; also on *Agropyron repens* and *Elymus glaucus*.

Hypocrea chionea E. & E. — On the bark and shreds of a decayed log of *Thuja occidentalis*. It was originally described from Ontario, Canada, collected by Dearness, and that seems to have been the only collection known. We found only about half a dozen stromata, pale chamois color, 1–2 mm. in diam., patellate. The asci are 16-spored, $85 \times 4\ \mu$. Spores vary, subglobose, subquadrate or subellipsoid, about $4\ \mu$ in diam.

Nectria balsamea Cke. & Pk. — On corticated dead branches of *Abies balsamea*.

Dothidiaceae

Phyllachora graminis (Pers.) F'k'l. — On *Elymus glaucus*.

Plowrightia morbosa (Schw.) Sacc. (*Dibotryon morbosa* (Schw.) T. & S.). — Not infrequent on *Prunus pennsylvanica*.

Sphaeriaceae

Bertia moriformis De Not. — On decorticated conifer wood. Not infrequent. This occurs throughout northern United States and Canada, on wood cf hardwoods as well as that of conifers.

Lasiosphaeria hirsuta (Fr.) Ces. & De Not. — On decorticated branches of *Alnus incana* and *Populus tremuloides*, apparently starting under the bark, which is later thrown off.

"Lasiosphaeria viridicoma (C. & P.) Sacc." (see Text Fig. 18). — On decorticated wood of *Alnus incana*.

This is not a Lasiosphaeria, but belongs somewhere else. It was described as *Sphaeria* (*Villosae*) *viridicoma* C. & P. in

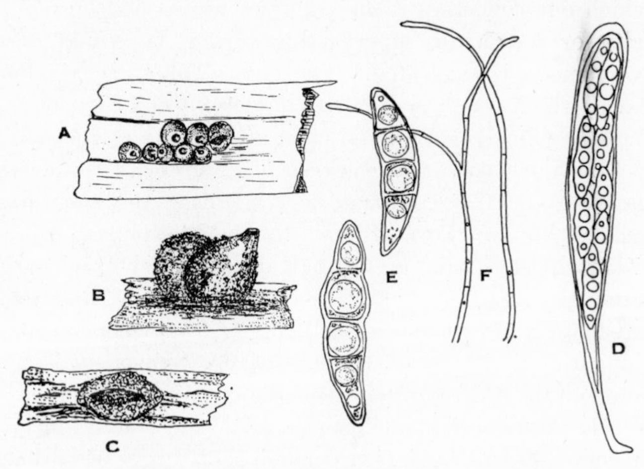

Fig. 18. "Lasiosphaeria viridicoma (C. & P.) Sacc." *a*, habit sketch of a cluster of perithecia; *b*, two nearly superficial mature perithecia, the circular opening in the ostiole of one of them showing; *c*, a view of a perithecium, showing the collapsed top of one of the ostioles; *d*, a slender-stalked ascus with ascospores; *e*, septate fusiform ascospores; *f*, filiform paraphyses

the *N. Y. State Mus. Rep.*, 29, p. 64, as occurring "on decaying beech wood and branches." This description is, however, not complete and the sizes of the perithecia as there given are too small. The spores are said to be lanceolate, whereas they are really fusiform. A good specimen is in our copy of Farlow Reliqueae No. 42. The genus Lasiosphaeria, with its composite content, has been thoroughly criticized by Von Höhnel (*Fragmente zur Mykologie*, XVI, No. 844). In summing up, Von Höhnel says: "I consider only those as true species of Lasiosphaeria whose perithecia are superficial and hairy, are without a beak, and bear hyaline, cylindric-vermiform, one-many-celled spores, which are curved in a characteristic manner." This appears to be a logical conception of the limitations of the genus. *L. hirsuta*, mentioned above, fits this characterization. By "hairy" he means spreading or stiff hairs, standing out from the perithecia. Those species, of which our collection is an example, whose perithecia have a felty or tomentose superficial covering, he would exclude. No remedy is suggested. The genus Heteronectria Penz & Sacc., which was based on one of these excluded species, viz. *L. ovina* (Pers.), is to be stricken out, says Von Höhnel.

Now the Cooke and Peck species, although its perithecia have a tomentose covering, does not have the Lasiosphaeria type of spore. Furthermore, the perithecia are erumpent, either through bark or through decorticated wood surfaces, although they may finally be quite superficial, and the asci have two walls, the outer rupturing and allowing considerable elongation as it approaches maturity. This latter is a character of the Pleosporaceae (sense of Lindau). Here we run into Leptosphaeria and Pocosphaeria, both containing species of very different habit, i.e. occurring on stems of herbaceous plants, grasses, etc.

The perithecia of some of our collection were overmature, almost superficial, and an inspection of the broad, prominent ostioles showed that quite a number opened by a slit instead of a round pore, and some of them were compressed. These are the characters, along with the tomentum or hairiness and the 3-septate (perhaps eventually 5-septate) fusiform hyaline spores, as well as the carbonaceous texture of the perithecia, which limit the genus Lophiotricha Richon. Other species, as is well known, among the Lophiostomataceae show this variable character, where some perithecia have rounded necks with pores, while others have compressed necks opening by slits. Combined with the other characters which indicate this family, the relationship seems unassailable. This would appear then to be the proper position for the species under discussion, and the name becomes **Lophiotricha viridicoma** (C. & P.) Kauff., *comb. nov.* (see Text Fig. 18). An emended description follows:

Perithecia erumpent, then superficial, in cespitose clusters of two to ten when in bark, more scattered or arranged in more irregular fashion when on decorticated wood, about 0.5 mm. in diam., ovate, black, somewhat longer than wide, carbonaceous, with a rather stout naked and black neck which is either rounded or more or less compressed, opening by a round pore or by a slit, clothed by a rather dense superficial *aeruginous-green tomentum.* Asci at length 145–160 × 10–15, elongated-clavate, subventricose upwards, thick-walled at first, rapidly elongating near maturity, tapering to a slender stalk. Ascospores fusiform, straight or curved, for a long time uniseptate, at length 3-septate (rarely 5-septate), somewhat constricted between the slightly enlarged central cells, hyaline, the exospore at length faintly brownish, 35–40 (45) × 7–9 (10) μ.

On naked wood or corticated branches of *Fagus grandifolia, Acer rubrum* and *Alnus incana.* Hitherto reported from New York (see *26th Rep. N. Y. State Mus.*, page 87) by Peck; from New Hampshire by Farlow; and now from northern Michigan. At first sight it is easily mistaken for a green Nectria. The decorticated surface of the old alder wood is somewhat blackened in the areas inhabited by the fungus. It matures slowly, and perithecia in which the spores are in an advanced state of maturity are scanty.

Rosellinia albolanata E. & E. — On decorticated wood of *Sambucus racemosa.*

Pleosporaceae

Didymosphaeria clematidis Fautr. — On dead stems of *Clematis virginiana.*

Leptosphaeria doliolum (Pers.) Ces. & De Not. — On dead stems of *Eupatorium purpureum.*

Leptosphaeria subconica Pk. — On dead stems of *Thalictrum subconica* Pk.

Pleospora alnea Kauff., sp. nov. (see Text Fig. 19). — PERITHECIA spherical, scattered or rarely in pairs, immersed in the bark, 350 to 450 μ in diam., raising the periderm slightly and piercing it with a very short, black, papillate ostiole, base may or may not reach the wood. ASCI subcylindrical, rounded at apex, short-stipitate, with double wall, 8-spored,

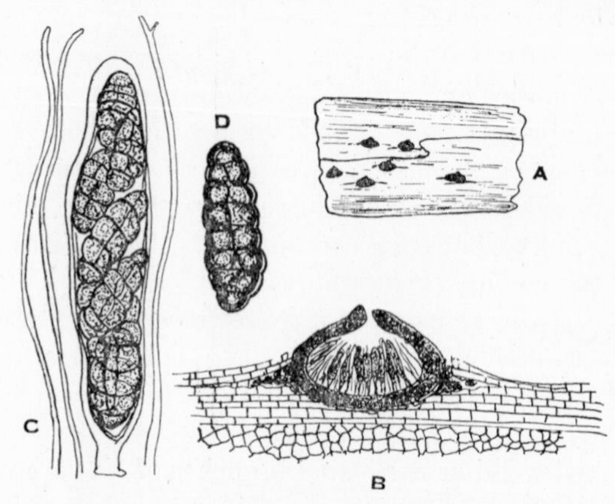

FIG. 19. PLEOSPORA ALNEA Kauff., sp. nov. *a*, habit sketch, showing scattered perithecia; *b*, a vertical section through a perithecium; *c*, an ascus with ascospores and filiform paraphyses; *d*, a many-celled ascospore

100–200 × 12–15 μ. ASCOSPORES elongated-ellipsoid, rounded-obtuse at ends, at length brownish honey-colored or darker, muriform, cross-septa 5 to 7, with several interrupted longitudinal septa, slightly constricted in the middle, 19–25 × 8–10 μ. PARAPHYSES filiform, abundant, hyaline.

On corticated dead branches of *Alnus incana*. Type collected by Delbert Swartz, September 2, 1927, at Rock River (Lake Superior), Michigan.

Where the loosened bark disappears, a small portion of it persists around some of the more closely grouped perithecia, but there is no stroma. The asci sometimes contain abnormally smaller spores which except for size have the same characters at maturity as the larger spores. Another ascomycete, with hyaline 2-celled ascospores, is scantily associated with the type.

VENTURIA CASSANDRAE Pk. — On living foliage of *Chamaedaphne calyculata.*

LOPHIOSTOMATACEAE

Lophionema cylindrosporum Kauff., sp. nov. (see Text Fig. 20). — PERITHECIA immersed except the small black, compressed, and

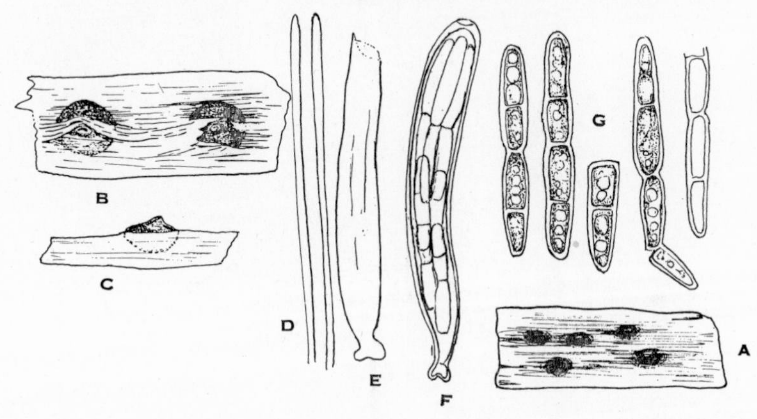

FIG. 20. LOPHIONEMA CYLINDROSPORUM Kauff., sp. nov. *a*, habit sketch, showing perithecia on substratum; *b*, sketch showing perithecia as immersed in substratum; *c*, diagram, side view of perithecia sunken into substratum; *d*, filiform paraphyses; *e*, an empty ascus; *f*, an ascus with ascospores; *g*, ascospores, some of them showing the manner in which they break at the septa

somewhat oblique ostiole, about 200 μ in diam., vertically flattened and shorter, with a black perithecial wall, carbonaceous. ASCI broadly elliptical, rounded above, short-stalked, with double wall, wall thicker at apex, 8-spored, about 85 $\times$ 17–20 μ. ASCOSPORES cylindrical, straight, rounded at ends, at first uniseptate and hyaline and constricted at the middle, becoming 3-septate and brown-tinged, 60–65 $\times$ 4–5 μ. PARAPHYSES filiform, equal, obtuse, hyaline, rather abundant, somewhat branched.

On old dead stems of *Eupatorium purpureum.* Type collected by C. H. Kauffman, August 30, 1927, Rock River (Lake Superior), Michigan.

The type material is scanty but this appears to be a clear-cut species. It differs from *L. vermisporum* (Ell.) Sacc., which is well figured on Plate 25 of Ellis' *N. Amer. Pyren.*, by its symmetrical spore halves, which show a constriction between

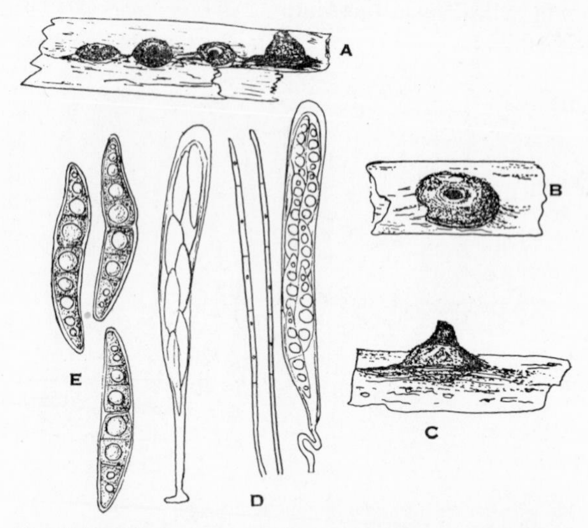

FIG. 21. LOPHIOSTOMA (LOPHIOTREMA) THALICTRI Kauff., sp. nov. *a*, habit sketch, showing partially immersed perithecia; *b*, a perithecium from which the neck has fallen off; *c*, a perithecium with the ostiole still prominent; *d*, asci with ascospores and filamentous paraphyses; *e*, septate fusiform ascospore

them, and which have fewer septa, and by the size of the asci and of the spores.

LOPHIOSTOMA CAULIUM (Fr.) De Not. — On dead stems of *Eupatorium purpureum*.

Lophiostoma (Lophiotrema) thalictri Kauff., sp. nov. (see Text Fig. 21). — PERITHECIA solitary and scattered, oval to subhemispherical, at first immersed except beak, at length nearly superficial, black, 300 to 500 μ in diam., depressed at maturity around the rather stout, more or less oblique and compressed ostiole which at length falls off, minutely rugulose and dull. ASCI about 140 × 10–12 μ, fusiform-subclavate, short-stipitate, 8-spored, gelatinous and quickly dissolving in water. ASCOSPORES fusiform, somewhat curved, acuminate-pointed at ends, 5–7 (9)-septate, hyaline, a few cells slightly enlarged, scarcely constricted. PARAPHYSES filamentous, few.

On old dead stems of *Thalictrum polygamum*. Type collected by C. H. Kauffman, August 30, 1927, at Rock River (Lake Superior), Michigan.

Lophiotricha viridicoma (C. & P.), comb. nov. (See under Lasiosphaeria.)

CLYPEOSPHAERIACEAE

ANTHOSTOMELLA ERUCTANS Fairman. — On decorticated wood of *Acer rubrum*.

VALSACEAE

ANTHOSTOMA MICROSPORUM Karst. — On bark of *Alnus incana*. The asci (sp. pt.) measure 27–30 × 3–4 μ. The spores are straight, pale brown, oblong, 4.5–6 × 1.5–2 μ. It is easily mistaken for a Eutypella because of its small spores; the spores are straight, however, instead of allantoid, and brown instead of hyaline, or may be merely tinged with brown.

DIAPORTHE BINOCULATA Ellis var. ILICIS E. & E. — On bark of *Nemapanthus mucronata*. Ascospores measure 14–17 × 7–8 μ, uniseptate, hyaline, constricted at middle, without appendages.

DIAPORTHE FAGINEA (Curr.) Sacc. — On bark of *Fagus grandifolia*. Although this collection is referred here provisionally, it is considered at least a form by Dr. Wehmeyer, and may need to be described under another name.

DIAPORTHE THELEBOLA (Fr.) Sacc. — On the bark of dead branches of *Alnus incana* and *Betula lutea*. This is common in the region. It is found under Melanconis in Ellis, *N. Amer. Pyren.*, p. 523. The asci measure 110–120 × 16–20 μ; the spores, 35–45 × 8–9 μ, appendaged at each end, not constricted, hyaline, uniseptate.

EUTYPA FLAVOVIRENS (Hoff.) Tul. — On decorticated wood of *Betula alba papyrifera* and *Acer rubrum*. This European species is reported by Ellis, *N. Amer. Pyren.*, p. 504, under *E. flavovirescens* (Hoff.) Sacc., and was known to him only from New York and N. Carolina. It is, however, distributed from coast to coast. I have it also from Oregon on *Quercus sp.* and on *Ceanothus cuneatus*. It is quite variable in its stromatic characters and departs quite a little from the usual appearance of species of Eutypa, the stromata being more isolated, usually forming elongated raised areas of various shapes. The yellow or greenish-yellow of the interior of the stromata are, however, quite distinguishing even in the sterile condition. Ellis (*N. Amer. Pyren.*) does not describe the spores of the American plants; they are allantoid, subhyaline (i.e. tinged with brown in the mass), 6–8 (9) × 1.5–2 μ. The perithecia are a quarter of a millimeter or less in diameter.

EUTYPA MILLIARIA (Fr.) Sacc. — On decorticated and blackened wood of *Sambucus racemosa*. This is seldom distributed in exsiccati, and American notices are rare. It appears to be easily confused with *E. Acharii* Tul. Wehmeyer says (*in litt.*) "*E. milliaria* is characterized by a rather rich development of stromatic hyphae about the perithecia which results in stromatic areas slightly raised above the wood-surface. *E. Acharii* is more like *E. sparsa* Romell, not raised above the wood surface, but with the wood heavily blackened about the perithecia." The asci of our collection are 95 μ long, slender and long-stalked, the spore-bearing part at upper end is short, 20–25 × 7–8 μ. The spores are allantoid, subhyaline, 7–8 × 1.5–1.8 μ.

EUTYPA SPARSA Romell. — On decorticated wood of *Populus tremuloides*. This European species, infrequent as it is, seems to be not at all reported for this country. Our collection agrees very well with the specimens in Sydow (Myc. Germ., No. 678) which are on *Populus tremula*. The surface of the wood is blackened and smooth, not raised, and the perithecia are scattered evenly beneath the surface. The asci are very small, measuring about 40–42 × 5–6 μ (sp. pt. 16–23 μ long).

The spores are allantoid, 6–7 (8)× 1–1.5 μ, hyaline. The stromatic substance is scarcely distinguishable.

EUTYPELLA ALNIFRAGA Nitschke. — On bark of *Alnus incana.* This is one of the closely related species clustering about *E. cerviculata.* It is not the species under the name of "*E. alnifraga*" as described by Winter in Rabenhorst (*Krypt. Flora*, p. 701). According to Wehmeyer (*in litt.*) it fits well the definition as given by Nitschke (*Pyr. Germ.*, p. 173). Its limiting characters are the strongly curved ascospores, the elongated divergent ostioles and its occurrence on Alnus. The spores are curved to an almost semicircular shape and measure 6–8 × 1.5–2 (2.5) μ.

EUTYPELLA ANGULOSA Nitschke. — On bark of *Betula alba papyrifera.* This also belongs to the "cerviculata" group, but is frequently quite marked by the fuller development of the stromata.

EUTYPELLA PRUNASTRI (Pers.) Sacc. — On bark of dead branches of *Prunus pennsylvanica.*

VALSA MICROSTOMA Nitschke. — On dead branchlets of *Abies balsamea.*

VALSA NIVEA (Hoff.) Fr. — Widely spread over dead bark of poplar.

MELANCONIDACEAE

CRYPTOSPORA FEMORALIS (Pk.) Sacc. — On bark of branchlets of *Alnus incana.* This species is well named because of the shape of the spores, which are like that of the femur bone, being knobby at both ends; they measure 40–80 × 5–9 μ, the larger sizes apparently being the mature ones. The asci are 8-spored, 90–100 × 17–20 μ. Ellis (*N. Amer. Pyren.*, p. 534) reports it also from California, although we have no Western collection.

MELANCONIS STILBOSTOMA (Fr.) Tul. — On bark of *Betula lutea.* Associated with the ascus stage was *Melanconium bicolor* Nees. For an account of the relation of these two spore forms see Wehmeyer (22).

Diatrypaceae

Diatrype platystoma (Schw.) Ellis. — On corticated branches of *Alnus incana* and *Acer rubrum*. Frequent.

Diatrypella betulina Pk. — On bark of *Betula alba papyrifera*.

Diatrypella discoidea C. & P. var. alni Cke. — On branchlets of *Alnus incana*.

Xylariaceae

Daldinia vernicosa (Schw.) Ces. & De Not. — On corticated wood of Prunus.

Hypoxylon cohaerens Fr. — On corticated wood of *Fagus grandifolia*. The length of the spore-bearing part of the asci is erroneously given in Ellis (*N. Amer. Pyren.*, p. 635). The asci (sp. pt.) measure 65–80 × 6–7 μ, with long slender stalk. The spores measure 9–12 × 4.5–5.5 μ.

Hypoxylon crustaceum Nitschke. — On rotten decorticated log of some deciduous tree. This species is poorly understood.

Hypoxylon fuscum Fr. — On corticated branchlets of *Alnus incana*. Common.

Hypoxylon fuscopurpureum (Schw.) Berk. — Covering fire-scorched logs of some hardwood tree for stretches of a meter or more. This species, incompletely described in Ellis (*N. Amer. Pyren.*, p. 649), seems to occur from coast to coast in this country. I have it from the Eastern seaboard, from Michigan and from Oregon. The material from Ontario, Canada, distributed by Bartholomew (Fungi Columbiana, Nos. 2122 and 2034) is scanty and does not show its spreading habit. No. 2034 is typical, the other somewhat doubtful. An emended description follows:

Stroma generally widely effused in elongated thin crusts often a foot or more in length, the perithecial-bearing portion about one-third millimeter thick, surface "Mars violet" (R.) or at length "deep liver brown," inseparably adnate, often with extensive and thin sterile margins or patches, purplish to black within, surface regularly but indistinctly areolate from the slightly raised mounds of each perithecium. Perithecia crowded, nearly monostichous, 4 per millimeter, oblong-ovate, immersed, opening by a minute, at first white-punctate ostiole. ASCI 8-spored, cylindrical, 90–105 × 7–9 μ (sp. pt. about 72 μ long). ASCOSPORES elliptic-ovate in one view, plano-convex in the other, at length black with a tint of purple, 12–14 (15) × 5–6 (7) μ.

This species appears to differ from *H. atropurpureum* Fr., which is said to have coffee-colored young stromata and smaller spores. It occurs on fallen trunks of various deciduous trees.

HYPOXYLON MARGINATUM (Schw.) Berk. — On bark of *Pyrus americana*. This is an extreme form of this species or may be distinct, but since the material is overmature, further collections are necessary. The typical form of this species occurs more often southward, as far as Georgia and the Gulf states.

HYPOXYLON MORSEI B. & C. — On corticated wood of *Alnus incana*. It occurs in Maine and from there across the continent to the Pacific.

HYPOXYLON MULTIFORME Fr. — On bark and decorticated wood of *Alnus incana*, *Betula lutea* and *Betula alba papyrifera*. Common.

HYPOXYLON RUBIGINOSUM Fr. — On decorticated wood of *Populus sp.*

NUMMULARIA REPANDA Nitschke. — On *Pyrus americana*.

XYLARIA CORNIFORMIS Fr. — On log of *Fagus grandifolia*. The stromata are young, covered by the conidial layer.

FUNGI IMPERFECTI

HISTIOMYCETES Von Höhnel

APIOSPHAERIA PINEA Sacc. — Superficial on decorticated conifer wood.

APIOSPHAERIA RUGULOSA Sacc. — Associated with *Hysterographium Mori*. On decorticated stick of *Alnus incana*. Conidia hyaline, straight, 3.5–4.5 (5) × 1.5 μ.

CYTOSPORA CERATOPHORA Sacc. — On bark of *Fraxinus nigra*. Conidia 4–5 × 1 μ, hyaline, allantoid.

CYTOSPORA CHRYSOSPERMA Fr. — Common on bark of Populus.

LIBERTELLA BETULINA Desm. — Covering large portions of a recently blown over tree of *Betula alba papyrifera;* on the bark.

LIBERTELLA BETULINA Desm. var. **amelanchieris** var., nov. Kauff. — On bark of *Amelanchier sp.* Type collected by Delbert Swartz, August 30, 1927, at Rock River, Michigan. The characters are like those of the fungus on birch, except that the spore horns are much paler, i.e. pale yellowish to whitish, and of course the host is different. The conidia are hyaline, curved, 14–15 × 1–1.25 μ. It is also not at all improbable that its perfect stage will be found to be a different species of Ascomycete from that to which *L. betulina* belongs.

LIBERTELLA FAGINEA Desm. — On corticated branches of *Fagus grandifolia.*

MELANCONIUM APIOCARPON Lk. — On corticated branches of *Alnus incana.* The conidia measure 14–16 × 8 μ.

MELANCONIUM BICOLOR Nees. — On bark of *Betula lutea,* associated with *Melanconis stilbostoma* of which it is the imperfect stage. See discussion by Wehmeyer (22).

MELANCONIUM PRUNI-LUSITANICAE Oud. — On bark of *Prunus pennsylvanica.* Conidia measure 10–14 × 7–8 μ. It has, therefore, much smaller conidia than *M. cerasinum* Pk., where the size is about 19–21.5 × 12–16 μ. The latter occurs on *Prunus virginianum* about Ann Arbor.

RHABDOSPORA INEQUALIS Sacc. & Roum. — On bark of branchlets of *Pyrus americana.* The conidia are hyaline, slightly curved, acute at ends, 40–48 × 1–1.5 μ.

SPHAERONEMA ACERINA Pk. — On bark of *Acer rubrum.* Common.

SPHAERONEMA PRUINOSUM B. & C. — On bark of *Amelanchier sp.*

STEGANOSPORIUM FAUTREYI Sacc. & Syd. — On dead corticated branchlets of *Betula lutea.* This species has been described quite incompletely, for example in the *Sylloge* where it occurs in Vol. 3 as *S. irregulare* (B. & C.) Sacc., and in Vol. 14 under *S. Fautreyi;* and also by Allescher in Rabenhorst. Essential additional points are brought out, however, by Diedicke in *Krypt. Flora der Mark Brandenburg;* especially the fact of the extensive septation of the spores and of the presence of a gelatinous envelope about them. The range of the spore size in our specimens is slightly larger than that given by any of these authors. Material which I collected in Virginia on *Betula nigra* has the same larger spore range, while, on the other hand, some collections examined show the smaller range. Here is a chance for the biometrician to discover "strains" of this species. The outstanding character of the conidia of this fungus is its sharply outlined dictyospory. The septa run at right angles, so that the spore is blocked out in a very regular manner, and where its base merges into the long slender pedicel, there is a row of 2 to 4 cells which the longitudinal septa do not penetrate; also at the apex of the spores only a single large cell is present. Elsewhere it has very regular quadrate cells each usually with a marked refractive oil-globule. The spores become dark brown, varying long-ellipsoid, subventricose or subclavate, and in fresh material usually show the gelatinous envelope. The spores of the Rock River and the Virginia collections measure 55–75 × 15–25 μ. Occasionally a branched pedicel is seen. The pedicels are 90 to 120 μ or more in length, about 3 μ in diameter. The fruiting mass, in vertical section, shows at times a slight tendency to form incomplete locules by the pushing up of the basal tissues.

STEGANOSPORIUM PIRIFORME (Hoff.) Corda. — On corticated branches of *Acer rubrum*. The conidia have 5–7 cross-walls, are muriform, and measure 40–50 × 16–19 μ.

HYPHOMYCETES

CERCOSPORA LATHYRI Dearn. & House. — On *Lathyrus maritimus* growing on the sandy beach of Lake Superior. The host plants in this area were attacked severely, showing that this parasite is quite virulent at times.

Oospora poricola Kauff., sp. nov. (see Text Fig. 22). — The fungus forms, in dried condition, pale honey-yellowish, flat or convex, and thin but firm and brittle cushions, which are one millimeter more or less in diam., circular or irregular and sometimes confluent; immersed in water these cushions become mucilaginous-milky from the innumerable conidia; mycelial layer thin; the mycelium is slender, branched, hyaline. Conidia formed in long chains, ellipsoid-ovate to oval or subelliptical, variable in size, one end rounded, the other

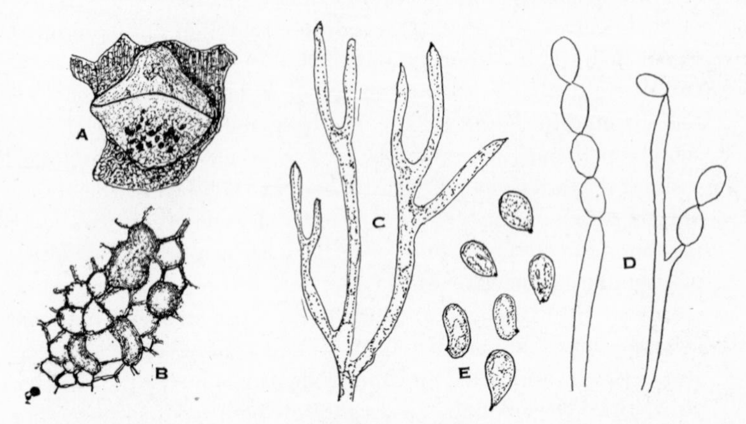

FIG. 22. OOSPORA PORICOLA Kauff., sp. nov. *a*, habit sketch, showing plaques on the pore surface of a polypore; *b*, a few of the pores enlarged, showing the cushions in the pore cavities; *c*, a portion of the spore-bearing mycelium; *d*, conidiophores with spores; *e*, conidiospores

more narrowed and subacute or obtusely pointed, hyaline or with the exospore a delicate tinge of color, 5×3.5 to $8–10 \times 4–5\ \mu$.

On the pore-surface of what is apparently *Trametes sepium*, which has the size and shape of *Fomes scutellatus*, but whitish throughout and abnormal. The Oospora is probably acting in a parasitic manner. The Trametes grew on *Alnus incana*. Type collected by C. H. Kauffman, August 30, 1927, at Rock River (Lake Superior), Michigan.

Whether these small patellate cushions were mistaken and described as a Hypocrea by the early mycologists could not be determined. The species of Hypocrea on Polypori have never been too well known, and a few seem to have been named of which the types are not accessible. *H. ochroleuca* B. & Rav., from its scanty description, might well have been something of the sort described above.

The same species, identical in every respect, is at Albany in the State Museum; Dr. House kindly sent it to me for study. The Polyporus on which it occurs was collected by Dr. House at Osceola, New York, September 21, 1921, on a dead trunk of *Fagus grandifolia*. The polypore host, as in my collection, is somewhat disturbed by the parasite, but not nearly so much so. When collected it had "a strong carrion odor," doubtless due to the fermentation caused by the parasite. The fruit-bodies of the host "formed imbricate masses over 10 feet along the trunk," and the pore-surface of them all show the Oospora cushions. It is my opinion that the host is *Trametes sepium* also.

Ramularia nemapanthae Cke. & Pk. — On *Nemapanthus mucronata*.

Sporotrichum laxum Nees. — On decayed débris under cedar trees.

Tubercularia vulgaris. — On dead branches of *Sambucus racemosus*.

BASIDIOMYCETES

PROTOBASIDIOMYCETES

UREDINALES

Calyptrospora columnare (A. & S.) Kuhn. — On *Vaccinium sp.*

Melampsoropsis Cassandrae (Pk. & Clint.) Arth. — On *Chamaedaphne calyculata*.

Peridermium decolorans Pk. — On *Picea mariana* needles.

Phragmidium occidentale Arth. — On *Rubus parviflorus*. This rust has here followed the host distribution to the eastern limit of the latter.

Uredinopsis mirabilis (Pk.) Magn. — On *Osmunda regalis*.

TREMELLALES

EXIDIA GLANDULOSA Fr. — On dead branches of alder.

HORMOMYCES FRAGIFORMIS. — On old conifer wood.

TREMELLA MESENTERICA Fr. — On rotten wood of poplar.

AUTOBASIDIOMYCETES

EXOBACIDIACEAE

EXOBASIDIUM CASSANDRAE Pk. — On foliage of *Chamaedaphne calyculata.*

AGARICACEAE

ARMILLARIA MELLEA (Vahl.) Sacc. — This occurs not infrequently on the base of trunks of living *Thuja occidentalis* in this region, although it may be seen as usual in various other relations. The fruit-bodies on cedar are in general more fuscous or sooty-fuscous, especially the stems, a color that one finds more often in the plants of the coniferous forests of the Rocky Mountains and the Northwest; these shades of color seem to be correlated with the form or forms definitely parasitic on the coniferous hosts, and are noticeably different from the brighter, yellowish honey-colored plants common in the hard-wood regions of Michigan. Heald (9) has recently given an excellent summary of the essential facts known about this species and its forms.

CANTHERELLUS INFUNDIBULIFORMIS Fr. — On sphagnum or moist places.

CLITOCYBE ECTYPOIDES Pk. — On conifer logs. Murrill (*N. Amer. Flora,* 9: 417) thinks this is *Omphalia chrysophylla* Fr., but the spores of the latter species measure 9–11 × 4–5 μ, and its gills are golden-yellow to egg-yellow. *C. ectypoides* occurs on logs in the conifer regions of northern North America, from coast to coast. Its spores often mature slowly, but when mature measure 6–7 (8) × 4–4.5 μ, a point I have tested in a number of fresh plants in different parts of the country. The gills vary in color from "pinkish-buff" to "honey-yellow" (R.). The pileus when moist is "clay color" to "tawny olive"

(R.) and glabrous — not flocculose as in *O. chrysophylla;* and the stem is solid, not hollow, covered by a dense, detersile whitish pruinosity. Although the stem often has a cartilaginous rind, its toughness seems to indicate that it had better be kept in the genus Clitocybe. It has no odor and the taste is slight. The basidia are 4-spored, and there are no cystidia. In *Agaricaceae of Michigan* I gave the range in size of pileus as 2–5 cm. The Rock River collections showed a range, not infrequently, of 3–8 (9) cm.

CLITOPILUS SUBVILIS Pk. — On the ground in swamps.

Collybia papilliformis Kauff., sp. nov. — PILEUS at first campanulate with more or less pointed papilla, margin incurved, then subexpanded and depressed around the papilla, finally almost plane, 1–2 cm. broad, rather fragile, *hygrophanous,* distinctly striate and creamy-buff with "Dresden-brown" (R.) papilla (moist), fading entirely to pale cream-buff after losing moisture, glabrous; flesh thin. GILLS adnate, at length sinuate, ventricose, *rather broad,* i.e. up to 3 mm. wide, close but not crowded, at first white then tinged incarnate, edge subserrate or eroded. STEM slender, 3–5 cm. long, 1–1.5 mm. thick, equal, hollow, at first subpellucid, pallid, then darker and at length "snuff-brown" (R.), glabrous, innately silky, even, strict when fresh. SPORES elliptic-oval, smooth, hyaline, 5–7 $\times$ 3–4 μ. Cystidia none. Gill-trama parallel. ODOR and TASTE mild, but odor becoming slightly nauseous after collecting.

On and attached to Sphagnum in sphagnous bogs. Type collected by C. H. Kauffman near Ann Arbor, Michigan, July 23, 1923; and again at Rock River (Lake Superior), Michigan, September 9, 1927.

Easily mistaken for a Mycena, this little agaric can be distinguished by its habit on Sphagnum, the spreading pileus at maturity, its darker contrasting papilla when the cap is moist, the fuscescent stem and by its microscopic characters. When dried all parts are some shade of fuscous.

COLLYBIA TUBEROSA Fr. — On humus where agarics had decayed. The color of the tubers was ochraceous-tawny.

COPRINUS RADIATUS Fr. (sense British authors). — On porcupine dung. The dung was brought to Ann Arbor, and the Coprinus developed readily on it. There are at least two conceptions of the fungus that belongs to this name. This plant is not the *C. radiatus* Fr. described in *Agaricaceae of Michigan*, but corresponds to the British conception as handed down in Cooke's Fig. A, Pl. 683, and the description in Rea (*Brit. Basid.*, p. 512). The spores are broadly ellipsoid, obtusely rounded at ends, 7–8.5 × 4.5–5.5 μ, dark purplish brown. It is a delicate little plant about 2–3 cm. high and the pileus has a diameter of 2–3 mm., whitish and minutely pulverulent.

CORTINARIUS ANOMALUS Fr.
CORTINARIUS ARMILLATUS Fr.
CORTINARIUS CINNAMOMEUS Fr.
CORTINARIUS EVERNIUS Fr.
CORTINARIUS FLEXIPES Fr. (minor)
CORTINARIUS GLANDICOLOR Fr.
CORTINARIUS OLIVACEUS Pk.
CORTINARIUS RAPHANOIDES Fr.
CORTINARIUS RIGIDUS Fr.
CORTINARIUS WHITEI Pk.

"ENTOLOMA NIDOROSUM." — This is a Leptonia-like plant, not markedly umbilicate, with a cap 2.5–5 cm. broad and with a strong nitrous odor when picked; the odor soon becomes less noticeable. The stem is somewhat cartilaginous, and might be considered sufficiently so to refer the plant to Leptonia. I know of no species of Leptonia with a nitrous odor. *Entoloma nidorosum* Fr. is as yet a species very vague in the minds of American mycologists and I fear this is true in Europe. I have collected nitrous specimens of Entoloma in Michigan, Wyoming and Oregon. It is, however, difficult to bring these various forms into a single limited species; nor do they, in all necessary characters, fit the Friesian and other European conceptions. Lange (12) gives the spores of *E. nidorosum* Fr. as 7–10 × 7–8 μ, subspheric. The spores of our collection measure 7–8.5 × 6–7 μ, also subglobose.

FLAMMULA GRAVEOLENS Pk. — Although this grew on Sphagnum beds, it appears to belong to this species of Peck. It had the strong odor given for that plant.

GALERA SPICULA Fr. — Not infrequent on mosses in the cedar swamps of the region.

HEBELOMA LONGICAUDUM Fr. (sense Ricken). — Growing among Sphagnum in cedar swamp.

HYGROPHORUS PALLIDUS Pk.
HYGROPHORUS PUNICEUS Fr.
HYGROPHORUS SPECIOSUS Fr.
LACTARIUS OCULATUS (Pk.) Burl.
LACTARIUS THEIOGALUS Fr.
LACTARIUS VIETUS Fr.

MARASMIUS ANDROSACEUS Fr. — On the bark and wood of dead branches of *Thuja occidentalis.* Also frequent on débris of other trees.

MARASMIUS SP. — This also occurred on fallen branchlets of Thuja. It differs from *M. thujinus* by its blackish stem and the attachment of the gills by a collar; from *M. filopes* Pk. by its blackish stem and from *M. minutus* Pk. by the collar. The gills are broad, distant, and attached by a collar. This is an undescribed species, but opportunity did not offer to study the fresh plant in detail. It is one of the minute species.

MARASMIUS THUJINUS Pk. — This species seems to have been reported but once (see *Bull. N. Y. State Mus.*, 67: 26. 1903). The spore-size was not given by Dr. Peck; this has been supplied by Pennington (*N. Amer. Flora*, 9: 281). Our plants had smooth, hyaline spores, lachrymoid in shape, pointed at one end, measuring 6–7 (8) × 3.5–4 μ. Cystidia none. The gill-trama is composed of slender parallel hyphae, 2.5–3 μ in diameter. Basidia 4-spored, about 22 × 5 μ; sterigmata very short. The trama of the pileus is differentiated into two layers, the inner composed of subgelatinous hyaline hyphae; the outer layer is dark brown, about 40 μ thick, and composed of very narrow, closely packed brown hyphae which are mixed with an amorphous substance. It would be interesting to determine which of these elements provides the reviving ability of the cap. The pileus and stem have a faint lilaceous tint. The stem is a very thin thread, 2–3 cm. long, inserted, glabrous or with scattered minute floccules, pallid except for the tint of lilac.

NAUCORIA MELINOIDES Fr.-Ricken. — On boggy black soil, near Sphagnum.

NOLANEA CAELESTINA Fr.-Lange. — Among Sphagnum in swamps. The spores are subglobose, sharply angled, 7–7.5 μ (inclusive of apiculus, 8–9 μ). Basidia 4-spored.

PANUS STIPTICUS Fr. — On conifer log.

PHOLIOTA SQUARRUSOIDES Pk. — On stump of birch.

PLEUROTUS PORRIGENS Fr. — On cedar log.

PLEUROTUS SEROTINUS Fr. — On dead trunk of *Betula lutea*.

PLICATURA FAGINEA (Schroet.) Karst. = *Trogia crispa*. — On branches of *Alnus incana* and *Betula lutea*.

PLUTEOLUS RETICULATUS Fr. — On conifer log.

PLUTEUS LEONINUS Fr. — On log.

PLUTEUS PELLITUS Fr. — On birch log.

TRICHOLOMA FUMOSILUTEUM Pk. — Among mosses, in cedar swamp.

TUBARIA FURFURACEA Fr. — On Sphagnum.

BOLETACEAE

BOLETINUS PALUSTER Pk. — In cedar swamps, always on very rotten wood remnants mixed with humus. This was quite fully described by Dr. Peck as *Boletus paluster* (*23rd Rep. of the N. Y. State Cabinet*, p. 132), later changed to Boletinus by him. It is said to grow among mosses, which are often the apparent substratum, but on close examination the plants are really attached to very decayed wood, which may be covered with moss. The color of the pileus is "rose dorée" to "Jasper red" (R.), the colored floccose-tomentose surface usually breaking up into appressed hairy scales. The flesh is yellowish-white in the pileus, golden-yellow in the stem. The tubes are large, angular and compound, 1–2 mm. in radial width, the main dissepiments somewhat gill-like, but forming deep subrectangular pockets. The stem is yellow above, clothed by a dark rose-red, subfloccose covering elsewhere. The spores measure 6–7 × 3–3.5 μ, tinged pinkish-yellowish under the microscope. No cystidia were found. It has been reported from Ontario to New Jersey. This is our first collection in Michigan.

BOLETINUS PICTUS Pk. — Frequent in sphagnous swamps.

CLAVARIACEAE

CLAVARIA PULCHRA Pk. — On moist ground.

PISTILLARIA PUSILLA Fr.-Pat. — Among the species of Pistillaria described with microscopic data, our plants are nearest to *P. pusilla* sense Patouillard (*Tab. Analyt.*, p. 23, Fig. 49). CLAVULAE 3–4 mm. high, with a distinct but slender sterile stipe extending about one third to one fourth of the whole length, fertile portion subcylindrical, 300–400 μ in diameter, obtuse or sub-acute; whole plant white and fleshy, *without a sclerotium*. SPORES hyaline, oval or subglobose, 3–3.5 μ; basidia sub-clavate, with 1, 2, 3 or 4 sterigmata and as many spores respectively, 18–20 × 3.5–4 μ.

Among débris composed of decaying leaves, etc., of Thuja, Alnus and Sphagnum, in cedar swamp.

The height of our plants was double that given by Patouillard (15), and the basidia are not by any means uniformly 4-spored, as given in his description.

Pistillaria thujicola Kauff., sp. nov. — FRUCTIFICATION 8–10 mm. tall, slender, about 0.5 mm. in thickness, pure white throughout, entirely fertile except that sometimes the minute tips are sterile, simple or forked dichotomously once or twice, slightly bulbillose at base and attached by radiating white hairs, branchlets when present acuminate-pointed, naked. SPORES oval-subglobose, minute, hyaline, 3–4 μ in diameter; basidia 2-spored, rarely 3-spored, subclavate, about 20–22 × 4–5 μ.

On inner side of loose bark of *Thuja occidentalis*. Type collected by C. H. Kauffman at Rock River (Lake Superior), Michigan, September 8, 1927.

The white color is retained after the plants are dried. The texture is fleshy, composed of parallel-lying hyphae, but not fragile. The hymenium in some mounts showed the presence of what appeared to be a parasite, forming cylindrical conidiophores intermixed with the basidia and bearing single Sepedonium-like, echinulate, rust-colored globose spores, 7–8 μ in diameter.

Hydnaceae

Asterodon ferruginosum (Karst.) Pat. — On decaying bark of *Betula lutea*.

Odontia barba-Jovis (With.) Fr. — On decorticated rotten log of *Thuja occidentalis*. This is thinly effused over a considerable area, white to "ivory yellow" (R.), the fertile portions becoming "cream color," subseparable, soft and flocculose. The spores are broadly elliptic-oval, hyaline, smooth, 6–8 × 4–5.5 μ, uniguttate. It agrees very well with the species as understood by Bourdot and Galzin.

Phlebia strigoso-zonata (Schw.) Lloyd. — On *Prunus pennsylvanica*. This is not infrequent on poplar in Michigan, but rare on other hosts. Burt says it has been reported also on beech and oak.

Thelephoraceae

Coniophora avellanea Burt. — On decorticated wood of *Thuja occidentalis*. The vinaceous-tinged, almost purplish color is unique; according to Ridgway, almost "Natal brown." The sterigmata are long and curved.

Corticium livido-caeruleum Karst. — On decorticated wood of *Thuja occidentalis*. It is lead-gray to slate-gray and is often found in the immature condition. Burt says it occurs on the "under side of coniferous rails, boards and shingles"; I have seen it mostly on coniferous logs in the forest, where it develops under rather restricted conditions of moisture, state of decay of the wood, and probably proper light conditions. It occurs throughout Europe and North America in conifer forests. I have it to the Pacific Coast, on various conifers. It is far from common.

Corticium roseum Fr. — On bark of dead branches of *Alnus incana* and other hardwoods. Frequent.

Corticium sociatum Burt. — On bark of *Thuja occidentalis* on which it forms numerous gregarious white patches up to a centimeter in length and half the width.

CORTICIUM SULPHUREUM Fr. — On very decayed pieces of *Thuja occidentalis*, where it forms yellow interweaving oözonium-like growths, interspersed with rhizomorphs. Only small fructifications were obtained and these were sterile. This seems to be frequent in very rotten conifer logs, but the determination must remain uncertain.

HYMENOCHAETE FULIGINOSA (Pers.) Bres. — On bark of *Thuja occidentalis* and on wood of *Alnus incana*.

HYMENOCHAETE SPRETA Pk. — On bark and wood of *Prunus sp.* The color has a marked reddish tinge, about that of "Kaiser brown" (R.). The spores measure $4 \times 2.5\ \mu$.

HYMENOCHAETE TABACINA Lév. — Common and variable, on a number of hardwood hosts.

HYPOCHNUS FUSCUS Fr. — On rotten decorticated wood of *Alnus incana*.

HYPOCHNUS SPONGIOSUS (Schw.) Burt. — On decayed wood of *Thuja occidentalis*.

HYPOCHNUS ZYGODESMOIDES (Ell.) Burt. — On very rotten wood of *Thuja occidentalis*.

PENIOPHORA CINEREA (Pers.) Cke. — On Acer, Amelanchier, Prunus, etc. Common.

PENIOPHORA GLOBULOSA Bres. — On bark or between the loose bark and wood of dead *Betula lutea*, often starting at the lenticels. Our specimens were whitish with creamy or pinkish-buff shades. By following the remarks of Burt (*Ann. Missouri Bot. Gard.*, Vol. 12, p. 282), one can easily recognize this species because of the peculiar structure of the cystidia.

PENIOPHORA VELUTINA (DC.) Cke. — Inside of loose bark of *Alnus incana*.

SOLENIA ANOMALA (Pers.) F'k'l. — On *Betula lutea*. Widely distributed and frequent in North America. Apparently our only brown Solenia.

STEREUM ABIETINUM Fr. — This rather rare species was found on a conifer log. The glaucous surface is distinctive and accounts for the name *S. glaucescens* Fr., which Burt considers a synonym.

STEREUM FASCIATUM Schw. — On fallen branches of *Populus grandidentata*.

STEREUM HIRSUTUM Fr. — Common on *Alnus incana*. Although not by any means limited to the genus Alnus, it is the field experience of the writer that it is far more often found on species of this genus throughout the coniferous regions of the North, in the Rocky Mountains and the Northwest. It is quite uncommon in the southern part of Michigan.

STEREUM RADIATUM Pk. — On charred log of *Thuja occidentalis*. It also occurs on *Larix laricina* about Ann Arbor. It is reported only on hemlock, spruce and pine by Burt. Easily recognized by the rich "Sudan brown" (R.) color, resupinate habit, and the shallow obtuse ridges on the surface. It may be considerably cracked in age on the hymenial surface.

STEREUM RUGOSUM Fr. — On *Populus tremuloides*.

STEREUM RUFUM Fr. — Common on dead poplar branches.

STEREUM SULCATUM Burt. — On a log of *Pinus Strobus*. This is one of four species easily confused by their superficial similarity: *S. Chailettii* Pers.-Fr. and *S. sulcatum* occur on conifers only, and are easily separable from each other by the character of their cystidia; those of *S. Chailettii* are twice as long and are slender, while *S. sulcatum* has short stubby cystidia. The other two species, *S. rugosum* Fr. and *S. Murrayi* (B. & C.) Burt, occur only on hardwoods. The latter has very many and easily noticeable rounded vesicular bodies in its hymenium; the former has dark rusty brown but small organs, like elongated basidia, in its hymenium, and bleeds in the fresh condition. All these are some shade of sordid whitish on the hymenial surface, tinged with slight pinkish or drab shades which vary with the age and environmental conditions during growth.

POLYPORACEAE

MERULIEAE

MERULIUS NIVEUS Fr. — On the bark of dead branches of *Alnus incana*.

MERULIUS TREMULOSUS Fr. — On top of a birch stump, intergrown with an old Polystictus; also on cedar wood.

Polyporeae

Poria candidissima (Schw.) Cke. — On rotten bark of *Abies balsamea* and on a large old fruit-body of *Fomes fomentarius* whose pore-surface it nearly covered. The spores of the plant on *Abies* are echinulate, 2–3 × 2–3 μ, clamp connections present; on *Fomes fomentarius*, 3–4 × 2–3 μ.

Poria crassa Karst. (?). — On stump of *Pinus Strobus*. No basidiospores could be found. It has, however, the other characters of that species. Though Karsten has referred thick specimens of *Poria xanthus* to *P. crassa*, the latter, as has been suggested by Romell, may be a distinct species. This specimen is sterile and so it is impossible definitely to refer this plant to this name.

Poria ferrea Pers.–Romell. — A stratose form on *Populus tremuloides;* also on old partially rotten branches of *Acer rubrum* and of *Acer spicatum*. Spores hyaline, oblong, 5–6 × 2.5 μ. On Acer, 4–6 × 1.5–2 μ.

Poria ferruginosa Fr. — Forming extensive patches on the bark of fallen branches and dead trunks of *Thuja occidentalis* and of *Betula lutea* in moist places; also on old bark of *Alnus incana* and decorticated wood of spruce (*Picea nigra?*). Spores 5–6 × 3 μ.

Poria lenis Karst. — On rotten decorticated wood of *Thuja occidentalis* and *Pinus resinosa*. Spores allantoid 4–5 × 0.7–1 μ.

Poria prunicola Murr. — At length forming thick stratose crusts on the bark of dead standing trunks of *Prunus serotina* and *Alnus incana*, the very young suborbicular fructifications usually starting at the lenticels. The affinities of this plant are with *Poria laevigata* Fr. and *P. betulina* Murr. Spores, hyaline, 4–5 × 3–4 μ. Cystidia rare. Pore mouths 4–6 per mm. Tubes whitish-stuffed.

Poria rufa Fr. — On coniferous wood.

Poria sinuosa Fr. — On old decaying bark of *Abies balsamea*. This is a soft floccose white plant when in good growing condition, with large alveolate pores, and easily becomes dingy or dirty brownish when handled, although the white color of the subiculum can be retained by careful drying. Old fructifications, near which the new growth may arise, are dirty dark brown.

PORIA SPISSA (Schw.) Cke. — On very rotten pine log. This is another large-pored species. The fructification was old and rather soft, apparently attacked by insects. The large tubes become agglutinated on drying so as to appear smaller. The color of the tubes in this condition approached "Pompeian red" (R.), although the dark yellow shades still persisted.

PORIA SUBACIDA Pk. — Only two collections of this variable and common Poria were made, one on *Pinus Strobus* and one on *Betula lutea*.

PORIA SUBFUSCOFLAVIDA Fr. — On decayed wood of *Thuja occidentalis*. At first "vinaceous-drab" (R.) with white margin, becoming cinereous. See Baxter's (1) paper in this volume.

PORIA UNDATA (Pers.) Bres. — On under side of log of *Betula lutea*. Basidia 4-spored. Spores 3–5 × 3–4 μ. This is resupinate, in which condition Lloyd says it is usually found; also known as a Polyporus.

PORIA VAPORARIA Fr. sense Romell. — On cut wood of *Thuja occidentalis*. Spores 6–7 × 2.5–3 μ.

PORIA VULGARIS Fr. var. CALCEA Romell. — On charred stump of *Pinus Strobus*. Spores ellipsoidal, 4 × 1 μ.

POROTHELIUM FIMBRIATUM Fr. — On old bark of *Betula lutea* and *B. alba*.

POLYSTICTUS ABIETINUS Fr. — As usual, common on bark of dead, standing and fallen trunks of *Abies balsamea;* also on other conifers.

POLYSTICTUS CINNAMOMEUS Fr. — On the ground, in mixed conifer forest.

POLYSTICTUS VELUTINUS Fr. — On old logs of *Betula lutea* and *Alnus incana*. This species goes generally unrecognized in this country. I do not find it in *North American Flora*. Overholts (*The Polyporaceae*) says he is not acquainted with it. Lloyd (*Mycological Notes*, letter no. 52) says he believes it to be the same as *P. pubescens;* elsewhere he says *P. Bar-*

tholemaei Pk. is *P. velutinus.* The description of Peck does not, however, fit the Friesian description, nor does it fit our plants. I think Peck probably had the correct view of *P. velutinus* Fr., as shown by his naming of one of my early collections from northern Michigan, of which I still have a part, and which is the same plant as those collected on this trip. Whenever I have been in the northern part of the state I have obtained this species and at first it is always confusing. One thinks immediately of *P. pubescens*, but closer examination invariably leaves one in doubt.

The fructification is decidedly thinner in well-developed and abundant material than in *P. pubescens*, the tubes are shorter, the pileus less pubescent, and other details are disturbing also. We were fortunate in getting spore-bearing material this time, and the spores are found to differ also from *P. pubescens*. They are oblong-elliptical, hyaline, smooth, and measure 5–6 × 2.5–3 μ. Cystidia none. This agrees with the description given by Rea (*Basidiomycetae*), as does every other item, and also with the Friesian description (*Hymen. Europ.*). All my former collections have turned dingy fulvous-lutescent in the herbarium. This change occurs also in nature and quite soon, depending on the weather; the tubes show the lutescent characteristic first. This color change, of course, is similar to that which occurs in *P. pubescens*. Fries placed *P. pubescens* in what we now call Polyporus, and *P. velutinus* in his section corresponding to Polystictus. This is as it should be. By doing so he recognized the more relative thickness of the pileus and the relatively longer tubes in *P. pubescens*, even though he called the latter "short" (for a Polyporus). I feel quite confident that the two species are autonomous. It does not seem to have a southern distribution, although it may follow the mountains.

When in good growing condition it is a whitish plant throughout ("albus" of Fries) and is corky-coriaceous, but becomes dingy lutescent and rigid when dry or in age. The pileus is gregarious or subimbricate, sessile, nearly plane, more or less dimidiate, 2–3 cm. wide radially, minutely pubescent, with one or few unicolorous zones separated by a slight furrow at times, becoming radially rugose or lined when dry, with a thin extended margin which is usually incurved when dry. The thickness varies but it is thicker behind, 2–3 (4) mm., tapering regularly to the very thin margin. Sometimes it is cuneately attached, sometimes by a broader base and often with a slight resupinate extension which may even bear tubes. The pores are round to subangular, with a slight sheen, about 4 per mm., but often larger by the breaking down of the thin dissepiments. The tubes are 1–3 mm. long, at first whitish but soon tinged. Rather frequent in the coniferous regions of northern Michigan.

POLYPORUS ALBELLUS Pk. — On corticated logs and fallen branches of *Prunus serotina*, *Betula lutea* and *Betula alba papyrifera*. There seems to be a considerable number of reasons why this has nothing to do with "*P. chioneus*" Authors, one of them being that the latter, a European species, is vaguely understood in Europe itself.

POLYPORUS BETULINUS Fr. — Common on birch.

POLYPORUS BOREALIS Fr. — On the stump of a recently cut spruce tree.

POLYPORUS BRUMALIS Fr. — On bark of a log of *Betula lutea*.

POLYPORUS ELEGANS Fr. — On rotten wood.

POLYPORUS GLOMERATUS Pk. — On the decorticated wood of a dead standing trunk of *Betula lutea*, developing at first under the bark, which is later pushed off.

POLYPORUS GUTTULATUS Pk. — On a pine log.

POLYPORUS LUCIDUS Fr. — On hemlock stumps and logs.

POLYPORUS OSSEUS Kalchbr. — On a stump of *Pinus Strobus*, and at the base of a living large trunk of *Pinus resinosa*. I have it also from Colorado where it grew at the base of a trunk of *Picea Engelmanni;* and from the Olympic Mountains in Washington, growing about 5 feet from the ground on a dead conifer trunk. It was reported by Kalchbrenner on Larix. It is clearly one of the species attacking conifer trees, and from all the conditions observed in the case mentioned above, it may be considered a parasite of the type producing butt rots of pine and other conifers. The fruiting bodies are collected rather rarely.

The pilei are frequently intergrown ("concrescent" per Fries) or, as was the case in several specimens of the present lot, the eccentric or lateral stipes may fork or are confluent. The horny glabrous pileus in the dry condition is characteristic. The color of the pileus is whitish-buff, but when dry is brownish-buff, about the color of manila paper and unicolorous. The thin margin becomes irregularly inrolled and crisped. The color of the short tubes varies from "light buff" to "warm buff" (R.). The tubes are about 1 mm. long. The pores have a resinous luster, are small, about 4–5 per mm., angular, the dissepiment thin and lacerate-fimbriate under a lens. The spores in one of the Rock River collections and in the Washington collection were alike. They are cylindrical, straight, hyaline, smooth, and measure 4–5.5 (6) $\times$ 1.5 μ. The basidia are 4-spored, small, about 15 $\times$ 3 μ. Cystidia of any notable type are lacking, although sometimes there are paraphyses-like outgrowths in the hymenium; these, however, may be secondary outgrowths.

Rea (18) gives the spores of what he includes as this species, subglobose, 4–5 μ in diameter. If the plant originally described from Hungary by Kalchbrenner has globose spores, then our American plant is probably unnamed.

POLYPORUS PICIPES Fr. — On decayed wood.

POLYPORUS RADIATUS Fr. — On corticated but rotten limbs of *Betula lutea*, lying on the ground.

POLYPORUS RESINOSUS Fr. (*P. benzoinus*, sense Lloyd). — On dead pine trunk.

POLYPORUS URSINUS Lloyd. — On conifer log.

FOMES CONCHATUS Fr. — On old log of some frondose tree, probably Fraxinus.

FOMES FOMENTARIUS Fr. — Common. On *Betula lutea* and *Betula alba papyrifera;* also on *Alnus incana*.

FOMES IGNIARIUS Fr. — On living trunks of *Fagus grandifolia;* also on *Alnus incana* (*teste* Swartz).

FOMES NIGRICANS Fr. — On living trunk of *Betula alba* and on dead trunks and logs of *Betula lutea;* also on *Alnus incana.* Sometimes the habit of the fruit-body is semiresupinate.

FOMES PINICOLA Fr. — Common on conifers.

FOMES ROSEUS (A. & S.) Cke. — On charred stump of *Pinus Strobus.*

FOMES SCUTELLATA (Schw.) Cke. — On dead trunks and branches of *Alnus incana.* Coker (4) has recently shown that this belongs to the section Ganoderma.

DAEDALEA CONFRAGOSA Fr. — The lamelloid form; on birch.

DAEDALEA UNICOLOR Fr. — On bark of dead maple.

IRPEX TULIPIFERA Schw. — On dead limbs of *Prunus serotina.*

TRAMETES CARNEA Nees. — On logs of *Pinus Strobus, Picea nigra* and *Thuja occidentalis.*

TRAMETES MOLLIS Fr. — On *Betula alba papyrifera.* Lloyd (*Mycol. Notes*) says "it is *T. mollis* of European authors, but the name has no application to it, and it is antedated by Persoon's name: *Trametes cervinus* Pers. It is really a Daedalea."

TRAMETES PINI Fr. and var. ABIETINA Pk. — On conifers.

TRAMETES SEPIUM Berk. — Several times this was found on decayed logs of *Thuja occidentalis.* Its colors are not generally made clear in descriptions. When young and growing it is white and spores are readily found. In age or after wintering it is sepia or fuscous, as the name implies. Frequently the new white growth appears with old portions either on the periphery or on the tube surface. The spores in fresh material are oblong, hyaline, smooth, 7–8 × 2.5 (3) μ; the basidia are 4-spored. The odor is slight.

UNIVERSITY OF MICHIGAN

LITERATURE CITED

1. Baxter, D. V. 1929. Some Porias from the Region of the Lake States II. Papers Mich. Acad. Sci., Arts and Letters, 9 : 39–46.

2. Boudier, Émile. 1905–10. Icones Mycologicae, 2 : Plate 404.

3. Burt, E. A. 1925. The Thelephoraceae of North America XIV. Ann. Mo. Bot. Gard., 12 : 213–357.

4. Coker, W. C. 1927. New or Noteworthy Basidiomycetes. Journ. Elisha Mitchell Sci. Soc., 43 : 129–144.

5. Dodge, B. O. 1914. Wisconsin Discomycetes. Trans. Wis. Acad. Sci. Arts and Letters, 17 : 1027–1056.

6. Durand, Elias J. 1902. Studies in North American Discomycetes II. Torr. Bot. Club Bull., 29 : 458–465.

7. —— 1908. The Geoglossaceae of North America. Ann. Mycol., 6 : 387–477.

8. Ellis, J. B., and Everhart, B. M. 1892. The North American Pyrenomycetes. Newfield, New Jersey.

9. Heald, F. D. 1926. Manual of Plant Diseases. New York.

10. Kauffman, C. H. 1918. The Agaricaceae of Michigan. Lansing, Michigan.

11. Kupfer, Elsie M. 1902. Studies on Urnula and Geopyxis. Torr. Bot. Club Bull., 29 : 137–144.

12. Lange, Jacob E. 1921. Studies in the Agarics of Denmark. Part IV : 23–41.

13. Macbride, Thomas H. 1899. The North American Slime Moulds. New York.

14. Overholts, L. O. 1915. The Polyporaceae of the Middle-Western United States. Washington University Studies, 3 : 3–96.

15. Patouillard, N. 1883. Tabulae Analyticae Fungorum. Poligny, France.

16. Pennington, L. H. Marasmius. North American Flora, 9 : 250–286.

17. Povah, A. H. 1929. Some Non-vascular Cryptogams from Vermilion, Chippewa County, Michigan. Papers Mich. Acad. Sci., Arts and Letters, 9 : 253–272.

18. Rea, Carlton. 1922. British Basidiomycetae. Cambridge, England.

19. Rehm, H. 1896. Die Pilze Deutschlands, Oesterreichs und der Schweiz. III Ascomyceten. Rabenhorst's Kryptogamen-Flora. Leipzig.

20. Seaver, Fred J. 1909. Discomycetes of North Dakota. Mycologia, 1 : 104–114.

21. Seaver, Fred J. 1914. A Preliminary Study of the Genus Lamprospora. Mycologia, 6 : 5–24.

22. Wehmeyer, L. E. 1926. Cultural Life Histories of Melanconis and Pseudovalsa. Mycologia, 18 : 257–272.

23. Winter, Geo. 1887. Die Pilze Deutschlands, Oesterreichs und der Schweiz. II Ascomyceten. Rabenhorst's Kryptogamen-Flora. Leipzig.

24. Zeller, S. M. 1922. Contributions to Our Knowledge of Oregon Fungi I. Mycologia, 14 : 173–199.

25. —— 1927. Ibid., II. Mycologia, 19 : 130–143.

SAND DUNE PLANTS OF KALAMAZOO COUNTY, MICHIGAN

LESLIE A. KENOYER

KALAMAZOO COUNTY lies in southwestern Michigan, thirty miles east of the Lake Michigan shore. As it is in the Kalamazoo morainic and outwash system, it contains a multitude of small lakes. About thirty-six of these equal or exceed one-half mile in length. The largest one, Gull Lake, is about five miles long and more than a mile wide. An interesting and varied flora is found about these lakes. The principal lines of vegetational succession are those characteristic of the peat bog and of the marl bog. One lake may be bordered by a shrub zone of *Potentilla fruticosa*, *Rhamnus alnifolia* and *Betula pumila*, accompanied by typical marl herbs, and give an alkaline reaction, while another lake in the same group has a zone of *Chamaedaphne calyculata*, *Vaccinium corymbosum* and *Sphagnum spp.*, and gives a strongly acid reaction. *Sarracenia purpurea* is found in both types, but the specimens of the peat are more thrifty than those of the marl. Some event, no doubt, in the early organic successional history of the lake determines which of these courses its development shall take.

On noting ridges of wind-blown sand along the shores of some of these lakes, I undertook to investigate the extent of their occurrence. In this region of prevailing "westerlies," the best developed dunes along the shores of the great lakes are on the east, where the sand washed up by the waves is most likely to be carried shoreward by the wind. I. D. Scott, in *Inland Lakes of Michigan*, mentions dunes only in connection with Black Lake and Douglas Lake among the small lakes, disregarding those which, like Crystal Lake, are lagoons cut off from the great lakes. In the former case the dunes are on top of an old terrace off the north shore; in the latter they are at the east end of the lake. The only dunes developed along the lakes of Kalamazoo County are along the east shore.

The best of these dunes is along the shore of Austin Lake, which, next to Gull Lake, is the largest in the county. This lake is two and one-half miles long and a little more than a mile wide. Dune conditions are found along all the east shore. For most of this length, the sand ridge is about six feet high and fifty feet back from the lake border. At the southeast portion is a splendid dune twenty feet high and one-fourth mile long, composed of pure white sand. Scott refers to a lack of shore adjustment in this lake due to the shallowness of the water, but the rounded contour of the leeward shore similar to that so frequent on the Great Lakes suggests to me a considerable adjustment.

The plants on the Austin dune are largely characteristic dune forms, including *Arctostaphylos uva-ursi* (found on the Lake Michigan dunes fifty miles distant, but not, I believe, elsewhere in Kalamazoo County), *Arabis lyrata, Solidago speciosa angustata, Selaginella rupestris* in a few small disappearing clumps, *Gaylussacia baccata, Vaccinium pennsylvanicum, Festuca octoflora, Artimesia caudata, Achillea millefolium, Tephrosia virginiana, Lespedeza hirta, Pteris aquilina, Lechea Leggettii* (a rare form for this region), *Helianthemum canadense, Poa compressa, Liatris scariosa, Polytrichum commune, Polytrichum juniperinum*, Leucobryum, Cladonia. That the dune is rather old is shown by the presence of trees of *Quercus velutina* up to forty years of age.

The dunes of next importance are those of Eagle Lake in Texas Township. Here is a ridge about ten feet high on which are found several of the more common sand plants, such as *Populus deltoides, Calamovilfa longifolia* (for which this is the only locality noted in the county), *Juncus balticus* and *Linaria canadensis* (see Pl. XLI, Fig. 1).

On the dunes of Pretty Lake, which extend for about half a mile along the east shore, and reach a height of six feet, are *Populus deltoides, Juncus balticus, glaucophylla* and *Salix longifolia.*

Other lakes having dunes are Bass, Harrison and West. West Lake has been cut off from Austin Lake by a wave-formed sand

PLATE XLI

Fig. 1. Dune on east shore of Eagle Lake. *Populus deltoides, Juncus balticus* and *Calamovilfa longifolia* are seen from left to right in the foreground. *Quercus velutina* occupies the background

Fig. 2. Dune front advancing over a swamp west of Rupert Lake, Alamo Township. *Ulmus americana*, *Benzoin aestivale* and *Sambucus canadensis* are being surrounded

PLATE XLII

Fig. 1. Dune complex near Cooper Center. Foreground is stabilized by *Poa compressa, Poa trivialis* (?) and *Agrostis alba*. In background there is an extensive blow-out

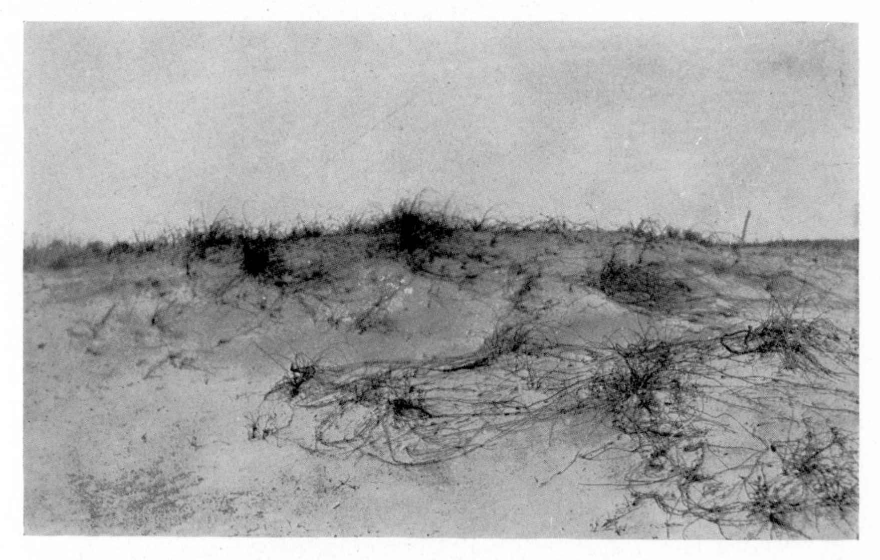

Fig. 2. Dune in Alamo Township. *Rubus villosus* is shown as a sand-binder

bar. Pickerel Lake and White's Lake also have slightly more sand accumulated on the east shore, and support some typical sand plants.

Of the lakes of the county which are at least one-half mile in diameter, about 20 per cent have sandy eastern shores with more or less developed dunes. The nature of the underlying soil, the contour of the shore, and the extent of shore adjustment are doubtless determining factors in dune formation. The vegetation of these dunes, while less varied than that of the Lake Michigan dunes, includes some of the same plants.

There are in the county several areas away from the lakes where glacial outwash sand has been left near the surface to be displaced by the prevailing westerly winds, forming typical dunes. These dunes may be ten to twenty feet in height, and in places give evidence of fairly rapid movement (see Pl. XLI, Fig. 2). The writer visited one such area in Cooper Township, four in Alamo Township, several along the west line of the county in Oshtemo and Texas townships and one near West Lake in Portage Township. Beginning at the last locality is a prominent line of sand ridges one-fourth mile wide extending westward for about six miles into Texas Township. In these areas *Agrostis alba*, *Poa pratensis*, *Poa compressa*, *Poa trivialis*, and *Cenchrus carolinianus* serve the rôle of sand-binding grasses (see Pl. XLII, Fig. 1). The principal tree is *Sassafras variifolium*. The shrubs are *Rhus typhina* and *Rubus villosus*, the latter assuming some importance as a sand binder (see Pl. XLII, Fig. 2). The more frequent herbs are *Asclepias syriaca*, *Asclepias amplexicaulis*, *Oenothera biennis*, *Krigia virginica*, *Linaria canadensis*, *Solanum carolinianum* and *Verbascum Thapsus*.

Western State Teachers College
Kalamazoo, Michigan

MEIOSIS IN *OENOTHERA FRANCISCANA**

CHANDRAKANT G. KULKARNI

OENOTHERA FRANCISCANA Bartlett (1) bred true to type for nine generations in the cultures of Davis and did not give in its progeny any mutations or variations (5). Since the tenth generation, however, this species has been giving in its progeny from selfed seed certain types of variants. Nearly half a dozen of these have arisen in *franciscana* cultures, which have not yet been reported upon by Professor Davis. Davis (5) has observed triploid plants in the F_2 generation of the cross *Oe. franciscana* × *Oe. biennis*, and one of the new variants of pure *Oe. franciscana* is very similar to these. Another type has been found to be a haploid.[1]

Although the history of the reduction divisions in the pollen mother cells of *Oe. franciscana* has been worked out thoroughly by Cleland (4), the writer decided to make a study of meiosis again to see whether the chromosome behavior during this critical period would throw any light on the origin of variants from self-pollinated seed.

The material on which these observations are based was collected in the cultures of Professor Bradley M. Davis [2] at the Botanical Garden, University of Michigan. The methods employed in fixing, dehydrating, embedding, cutting and staining were the same as those used in other work recently reported.

The descriptions of the early prophase stages of the hetero-

* Paper from the Department of Botany, University of Michigan, No. 291.

[1] A detailed history of the meiosis in the pollen mother cells of this plant and its genetic relations to the parent species will be published very soon elsewhere, by Bradley M. Davis and Chandrakant G. Kulkarni.

[2] The writer is grateful to Dr. Davis for allowing him to collect the material from his cultures.

typic division conform generally to the account of these stages given by Cleland (4). In the later stages of second contraction Cleland (4) finds a closed chain of four chromosomes to which are linked two two-linked chains; each link is made up of a pair of chromosomes. These links separate from the chain of four into bivalent pairs in later stages of second contraction. During diakinesis he observes a closed chain of four chromosomes and five pairs in his preparations (Fig. 28). "The circle of four, however, does not break up in diakinesis, but remains until the disappearance of the nuclear membrane, and even later, being often seen during the formation of the equatorial plate and occasionally at metaphase (Fig. 29)." All my preparations show a closed chain of four chromosomes during second contraction (Figs. 1, 3 and 4), to which are linked ring-shaped pairs of bivalent chromosomes (Fig. 1). These observations are quite in agreement with the observations of Cleland. The chain of four chromosomes, however, breaks into two pairs at diakinesis before the nuclear membrane disappears (Figs. 5–6). None of my preparations showed a closed chain of four at the equatorial plate or at metaphase. All my preparations showed seven pairs of chromosomes at diakinesis and metaphase. Heterotypic metaphases are normal in most cases.

Non-disjunction phenomena occur rarely during the heterotypic anaphase, in the nuclei of some pollen mother cells. This would result in six chromosomes passing to one pole and eight to the other (Figs. 7–9), instead of seven to each. A lengthwise split appears in the chromosomes during the late telophase, but it does not become conspicuous until late in the interkinesis (Fig. 10). The homoeotypic divisions are regular and occur simultaneously. The segmentation of the protoplasm to form four spores is effected by vacuolization and furrowing. This process is quite similar to that described in great detail for *Oenothera pratincola* (7). The method of the formation of pollen grains in this species also resembles that of *Oe. pratincola* (7). Most of the pollen grains have three discs ("interstitial bodies") but occasionally a pollen grain with four of these is found (Fig. 11).

Although the exact nature of only one of the sports of *Oenothera franciscana* has been determined, namely, the haploid "pointed tips," it is likely that some, at least, of the remaining ones will belong to the set of seven or more possible non-disjunctional types, several of which are known for *Oe. Lamarckiana* and which presumably may be established for all the mutating Oenotherae. The non-disjunctional types, one (or possibly two) triploids and a tetraploid, are what may logically be expected to turn up sooner or later in every species. It is noteworthy that the only plant genus besides Oenothera which has yielded a set of non-disjunctional types is Datura (2), which has been parallel to Oenothera in giving one of the two other known haploid types (3). A haploid plant from a hybrid has been observed by Gaines and Aase (6) in Triticum.

University of Michigan

LITERATURE CITED

1. Bartlett, H. H. 1914. *Oe. franciscana* and *Oe. venusta* spp. novv. Rhodora, 16 : 33–37.
2. Blakeslee, Albert F., Belling, John, and Farnham, M. E. 1920. Chromosomal Duplication and Mendelian Phenomena in Datura Mutants. Science, 52 : 388–390.
3. Blakeslee, Albert F., Belling, John, Farnham, M. E., and Bergner, A. Dorothy. 1922. A Haploid Mutant in the Jimson Weed. Science, 55 : 646–647.
4. Cleland, R. E. 1922. Reduction Divisions in the Pollen Mother Cells of *Oe. franciscana*. Am. Journ. Bot., 9 : 391–413.
5. Davis, Bradley Moore. 1916. The Hybrids of *Oenothera biennis* and *Oenothera franciscana* in the First and Second Generations. Genetics, 1 : 197–251.
6. Gaines, E. F., and Aase, Hannah C. 1926. A Haploid Wheat Plant. Am. Journ. Bot., 13 : 373–385.
7. Kulkarni, Chandrakant G. Meiosis in the Pollen Mother Cells of Some Strains of *Oenothera pratincola* Bartlett. Bot. Gaz. (*In press.*)

EXPLANATION OF PLATE XLIII

All figures except Figure 9 were drawn with the aid of an Abbé camera lucida, under a Zeiss microcope, with a Zeiss compensating ocular 20 × and a 1.5 mm. apochromatic objective. Figure 9 was drawn with 20 × and an objective having an aperture 0.65. The figures have been reduced about one half in reproduction.

FIG. 1. Heterotypic prophase, early second contraction, showing a closed chain of four chromosomes to which are linked ring-shaped pairs of bivalent chromosomes

FIG. 2. Heterotypic prophase, a later second contraction stage. Note the two two-linked pairs of chromosomes and three pairs of chromosomes

FIGS. 3–4. Heterotypic prophase, second contraction, showing a closed chain of four chromosomes and five pairs of chromosomes

FIGS. 5–6. Heterotypic prophase, diakinesis, nuclear membrane still intact, showing seven pairs of chromosomes

FIG. 7. Late anaphase, showing an unequal distribution of chromosomes (6 and 8)

FIG. 8. Late anaphase, showing the normal distribution of seven chromosomes to each pole

FIG. 9. Late anaphase, showing irregular distribution; only one cell having eight chromosomes is shown

FIG. 10. Interkinesis, showing eight split chromosomes

FIG. 11. An abnormal pollen grain, showing four interstitial bodies

PLATE XLIII

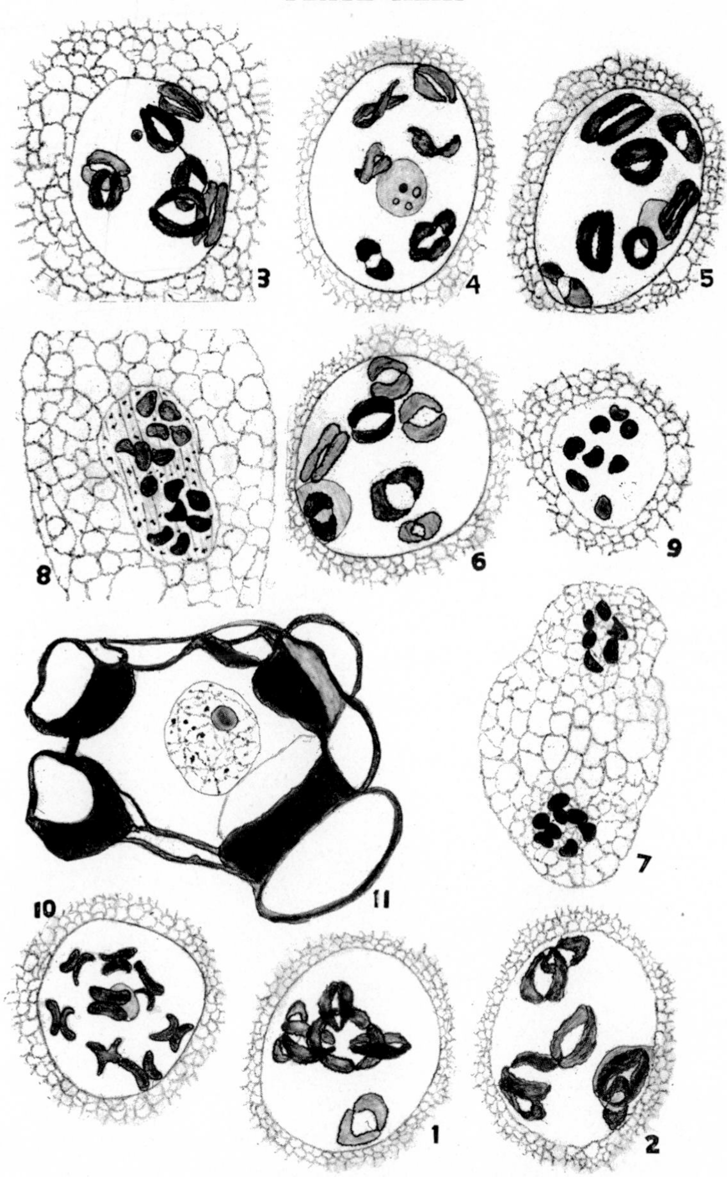

Meiosis in *Oenothera franciscana*

THE EFFECT OF ENVIRONMENTAL FACTORS ON THE SPORE SIZE OF *PESTALOZZIA GUEPINI* *

CARL D. LA RUE

ALTHOUGH some fungi show remarkable variation in spore size, depending upon the medium on which they are grown, this has not been found true for strains of *Pestalozzia Guepini*. On the contrary, strains isolated by La Rue and Bartlett (3), and studied in detail by the writer over a period of years (2), showed a remarkable constancy. These studies were made, however, on clones grown on media of as constant composition as could well be secured in order to eliminate fluctuations due to change in substrata. An attempt was made to see whether similar constancy would result from growth of the clones on varying substrata.

Pestalozzia Guepini exists in tropical and temperate regions as a parasite on many plants and as a saprophyte on a wide range of substances. It was possible, therefore, to grow it on many different substrata.

As a test of the effect of substratum on spore size, as many different fruits and vegetables as possible were secured at one time. Pieces of each of these were put into test tubes, a small amount of distilled water was added to each, and the whole lot of tubes was autoclaved.

Two strains of the fungus were selected for study, and transfers were made from tube cultures of these which had been grown from single spores. A mass of spores was placed on each of the nutrient substances, which were then set together in a dark culture room with a temperature of from 22° C. to 28° C.

On most of the substances growth of the mycelium was very

* Paper from the Department of Botany, University of Michigan, No. 295.

rapid, but on some it was rather slow. Great variations developed in the amounts of mycelium produced on the different substances, and the differences in the appearance of the mycelium from the same clone growing on different substances were equally apparent.

These differences for Clones 1 and 2 are summarized in Tables I and II.

GROWTH OF MYCELIUM

Clone 1 produced a very rapid and abundant growth on pea, coconut, onion, canteloupe, peach, turnip, banana and carrot. On carrot petiole, beet, beet petiole, banana peel, pepper and cucumber the mycelium was sparse and of slow growth.

Clone 2 grew rapidly and produced a luxuriant mycelium on coconut, beet, sweet potato, asparagus, carrot, potato, banana, canteloupe and cabbage. The slowest and least abundant growth was produced on apple, banana peel, pepper and beet petiole.

SPORULATION

Clone 1 gave an exceptional production of spores on several substrata which in order of abundance of spores were: oatmeal agar, potato, beet, pea, bean, asparagus, cucumber and carrot. Spore production was poor on carrot petiole, beet petiole, banana peel and lettuce. These substances are all low in carbohydrate content, which is an important factor for spore production, at least in Pestalozzia.

Clone 2 produced abundant masses of spores on the following substances listed in the order of abundance: bean, beet, potato, pea, coconut, canteloupe, cucumber and turnip.

Spore production was low on carrot petiole, beet petiole, lettuce and banana peel.

Spores were produced earliest in Clone 1 on beet, pea, bean and coconut in order, and latest on prune agar, oatmeal agar, beet petiole and banana peel.

In Clone 2 spores appeared earliest on asparagus, bean, beet, tomato and radish in the order given. Late spore production in this clone was noted on oatmeal agar, coconut, sweet potato, beet petiole, cabbage and peach.

SPORE SIZE

Measurements were made of 100 spores taken at random from each different culture. The results for Clone 1 are shown in Table III, and for Clone 2 in Table IV.

Although the substrata chosen are very different in chemical content, in water content and in hydrogen ion concentration the variations in spore size are slight and apparently of no significance whatever.

THE EFFECT OF CONCENTRATION OF SUBSTRATUM

In this test Coons' agar (1) was used and was made up in the following concentrations: normal, × 5, × 10, × 15, × 20, × 25 and × 30. The different concentrations were made up on the same day, and tubes of agar of each type were inoculated on the same day with masses of spores from single-spore cultures of each of three clones. All the tubes were allowed to grow in the dark in a culture chamber with a temperature range of from 22° C. to 28° C.

Eventually all the cultures developed normal growth except Clone 3 × 20 which became contaminated with bacteria, and never grew normally nor developed spores.

One hundred spores were measured from each of the cultures. The results for Clone 1 are given in Table V, for Clone 2 in Table VI, and for Clone 3 in Table VII. The variations in range and mean of spore size are not significant.

THE EFFECT OF TEMPERATURE ON SPORE SIZE

For this test a number of tubes were poured from one lot of prune agar. Three tubes were inoculated from Clone 1 and three from Clone 2. In each case masses of spores produced by single-spore cultures were used.

One culture from each clone was placed in a dark cold room at a temperature of from 0 to 4° C. Another from each clone was put in a dark culture chamber at a temperature of from 22° C. to 28° C. The remaining two cultures were kept in the dark in an incubator maintained at a temperature of 37.5° C.

The cultures kept in the cold room at 0–4° C. grew slowly, but produced no spores. After three weeks they were removed to the culture chamber at 22–28° C. Here they fruited normally.

The cultures in the culture chamber at 22–28° C. grew and sporulated normally.

The culture of Clone 2 kept at 37.5° C. developed a bacterial contamination and produced no spores. That of Clone 1 formed spores slowly but in considerable numbers.

One hundred spores were measured from each of the cultures in the usual way. The results are shown in Table VIII. The variations in range and spore size are not significant.

DISCUSSION

Stevens and Hall (6) record various changes, due to changes of substratum, in the growth and appearance of several different species of fungi. Further, these workers record spore measurements which show great changes in spore size due to alteration in the composition of substrata. Although no specific statement is made as to the source of the colonies from which the measured spores were taken, it may be presumed that they were derived from single-spore cultures and did not represent mixtures of clones. Otherwise it would have been useless to make comparisons of the cultures.

More recently Stevens (5) has made a study of the effects of environmental factors on the growth of the mycelium and on the spore size of *Helminthosporium sativum*. He finds that spore size, as well as type of mycelium and rate of mycelial growth, may be changed greatly by the use of different media.

Leonian (4) finds that the sporangia of various species of Phytophthora show great changes in size due to the use of different media.

The type of medium used and its richness have been found by a host of workers to exercise a profound effect on the type and abundance of growth of mycelium, as well as on the fruiting habits of fungi. The effect of environmental factors on spore size has been studied carefully by a relatively small number of investigators and in only a few groups. Most of these find that spore size is readily altered by change of substratum. The results of the writer are a direct contradiction of those of these observers. These findings can be harmonized with those of Stevens, Stevens and Hall, Leonian and others only by the assumption that the fungi of different groups show a wide variability in their response to environmental factors. This variability may be even greater in regard to spore size than in respect to growth characteristics.

From this it is obvious that the dependability of spore measurements as criteria in the delimitation of species will depend largely on the constancy of spore size within a given group. It is incumbent upon one who proposes to make use of spore measurements as a means of distinguishing species, or varieties, to study very carefully this characteristic of the forms under consideration.

SUMMARY

1. Mycelial growth, spore production, and spore size of two strains of *Pestalozzia Guepini* were studied on a number of substrata. The effect of concentration of nutrients on spore size on three strains of the fungus was studied. The effect of temperature on growth, development of spores and spore size was investigated on two different strains.

2. Growth habit and rate of spore production varied considerably on the different media, but spore size was not changed.

3. Change in the concentration of nutrients did not effect a change in spore size.

4. Different temperatures decidedly affect the growth of mycelium and the number of spores produced, but do not affect spore size.

5. The dependability of spore measurements in delimiting species and strains is closely connected with the constancy of spore size in the forms concerned. Those who use this criterion should study carefully the variability of spore size in the forms considered.

University of Michigan

TABLE I

GROWTH AND SPORULATION OF STRAIN 1 ON VARIOUS SUBSTRATA

Substratum	Time of Development		
	2 days	3 days	4 days
Apple	Dense, cottony mat, no spores	Extensive mycelium, spores forming	Spores abundant
Asparagus	Flat, cottony mycelium, spores forming	Sparse mycelium, enormous number of spores	Unchanged
Banana pulp	Dense mycelium, spores at center	Shaggy concentric rings of mycelium, spores very numerous	Unchanged
Banana peel	Sparse mycelium, some spores	Very sparse mycelium, spores forming	Spores abundant
Bean pod	Feathery mycelium, spores abundant	Feathery mycelium, spores very numerous	Spores abundant
Beet	Very sparse mycelium, spores abundant	Sparse mycelium, spores in enormous numbers	Unchanged
Beet petiole	Sparse, erect mycelium, no spores	Loose, shaggy mycelium, spores forming	Spores fairly abundant
Cabbage	Plush-like hyphae, spores forming at center	Odor present, shaggy mycelium, spores in center	Spores abundant
Canteloupe	Very dense mycelium, no spores	Shaggy mycelium, spores in center	Unchanged
Carrot	Dense tuft of mycelium, spores very abundant	Flat mycelium, spores abundant	Spores abundant
Carrot petiole	Sparse fluffy mycelium, no spores	Very little aërial mycelium, many spores	Spores abundant
Coconut	Dense, cottony mat, no spores	Extensive mycelium, spores abundant	Spores very abundant
Coons' agar	Growth over all surface but almost no aërial mycelium, spores forming	Thin weft of mycelium over surface, spores abundant	Spores abundant
Cucumber	Loose mat of mycelium, spores forming	Loose mat of mycelium, enormous number of spores	Unchanged
Lettuce	1 cm. diameter spot of mycelium, spores in center	Sparse growth of shaggy mycelium, spores forming in center	Unchanged
Oatmeal agar	Almost no aërial mycelium, no spores	Flat mycelium, no spores	Spores abundant
Onion	Concentric rings of densely tufted mycelium, spores in center	Small amount of shaggy mycelium, spores abundant	Spores abundant
Pea pod	Fluffy mycelium, spores appearing	Extensive mycelium, spores very abundant	Spores more numerous
Peach	Erect dense hyphae, no spores	Shaggy mycelium, spores abundant	Unchanged
Pepper	Small spot of erect mycelium, no spores	Scanty mycelium, spores fairly abundant	Spores fairly abundant
Potato	Concentric rings of flat, silky mycelium, no spores	Dense, cottony mycelium, spores abundant	Spores abundant
Prune agar	Spot of mycelium, 3 mm. in diameter, no spores	Spot of mycelium rings of 2 cm. in diameter, no spores	Spores abundant
Radish	Loose, cottony mycelium, strong odor, no spores	Strong odor, flat mycelium, enormous number of spores	Unchanged
Sweet potato	Dense mycelium, no spores	Dense mycelium, many spores	Spores abundant
Tomato	Erect hyphae, many spores	Shaggy mycelium, spores numerous	Spores abundant
Turnip	Dense mat of mycelium, no spores	Shaggy mycelium, spores abundant	Unchanged

TABLE II

Growth and Sporulation of Strain 2 on Various Substrata

Substratum	Time of Development		
	2 days	3 days	4 days
Apple	Thin mat of mycelium, no spores	Extensive cottony mycelium, no spores	Spores fairly abundant
Asparagus	Dense, central mat of mycelium, scattered outlying hyphae, some spores formed	Rings of cottony mycelium, sharply bounded feathery edge, spores at center	Spores few
Banana peel	Very sparse growth of hyphae, no spores	Sparse mycelium, concentric rings, spores forming in center	Spores abundant
Banana pulp	Cottony mass of mycelium, no spores	Dense, cottony mycelium, no spores	Spores few
Bean pod	Thin layer of hyphae, spores forming	Extensive, fluffy mycelium, spores at center	Spores abundant
Beet	Very dense, flat mycelium, no spores	Dense, cottony mycelium, many spores	Spores abundant
Beet petiole	Scattered hyphae, no spores	Thin mycelium with cottony masses, no spores	Spores few
Cabbage	Cottony mycelium over surface, strong odor, no spores	Dense, cottony mycelium, no spores	Spores few
Canteloupe	Very dense, cottony mycelium, no spores	Shaggy mycelium, no spores	Spores few
Carrot	Dense mat of mycelium, concentric appearance, no spores	Rings of cottony mycelium, no spores	Spores few
Carrot petiole	Slight growth, erect hyphae, no spores	Very little mycelium, some spores forming	Spores abundant
Coconut	Small mat, very dense hyphae, no spores	Extensive cottony mycelium, no spores	Spores few
Coons' agar	Cottony mass, erect hyphae on edges, no spores	Dense, cottony mycelium, no spores	Spores few
Cucumber	Slight growth, no spores	Thin mycelium, spores forming	Spores few
Lettuce	Cottony mycelium, no spores	Shaggy mycelium, some spores	Spores few
Oatmeal agar	Flat mycelium, no spores	Flat mycelium with shaggy spots	No spores
Onion	Small mat of very erect hyphae, no spores	Small spot of loose shaggy mycelium, no spores	Spores few
Pea pod	Small mat of hyphae, no spores	Extensive mycelium, many spores forming	Spores fairly abundant
Peach	Cottony tuft of mycelium, no spores	Dense, cottony mycelium, no spores	Spores few
Pepper	Very slight growth, no spores	Very scanty mycelium, no spores	Spores few
Potato	Dense mass of mycelium, concentric appearance, no spores	Dense, cottony mycelium, no spores	Spores few
Prune agar	Small spot of hyphae, no spores	Flat mycelium with shaggy spots, no spores	Spores few
Radish	Thin, cottony mycelium, very strong odor of decaying radish, spores forming	Dense, cottony mycelium, spores forming at center	Spores few
Sweet potato	Very dense flat mycelium, no spores	Extensive cottony mycelium, no spores	Spores few
Tomato	Cottony mycelium over surface, no spores	Shaggy mycelium, some spores at center	Spores fairly abundant
Turnip	Flat, cottony tuft, no spores	Dense, cottony mycelium, no spores	Spores few

TABLE III

SPORE LENGTHS OF CULTURES OF CLONE 1 GROWN ON VARIOUS MEDIA

Values in μ, 100 spores measured from each culture

Substratum	Range	Mode	Mean
Apple	16.4–26.9	21.1	21.54
Asparagus	17.5–25.7	21.1	21.43
Banana pulp	17.5–25.7	21.1	21.18
Banana peel	16.4–25.7	21.1	21.79
Bean pod	16.4–25.7	21.1	21.72
Beet	16.4–26.9	21.1	21.42
Beet petiole	16.4–26.9	21.1	21.60
Cabbage	16.4–24.6	21.1	20.99
Canteloupe	17.5–24.6	21.1	21.46
Carrot	17.5–28.1	21.1	21.90
Carrot petiole	17.5–26.9	21.1	21.32
Coconut	16.4–28.1	21.1	21.40
Coons' agar	17.5–26.9	21.1	20.90
Cucumber	16.4–26.9	21.1	21.27
Green onion	17.5–25.7	21.1	21.11
Lettuce	16.4–23.4	21.1	20.87
Oatmeal agar	16.4–25.7	21.1	20.94
Pea pod	16.4–25.7	21.1	20.80
Peach	17.5–28.1	19.9	21.04
Pepper	16.4–25.7	21.1	21.02
Potato	16.4–28.1	21.1	21.41
Prune agar	16.4–25.7	21.1	20.73
Radish	18.7–23.4	21.1	21.01
Sweet potato	16.4–25.7	21.1	21.69
Tomato	17.5–25.7	21.1	21.64
Turnip	16.4–26.9	21.1	20.69

TABLE IV

SPORE LENGTHS OF CULTURES OF CLONE 2 GROWN ON VARIOUS MEDIA

Values in μ, 100 spores measured from each culture

Substratum	Range	Mode	Mean
Bean pod	15.2–25.7	21.1	20.57
Beet	17.5–24.6	21.1	20.87
Cabbage	16.4–26.9	21.1	20.72
Canteloupe	16.4–25.7	21.1	20.91
Coons' agar	17.5–26.9	21.1	20.90
Oatmeal agar	16.4–24.6	21.1	20.50
Pea pod	17.5–25.7	19.9	20.59
Pepper	17.5–24.6	21.1	20.85
Potato	16.4–28.1	21.1	20.75
Radish	16.4–24.6	18.7	20.33
Turnip	17.5–24.6	19.9	20.19

TABLE V

LENGTHS OF SPORES OF CULTURES OF CLONE 1 GROWN ON MEDIA WITH VARIOUS CONCENTRATIONS OF COONS' AGAR

Values in μ, 100 spores measured from each culture

Number of times normal concentration	Range	Mode	Mean
1	16.4–25.7	21.1	21.60
5	16.4–29.3	21.1	22.11
10	18.7–24.6	21.1	21.74
15	17.6–25.7	21.1	21.20
20	16.4–28.1	21.1	21.01
25	16.4–29.3	18.7	21.27
30	16.4–28.1	21.1	21.18

TABLE VI

LENGTHS OF SPORES OF CULTURES OF CLONE 2 GROWN ON MEDIA WITH VARIOUS CONCENTRATIONS OF COONS' AGAR

Values in μ, 100 spores measured from each culture

Number of times normal concentration	Range	Mode	Mean
1	16.4–25.7	21.1	21.28
5	16.4–28.1	21.1	21.36
10	16.4–25.7	21.1	20.34
15	16.4–24.6	21.1	20.80
20	16.4–25.7	21.1	20.17
25	16.4–29.3	21.1	20.61
30	16.4–25.7	21.1	20.45

TABLE VII

LENGTHS OF SPORES OF CULTURES OF CLONE 3 GROWN ON MEDIA WITH VARIOUS CONCENTRATIONS OF COONS' AGAR

Values in μ, 100 spores measured from each culture

Number of times normal concentration	Range	Mode	Mean
1	16.4–23.4	19.9	19.82
5	14.0–25.7	19.9	19.54
10	16.4–24.6	21.1	20.20
15	14.0–24.6	21.1	19.59
20	——	——	——
25	15.2–29.3	19.9	20.27
30	15.2–24.6	19.9	19.14

TABLE VIII

LENGTHS OF SPORES OF CULTURES OF CLONES GROWN UNDER DIFFERENT TEMPERATURE CONDITIONS

Values in μ, 100 spores measured from each culture

Clone	Temperature	Range	Mode	Mean
1	0°– 4° C.	14.0–26.9	19.9 and 21.1	20.17
	22°–28° C.	14.0–23.4	21.1	20.97
	37.5° C.	15.2–25.7	21.1	20.61
2	0°– 4° C.	15.2–25.7	21.1	20.70
	22°–28° C.	16.4–25.7	21.1	20.31

BIBLIOGRAPHY

1. COONS, G. H. 1916. Factors Involved in the Growth and the Pycnidium Formation of *Plenodomus fuscomaculans*. Journ. Agr. Res., 5 : 713–769.
2. LA RUE, C. D. 1922. The Results of Selection within Pure Lines of *Pestalozzia Guepini*, Desm. Genetics, 7 : 142–201.
3. LA RUE, C. D., AND BARTLETT, H. H. 1922. A Demonstration of Numerous Distinct Strains within the Nominal Species *Pestalozzia Guepini*, Desm. Am. Journ. Bot., 9 : 79–92.
4. LEONIAN, L. H. 1925. Physiological Studies on the Genus Phytophthora. Am. Journ. Bot., 12 : 444–498.
5. STEVENS, F. L. 1922. The Helminthosporium Foot-Rot of Wheat, with Observations on the Morphology of Helminthosporium and on the Occurrence of Saltation in the Genus. Ill. Nat. Hist. Survey, Bull. No. 14 : 77–185.
6. STEVENS, F. L., AND HALL, J. G. 1909. Variation of Fungi Due to Environment. Bot. Gaz., 48 : 47–71.

THE NATIVE HABITAT OF THE PARÁ RUBBER TREE *

CARL D. LA RUE

THE idea has long been current that the Pará rubber tree, *Hevea brasiliensis*, is a swamp tree and reaches its best development in the swamps of the lower valley and in the delta region of the Amazon. This belief was probably spread by travelers who saw rubber trees in the region near Pará and did not penetrate far enough into the interior to realize the error of their early impressions. Indeed, most of the inhabitants of Pará have never been in the interior and so are able to give only an incorrect picture of the growth of a plant so important to them.

When Pará rubber trees were grown from seeds introduced to Kew by Wickham (3) and thence shipped to Ceylon and Singapore, a number of these, at least, were planted in rather low ground where they did not thrive very well. Early plantings of seeds of these first trees were made in wet ground, but the error was soon discovered, and later plantings were made on well-drained soil. In present day plantings the problem of drainage is a serious one whenever swampy areas must be used. It is universally recognized that whatever its native habitat may be the Pará rubber tree can be grown profitably only on friable, well-drained soil which allows the development of a deep root-system.

Along the banks of the lower Amazon and those of its lower tributaries, one finds many trees growing at low levels where their roots are covered by water for some time each year. These trees are those which have given rise to the idea that rubber trees must grow under such conditions.

There is every evidence, however, that such trees merely en-

* Paper from the Department of Botany, University of Michigan, No. 296.

dure this habitat, not that they find it essential, or even satisfactory. An examination of these trees was made by the writer to determine their condition, with the result that all were found stunted and generally poor in development for their years.

The root-systems of trees growing on soil just above the level of low water were found to be confined to the soil above the level of ground-water during the season of low water. Roots which extend down into the water are killed. In some places the trees have all their roots spread out in a flat layer little more than six inches in thickness. There are no large roots such as are found on normal trees, and the whole root-system is obviously abnormal, with many stunted and contorted, and many dead, roots.

The growth of the trunks is unsatisfactory also, and all the trees are small for their age. Almost all have the swollen bases and tapering trunks which are found on eastern plantations either on poorly drained soils, or on very sandy tracts (*permatangs*). Normal trees have a cylindrical lower trunk, and one is able to tell a great deal concerning the value of a plantation by the shape of the trees alone.

The bark on these trees is very thin and hard, and in most of them the number of rows of latex vessels is small as compared with those in the bark of up-river trees (1). There is an unusual development of stone cells in the bark of these trees. The wounds made in the bark by tapping heal slowly.

Many of the trees of the flood-plain lands have tops which are dying, one of the good indications of an unsatisfactory root condition. The leaves are pale green and generally unhealthy in appearance as contrasted with those of trees growing under better conditions.

The production of the trees of the lowland is usually poor, although some trees are found which have relatively high yields. Naturally, with the low prices of rubber which have been current for several years, a great many of these trees are not worth tapping at all.

In a few places where the alluvial soil is deep enough to allow the development of a good root-system, large trees are found, which are in a flourishing condition and which yield large quantities of latex. Such trees, however, are so exceptional as to be negligible in the great number of trees examined, and their development indicates clearly that the Pará rubber tree needs a greater depth of soil than is usually found in swampy districts.

The quality of the rubber from the lower Amazon, the so-called "islands" rubber, has always been low. At present little is known of the effect of the physical condition and the chemical composition of soils on the quality of rubber, so we cannot state that the cause of the poor quality is the habitat. This is even more true in the light of our knowledge of the methods of preparation of rubber which are used in this region. Most of the rubber is collected in a very careless manner, and no effort is made to keep the latex clean. The latex is then allowed to coagulate naturally and the rubber is not washed. Most of it comes into Pará as a wet, putrid mass of very low value. One can hardly doubt that the preparation is the greatest cause of defects in the quality of the rubber.

The trees of the island region near the mouth of the Amazon are of the white variety of *Hevea brasiliensis*, the same variety as that planted on the plantations in the Near East. That this variety is capable of better growth than that described above is shown by the splendid development of trees on the best plantations of Sumatra, Java, the Federated Malay States, and other places. It is demonstrated also by the large trees on the plateaus along the Tapajos, where trees of great size and high yield are found.

On the upper rivers one finds many trees of the white variety, well developed on the uplands, but small and stunted on the flood-plains. The flood-plain trees are in all respects the same as those of the islands region because their environment is essentially the same.

Trees of this variety on the river banks and the plateaus back from the rivers have all the characteristics of healthy normal trees. Their root-systems are both deep and extensive, and there is a complete absence of the swollen root-crowns found on the flood-plain trees. The trunks are cylindrical, with relatively thick soft bark, rich in latex vessels. The leaves are dark green and are borne on sound branches, which are a distinct contrast to the unhealthy tops of the trees in swampy ground.

It is only along the upper tributaries of the Madeira, the Purús, etc., that one finds the black variety of *Hevea brasiliensis* (1). Along the Madre de Dios and the Tahuamanu rivers in Bolivia, and the Acré River in Brazil, the writer found great numbers of huge trees of this variety. These are the finest rubber trees seen anywhere in the Amazon Valley. They have all the characteristics of growth already described in connection with trees of the white variety in a good habitat. In addition to spreading root-systems, cylindrical trunks, spreading crowns, healthy leaves and the like, they have exceedingly soft bark of unusual thickness. The bark is dark purple and has a remarkable development of latex vessels. The yield of these trees is very high, and the quality of the rubber is the best known.

None of these trees are found on the flooded land, but invariably grow on the upland. Apparently they are less tolerant of unfavorable conditions than the trees of the white variety, for it seems hardly possible that the seeds have not been carried down to the alluvial lands innumerable times during the existence of the variety.

While the habitat of the Pará rubber tree is under discussion, mention may be made of the theory that the black variety is merely a habitat variation of *Hevea brasiliensis*. This theory cannot be held by anyone who has seen the white variety in the upriver country, where it still remains distinct, though the black variety is found in the same area.

It is not possible at present to locate the original home of *Hevea brasiliensis*, but it must have been somewhere in the uplands drained by the Beni, the Abuná, the Acré, the upper Purús and the upper Juruá. This is also the opinion of Marbut (2) who studied the soils of these regions. Wherever it originated it could have spread throughout this region by land, and have descended the rivers to the Amazon, and finally down to the mouth of that river. *Hevea brasiliensis* has not spread to the north side of the Amazon, or, if so, not to any considerable extent.

The tolerance of the white variety of unfavorable conditions in alluvial lands has allowed it to travel rapidly down the rivers and penetrate into the jungles from the river banks. Accordingly, it now has an extensive distribution in the lower valley of the Amazon.

The inability of the black variety to endure conditions on the flood-plains may be the cause of its limited distribution, since it could spread only by land, and has not yet had sufficient time to spread over the great area covered by the white variety.

The Pará rubber tree in its most favored localities is accompanied by the *castanha*, *Bertholletia excelsa*, the Brazil-nut tree. This tree is never found on alluvial land (*varzea*), but always on the uplands (*terra firma*). The satisfactory development of the Brazil-nut tree is a fair indication that the region and soil will be favorable for the growth of *Hevea brasiliensis*, whether it now grows there or not. While the rubber tree can live in more unfavorable conditions than the *castanha*, its requirements for successful growth are the same. The idea that the Pará rubber tree originated in a swampy region is no longer tenable.

SUMMARY AND CONCLUSIONS

1. The white variety of *Hevea brasiliensis*, the Pará rubber tree, is frequently found growing in low or swampy land, but it does not thrive in such a situation.
2. Both the white and the black varieties of the species grow best on friable well-drained soils.
3. The black variety appears to be unable to live in swampy soils.
4. The species probably originated on the uplands drained by the Madeira, Purús and Juruá rivers and their tributaries.
5. The inability of the black variety to live in flood-plain soils may have prevented its spread by the rivers and so may have limited its distribution, which is much less extensive than that of the more tolerant white variety.

UNIVERSITY OF MICHIGAN

LITERATURE CITED

1. La Rue, Carl D. 1926. The Hevea Rubber Tree in the Amazon Valley. U. S. Dept. Agric. Dept. Bull., No. 1422 : 1–70.

2. Schurz, W. L., Hargis, O. D., Marbut, C. F., and Manifold, C. B. 1925. Rubber Production in the Amazon Valley. Trade Promotion Series, No. 23. Crude Rubber Survey. U. S. Dept. of Commerce.

3. Wickham, H. A. 1908. On the Plantation, Cultivation, and Curing of Pará Indian Rubber. 78 pages. Illustrations. London.

A SPECIAL REACTION TO LIGHT BY THE MYCELIUM OF *CLAVICEPS PURPUREA* *

ADELIA McCREA

SEVERAL years ago, in connection with studies being made on *Claviceps purpurea* (Fr.) Tul. in the Cryptogamic Laboratory of the University of Michigan, it was noticed that part of a series of capsule cultures began to show a very faint pinkish tinge about two weeks after planting, while the others remained unchanged. In attempting to account for this difference, the fact was brought out that the colored ones were nearer the source of light. At this time, light came from a north window on a court, in the month of February. No factor other than light seemed involved; so, to test the point, a cupboard was placed directly before the window, and it was found that all of the cultures promptly assumed the pinkish color.

The effect of light on fungus mycelium with reference to color production has been little studied. Kosaroff (4; cited by Robinson), working with *Pyronema confluens* Tul. (*P. omphaloides* (Bull.) Fuckel), found that light exercises a modifying influence on the depth of color. Robinson (6) in 1926 reported for the same organism that the characteristic pink pigment of this fungus never develops in darkness; and he carried on sufficient experimentation, using liquid screens, to convince him that it is the "blue end" of the spectrum which is responsible for the appearance of this color in the mycelium. Bessey (1) worked with two Fusaria isolated from sesame, and two Neocosmospora cultures, *N. vasinfecta* (Atk.) and *N. vasinfecta* var. *nivea* Smith. He found that

* Paper from the Department of Botany of the University of Michigan, No. 282.

an intense orange color is produced in all these fungi in response to light. By the use of colored liquids, he proved that the effective rays are those of the blue portion of the spectrum. Smith and Swingle (7), working independently at about the same time, reported that the characteristic salmon color of *Fusarium oxysporum* is due to the rays of the blue area of the spectrum. Using the same liquid filters, they likewise established that *Neocosmospora vasinfecta* also produces its color in response to stimulation by the blue rays only. Brefeld (3) reports that he observed in his cultures of *C. purpurea* grown on nutrient solution a gradation of color from yellow through purple and finally to brown. Meyer (5) confirmed the yellow-to-brown coloration, but did not record the violet or purple seen by Brefeld. Bonns (2), in his more recent work on *C. purpurea*, mentions the occasional appearance of a "dark purple" when grown on certain substrata; but he, as well as Brefeld and Meyer, did not follow up the matter to ascertain the conditions under which color appears.

Experimental. — More recently the matter was again taken up by the writer and a definite study was made of color production in the cultures of this fungus with respect to the influence of light. Cultures were grown upon a modified Leonian's agar medium,[1] with the nutrients in double the original quantities. For this part of the work light reached the cultures after passing through only the common types of clear glass, such as window glass, test tubes and battery jars.

Experiments with ordinary glass. — Before the cultures were exposed to the light, they were grown in the dark, usually for two weeks, in large test tubes, 35 × 240 mm., on agar slants of 75 c. c. Controls were kept in the dark cupboard throughout. In the dark, the color of the mat produced by the fungus in the cultures is constant — "tilleul buff" (Ridgway), a sort of very pale flesh-color.

[1] The medium as used had the following formula:

Magnesium sulphate....	1.25 gms.	Maltose............	12.50 gms.
Dihydrogen potassium phosphate...........	2.50 gms.	Malt Extract.........	12.50 gms.
Peptone (Witte's).......	1.25 gms.	Agar-agar............	6%
		Water................	1000 c.c.

When the cultures had developed a good mat, they were exposed to direct light which now came from a southern exposure on the fourth floor, facing the open campus. The experiments began in March, were repeated in April, and again in May. The test tube cultures were exposed simultaneously as follows:

a. Outside the window, on the ledge. In this position, the light passed through only one layer of glass, that of the test tube.

b. A second set of cultures was placed on a table, inside the closed window; hence light passed through two layers of glass: window and test tube.

c. For a third set, the tubes were placed within an ordinary battery jar on the table, making three layers of glass.

d. The fourth set of cultures were put in a nest of two battery jars on the table, so that light passed through four thicknesses of glass: window, outer jar, inner jar and test tube.

Other factors were eliminated as much as possible, the chief variant being temperature. Careful tests on this point showed that, within the range permitting the usual growth of the organism, *temperature does not influence color production.*

In each of the four situations described above, the culture surface became a beautiful, deep shade of red, corresponding very closely to Ridgway's "carrot red." This was much more striking than any previously obtained, and may be considered the characteristic reaction of such cultures to light, under clear atmospheric conditions. The controls in all cases retained throughout the experiment the typical "tilleul buff" (R.) of the cultures grown in darkness.

In this phase of the work cultures were left continuously exposed at the window. It was observed that the color might fade and, later, again appear. More recent microscopic study of this phenomenon indicates that it is due, not to any ebb and flow of color, but to a temporary obscuring of the surface by additional aërial and marginal growth which at first is white, but may later develop the typical color. When the actively growing period is past and the culture has become mature, the deep red color may persist unchanged for several months.

The duration of exposure necessary to stimulate the mycelium to color production is not great. It needs no more than an hour of direct exposure to strong sunlight through glass. When, for example, cultures grown in small glass capsules in the dark are placed in bright sunshine for one hour, and again returned to the dark cupboard, they develop the red color within a few hours.

The following points may, therefore, be considered quite definitely established by this part of the work: first, that color is produced in this mycelium in response to light; second, the stimulus necessary for color production is not inhibited by four thicknesses of ordinary glass, such as that used in windows, test tubes and battery jars; third, the appearance of color does not depend upon the "far" ultra-violet rays, because window glass does not transmit the rays beyond 0.310 μ; and, fourth, that an exposure as brief as one hour through one thickness of glass suffices to induce the typical reaction within the next few hours.

Experiments with special glass filters. — In order to study more closely in which general part of the spectrum the activating rays might lie, a set of boxes was provided to control the light. The dimensions were 16 by 16 by 16 inches, each box being fitted with a door on one side and with a window of four panes, each $6\frac{1}{2}$ inches square, of the various filter glasses under test. One smaller box, 10 by 10 by 10 inches, had a single square pane.

The filter glasses used comprised five of the Corning [2] types, and one of "Vita glass," [3] having the following designations: Corning, G–38–L; G–53–C; G–38–H; G–34–R; and G–555–BE, analyses of which will be found in the table of results following (Table I). Vita glass was of the "clear" type.

These boxes were used both indoors and out. *Indoors,* they were placed before the south window which could be opened for any desired length of time during the hours of direct sunlight. The cultures were contained in glass capsules placed on the floor of the box, so that light reached them after passing through the colored screen and the capsule glass. Except during the four or five hours

[2] The Corning glass filters were obtained from Corning Glass Works, Corning, New York.

[3] The Vita Glass Corporation of New York City very kindly provided this material.

when the window was opened each sunny day, the window glass made a third layer.

When the boxes were used *outdoors*, they were placed, with windows uppermost, upon a porch roof about twelve feet above the ground, with full exposure to light. *In this situation the covers of the capsules were removed.* The under side of each box window was sterilized with bichloride of mercury followed by alcohol. Sterile cotton "collars" or "rings" for the capsules had been prepared between sheets of parchment paper. As the cover of each capsule was removed, one of these cotton rings was quickly put in place, the capsule pressed up under the glass and securely blocked in position. The intervening sheet of parchment paper was then drawn off the cotton, leaving nothing but the single layer of filter glass between the light and the surface of the culture. When the cultures were all in place and the door closed, no light could reach the mycelium except that which filtered through the special glass. Practically all the cultures remained sterile; so it is safe to say that, with reasonable care and dexterity, contamination can be avoided by this method.

This experiment was repeated twice, under very nearly these exact conditions. With one exception, viz. Filter G–38–L, the results of the three series were entirely consistent, and may be said to establish the following points:

1. Production of the red color in the mycelium is due to the shorter rays of the spectrum: the blue, the violet, and perhaps, the "near" ultra-violet. The intense red color was obtained, for example, under G–555–BE, which bars all yellow, all green and the blue-green. The usual color, although less intense, occurs under G–53–C which bars red, yellow and green, transmitting only the "near" ultra-violet, the violet and part of the blue. (This glass is thick and so very dark that light is dim.) The color is practically lacking under the glass, G–34–R, which bars (of the visible spectrum) only the violet, the blue and the blue-green; and under G–38–H, which bars only the ultra-violet, the violet, and all of the blue except a little lying in the blue-green area.

2. There is no evidence that the presence of the long rays of the spectrum has any inhibiting effect upon color production.

TABLE I

DATA ON FILTER GLASSES

GLASS	RANGE	BARS	TRANSMITS	EFFECT
G–38–L 5 mm.	0.380 to 0.720 μ	Ultra-violet, beyond 0.380 μ	All visible rays	* Indoors: very slight color. 0 to I Outdoors: good color. III
G–53–C 4 mm.	0.385 to 0.470 μ	Green, yellow, red	Near ultra-violet, violet, part blue	Typical, although less intense, owing to dim light Indoors: II Outdoors: II to III
G–38–H 3 mm.	0.460 to 0.700 μ	Ultra-violet, violet, part blue	From blue-green to red, inclusive	Color lacking or very pale Indoors: 0 to I Outdoors: 0 to I
G–34–R 3 mm.	0.550 to 0.710 μ	Violet, blue, green	From yellow to red, inclusive	Color lacking or very pale Indoors: 0 to I Outdoors: 0 to I
G–555–BE 8 mm.	Broken 0.385–0.490 0.595–0.720μ	Yellow, green, blue-green	Near ultra-violet, violet, blue, orange, red	Typical carrot red Graded as IV
Vita glass 2 mm.	From near 0.270 μ to limit of visible spectrum	None	All visible, and part of invisible	Typical carrot red Graded as IV
Capsule Test tube Glass jars	Spectral characteristics unknown			Typical carrot red Graded as IV

NOTE: Ultra-violet, less than 0.400 μ
Violet.........0.400 to 0.435
Blue..........0.435 to 0.490
Green.........0.490 to 0.574
Yellow........0.574 to 0.595
Orange........0.595 to 0.626
Red...........0.626 to 0.720, approximately

* This is the inconsistency above referred to, and is believed due to the

Filter G–555–BE, which allows the activating rays to pass, gives the normal color, although it transmits all the orange and the red, cutting out only the yellow and the green areas. Vita glass transmits all the visible spectrum, as well as a considerable portion of the ultra-violet; yet the typical color is produced under it. Again, so far as we know, all the visible rays pass through the glass of the capsules and test tubes; and here too the reaction of the mycelium is typical.

The table on page 250 gives data on the types of glass used, and a summary of their effect upon color production both indoors and out. For convenience, the depth of color is indicated by O, the lack of response by IV, which signifies the typical "carrot red," with the intermediate color-intensity by I, II and III.

Location of pigment. — Microscopic examination of the colored mycelium, with Bausch and Lomb 3 mm. objective with 15 × and 25 × oculars, showed that the color is located only in the walls of the mycelium and the conidiospores; it seems clearly not present in the protoplasm or vacuoles. Color is very faint under the microscope, and only in mass can the pinkish tinge be easily noted in a mount.

Nature of pigment. — Color was quickly and completely removed from *fresh* mycelium by acetone or alcohol. In each test, the solvent became quite deeply colored, suggestive of carotin in solution. These extracts were evaporated and the oily residues tested for carotin, with arsenic trichloride, but results were negative. Nothing further is known at this time as to the nature of the pigment.

My sincere thanks are due to Professor C. H. Kauffman, under whose direction this work was done.

University of Michigan

fact that outdoors the light passed only through the colored screen, while indoors the capsule covers also intervened. Since, however, the maximum color cannot be secured with this glass either indoors or out, it is probable that the "near" ultra-violet rays are necessary for its full production; i.e. those between 0.310 μ which pass window glass, and 0.380 μ which is the cut-off of Filter G–38–L. (This glass is used in lenses, to protect the eyes from the ultra-violet rays from lamps or sunshine.)

LITERATURE CITED

1. Bessey, Ernst A. 1904. Über die Bedingungen der Farbbildung bei Fusarium. Flora, 93 : 301–334.

2. Bonns, Walter W. 1922. A Preliminary Study of *Claviceps purpurea* in Culture. Am. Journ. Bot., 9 : 339–353.

3. Brefeld, O. 1891. Untersuchungen aus dem Gesammtgebiete der Mykologie (Ascomyceten II), 10 : 192–193.

4. Kosaroff, P. 1906. Beiträge zur Biologie von *Pyronema confluens*. Arb. a. d. kais. biol. Anst. f. Land- u. Forstwirtsch., V : 3.

5. Meyer, B. 1888. Untersuchungen über die Entwickelung einiger parasitischer Pilze bei saprophytischer Ernährung. Landw. Jahrb., 17 : 915–945.

6. Robinson, Wilfrid. 1926. The Conditions of Growth and Development of *Pyronema confluens*. Ann. Bot., 40 : 245–272.

7. Smith, E. F., and Swingle, D. B. 1904. The Dry Rot of Potatoes Due to *Fusarium oxysporum*. Bull. 55, Bureau of Plant Industry, U. S. Dept. of Agr.

SOME NON-VASCULAR CRYPTOGAMS FROM VERMILION, CHIPPEWA COUNTY, MICHIGAN

ALFRED H. POVAH

THROUGH the generosity of the Honorable George Shiras, 3d, there were made possible the expeditions to the Whitefish Point Region which have resulted in a knowledge of the flora and fauna of the northeastern part of the state of Michigan. These expeditions were carried on as a coöperative project by the Michigan Geological and Biological Survey and the Museum of Zoölogy of the University of Michigan, with the assistance of Mr. George Shiras, 3d. The writer spent approximately two months (June 24 to August 22) in 1914 at Vermilion, Michigan, as cryptogamic botanist of the Shiras Expedition.

Although especial attention was given to fungi, a small collection of Algae and a slightly larger collection of liverworts and mosses were made. The season was too dry for ideal collecting. In fact, a period of twenty-six days without rain resulted in such a dearth of specimens that much time and effort were expended in fruitless search for specimens. The writer realizes that in one season, and that a very dry one, it would be impossible to make a complete collection of the Thallophytes and Bryophytes of the region. Subsequent visits would be necessary. Nevertheless, the list of specimens obtained has sufficient additions to our state flora to make it worthy of record. In the algae, three species occurring in the East, viz. *Tetraspora lubrica* (Roth) Ag. var. *lacunosa* Chauvin, *Stigeoclonium amoenum* Kütz. and *Vaucheria Dillwynii* (Web. & Mohr) Ag., were collected. Among the fungous collections some of the more interesting are: **Lasiobolus longisetosus,** sp. nov., *Merulius gyrosus* Burt (named and known only from this collection), *Odontia vesiculosa* Burt ined., *Peniophora* *ludoviciana* Burt (only the second collection of this rare species), *Hypoxylon albocinctum* E. & E., *Endogone sphagnophila* Atkins. and *Entomophthora rhizospora* Thaxt.

The region is interesting to a collector because of its varied topography and vegetation. Some types are:

(1) virgin forest — white pine, hemlock, balsam fir, white birch, yellow birch with a small admixture of beech, hard maple and mountain ash;

(2) second growth pine forest — white, Norway and jack pine with a very few birches;

(3) spruce-cedar swamp — black spruce, white cedar and balsam fir with a few birches, soft maple and mountain maple;

(4) sand dunes — along the shore of Lake Superior with the low, moist places covered with woods of pine, maple, spruce, fir and poplar;

(5) tamarack bog — tamarack black spruce, sphagnum, alder, etc.;

(6) black ash swamp.

For more detailed information the reader is referred to the report of the phanerogamic botanist, Mr. C. K. Dodge (7).

The specimens have been deposited in the herbarium of the University of Michigan under the name Shiras Collections. An asterisk after the species denotes that this is the first or earliest Michigan collection in the University of Michigan Herbarium. Duplicates are in the author's herbarium.

Grateful acknowledgment is hereby made to those who have examined and named specimens, especially Professor C. H. Kauffman, the Agaricaceae; Dr. E. A. Burt, the Thelephoraceae; the late C. G. Lloyd, the Polyporaceae; Dr. L. O. Overholts, the porias; Dr. E. B. Mains, the Uredinales; Professor E. N. Transeau, the Algae; and Dr. A. Le Roy Andrews, the Sphagnaceae.

THALLOPHYTA

Algae

Zygnemaceae

Spirogyra varians (Hass.) Kütz. — In pool in swamp.

Tetrasporaceae

Tetraspora lubrica (Roth.) Ag. var. lacunosa Chauvin. * — Transeau says this variety occurs in the East. In pool in swamp.

Ulothricaceae

Ulothrix zonata (Web. & Mohr) Kütz. * — With gametes and zoöspores. On piles of dock in Lake Superior.

Chaetophoraceae

Draparnaldia plumosa Ag. — On stem in slow-moving stream.

Chaetophora incrassata (Huds.) Hazen. * — On boards in race, in rapidly flowing water.

Stigeoclonium amoenum Kütz.*— Two collections from ditch with slow-moving water. According to Transeau, this is a new record west of the Atlantic seaboard for the species.

Vaucheriaceae

Vaucheria Dillwynii (Web. & Mohr) Ag. * — Almost submerged in cedar swamp. Previously known only from Massachusetts and New Jersey, according to Transeau.

Vaucheria geminata (Vauch.) DC.*— In pool in swamp.

Vaucheria geminata (Vauch.) DC. var. racemosa (Vauch.) Walz.* — In pool in wet pasture.

Vaucheria sessilis (Vauch.) DC.*— In pool in swamp.

Fungi

MYXOMYCETES

Ceratiomyxa fruticulosa (Muell.) Macbr. — On rotten log.

Badhamia macrocarpa (Ces.) Rost. * — On moss and leaves in swamp.

Fuligo ovata (Schaeff.) Macbr. — In cedar swamp.

Fuligo violacea Pers. — On log in hardwood forest.

Physarum notabile Macbr. (*P. nephroideum* Rost.). — On rotten log in mixed forest.

LYCOGALA EPIDENDRUM (Buxv.) Fr. — On rotten log in bog.

TRICHIA DECIPIENS (Pers.) Macbr. — On rotten log in alder thicket.

TRICHIA FAVOGINEA (Batsch) Pers. * — On logs in swamp and mixed woods.

HEMITRICHIA STIPITATA Mass. — On rotten log in black ash swamp.

ARCYRIA DENUDATA (L.) Sheld. — On rotten log in swamp.

COMATRICHA FLACCIDA (List.) Morg.* — On decaying birch log. Rare.

COMATRICHA IRREGULARIS Rex. * — On coniferous log in spruce bog. Beardslee (2) reports having found this in Montmorency Co., Michigan, but no specimens are in the University of Michigan Herbarium.

STEMONITIS FENESTRATA Rex.* — On rotten logs in mixed forest.

STEMONITIS FUSCA (Roth.) Rost. (*S. maxima* Schwein.). — On rotten logs in low, wet places in forest and in bog.

STEMONITIS SPLENDENS Rost. (*S. Morgani* Pk.). — On rotten birch bark.

TUBIFERA FERRUGINOSA (Batsch) Macbr. — On stump. According to Macbride (11), this species is more common in the north and this is substantiated by the fact that there is a single local (Washtenaw County) collection, made by V. M. Spalding in 1889, in the University of Michigan Herbarium.

PHYCOMYCETES

ENDOGONE SPHAGNOPHILA Atkins. * — Two collections of this interesting yellow fungus were made from the tips of *Sphagnum sp.* growing in wet places in the forest. Thaxter (17) found it in Maine and Atkinson (1) collected it in New York and Maryland.

ENTOMOPHTHORACEAE

ENTOMOPHTHORA RHIZOSPORA Thaxt.* — *Fide* Roland Thaxter. The zygosporic stage on caddis flies was found on the under side of a black ash stump in a dried-up swamp. Thaxter (16) found this species in Maine and North Carolina.

Mucoraceae

Mucor hiemalis Wehmer.* — On bear and porcupine dung and on an old bone in the forest. These collections are numbers four, five and six respectively of Povah (13).

Mucor ramannianus Moeller.* — On decaying mushroom in swamp. Povah (13) number two.

Sporodinia grandis Lk. — On decaying mushroom in swamp.

Peronosporaceae

Peronospora effusa (Grev.) Rabenh. — On *Chenopodium album* L. (Specimen destroyed by fungi.)

ASCOMYCETES

Geoglossaceae

Mitrula phalloides (Bull.) Chev.* — Attached to leaves in pools.

Microglossum fumosum (Pk.) Dur.* — Among moss in cedar swamp.

Geoglossum glabrum Pers.* — Among moss in wet places in swamp.

Geoglossum nigritum Cke.* — Among moss in cedar swamp.

Spathularia velutipes Cke. & Farl.* — On rotten log in forest.

Leotia lubrica Pers.* — On ground in cedar swamp.

Cudonia circinans (Pers.) Fr.* — On rotten log in forest.

Vibrissea truncorum (Alb. & Schwein.) Fr.* — On rotten stick in pool.

Trichoglossum hirsutum (Pk.) Dur.* — In swamp among moss.

Pezizaceae

Lachnea hemispherica (Wigg.) Gill.* — On dead twigs in cedar swamp.

Lachnea scutellata (L.) Gill.* — On log in corduroy road and in forest. Common.

Lachnea stercorea (Pers.) Gill. var. gemella Karst.* — On deer dung in forest and on cow dung in pasture.

PLICARIA BADIA (Pers.) Fuckl.* — On logs in wet woods and swamps. Common.

PLICARIA PUSTULATA (Hedw.) Fuckl.* — Common on the ground in wet places. The spores in our specimens are slightly larger (16–20 × 12–14 μ) than Rehm's (14) measurements.

NEOTIELLA NIVEA Romell.* — On rotten leaves in wet woods.

HUMARIA APPLANATA (Hedw.) Rehm.* — On ground in cedar swamp.

HUMARIA RUTILANS (Fr.) Sacc.* — On and among *Polytrichum sp.* in sandy soil.

HUMARIA SACCHARINA Bres. * — On alder twig in swamp. In Europe this occurs on basswood.

ASCOBOLACEAE

Lasiobolus longisetosus, sp. nov. *

Apothecia crowded, pale orange when fresh, fading to tan, 0.4–1.0 mm. in diameter; setae hyaline or tinged yellow, nonseptate, unbranched (250–) 450–600 (–700) μ long, at largest place near the base 20–40 μ in diameter, slightly tapering below; asci not staining blue with iodine, elongate-clavate, 160–180 × 10.5–17.5 μ, eight-spored; spores obliquely uniseriate or irregularly biseriate, hyaline, broadly elliptical, smooth, 17.5–21 × 7.5–10.5 μ; paraphyses hyaline, filiform, septate, branched, slightly swollen at the tips. On deer dung. August 15, 1914. Vermilion, Chippewa County, Michigan. Type in the University of Michigan Herbarium, Shiras Collection No. 338 and in Povah Herbarium No. 1110.

This species is related to *L. equinus* (Müll.) Karst., but differs from it in the smaller apothecia, the much longer setae, the smaller asci and spores. *L. longisetosus* was again collected in 1927 at Rock River, Alger County, Michigan.

ASCOPHANUS FLAVUS Karst.* — On cow dung in wooded pasture.

HELOTIACEAE

CHLOROSPLENIUM AERUGINOSUM (Oeder) De Not. — On wood along shore of Lake Superior.

DASYSCYPHA AGASSIZII (B. & C.) Sacc.* — Common on dead branches of *Abies balsamea* (L.) Mill.

DASYSCYPHA NIVEA Sacc.* — On rotten log in dried-up swamp.

HYMENOSCYPHA ALBIDA (Rob.) Phill.* — On decayed leaves in swamp. The spores in our specimens, measuring 13–17 × 3–4 μ, are slightly wider than those in European specimens.

MOLLISIACEAE

MOLLISIA CINEREA (Batsch) Karst. — On wood of old birch.

TRYBLIDIACEAE

SCLERODERRIS ACERICOLA (Pk.) Sacc.* — On dead twigs of *Acer rubrum* L. associated with *Sphaeronema acerinum* Pk. Saccardo (15) mentions this association and suggests that the two are phases of the same fungus.

PHACIDIACEAE

RHYTISMA ANDROMEDAE (Pers.) Fr. — Parasitic upon the leaves of *Andromeda glaucophylla* Link.

HYSTERIACEAE

GLONIUM LINEARE (Fr.) De Not. — On birch bark.

ERYSIPHACEAE

MICROSPHAERA ALNI (DC.) Wint. — On *Alnus incana* (L.) Moench.

UNCINULA SALICIS (DC.) Wint. — On *Salix sp.*

HYPOCREACEAE

CHILONECTRIA CUCURBITULA (Curr.) Sacc.* — On dead, fallen *Abies balsamea.*

NECTRIA CINNABARINA (Tode) Fr. — On dead maple.

CORDYCEPS MILITARIS (L.) Link.* — On insect remains on old log.

DOTHIDIACEAE

PLOWRIGHTIA MORBOSA (Schwein.) Sacc. — Common on living *Prunus pennsylvanica* L.

AMPHISPHAERIACEAE

TREMATOSPHAERIA MINUTA Berlese.* — On bark of *Betula sp.* This fungus occurs upon *Salix cinerea* in Italy.

Pleosporaceae

Venturia pulchella Cke. & Pk.* — On living leaves of *Chamaedaphne calyculata* (L.) Moench. Specimens in the University of Michigan Herbarium are from New Hampshire, New Jersey, and Ontario, Canada.

Xylariaceae

Daldinia concentrica (Bolt.) Ces. & De Not. — On dead birch.

Daldinia vernicosa (Schwein.) Ces. & De Not. — On birch stump.

Xylaria hypoxylon (L.) Grev.* — On rotten birch log.

Hypoxylon albocinctum E. & E.* — Two collections, one on an old Poria growing on a birch log and the other on a dead maple in a swamp. The specimen on the Poria shows the ashy color of the young stroma, the collection from maple shows the purplish black of the mature stroma. A distinctive feature of this species is the fact that the bark beneath the stroma is whitened and circumscribed by a black line, as pointed out by Ellis and Everhart (8).

Hypoxylon fuscum (Pers.) Fr. — Common on dead branches of *Alnus incana* (L.) Moench.

Hypoxylon multiforme Fr.* — Common on birch.

BASIDIOMYCETES

USTILAGINALES

Cintractia caricis (Pers.) Magn. * — On *Carex aquatilis* Wahlenb. Host identified by H. A. Gleason.

UREDINALES

Melampsoraceae

Chrysomyxa Cassandrae Pk. & Clint. II. — On *Chamaedaphne calyculata* (L.) Moench.

Chrysomyxa Ledi (Alb. & Schwein.) De By II. * — On *Ledum groenlandicum* Oeder.

Cronartium cerebrum (Pk.) Hedg. & Long I.* — On *Pinus Banksiana* Lamb. Exceedingly common on the northern scrub pine, some trees having hundreds of galls.

Melampsora Bigelowii Thüm. II. — On *Salix sp.*

Uredinopsis Osmundae Magn. II. * — On *Osmunda cinnamomea* L.

Pucciniaceae

Puccinia mesomegala Berk. & Curt. III. * — On *Clintonia borealis* (Ait.) Raf.

Caeoma nitens Burr. — On *Rubus villosus* Ait.

Aecidium Peckii De Toni. — On *Oenothera muricata* var. *canescens* (T. & G.) Robinson.

Aecidium Grossulariae Schum. — On *Ribes triste albinervum* (Michx.) Fernald.

Auriculariaceae

Hirneola Auricula-Judae (L.) Berk. — On fallen log.

Tremellaceae

Tremella mycetophila Pk. — On *Collybia dryophila* Fr.

Dacryomycetaceae

Ditiola conformis Karst. * — On rotten birch stick. Burt (5) says this fungus is rare and records it from Ontario, Vermont and New York.

Calocera palmata (Schum.) Fr. * — Among moss in swamp.

Guepinia spathularia (Schwein.) Fr. * — On rotten log.

Thelephoraceae

Thelephora terrestris (Ehrh.) Fr. * — Common on ground in burned area.

Aleurodiscus amorphus (Pers.) Rabenh. * — On dead fallen *Abies balsamea*. Burt (4) reports this species as infrequent.

Hymenochaete tabacina (Sowerb.) Lév. — Common on *Betula lutea* Michx., *Pyrus americana* (Marsh) DC., *Alnus incana*, *Acer spicatum* Lam., and *Fagus grandifolia* Ehrh.

STEREUM FASCIATUM Schwein. * — Common on maple and beech logs.

STEREUM HIRSUTUM (Willd.) Fr. * — On dead alder.

STEREUM MURRAYI (B. & C.) Burt. * — Common on dead birch logs.

STEREUM RUFUM Fr. — On dead poplar.

CYTIDIA SALICINA (Fr.) Burt. — On rotten stick on beaver house.

PENIOPHORA AURANTIACA Bres. * — On dead alder.

PENIOPHORA INCARNATA (Pers.) Karst. — On dead maple in swamp.

PENIOPHORA LUDOVICIANA Burt. * — On black ash stump in dried-up swamp. When fresh the color is orange-yellow. The fructification extends irregularly for 9 cm. and measures 2.5 cm. at its widest point. Burt (6) named this species from material collected by Langlois at St. Martinville, Louisiana. The present collection is the only other material Burt has received. The species appears to be rare but the two collections are from such widely separated localities that searching will undoubtedly yield further collections.

PENIOPHORA COCCINEO-FULVA (Schwein.) Burt. * — On old *Poria sp.* growing on a birch log. The fungus usually grows on wood or bark.

CORTICIUM GALACTINUM (Fr.) Burt. * — On rotten log.

CLAVARIACEAE

CLAVARIA CRISTATA Pers. * — Common on rotten logs in the pine forest.

CLAVARIA FILIPES B. & Rav. * — Among moss in swamp.

CLAVARIA PULCHRA Pk. * — Among moss in swamp.

CLAVARIA STRICTA Pers. * — On rotten log in mixed forest.

PHYSALACRIA INFLATA (Schwein.) Pk. * — On rotten log.

HYDNACEAE

ODONTIA VESICULOSA Burt ined. * — *Fide* Burt. On dead birch in swamp. The spores are hyaline, oval to elliptical, and measure $8\text{–}12 \times 3\text{–}4\ \mu$.

RADULUM BENNETTII B. & C. * — On dead bark at base of living birch.

PHLEBIA RADIATA Fr. * — On rotten birch stump in swamp.

ASTERODON FERRUGINOSUM Pat. * — On rotten birch log. This is *Hydnochaete setigera* Pk. Although the plant usually grows as a very thin crust on logs, the present collection is 1.5 cm. thick and shows ten distinct annual layers.

HYDNUM LACINIATUM Leers. * — On rotten birch log.

HYDNUM OCHRACEUM Pers. — On rotten log.

HYDNUM PULCHERRIMUM B. & C. * — On rotten birch log.

IRPEX LACTEUS Fr. * — On dead *Prunus pennsylvanica* L.

IRPEX TULIPIFERA (Schwein.) Fr. — On rotten beech log.

POLYPORACEAE

MERULIUS GYROSUS Burt. * — On rotten birch log. August 14, 1914. Vermilion, Michigan. This species, known only from this the type collection, is described by Burt (3) as follows:

"Type; in Mo. Bot. Gard. Herb.

"Fructification resupinate, effused, membranaceous, the margin cottony, whitish, here and there free; hymenium drying Capucine-buff, even near the margin, with the folds but little elevated, obtuse, not forming pores; in structure 400 μ thick, with the folds standing out 200–400 μ further, composed of interwoven, branching, hyaline hyphae 3.5–4 μ in diameter, nodose septate, incrusted near the substratum; no cystidia; spores hyaline, even, often slightly curved, $4.5\text{–}5 \times 1\text{–}2\ \mu$.

"On rotten birch log. Michigan. August. Rare.

"This species is related to *M. fugax*, but its hymenium has stouter, more obtuse folds than those of *M. fugax*, and the spores are of the slender curved type. *M. borealis* of Lapland has very similar aspect and coloration but with thinner folds, non-incrusted hyphae, and longer spores; perhaps future collections of *M. gyrosus* may show that these differences are not constant.

"Specimens examined: Michigan, Vermillion [*for* Vermilion], A. H. W. Povah, 7, type (in Mo. Bot. Gard. Herb. 9088)."

Portions of the type collection are also in the University of Michigan Herbarium, Shiras Collection, No. 312, and in Povah Herbarium, No. 616. A collection from Colorado in the University of Michigan Herbarium labeled *M. gyrosus* Burt should, in the opinion of the writer, be referred to *Radulum Bennettii* B. & C.

Poria betulina (Murr.) Lloyd. * — On birch in swamp. Murrill (12) records Maine and New Hampshire. Kauffman (9) adds New York. The range of this fungus will probably be shown to be co-extensive with the birch upon which it grows.

Poria fulvida E. & E.* — On maple log. The specimen agrees well with Murrill's (12) description of *Fuscoporia fulvida* (E. & E.) Murr., although the host and locality are widely separated.

Poria obliquiformis (Murr.) Sacc. & Trott. * — On maple log. This is the *Fomitiporia obliquiformis* of Murr. (12). A later collection in the University of Michigan Herbarium is on *Prunus serotina* Ehrh.

Poria ornata Pk. * — On rotten birch log. This species superficially resembles *P. subacida* Pk., which, however, grows on coniferous wood.

Poria papyracea (Schwein.) Cke. * — On the under side of dead twigs of *Thuja occidentalis* L. on living tree. Specimens submitted to C. G. Lloyd were called *Trametes serpens* Fr., with the comment that there were three distinct plants passing under that name. Weir (18) settled the difficulty.

Poria pereffusa (Murr.) Sacc. & Trott. * — This is *Fomitiporia pereffusa* Murr., although the cystidia in our specimens measure slightly larger ($27–31 \times 5–6$ μ) than in Murrill's description. On beech log.

Poria prunicola (Murr.) Sacc. & Trott. — On dead *Prunus pennsylvanica* L.

Poria rufa Fr. * — On under side of spruce log. The mahogany red pore surface and the white margin are very striking.

Poria subacida Pk. — On coniferous logs. Not uncommon.

Poria subincarnata (Pk.) Overh.* — On coniferous log.

Porothelium fimbriatum (Pers.) Fr. — On rotten birch log.

FOMES APPLANATUS Fr. — Rather common on birch, beech and maple.

FOMES IGNIARIUS (L.) Fr. * — Very common on birch.

FOMES FOMENTARIUS Fr. — Very common on birch.

FOMES NIGRICANS Fr. * — Common on dead and occasional on living birch.

FOMES ROSEUS (A. & S.) Cke. — Not uncommon on coniferous logs.

FOMES PINICOLA Fr. — Very common on coniferous wood. Collections were obtained from pine, balsam fir and spruce. One collection is rather unusual in that the upper surface shows a yellow-brown varnished appearance. When fresh, the pores and context were sulphur yellow. Microscopic study shows the characteristic structure of *F. pinicola.*

FOMES SCUTELLATUS Schwein.* — On dead birch in swamp; also on alder.

POLYPORUS ALBELLUS Pk. * — On dead alder and on birch stump.

POLYPORUS ALBOLUTEUS E. & E. * — On dead coniferous log. According to C. G. Lloyd, this is only the second collection sent to him from east of the Rocky Mountains. Our specimen is resupinate and measures 9.5×4.5 cm. The pores are 1–3 mm. in diameter. The orange color and large pores are distinctive.

POLYPORUS CHIONEUS Fr. * — On dead birch.

POLYPORUS ELEGANS (Bull.) Fr. — On dead birch. Not uncommon. Lloyd (10) comments upon a New York specimen with spines. One specimen in this collection shows three spines, one 3 mm. long.

POLYPORUS FRAGILIS Fr. — A very young specimen was collected upon a fallen spruce log. Our specimen agrees very well with a collection in the University of Michigan Herbarium from New Richmond, Michigan, identified by Lloyd.

POLYPORUS GUTTULATUS Pk.* — On old coniferous stump.

POLYPORUS LUCIDUS (Leys.) Fr. — American form on hemlock. Not uncommon.

POLYPORUS NIDULANS Fr. * — On dead *Betula lutea* Michx.

POLYPORUS PARGAMENUS Fr. — Common on dead birch. One collection on the base of a living birch.

Polyporus perennis (L.) Fr. * — On sandy wooded ridge.

Polyporus picipes Fr. — Common on rotten logs in the forest.

Polyporus resinosus (Schrad.) Fr. — Rather common on coniferous logs.

Polyporus schweinitzii Fr. * — Very common on coniferous logs. One collection from the base of a living *Pinus Strobus* L.

Polyporus Spraguei B. & C. — On rotten birch log.

Polyporus sulphureus (Bull.) Fr. — Occasional on pine logs.

Polyporus ursinus Lloyd. * — On rotten balsam fir log.

Polyporus volvatus Pk. * — On stump of *Pinus resinosus* Ait. (Specimens destroyed by insects.)

Polystictus abietinus Fr. * — Common on pine logs.

Polystictus balsameus Pk. * — A single collection from the base of a living balsam fir.

Polystictus hirsutus Fr. — Fairly common on dead alder.

Polystictus versicolor (L.) Fr. — Common on birch and maple.

Trametes carnea (Nees) Cke.* — Rather rare on coniferous logs.

Trametes cervina (Pers.) Fr.* — Rare. On dead maple in swamp.

Trametes cinnabarina (Jacq.) Fr. — Not uncommon on birch logs.

Trametes pini (Brot.) Fr. — Common on pine logs.

Trametes variiformis Pk. * — On rotten spruce log. Not common.

Daedalea confragosa (Bolt.) Fr. — On rotten birch log. Infrequent.

Lenzites sepiaria Fr. — Common on coniferous wood.

Boletaceae

Boletinus porosus (Berk.) Pk. — On rather dry sphagnum in woods.

Boletus scaber Fr. — In woods.

Boletus separans Pk. — In pine forest.

Boletus versipellis Fr. — In mixed forest.

Agaricaceae

Amanita frostiana Pk.* — A single specimen in hemlock woods.

Amanita muscaria Fr. — Very abundant under pines, especially at Whitefish Point, Michigan.

Cantharellus infundibuliformis (Scop.) Fr. — In cedar swamp.

Claudopus nidulans Pers. — On rotten log.

Clitocybe ectipoides Pk. — On rotten coniferous log.

Clitocybe laccata (Scop.) Fr. — Common in pine woods and occasional in swamp.

Collybia dryophila Fr. — On rotten birch log.

Collybia platyphylla Fr. — On sandy wooded ridge.

Crepidotus mollis Fr. — On rotten black ash stump.

Hygrophorus miniatus Fr. — Very common in bogs and swamps.

Hypholoma sublateritium var. perplexum Pk. — On ground under cedars.

Lentinus cochleatus Fr. — On rotten birch stump and on rotten log in swamp.

Lentinus lepideus Fr. — Exceedingly common. On driftwood along the shore of Lake Superior and on logs and stumps in swamps.

Marasmius rotula (Scop.) Fr. * — On rotten birch twigs in forest.

Omphalia campanella Fr. * — On moss-covered coniferous log in swamp.

Pholiota squarrosoides Pk. — On rotten birch in woods.

Pleurotus sapidus Kalchbr. — Common on birch and maple.

Psalliota campestris Fr. — On old manure pile in old lumber camp.

Russula chamaeleontina Fr. — In wet cedar swamp.

Russula delica Fr. — In sandy woods.

Plicatura nivea (Fr.) Karst. * (*Trogia alni* Pk.). — On trunks of living maple and on dead yellow birch.

GASTEROMYCETES

Lycoperdon pulcherrimum B. & C. — On dead birch log.

Lycoperdon pyriforme Schaeff. — On base of birch tree.

LYCOPERDON PYRIFORME var. TESSALATUM Pers. — On rotten birch log.

GEASTER CORONATUS (Schaeff.) Schroet.* — On rotten, moss-covered log.

BOVISTA PILA B. & C. — In vegetable garden.

SCLERODERMA VERRUCOSUM (Bull.) Pers. — On sand dune.

ASTRAEUS STELLATUS (Scop.) E. Fischer. — Very common on sand dunes.

FUNGI IMPERFECTI

SPHAERONEMA ACERINUM Pk. — Very common on dead maple twigs.

CYTOSPORA LEUCOSPERMA (Pers.) Fr. — On maple beaver cutting in beaver dam.

CAMAROSPORIUM ACERINUM E. & E. * — On dead twigs of *Acer spicatum* Lam. The spores in our specimens, measuring 12–14 μ, are slightly wider than in the description.

CYTOSPORINA CERVICULATA Sacc. * — On dead alder branches.

RHABDOSPORA INAEQUALIS Sacc. & Roum. * — On dead twigs on living *Pyrus americana* (Marsh) DC.

SPHAERONAEMELLA OXYSPORA (Berk.) Sacc. * — On old decaying *Polyporus resinosus.*

LIBERTELLA BETULINA Desm. * — On fallen birch twigs.

STYSANUS BERKELEYI (Mont.) Sacc. * — On old *Fomes fomentarius.*

TUBERCULARIA VULGARIS Tode. — On alder twigs in swamp and on old *Plowrightia morbosa.*

BRYOPHYTA

HEPATICAE

MARCHANTIA POLYMORPHA L. — In swamp beside ditch. June. Antheridiophores and archegoniophores present.

PTILIDIUM CILIARE (L.) Nees. — On bark of birch trees. June. Fruiting.

PTILIDIUM PULCHERRIMUM (Web.) Hampe. * — On bark of white cedar in swamp. June. Fruiting.

RADULA COMPLANATA (L.) Dumort. * — On exposed root on conifer by stream.

FRULLANIA ASAGRAYANA Mont. — On bark of trees in wet places.

FRULLANIA BRITTONIAE Evans. * — On bark of fallen white cedar in swamp.

JUNGERMANNIA LANCEOLATA L. — On rotten logs in swamp. June. Fruiting.

LOPHOZIA MARCHICA (Nees.) Steph. — On rotten stump beside spring.

MUSCI

SPHAGNALES

SPHAGNUM GIRGHENSOHNII Russ. — In wet places in forest. August. Sporophytes.

SPHAGNUM RECURVUM Beauv. — In hemlock forest. August. Sporophytes.

SPHAGNUM SQUARROSUM Crom. * — Four collections, three from cedar swamps, and one from low, wet place in the forest. August. Sporophytes.

BRYALES

DICRANACEAE

CERATODON PURPUREUS (L.) Brid. — Common in open sandy places.

DICRANUM FUSCESCENS Turn. * — At base of tree on mound in swamp.

DICRANUM UNDULATUM Ehrh. — On the ground in woods.

LEUCOBRYACEAE

LEUCOBRYUM GLAUCUM (L.) Schimp. — On a high ridge through swamp.

POTTIACEAE

BARBULA FALLAX Hedw. * — On sand along shore of Lake Superior.

ORTHOTRICHACEAE

ULOTA CRISPULA Bruch. — On dead twigs of white cedar.

Funariaceae

Funaria hygrometrica (L.) Schreb. — Very common on half-buried logs in swamp.

Bryaceae

Bryum bimum Schreb. — On earth in wet places in woods.

Pohlia nutans (Schreb.) Lindb. — Common on stumps in swamp.

Mniaceae

Mnium Drummondii B. & S. — On rotten logs in swamp. Rare.

Mnium medium B. & S. — On ground in wet white cedar swamp. Rare.

Mnium punctatum (L.) Hedw. * — Along bank of stream in swamp. Rare.

Mnium rostratum Schrad. * — In wet places in swamp. Rare.

Mnium spinulosum B. & S. — On rotten wood in wet places. Common.

Neckeraceae

Neckera pennata (L.) Hedw. — Very common on trunks of trees in moist woods growing up to eight or ten feet above the ground.

Hypnaceae

Hypnum fertile Sendt.* — Along edge of dried-up swamp growing mixed with *Climacium dendroides*. Not common.

Hypnum haldaneanum Grev. — Common on rotten stumps and logs in swamp.

Hypnum crista-castrensis L. — On rotten log in swamp. Not rare.

Plagiothecium striatellum (Brid.) Limpr. — On wet ground in swamp.

Stereodon imponens (Hedw.) Lindb. * — On rotten log in swamp.

Dendroidaceae

Climacium dendroides (L.) Web. & Mohr. — At edge of dry swamp under conifers.

GEORGIACEAE

GEORGIA PELLUCIDA (L.) Rabenh. — Common on stumps in swamp.

POLYTRICHACEAE

POLYTRICHUM COMMUNE L. — Very common on sandy soil.

POLYTRICHUM JUNIPERINUM Willd. — Very common on sandy soil.

POLYTRICHUM OHIENSE Ren. & Card. — On sandy bank along road at edge of woods. Not common.

POLYTRICHUM PILIFERUM Schreb. — Common on sandy soil. In moist, low places along the shore of Lake Superior.

NORTHWESTERN UNIVERSITY
EVANSTON, ILLINOIS

LITERATURE CITED

1. ATKINSON, G. F. 1918. The Genus Endogone. Brooklyn Bot. Gard. Mem., 1 : 1–17.
2. BEARDSLEE, H. C. 1917. Michigan Collections of Myxomycetes. Nineteenth Rept. Mich. Acad. Sci., pp. 159–162.
3. BURT, E. A. 1917. Merulius in North America. Ann. Mo. Bot. Gard., 4 : 328.
4. —— 1918. The Thelephoraceae of North America. IX. Aleurodiscus. Ann. Mo. Bot. Gard., 5 : 181.
5. —— 1921. Some North American Tremellaceae, Dacryomycetaceae, and Auriculariaceae. Ann. Mo. Bot. Gard., 8 : 386.
6. —— 1925. The Thelephoraceae of North America. XIV. Peniophora. Ann. Mo. Bot. Gard., 12 : 244.
7. DODGE, C. K. 1921. Observations on the Wild Plants at Whitefish Point and Vermilion, near the South Shore of Lake Superior, and other parts of Chippewa County, Michigan, in 1914. Mich. Biol. and Geol. Survey Publ., 31, Biol. Ser. 6, pp. 125–164.
8. ELLIS, J. B., AND EVERHART, B. M. 1892. The North American Pyrenomycetes. Newfield, N. J.
9. KAUFFMAN, C. H. 1915. The Fungi of North Elba. N. Y. State Mus. Bull., 179 : 91.
10. LLOYD, C. G. 1920. Mycological Notes, 64 : 1003. Fig. 1833.

11. MACBRIDE, T. H. 1922. The North American Slime Moulds. New York.

12. MURRILL, W. A. 1907. North American Flora, 9 : 12.

13. POVAH, A. H. W. 1917. A Critical Study of Certain Species of Mucor. Bull. Torrey Bot. Club, 44 : 241–259; 287–313.

14. REHM, H. 1896. In Rabenhorst's Kryptog. Flora Deutsch., Österreich und der Schweiz. Bd. I, Abt. 3, pp. 1013.

15. SACCARDO, P. A. 1889. Sylloge Fungorum, 8 : 599–600.

16. THAXTER, R. 1888. The Entomophthoreae of the United States. Boston Soc. Nat. Hist. Mem., 4 : 133–201.

17. —— 1897. New or Peculiar Zygomycetes. 2. Syncephalastrum and Syncephalis. Bot. Gaz., 24 : 12.

18. WEIR, J. R. 1923. Poria papyracea (Schwein.) Cke. Phytopathology, 13 : 187.

THE HYDROGEN ION CONCENTRATION OF THE HABITATS OF THE BRYOPHYTES AND PTERIDOPHYTES OF THE DOUGLAS LAKE REGION *

JOSEPH J. ROBINOVE AND CARL D. LA RUE

FOR some time one of the authors has been interested in a study of the life-histories and the genetic behavior of the green cryptogams, particularly the bryophytes. At the same time one of his students has been engaged in similar studies on the pteridophytes. These studies have involved the cultivation of bryophytes and pteridophytes in the laboratory and the greenhouse. Among other things, it became desirable to know to what extent success in growing species of the various groups might be due to the hydrogen ion concentration of the media used. Accordingly an attempt was made to discover the relation of the forms to the soil reactions of their normal habitats.

This work was done during the summers of 1926 and 1927 at the University of Michigan Biological Station located on Douglas Lake, Cheboygan County, Michigan. That this region is rich in species of bryophytes has been shown in the lists made by Nichols (6). The number of species of pteridophytes is not particularly large, but there is a good representation of most of the groups in the list by Gates and Ehlers (4). The range of the habitats is not great, but for preliminary work of this sort they show sufficient variability.

Collections were made from a number of localities near the station, as well as from the Big Stone Bay region on the shores of Lake Michigan. The places of collection need not be discussed

* Paper from the Department of Botany of the University of Michigan, No. 294, reporting work conducted at the University of Michigan Biological Station.

here, inasmuch as they have been treated from a vegetational standpoint by Gates (3).

METHOD

The method used was similar to that devised by Wherry (7). In each test a sample of the medium in which the plant was growing, soil, humus, rotten wood, etc., was brought into the laboratory with a specimen of the plant for determination. Whenever possible, determination of the hydrogen ion concentration was made at once. A La Motte colorimeter was used, and the indicator dyes used were supplied by the La Motte Chemical Co. The indicators used were phenol red 0.02 per cent solution; brom-cresol purple 0.04 per cent; brom-phenol blue 0.04 per cent; and brom-cresol green 0.04 per cent.

The soil or other medium to be tested was put in a test tube and covered with distilled water which had been tested for neutrality. Equal volumes of the medium and of distilled water were used, and the tubes were then shaken vigorously to mix the water and medium thoroughly. The mixture was allowed to stand for an hour, after which the clear liquid was decanted into a clean tube and set aside for a short time to allow any particles to settle to the bottom, or float to the surface.

The pH tests were made by using 10 c. c. of the solution with 0.5 c. c. of the indicator. The colors were matched with the colorimeter tubes. These tubes were graduated to 0.2 pH and readings were taken to 0.1 pH. Border-line cases were checked by other indicators. Since there was very little clay in these soils, no difficulty was experienced with turbidity. The decanted liquid was usually clear and free from sediment or suspended materials. Filtration was unnecessary, and, since its effect on the pH value of solutions has not yet been tested fully, was avoided.

The species studied and the pH ranges of each are shown for the bryophytes in Table I and for the pteridophytes in Table II.

TABLE I

HYDROGEN ION CONCENTRATION OF THE BRYOPHYTES OF THE DOUGLAS LAKE REGION

The Bryophytes are listed according to the usage of Evans and Nichols (2); the Pteridophyte nomenclature follows Gray's Manual.

SPECIES	Number of samples	pH range	Average
MARCHANTIACEAE			
Conocephalum conicum (L.) Dumort........	9	4.2–8.0	6.3
Marchantia polymorpha L................	6	5.2–7.8	6.3
METZGERIACEAE			
Pellia neesiana (Gottsche) Limpr...........	7	6.4–7.0	6.7
Riccardia latifrons Lindb..................	8	4.8–6.6	5.4
Riccardia multifida (L.) S. F. Gray..........	2	4.6–4.6	4.6
Riccardia sinuata (Dicks.) Trevis...........	1		7.0
JUNGERMANNIACEAE			
Bazzania trilobata (L.) S. F. Gray..........	8	4.6–6.2	5.2
Blepharostoma ciliata....................	2	4.0–5.0	4.5
Blepharostoma trichophyllum (L.) Dumort...	7	4.2–6.2	5.4
Calypogeia trichomanis (L.) Corda..........	19	4.0–6.6	5.4
Cephalozia catenulata (Huben.) Spruce.......	2	5.1–5.2	5.2
Cephalozia curvifolia (Dicks.) Dumort........	2	4.2–6.0	5.1
Cephalozia fluitans (Nees) Spruce...........	2	4.9–5.0	5.0
Cephalozia media Lindb..................	19	4.0–7.0	5.5
Cephalozia pleniceps (Aust.) Lindb..........	1		6.0
Chiloscyphus fragilis (Roth) Schiffn..........	1		6.8
Chiloscyphus rivularis (Schrad.) Loeske.......	2	6.4–6.6	6.5
Frullania eboracensis Gottsche.............	8	5.0–6.8	5.7
Jamesoniella autumnalis (D. C.) Steph.......	20	4.2–6.2	5.3
Lepidozia reptans (L.) Dumort.............	5	4.2–5.8	5.0
Lophocolea heterophylla (Schrad.) Dumort....	14	4.0–7.0	5.2
Lophocolea minor Nees..................	2	4.8–6.4	5.6
Lophozia barbata (Schreb.) Dumort	1		5.8
Lophozia incisa (Schrad.) Dumort...........	1		5.6
Lophozia porphyroleuca (Nees) Schiffn........	2	4.8–6.2	5.5
Mylia anomola (Hook.) S. F. Gray..........	2	4.4–4.6	4.5
Plagiochila asplenioides (L.) Dumort.........	1		6.8
Porella platyphylloides (Schwein.) Lindb......	7	5.6–6.4	6.1
Ptilidium ciliare (L.) Nees................	1		5.0
Ptilidium pulcherrimum (Wed.) Hampe.......	16	4.6–6.8	5.1
Radula complanata (L.) Dumort	7	4.4–6.8	5.6
Scapania nemorosa (L.) Dumort............	1		6.2
Trichocolea tomentella (Ehrh.) Dumort......	8	4.4–6.6	5.6

TABLE I (*Continued*)

HYDROGEN ION CONCENTRATION OF THE BRYOPHYTES OF THE DOUGLAS LAKE REGION

SPECIES	Number of samples	pH range	Average
SPHAGNACEAE			
Sphagnum fuscum (Schimp.) H. Klinggr.	2	4.8–5.8	5.3
Sphagnum squarrosum Crome	8	3.8–7.4	5.3
Sphagnum wulffianum (Girg.)	2	4.6–5.4	5.0
DICRANACEAE			
Ceratodon purpureus (L.) Bird	6	4.4–7.0	5.4
Dicranum flagellare Hedw.	14	3.8–6.4	5.3
Dicranum montanum Hedw.	8	4.0–6.2	5.3
Dicranum rugosum (Hoffm.) Bridg.	2	5.0–5.2	5.1
Dicranum scoparium (L.) Hedw.	12	4.0–6.6	5.0
Dicranum undulatum Ehrh.	6	4.4–6.2	5.0
Dicranum viride (Sull. & Lesq.) Lindb.	14	4.4–6.0	5.2
LEUCOBRYACEAE			
Leucobryum glaucum (L.) Schimp.	4	4.8–5.6	5.3
FISSIDENTACEAE			
Fissidens adiantioides (L.) Hedw.	1		6.2
Fissidens cristatus Wills.	2	6.2–6.2	6.2
Fissidens osmundioides (Sw.) Hedw.	2	6.0–7.2	6.6
POTTIACEAE			
Encalpyta ciliata (Hedw.) Hoffm.	2	6.2–6.6	6.4
Tortula mucronifolia Schwaegr.	2	6.2–6.6	6.4
ORTHOTRICACEAE			
Orthotrichum speciosum Nees	3	5.9–6.2	6.1
FUNARIACEAE			
Funaria hygrometrica (L.) Schreb.	3	5.2–6.6	6.1
BRYACEAE			
Bryum caespiticium L.	19	4.0–7.0	5.4
Leptobryum pyriforme (L.) Wils.	1		5.8
Pohlia nutans (Schreb.) Lindb.	6	4.2–6.4	5.0
Rhodobryum roseum (Weis.) Limpr.	4	5.8–7.1	6.5
MNIACEAE			
Mnium affine ciliare (Grev.) C. M.	9	3.9–7.3	5.8
Mnium marginatum (Dicks.) Leyss.	4	5.2–6.5	5.0

TABLE I (*Continued*)

HYDROGEN ION CONCENTRATION OF THE BRYOPHYTES OF THE DOUGLAS LAKE REGION

SPECIES	Number of samples	pH range	Average
Mnium marginatum (Dicks.) Beauv.	2	5.2–6.6	5.8
Mnium punctatum (L.) Schreb.	2	5.2–6.8	6.0
Mnium punctatum var. elatum (L.)Schreb.	5	4.8–6.8	5.6
Mnium rostratum Schrad.	3	6.0–6.8	6.5
Mnium stellare Reich.	1		5.4
AULACOMNIACEAE			
Aulacomnium palustre (L.) Schwaegr.	14	4.4–6.6	5.5
BARTRAMIACEAE			
Bartramia pomiformis L.	1		5.6
Philonotis fontana (L.) Bridg.	7	4.0–8.2	6.8
FONTINALACEAE			
Fontinalis novae-angliae Sull.	1		7.2
LEUCODONTACEAE			
Leucodon sciuroides (L.) Schwaegr.	1	4.6–6.8	6.2
NECKERACEAE			
Neckera pennata (L.) Hedw.	10	4.2–7.2	6.0
LESKEACEAE			
Anomodon attenuatus (Schreb.) Huben.	8	6.0–7.1	6.5
Anomodon minor (Beauv.) Furn.	1		6.4
Elodium lanatum (Stroem.) Broth.	1		6.1
Thuidium abietinum (L.) Br. & Sch.	3	6.4–7.0	6.7
Thuidium delicatulum (L.) Br. & Sch.	8	5.0–6.6	5.7
Thuidium recognitum (Hedw.) Lindb.	10	4.6–8.0	6.0
HYPNACEAE			
Amblystegium irriguum (Wils.) Br. & Sch.	1		6.0
Amblystegium riparium (L.) Br. & Sch.	2	6.2–6.4	6.3
Amblystegium serpens (L.) Br. & Sch.	3	6.4–7.4	6.8
Calliergon cordifolium (Hedw.) Kindb.	4	6.0–6.6	6.3
Calliergon giganteum Schimp.	5	5.8–7.8	6.6
Drepanocladus aduncus (L.) Warnst.	2	6.2–7.1	6.6
Heterophyllum haldanianum (Grev.) Kindb.	2	4.2–5.2	4.7
Hylocomium splendens (Hedw.) Br. & Sch.	4	4.2–7.0	5.7
Hypnum schreberi Willd.	9	4.4–6.8	5.5

TABLE I (*Continued*)

HYDROGEN ION CONCENTRATION OF THE BRYOPHYTES OF THE DOUGLAS LAKE REGION

SPECIES	Number of samples	pH range	Average
Ptilium crista-castrensis (L.) De Not.	3	4.8–6.6	5.8
Rhytidiadelphus triquetris (L.) Warnst.	10	4.0–7.8	5.6
Stereodon fertilis (Sendt.) Lindb.	1		6.2
Stereodon imponens (Hedw.) Lindb.	3	4.4–6.2	5.1
Stereodon lindbergii (Mitt.) Warnst.	16	4.3–6.8	5.5
Stereodon recurvans (Schwaegr.) Broth.	2	5.0–5.2	5.1
BRACHYTHECIACEAE			
Bryhnia novae-angliae (Sull & Lesq.) Grout.	1		6.0
DENDROIDACEAE			
Climaceum dendroideum (L.) Web. f. & Mohr.	11	5.4–6.6	6.0
BAUXBAUMIACEAE			
Bauxbaumia aphylla L.	1		6.4
GEORGIACEAE			
Georgia pellucida (L.) Rabenh.	16	4.0–6.8	4.8
POLYTRICHACEAE			
Catherinea undulata (L.) Web. f. & Mohr.	1		6.8
Polytrichum commune L.	4	4.6–6.7	5.3
Polytrichum juniperinum Willd.	17	4.4–6.7	5.2
Polytrichum piliferum Schreb.	2	4.8–5.4	5.0

TABLE II

HYDROGEN ION CONCENTRATION OF THE PTERIDOPHYTES OF THE DOUGLAS LAKE REGION

SPECIES	Number of samples	pH range	Average
POLYPODIACEAE			
Phegopteris dryopteris (L.) Fée	3	6.0–7.6	7.0
Phegopteris robertiana (Hoffm.) A. Br.	1		7.4
Pteris aquilina L.	3	4.6–6.8	5.4
Asplenium filix-femina (L.) Bernh.	8	6.0–8.2	7.0
Aspidium cristatum (L.) Sw.	4	6.0–6.6	6.2
Aspidium spinulosum (O. F. Muller) Sw.	8	4.2–6.4	5.3
Aspidium spinulosum var. intermedium (Muhl.) D. C. Eaton	8	4.8–6.4	5.8
Aspidium thelypteris (L.) Sw.	9	4.8–8.2	6.3
Cystopteris bulbifera (L.) Bernh.	3	7.4–8.2	7.8
Onoclea sensibilis (L.)	8	4.8–8.0	6.1
Onoclea struthiopteris (L.) Hoffm.	1		7.3
OSMUNDACEAE			
Osmunda cinnamomea D. L.	5	4.2–5.8	5.0
Osmunda regalis (L.)	8	4.2–6.8	6.0
OPHIOGLOSSACEAE			
Botrychium ramosum (Roth) Aschers.	2		6.2
Botrychium simplex E. Hitchcock	1		6.6
Botrychium virginianum (L.) Sw.	9	5.2–8.0	6.2
EQUISETACEAE			
Equisetum arvense L.	9	6.4–7.8	6.8
Equisetum hyemale L.	2	7.4–7.6	7.5
Equisetum hyemale robustum (A. Br.) A. A. Eaton	1		7.4
Equisetum fluviatile L. (Pipes)	2	5.6–5.8	5.7
Equisetum littorale Kuhlewein	1		8.0
Equisetum palustre L.	3	5.0–6.2	5.2
Equisetum scirpoides Michx.	3	5.2–7.8	6.5
Equisetum sylvaticum L.	5	5.2–8.2	6.9
Equisetum variegatum Schleich.	6	7.6–8.0	7.8
Equisetum variegatum var. Nelsoni A. A. Eaton	2	7.7–8.5	8.1
LYCOPODIACEAE			
Lycopodium annotinum L.	4	5.8–6.2	6.0
Lycopodium clavatum L.	6	5.5–6.4	5.3
Lycopodium lucidulum Michx.	1		6.6
Lycopodium obscurum L.	3	6.2–6.5	6.4
Lycopodium tristachyum Pursh.	2	5.4–6.6	6.0
SELAGINELLACEAE			
Selaginella selaginoides (L.) Link	2		7.8
Selaginella rupestris (L.) O. Spring	1		7.2

It is scarcely to be expected that mosses and liverworts which grow on a great variety of substrata would be affected greatly by the general soil conditions in any given locality. Many of the forms are epiphytic; others grow on decaying logs and stumps, still others in water, and only those rooted directly in the soil could be expected to be affected by the reaction of the soil. In some places, however, the soil water may penetrate the substratum of a plant sufficiently to influence its reaction.

In most situations the composition of the substratum of the bryophytes as well as its reaction varies greatly over a few square feet, sometimes over even a few square inches of surface. For instance, where a stream flows through a locality from which collections have been made, the plants growing in the water may have a habitat of very different reaction from that of those on the bank. Likewise, plants on the soil at the edge of the bog may experience a very different living condition from those growing on peat in the center of the bog. Therefore, although all the plants secured on a given collecting trip were studied as one set, these sets are of no particular significance and are not presented.

What has been said of the bryophytes in relation to their habitats is true of the pteridophytes, only in a much lesser degree. These forms are more often rooted in the soil than are the bryophytes, but a great many of them are found in almost identical situations. The number of epiphytic plants in this group is very small and such as occur are much nearer the ground than many of the bark-inhabiting species of mosses and liverworts. In general the particular area in which a fern or club moss grows is of no great importance as an indication of reaction of its substratum; data on localities are, therefore, omitted.

Collections were made in the following places near the Biological Station: The Gorge, Bryant's Bog, Fairy Island, Grapevine Point, Mud Lake Bog, Smith's Bog, Reese's Bog, Burt Lake, Vincent's Lake, Carp Creek, Ingleside, Maple River and North Fishtail Bay. In addition to these, a considerable number of samples was taken from the Big Stone Bay region along the shore of Lake Michigan.

Most of the soils in Cheboygan County are sandy and have

been wooded. Where the land has been cut and burned over, very little humus is left, but in the well-developed forests and in the swamps and bays there is a great deal of humus on the surface and incorporated with the upper layers of the soil. In such a region one would naturally expect to find a large number of habitats with an acid reaction, and the tests bear out that expectation. No species of bryophyte of which more than one sample was tested had a substratum with an average pH above 7.0. From the data secured it is not possible to conclude that any moss or liverwort prefers an alkaline or even a neutral soil reaction; it is very desirable, however, to have data from a region where the general reaction of the soil is alkaline, before any sweeping conclusions are made as to the preference of an acid reaction.

The fact that a species is found growing under certain conditions is as likely to indicate tolerance of those conditions as preference for them. Usually, where the data in Table I show limited ranges for species, it will be seen that the number of determinations is small. Almost every species for which a fairly large number of determinations are shown will be found to show ability to thrive in a great range of habitats. Table III shows the variation in pH of some species with an unusually wide range.

TABLE III

HYDROGEN ION DETERMINATIONS OF HABITATS OF BRYOPHYTES AND PTERIDOPHYTES WHICH SHOW UNUSUAL RANGES

The actual number of samples of species listed will be found in Tables I and II.

BRYOPHYTES

SPECIES	pH						
Aulocomnium palustre....	4.4	4.6	5.0	5.2	5.4	5.7	6.0
	6.6						
Blepharostoma trichophyllum..................	4.2	5.0	5.6	5.8	6.0	6.1	6.2
Bryum caespiticium	4.0	4.4	4.6	4.8	5.0	5.2	5.4
	5.6	6.3	6.4	6.6	7.0		
Calypogeia trichomanis ...	4.0	4.2	4.3	4.8	5.0	5.2	5.4
	5.8	6.0	6.1	6.2	6.3	6.4	6.6
Cephalozia media	4.0	4.2	4.4	4.6	5.0	5.2	5.6
	6.0	6.1	6.2	6.3	6.4	6.6	
Ceratodon purpureus	4.4	5.2	5.4	7.0			
Climacium dendroides	5.4	5.6	5.8	6.1	6.2	6.3	6.6
Conocephalum conicum...	4.2	5.0	5.8	6.2	6.6	6.8	7.4
	8.0						
Dicranum flagellare	3.8	4.0	4.4	4.6	4.8	5.0	5.2
	6.0	6.2	6.4				
Dicranum montanum.....	4.0	4.2	4.6	6.0	6.2		
Dicranum scoparium	4.3	4.4	4.8	5.0	5.2	5.4	6.6
Dicranum viride	4.4	4.6	4.8	4.9	5.0	5.2	5.6
	6.0						
Frullania eboracensis	5.0	5.4	5.8	5.9	6.0	6.8	
Georgia pellucida	4.0	4.1	4.2	4.4	4.8	5.0	5.2
	6.0	6.4	6.8				
Hypnum schreberi	4.4	4.6	4.8	5.2	5.8	6.0	6·2
	6.4	6.8					
Jamesoniella autumnalis ..	4.2	4.6	4.8	5.0	5.2	5.6	5.8
	6.0	6.2	7.0				
Leucodon sciuroides......	4.6	5.8	6.0	6.2	6.4	6.6	6.8
Lophocolea heterophylla..	4.0	4.2	4.4	4.6	4.8	5.0	6.0
	6.1	6.2	6.6	7.0			
Marchantia polymorpha...	5.2	5.8	5.9	6.4	6.8	7.8	
Mnium affine ciliare......	3.9	5.2	5.3	5.7	6.0	6.2	
	6.3	6.8	7.3				
Neckera pennata.........	4.2	5.0	5.6	6.0	6.2	6.4	6.7
	7.2						
Pellia neesiana...........	5.0	6.4	6.6	6.8	7.0		
Philinotis fontana........	4.0	6.8	7.0	7.3	7.4	8.2	

TABLE III (*Continued*)

HYDROGEN ION DETERMINATIONS OF HABITATS OF BRYOPHYTES AND PTERIDOPHYTES WHICH SHOW UNUSUAL RANGES

BRYOPHYTES

SPECIES	pH						
Polytrichum juniperinum..	4.4	4.6	4.8	5.0	5.2	5.4	5.6
	6.2	6.6	6.7				
Porella platyphylloidea....	5.6	5.8	6.0	6.2	6.4		
Ptilidium pulcherrimum ..	4.6	4.8	5.0	5.4	5.8	6.0	6.8
Radula complanata.......	4.4	4.6	5.0	5.9	6.2	6.8	
Rhytidiadelphus triquetris	4.0	4.6	5.0	5.2	5.8	6.2	6.4
	7.8						
Riccardia latifrons........	4.6	4.8	5.2	6.0	6.1	6.6	
Sphagnum squarrosum....	3.8	4.6	4.7	5.2	6.0	7.4	
Stereodon lindbergii......	4.3	4.4	4.8	5.0	5.4	5.6	5.7
	6.0	6.2	6.3	6.4	6.8		
Thuidium recognitum.....	4.6	5.0	5.2	6.0	6.2	6.4	6.6
	8.0						

PTERIDOPHYTES

SPECIES	pH							
Asplenium filix-femina....	6.0	6.4	6.6	7.0	7.4	7.6	8.2	
Aspidium spinulosum.....	4.2	5.0	6.0	6.2	6.4			
Aspidium spinulosum var. intermedium...........	4.8	5.2	6.2	6.4				
Aspidium thelypteris......	4.8	5.0	5.8	6.0	6.1	6.2	6.4	6.8
	7.6	8.2						
Botrychium virginianum..	5.2	5.6	6.0	6.2	7.6	8.0		
Equisetum arvense.......	6.2	6.4	6.6	7.2	7.7	7.8		
Equisetum variegatum....	7.2	7.6	8.0	8.4				
Lycopodium annotinum...	5.8	6.0	6.2					
Lycopodium clavatum....	5.0	5.1	5.4	5.5	6.1	6.4		
Onoclea sensibilis.........	4.8	5.0	5.6	6.4	6.6	7.0		
Osmunda cinnamomea....	4.2	5.2	5.4	5.8				
Osmunda regalis	4.2	5.0	5.2	5.8	6.6	6.8	7.8	
Pteris aquilina...........	4.6	4.7	4.8	5.2	6.2	6.3	6.4	6.5
	6.6	6.8						

A few species (*Climaceum dendroideum*, *Jamesoniella autumnalis*, *Lophocolea heterophylla* and *Porella platyphylloidea*) show a very limited range, though the number of determinations for each is fairly large. These plants are rather restricted in the habitats in which they are found and it may be that the determinations really show the preferences of these plants. But for most of the species studied it is possible to infer only that a much larger number of determinations must be made before anything like a preferred range can be indicated.

Sphagnum mosses are usually considered as forms which have a definite preference for acid habitats, but one specimen of *Sphagnum squarrosum* was found in an alkaline habitat (pH 7.4). This was checked carefully because it was suspected to be an erroneous determination, but proved correct. This sample was found growing in the water of Carp Creek not far from its origin in the springs which flow out from underlying layers of limestone. The water here showed a pH 7.6 as determined by Creaser (1). It is likely that further examinations will reveal other examples of the growth of Sphagnum in alkaline water.

The ferns are like the mosses and liverworts in showing a wide range of habitat reactions. Almost all the species for which a considerable number of determinations were secured vary greatly in the pH values of the substrata. The majority of these show an extension from acid reactions well into the alkaline range. A few species of restricted habitat fail to reveal any alkaline reaction, so far as they were tested here.

The lycopods in this region have only acid habitats, which is to be expected from their limited distribution.

The species of Equisetum are rather general in their distribution. Of the species and varieties tested, two show only acid habitats, four only alkaline substrata, and the remainder habitats ranging from acid to alkaline.

Two species of Selaginella were tested, but only one determination for each was secured, so that little emphasis can be put on the fact that both samples were alkaline.

DISCUSSION

Wherry (7) has emphasized the importance of soil reactions as a factor in plant distribution, and has shown by pH determinations what has long been known from observation, that certain plants are absolutely restricted to acid habitats, while others prefer neutral or alkaline soils.

Gustafson's work tends to prove that soil reactions play an important part in the distribution of certain plants on the shore of an inland lake in Michigan.

Only a small number of the fern species studied by Wherry were collected and tested in this study. Most of the data on these species agrees fairly well with Wherry's results. The number of determinations is not great enough to enable us to attempt to align them with his theory that northern ferns tend to prefer alkaline habitats.

So far as the bryophytes are concerned, it appears easy to over-emphasize the influence of the reaction of the habitat on the growth of the plants. There are, in any type of plant, many other factors in the soil or substratum which may be of equal weight, while with the bryophytes it is almost certain that some of these are of greater importance than the pH value.

SUMMARY

(1) The hydrogen ion concentrations of the habitats of about one hundred species of bryophytes and thirty-three species of the pteridophytes are presented.

(2) On account of the small number of determinations for many of the species of pteridophytes no definite conclusions can be drawn, but there are indications that many of the plants can tolerate a wide range of soil reactions.

(3) With some exceptions, the bryophytes show ability to thrive on substrata of highly variable reactions.

The authors are indebted to Professor George E. Nichols of Yale University and the University of Michigan Biological Station for aid in the collection and identification of many of the species listed in this paper.

University of Michigan

BIBLIOGRAPHY

1. CREASER, C. W., AND BROWN, H. W. 1927. The Hydrogen-ion Concentration of Brook-trout Waters of Northern Lower Michigan. Ecology, 8 : 98–105.

2. EVANS, A. W., AND NICHOLS, G. E. 1908. The Bryophytes of Connecticut. Conn. State Geol. and Nat. Hist. Survey, Bull. 11 : 1–204.

3. GATES, F. C. 1912. The Vegetation of the Region in the Vicinity of Douglas Lake, Cheboygan County, Michigan. Rept. Mich. Acad. Sci., 14 : 46–106.

4. GATES, F. C., AND EHLERS, J. H. 1924. An Annotated List of the Higher Plants of the Region of Douglas Lake, Michigan. Papers Mich. Acad. Sci., Arts and Letters, 4: 183–284. Additions to this list are published *ibid.*, 8 : 111–120.

5. GUSTAFSON, F. G. 1926. Plant Distribution as Affected by the Hydrogen Ion Concentration of the Soil. Papers Mich. Acad. Sci., Arts and Letters, 6 : 237–246.

6. NICHOLS, G. E. 1922. The Bryophytes of Michigan with Particular Reference to the Douglas Lake Region. Bryologist, 25 : 41–58.

7. WHERRY, E. T. 1922. Soil Acidity — Its Nature, Measurement and Relation to Plant Distribution. Ann. Rept. Smithsonian Institution, 1920. Pp. 247–268.

A CYTOLOGICAL STUDY OF A BISPORED FORM OF *PSALLIOTA CAMPESTRIS* *

JOHN E. SASS

CERTAIN cultivated forms of the common field mushroom, *Psalliota campestris* Fr., have two-spored basidia, whereas in the wild forms of this species the basidia are normally four-spored. This character has been observed by a number of investigators. Goebel (6, p. 134) may have made the illustrations for his textbook from a cultivated form. Maire (10) stated that the form which he used for cytological study of this species had two-spored basidia. Atkinson (1) found that in several commercial varieties which he examined the basidia were two-spored. He made two collections of supposedly wild forms of *Psalliota campestris* which were two-spored. Buller (4, 5) found that in cultivated forms the basidia are mostly two-spored, but there are among them occasional one-spored basidia. In the four-spored wild forms Buller observed some three-spored basidia. Doubtless most recent mycologists have observed these facts.

Very little cytological work has been done on two-spored Hymenomycetes. A comprehensive review of work on these forms is given by Bauch (2). Several cases illustrating distinctly different modes of nuclear behavior will be briefly described here.

Maire (10) studied the nuclear phenomena in the hymenium of a two-spored form of *Psalliota campestris*. He showed that the young basidia are binucleate and that these two nuclei fuse. The fusion nucleus normally undergoes two divisions, resulting in four nuclei in the basidium. Two sterigmata and two spores develop on the basidium and two nuclei enter each spore. The two nuclei in the spore divide once, so that the mature spore contains four

* Paper from the Department of Botany of the University of Michigan, No. 284.

nuclei. Maire stated that in some basidia the fusion nucleus divides but once and each of the two spores receives one nucleus. This nucleus may then divide once or twice. Maire did not give any figures in support of his account of the nuclear phenomena in the hymenium and he did not mention the chromosome number. He presented no data on the nuclear phenomena in the vegetative mycelium.

Lewis (9) reported a somewhat different condition in *Amanita bisporigera* Atk. In this two-spored species karyogamy occurs in the basidium, followed by two divisions of the fusion nucleus, giving rise to four nuclei in the basidium. According to Lewis, two of these nuclei degenerate and each of the two spores receives one nucleus. Lewis did not publish any data on nuclear behavior in the vegetative mycelium of his plant.

A third type of nuclear behavior, which differs radically from the preceding cases, was reported by Bauch (2). He found a two-spored form of *Hygrophorus virgineus* Fr. (*Camarophyllus virgineus* (Wulf)) which, he says, is indistinguishable from the more common four-spored form, except for the spore number and spore size. In these two "races," as Bauch designates them, he found marked differences in nuclear behavior. He showed that in the four-spored form the usual scheme of meiosis occurs. Each of the four spores receives one nucleus which divides once. In the two-spored form, however, the young basidia are uninucleate. There is no karyogamy and the single nucleus divides but once. In the prophases of this division Bauch found no condition comparable to diakinesis. Each of the two spores receives one nucleus which undergoes one division in the spore. Bauch also determined that in the four-spored form the cells of the hyphae are binucleate and there are clamp connections at the septa. In the two-spored form the hyphal cells are uninucleate and there are no clamp connections. He gives no figures of the mycelium and does not make clear the method used in obtaining his data. In the basidia of the four-spored form Bauch found the diploid chromosome number to be eight. He counted four chromosomes on the spindle of the division occurring in the basidium of the two-spored form and concluded that this form is haploid. Bauch, therefore, believes that the nuclear phenomena in the two-spored form of *Hygrophorus virgineus* Fr. can be interpreted as a case of "haploid parthenogenesis."

Kühner (8) studied the cytology of a two-spored form of *Mycena galericulata* Scop. He found that the subhymenial cells and the basidia are uninucleate and that only one division occurs in the basidium. Each spore receives one nucleus which divides once, making the mature spore binucleate. The nuclear behavior in this form resembles that of the haploid, two-spored form of *Hygrophorus virgineus* as reported by Bauch.

The mycelium of *Psalliota campestris* was first studied in detail by Hirmer (7). He did not state whether his material was two-spored or four-spored; consequently, we cannot incorporate his results into a consistent scheme with other data on this species. Hirmer found that in his plant the cells of the vegetative mycelium are multinucleate. As many as eleven nuclei may be present in a cell. Clamp connections were not found, nor did he observe the nuclei to be definitely associated in pairs. Several nuclei may undergo simultaneous division. The trama cells near the hymenium are described as having fewer nuclei than the cells of vegetative hyphae, while the immediately subhymenial cells are definitely binucleate. The young basidia are binucleate and karyogamy occurs. Hirmer's figures of the basidium and its nuclei are semidiagrammatic, showing no details of the fusion nucleus, and he gives no data beyond the fusion nucleus stage.

MATERIALS AND METHODS

The two-spored *Psalliota campestris* studied by the writer can be collected during practically the entire year in a local greenhouse. Material in the freshest possible condition is thus available for fixing and for tissue cultures. There are two well-defined "varieties" growing in this greenhouse, a pure white variety and a much more common one with a fuscous pileus. In the present study the fuscous variety was used exclusively.

Interpretations of the cytological phenomena observed in fixed material should take due account of special effects produced by different killing fluids. For this reason several killing fluids and various stain combinations were used in this study. The interpretations here presented are based largely on observations made on material fixed in acetic-formalin-alcohol, Bouin's picro-formol and Flemming's weaker and stronger solutions. Iron haematoxylin, basic fuchsin and safranin-crystal-violet were used as stains.

A modification of what may be called the "agar-film method" was used in the study of vegetative mycelium obtained from tissue cultures. A brief outline of the method used follows: Place a *perfectly clean* and sterile slide in a sterile damp chamber. Spread over the center of the slide two drops of a sterile medium containing 0.2 per cent agar and 0.5 per cent malt extract. Inoculate this film with a piece of mycelium and incubate. When the mycelium radiating from the inoculum has grown out for some distance, transfer the slide to a dry petri dish and allow the agar film to dry down somewhat. This latter process is a critical operation requiring patience and some practice with the method. At the proper stage of drying, as determined by trials, fix the preparation in the following solution:

95 per cent alcohol	50 c. c.
1 per cent glacial acetic acid	45 c. c.
40 per cent formalin	5 c. c.

This solution fixes the mycelium very well and hardens the agar film in 30 minutes. Rinse in 50 per cent alcohol; then wash thoroughly in distilled water. Finally mordant and stain in iron haematoxylin. A form of this method was used by Hirmer (7).

A simple and practical illuminator was also developed during the course of this study. It was found that a parabolic reflector from an automobile headlight projects an intense field of light 5 cm. in diameter on a sheet of ground glass placed about 40 cm. from the bulb. A device was made for providing accurate lateral and axial adjustment of the bulb. A variable transformer furnishes six-volt current for the lamp. If a beam of sunlight is passed through a one-liter Pyrex distilling flask filled with water, the rays converge approximately 5.8 cm. from the surface of the flask. A ground-glass screen placed 1.5 cm. from the flask intercepts a fairly even field of light 2.5 cm. in diameter. The reflector, the screen and the flask are now combined. The bulb in the reflector is adjusted until an evenly illuminated disk of light is projected on the screen. The flask is then placed about 1.5 cm. beyond the screen. A brilliant but soft light is thus obtained. The units are enclosed in a metal body. Wratten filters were used to obtain maximum definition of details in stained preparations.

NUCLEAR PHENOMENA IN THE HYMENIUM

In the form of *Psalliota campestris* which was investigated, the subhymenial cells are pseudo-parenchymatous, and have very irregular outlines in section. Nuclei can be stained sharply only in cells in and near the hymenium and counts of nuclei are dependable only in these cells. Immediately below the hymenium the cells are distinctly binucleate (Fig. 1). Cells farther away from the hymenium are multinucleate and nuclear pairing is very obscure. In the interior of the trama the staining properties of the nuclei are very poor and the observer is likely to be confused, when counting nuclei, by the numerous discoid basophilic bodies which are present in pairs at the septa.

The young basidia are binucleate (Fig. 2) and karyogamy occurs while the basidia are relatively small. As the basidium enlarges, the fusion nucleus also enlarges and moves upward in the basidium (Fig. 3). Up to this point in the nuclear cycle, the writer's observations confirm the results reported by Maire (10) and Hirmer (7). Just before meiosis the fusion nucleus is less than 3 μ in diameter. This is about half as large as the corresponding nuclei of certain agarics in which the details of meiosis have been worked out. Owing to the small size of the nuclei in the form of Psalliota studied by the writer, the early phases of meiosis have not been followed. The outline of the fusion nucleus is indicated in an overstained preparation by a line of demarcation between the clear nuclear lymph and the finely granular cytoplasm. A minute but distinct nucleolus and a very lightly stained peripheral reticulum can be demonstrated. The nucleolus decreases in size somewhat and a number of karyosomes appear on the reticulum. The first prophase stage which can be traced readily with the camera lucida shows a condition resembling diakinesis. The chromosomes are short, beaded or constricted bodies, observed in some basidia to have tapering ends that suggest remnants of a spireme condition. There are some indications of pairing of the chromosomes (Figs. 4–5).

Just before spindle formation there are eight to ten chromatin bodies. One of these probably is the nucleolus. In heterotypic anaphase figures, one deeply staining body is regularly found quite apart from the spindle. This body is at first scarcely smaller than the chromosomes and it may lie in any direction from the spindle (Fig. 6). The chromosomes are nearly alike in size, and number approximately eight. Interpretation is difficult here because of the constricted character of the chromosomes. They become distributed along the entire spindle and can be counted best at this stage (Fig. 7). It is frequently possible to observe a distinct body at each end of the spindle. The writer believes that these bodies are members of the chromosome complement and that their position is due to the peculiar stringing out of chromosomes that is characteristic of the heterotypic spindle in this subject.

The two compact chromosome groups resulting from the first division do not reconstruct into nuclei, but enter into the second division (Figs. 8–9). The second division figure may resemble the division of a single chromatin body, but in favorable cases the four chromosomes can be observed at metaphase. Maire (10) and Bauch (2) show such figures. In many basidia with simultaneous homotypic figures, one or two minute, deeply stained bodies were observed lying apart from the spindles (Fig. 9). In the four nuclei resulting from meiosis, the nucleolus is a minute, deeply staining body. In heavily stained preparations the nuclear outline can be distinguished, but no reticular structure has so far been demonstrated in these spore nuclei by the writer (Fig. 10).

Sterigmata on the basidium rarely appear during the second nuclear division; usually they appear after the basidium has attained its maximum size and contains four nuclei. As the two sterigmata enlarge, the nuclei do not take the stain readily. The chromatic material becomes irregular in outline. Stages of the migration of the nuclei into the sterigmata and spores were observed. The migration may begin when the sterigmata are relatively small (Figs. 12, 15, 16). In some cases, however, four nuclei can be observed still in the basidium even after small spores are already formed on the sterigmata (Fig. 14). Each of the two spores normally receives two nuclei which divide once while the spore is still thin-walled (Figs. 19, 22). The mature spore thus contains four nuclei (Figs. 17, 20).

In some basidia there seems to be but one division. Apparently full-sized basidia containing two nuclei have been observed. No way of distinguishing monosterigmatic from bisterigmatic basidia in microtome sections has been found. Consequently the behavior of the nuclei in monosterigmatic basidia has not been worked out. Because of the comparative scarcity of monosterigmatic basidia, it is highly probable that the observations reported in this paper represent phenomena in the normal two-spored basidia.

NUCLEAR BEHAVIOR IN THE VEGETATIVE MYCELIUM

By means of the technique previously described, the nuclei in the vegetative hyphae can be readily demonstrated. Cultures were made from pileus tissue and the inoculum for the agar-film preparations was taken from these cultures. Bensaude (3) emphasized the fact that the significant nuclear phenomena of the mycelium occur in the *actively growing* terminal cells of vegetative mycelium. The writer's observations, therefore, were made largely on the peripheral hyphae of an actively growing mycelium. In the present form of *Psalliota campestris* the terminal hyphal cells and the cells near the end are multinucleate, the number of nuclei ranging from four to ten (Fig. 23–24). These nuclei are relatively small. The greater part of the nucleus consists of a deeply staining body, surrounded by a clear area in which there may be one to three lightly stained granules. The diameter of the nucleus is somewhat less than the thickness of the hypha. The intercalary hyphal cells have, in general, fewer nuclei. These nuclei are nearly as large as the diameter of the hypha (Fig. 25). There is no certainty as to the association of nuclei in pairs, although the nuclei may be more or less grouped. In these groups of nuclei, stages of simultaneous division of several nuclei have been observed. In some cases only one nucleus of a group has been found in a stage of division.

Clamp connections were not found in this fungus. The septa are plain cross walls. On each side of the cross wall, there is a lenticular basophilic body, such as is described by Maire (10). These bodies are unlike in size and staining properties. The smaller one, which is paler than the larger when stained with haematoxylin, is on that side of the septum near the tip of the hypha. No suggestion is offered here concerning the origin and function of these bodies. The results reported by Hirmer on a form of *Psalliota campestris* are verified by the writer's observations, and it is possible that Hirmer worked with a two-spored form.

DISCUSSION

Since the discovery of heterothallism and homothallism in the Hymenomycetes, the attention of cytologists has been focused on the nuclear cycle in these fungi. It is difficult to find a Hymenomycete in which the complete nuclear cycle can be followed. Although in some species the phenomena in the basidium can be readily studied, difficulties are encountered in germinating spores or obtaining cultures for the study of the mycelium. Peculiar staining reactions of the nuclei or of cell inclusions are troublesome in certain species. The situation is further complicated if the basidia of a species bear a variable number of spores. When studying microtome sections of such a form, the observer is not always certain of the full number of sterigmata on any given basidium. If the mycelium of a species is favorable for study by the special methods herein described, the data on nuclear behavior are quite reliable, since there is no cutting away of parts of cells as in microtome sections. In view of the conditions mentioned, any interpretation should take into account the limitations imposed by these properties of the Hymenomycetes.

Maire (10) did not make clear the evidence from which he concluded that in some basidia only one division occurs. The writer has observed apparently binucleate basidia with two well-developed sterigmata, and since the sterigmata usually appear after the last division, it is possible that only one division occurs in some basidia. I have also found apparently monosterigmatic, binucleate basidia, but there is no reliable criterion for distinguishing monosterigmatic basidia in sections. Proof that in some basidia only one nuclear division occurs would afford a cytological basis for the occurrence of one-spored basidia in a normally two-spored form.

In contrast to the two-spored form of *Hygrophorus virgineus* studied by Bauch, the fungus studied by the writer is a diploid form, in which karyogamy and meiosis normally occur. Since the details of these phenomena are at the limits of microscopic visibility, they furnish no clue to the cytological basis for the presence of the two-spored character in a diploid form.

The study of nuclear behavior in the mycelium should begin with the germ tube. Neither Maire nor Hirmer submitted data on nuclear behavior during germination. The writer has hitherto been unable to germinate the spores of this form. This leaves a serious gap in our knowledge of the nuclear cycle of this fungus. As shown by Hirmer and confirmed by the writer, the peripheral cells of an actively growing mycelium are multinucleate, containing as many as ten nuclei (eleven, according to Hirmer). In older cells there are fewer nuclei, resulting apparently from the production of additional septa. In these plants septum formation does not seem to be directly associated with nuclear phenomena, and the several nuclei seem to be able to function as independent units. The grouping of nuclei is probably the result of successive divisions of several nuclei and not of nuclear association.

There is no reason to believe that any significant nuclear phenomena occur during the organization of the carpophore, prior to the differentiation of the hymenium. My observations indicate a progressive decrease in the number of nuclei per cell during the early initiation of the fertile portion of the gill, until finally the subhymenial cells and young basidia are binucleate.

The question now arises: What is the mechanism by which the several nuclei of the hyphal cell are sorted out, ultimately into pairs? There is at present no direct evidence bearing on this point. All the nuclei of the hyphal cell are morphologically alike, so far as has been shown by present methods. If the nuclei are separated by the random production of septa, it would be possible for sister nuclei to appear in a basidium and there fuse. This hypothesis does not harmonize with the accepted idea of the sexual nature of karyogamy in the basidium, for very few cases are known in which sister nuclei enter into gametic union. It seems more probable to the writer that in the multinucleate hyphal cells of this form, there are present nuclei of opposite sex, even if there is no evidence here of the striking synkaryons observed in certain other species. The sorting out of nuclei at the time the cells become binucleate may not be a random process, and it may well be that the subhymenial cells in which two nuclei of opposite sex occur may be the source of functioning two-spored basidia.

SUMMARY

A cytological study of the hymenium and the vegetative mycelium of a two-spored form of *Psalliota campestris* shows the following nuclear cycle in this form.

1. The subhymenial cells are definitely binucleate. The trama cells farther from the hymenium are multinucleate.
2. The young basidia are binucleate. Karyogamy and meiosis occur in the basidium.
3. Certain details of meiosis are given, showing that this form is diploid. The 2 $\times$ chromosome number is $\pm$ 8.
4. Four nuclei are formed in each basidium and each of the two spores normally receives two nuclei.
5. There is some meager evidence that in some basidia only one division occurs.
6. The present data do not show definitely the facts concerning nuclear phenomena in one-spored basidia.
7. The terminal cells of actively growing vegetative mycelium are multinucleate. The older cells of the mycelium contain relatively fewer nuclei.
8. No evidence of synkaryons was found in the vegetative mycelium.

The writer wishes to acknowledge his debt to Professor C. H. Kauffman under whose guidance this study was conducted.

University of Michigan

LITERATURE CITED

1. Atkinson, G. F. 1906. The Development of Agaricus campestris. Bot. Gaz., 42 : 241–264.

2. Bauch, Robt. 1926. Untersuchungen über zweisporige Hymenomyceten. Zeitschr. f. Bot., 18 : 337–387.

3. Bensaude, Mathilde. 1918. Recherches sur le cycle évolutif et la sexualité chez les Basidiomycètes. Nemours. Pp. 1–156.

4. Buller, A. H. R. 1909. Researches on Fungi. Vol. I. Winnipeg.

5. Buller, A. H. R. 1922. Researches on Fungi. Vol. II. Winnipeg.

6. Goebel, K. 1887. Outlines of Classification and Special Morphology of Plants. Oxford edition. Pp. 134.

7. Hirmer, Max. 1920. Zur Kenntnis der Vielkernigkeit der Autobasidiomyceten I. Zeitschr. f. Bot., 12 : 657–674.

8. Kühner, R. 1927. Étude cytologique de l'hymenium de Mycena galericulata. Le Botaniste, 18 : 169–176.

9. Lewis, C. E. 1906. The Basidium of Amanita bisporigera. Bot. Gaz., 41 : 348–352.

10. Maire, René. 1902. Recherches cytologiques sur les Basidiomycètes. Bull. Soc. Myc. France, 18 : 1–209.

EXPLANATION OF PLATES

The drawings were made with a camera lucida. The lenses used were a Zeiss apochromat 2 mm. N. A. 1.3, Zeiss compensating oculars and Bausch and Lomb hyperplane oculars.

Figures 1–22 are at a magnification of approximately 2800. Figures 23–25 are at a magnification of 1400.

PLATE XLIV

FIG. 1. Subhymenial cells, with synkaryons, and two basophylic bodies at a septum

FIG. 2. Young basidium containing two nuclei

FIG. 3. The fusion nucleus in a basidium

FIGS. 4–5. Late premeiotic figures resembling diakinesis

FIG. 6. Heterotypic division of the fusion nucleus, nucleolus still evident

FIG. 7. Heterotypic division, nucleolus no longer evident

FIG. 8. Telophase of the first division

FIG. 9. Homeotypic division. Simultaneous division of two chromosome groups

FIG. 10. Basidium with four nuclei

FIG. 11. Two small sterigmata on a basidium with four nuclei

FIG. 12. One nucleus in each sterigma and two nuclei still in the basidium. No evidence of nuclear degeneration

PLATE XLV

FIG. 13. Two nuclei near the base of a sterigma

FIG. 14. Two nuclei near a sterigma and two others some distance down in the basidium

FIGS. 15–16. Two nuclei in a sterigma

FIG. 17. Two-spored basidium, each spore containing four nuclei

FIG. 18. A thin-walled spore containing one nucleus

FIGS. 19–20. Thick-walled spores containing two and four nuclei, respectively

FIG. 21. Spore with spindle of mitosis of one nucleus

FIG. 22. Spore containing spindles of the simultaneous division of two nuclei

FIG. 23. Terminal cell of hypha of vegetative mycelium. Only the chromatin material of the nuclei is evident. Some nuclei apparently in stages of division

FIG. 24. Intercalary cell near the end of a hypha

FIG. 25. Intercalary cell of old mycelium. Outline of the entire nucleus evident. Basophilic bodies at the septa

PLATE XLIV

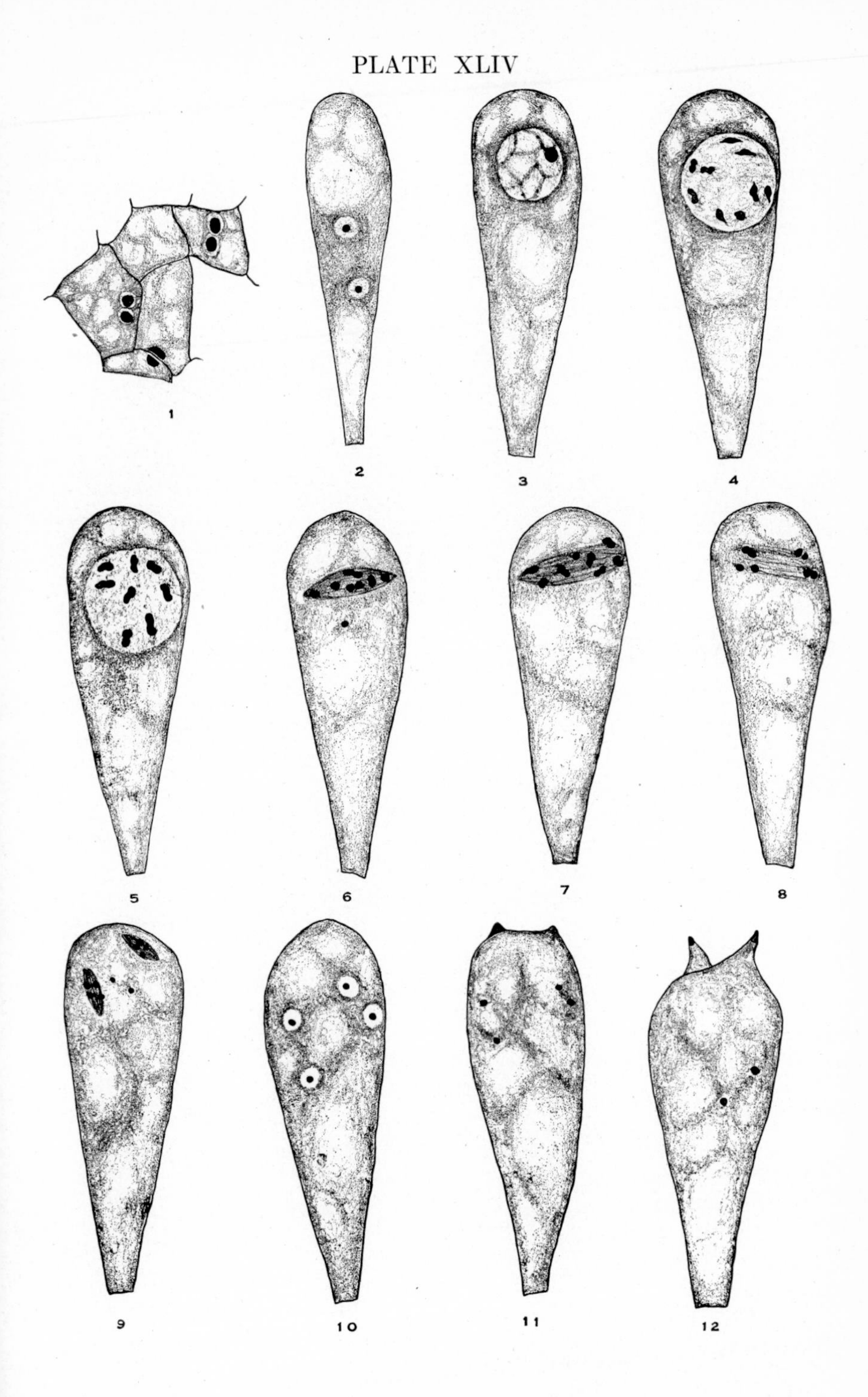

PLATE XLV

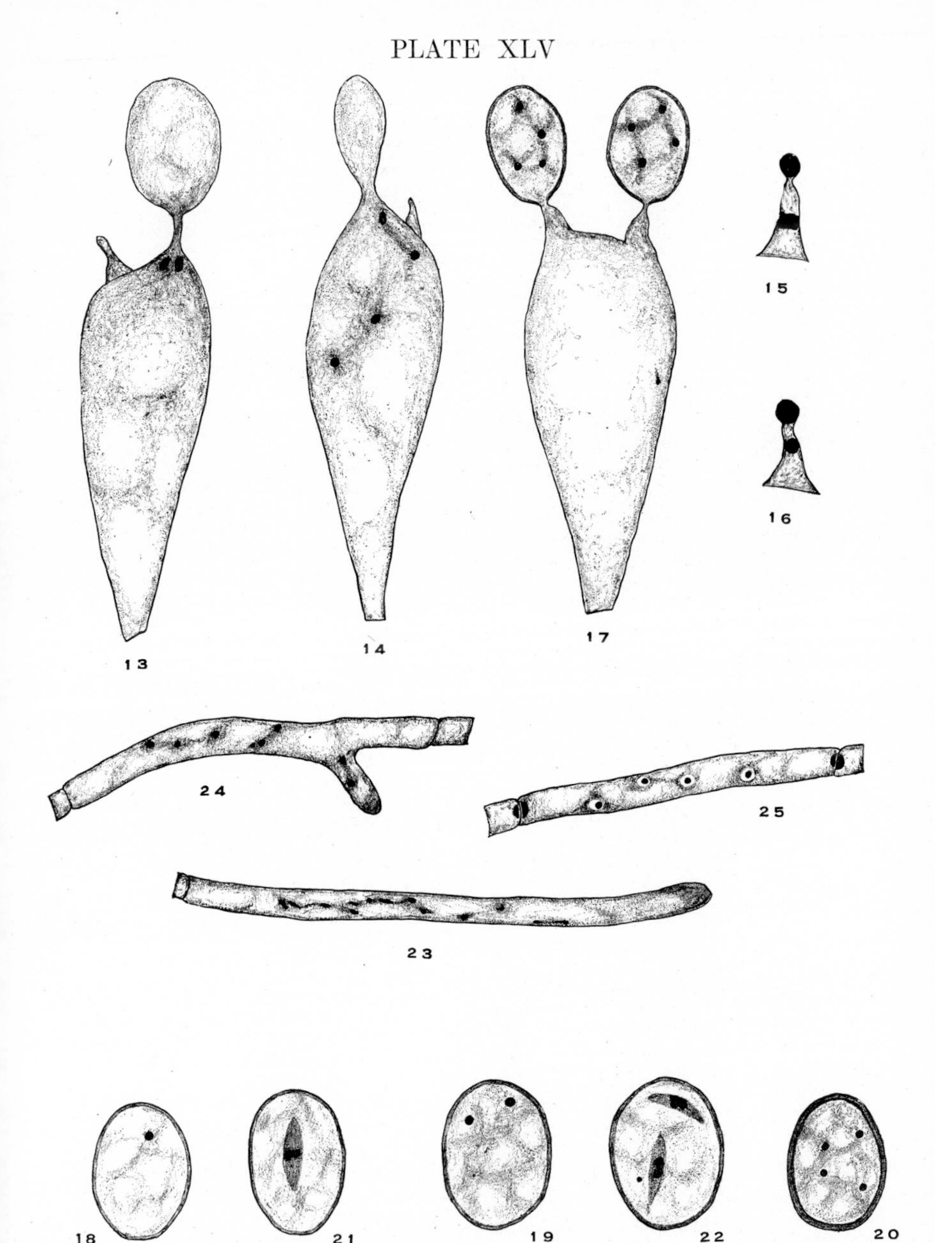

SPORE GERMINATION OF *LYCOPERDON PYRIFORME* *

DELBERT SWARTZ

CUNNINGHAM (4) in a recent paper states that the spores of the Lycoperdaceae have never been germinated. A brief review of the literature on the subject will show this to be the generally accepted status of spore germination in this group at the present time. This view is held today in spite of the report by Hoffman (7) in 1859 of successful germinations of the spores of *Lycoperdon echinatum* Pers., *Lycoperdon gemmatum* Batsch. and *Bovista plumbea* Pers. The details of the methods used as well as the details of the germination process were not given. This low percentage of germination combined with negative results obtained by himself and Brefeld (2) led DeBary (5), 1884, to state that the spores of the Lycoperdaceae had never been germinated. DeBary goes on to say that there seemed to be no reasons why the spores of this group should not germinate because of their relationship to certain forms whose spores had been germinated. Brefeld and DeBary were of the opinion that a study of special conditions surrounding the germination process would lead to successful experiments in this group. From the time of DeBary until the work of Miss Ferguson (6), 1902, there were no further reports of investigations on spore germination of a general nature. Miss Ferguson in reporting results obtained in the study of germination of many species of the higher Basidiomycetes reported failure to obtain germination in *Calvatia cyathiforme* Bosc., *Lycoperdon pyriforme* (Schaeff.) Fr., *Lycoperdon gemmatum* Batsch. and *Lycoperdon Wrightii* B. & C. The spores of the species named above were subjected to special conditions such as alternate cold

* Paper from the Department of Botany of the University of Michigan, No. 283.

and heat, continued cold, continued high temperature. Also germination trials were made in special media such as bean, beet, Lepiota decoctions as well as in distilled and tap water and in sugar solutions. They were not brought to germination. Miss Cool (3), 1912, working with species of Lycoperdon, reports, "Versagten die Keimung auch nach einjährigem Aufbewahren." Similarly for *Bovista nigrescens* and *Geaster sp.* she reports "Versagten die Keimung auch nach Aufbewahren."

From the results obtained by these investigators, it is quite evident that there are logical grounds for doubting the results of Hoffman. Therefore, the statement of Cunningham sums up the opinions held today, namely, that nothing is known concerning the germination of the spores of this group.

Preliminary studies made by the writer led in every case to negative results; it soon became clear that special difficulties had to be overcome in such a study. A hypothesis was set up which rested on the probability that special combination of factors might be needed. An attempt was made to analyze the probable factors entering in and then to apply various conditions for germination.

The spores of the species of Lycoperdaceae are very small, with a diameter varying from 3 to 7 μ, and possessed of a very thick wall in proportion to the diameter of the spore. These two facts render it quite difficult to make any observations on the details in the interior of the spores. The question arose whether the structure of the spore wall made it, in some way, impermeable to water. The heavy wall which is in some species covered with warts or spines seemed to present a barrier to the water's entering the spore. Early experiments seemed to show that water was unable to penetrate the spore wall unless the wall was previously changed mechanically. (This will be discussed later.)

Bacteria were found to be frequently present in fruit bodies ripened under natural conditions; the rapid development of these prevented the use of a nutrient solution or the usual solid substrata for testing germination. One might associate the rather thick wall with a required resting period. The writer has not found any record in which the lack of germination has been thought due to a rest period, and has made no effort to determine the necessity of a rest period in the spores studied.

As noted above, it was deemed necessary to create some mechanical disturbance in the wall of the spore which would change its character and perhaps facilitate water absorption. Consequently, during the summer of 1927 the writer decided to determine the effect of alternate wetting and drying. The following species were used: *Calvatia saccata* (Fr.) Lloyd, *Bovista pila* B. & C., *Lycoperdon gemmatum* Batsch., *Lycoperdon atropurpureum* Vitt. Spore suspensions were made of each of these forms and agitated at frequent intervals during the day. At night before the writer left the laboratory the water of the suspensions was filtered off, and the spores were deposited on the filter paper used. The spores were usually completely dried by the following morning, at which time they were removed from the surface of the filter paper and again placed in suspension in distilled water. Moist chambers were prepared daily to determine the stage at which germination would take place. Negative results were obtained in every species used except *Calvatia saccata*. Spore changes here, such as an increase in size combined in a few tests with a germ tube, gave evidence of activity within the spore. When this experiment was repeated, it was found that at the end of the third day a few spores had germinated. The germ tube thus formed was, however, so similar in appearance to the pedicel of the spore, and occurred so rarely, that rechecking was thought to be necessary. At this point the work had to be discontinued.

Early experiments conducted in the fall failed to give any positive results, but the average temperature of the laboratory was considerably lower than it had been during the summer when encouraging results had been obtained. Temperatures during the summer had been between 75° and 85° F. most of the time, and the laboratory temperature was never above 72° F. during the fall and winter, and frequently much lower. In order to get a temperature approximating that of the previous summer a constant temperature oven was used and kept at 28° C.

The first spores tried were those of *Lycoperdon pyriforme*. The water was allowed to dry out of a spore suspension which had been placed in the bottom of a petri dish[1] and kept in the constant temperature oven. When the water had evaporated, additional sterile distilled water was added. Frequent microscopic mounts were examined for any evidences of germination. At the end of six days the spores had swollen slightly, tending at times to be more or less lemon-shaped instead of the normal spherical shape, although not all spores assume the lemon shape as they germinate. After the spores had swollen somewhat, elongation took place. During this swelling and elongation the color of the spore became of lessened intensity. Enlargement and elongation were followed by germination, the details of which follow. The now swollen, enlarged and elongated spore began to show very pronounced vacuolar regions in the interior. Very often the most evident vacuoles occur one at either end of the spore. At this stage the spore is two to four times as large as the normal spore. Also at this time the elongated spore may become septate and germ tubes are then sent out from either one or both of the component cells, or more commonly the spore does not become septate, but sends germ tubes out directly. The number of germ tubes sent out varies from one to four. These germ tubes, which may preferably be called the primary mycelium, following Bensaude (1), are relatively very heavy; they have a diameter at least half as great as that of the swollen spore, sometimes almost equal to that of the germinating spore. The outer wall of the spore has been left behind and is partially digested; fragments of it may be seen in the water surrounding the spore.

Stained preparations of the stages described in the preceding paragraph show the mycelium to consist of several relatively short cells with one nucleus in each cell. The nuclei are very small; the one or two nucleoli in the nucleus stain deeply and are seen as small deep blue bodies in the central part of the cell. The nucleoli occupy, as usual, only a small proportion of the space within the nuclear boundary; the remainder is rather hyaline and takes scarcely any stain. The nuclei occupy about three fourths

[1] For reasons of convenience in staining, the spore suspensions in later experiments were placed on slides in petri dishes, and the water allowed to evaporate.

of the diameter of the germ tubes. The septa are relatively numerous and the cells correspondingly short.

The percentage of germination is rather low in each of the successful attempts at germination. At first only a few swollen spores can be seen among the spores of the suspension. The majority of the spores in any field are unswollen normal spores with here and there groups of germinating spores in different stages of germination. The number of germinating spores increases day after day, and it is possible for several days to see the successive developmental stages. It is hoped that improved methods may increase the percentage and bring out greater details than those presented in this preliminary report.

The writer wishes to express his grateful appreciation for many helpful suggestions and criticisms to Dr. C. H. Kauffman, under whose direction this investigation was done, and to Mr. J. E. Sass for helpful suggestions on methods of staining the germinated spores.

University of Michigan

LITERATURE CITED

1. Bensaude, Mathilde. 1918. Recherches sur le cycle évolutif et la sexualité chez les Basidiomycètes. (Printed separately, Nemours.)

2. Brefeld, O. 1877. Botanische Untersuchungen über Schimmelpilze. Heft III : 174–180.

3. Cool, Catharina. 1912. Beiträge zur Kenntnis der Sporenkeimung und Reinkultur der höheren Pilze. Mededeel. uit het Phytopatholog. Laborat. "Willie Commelin Scholten" III : 1–38.

4. Cunningham, G. H. 1926. Development of *Lycoperdon depressum* Bon. New Zealand Journ. of Sci. and Tech., 13 : 228–232.

5. DeBary, A. 1887. Comparative Morphology and Biology of the Fungi, Mycetozoa and Bacteria (Eng. transl.). Oxford.

6. Ferguson, Margaret C. 1902. A Preliminary Study of the Germination of the Spores of *Agaricus campestris* and other Basidiomycetous Fungi. U. S. D. A. Bull., 16 : 1–40.

7. Hoffman, H. 1859. Über Pilzkeimungen. Bot. Zeit., 17 : 209–214; 217–219.

DESCRIPTION OF PLATE XLVI

Figures 1, 8, 9, 10 were drawn from mounts under 2000 magnification (25 × ocular; 1.9 oil immersion objective). Figures 2–7 were drawn at approximately 1000 magnification (15 × hyperplane ocular; 63 × apochromatic objective). Reduction one third.

Fig. 1. Normal spores, from a specimen that has been dry for several months. Note that the spores are not smooth as described

Fig. 2. Showing the earliest indications of germination, and the appearance of vacuolar regions within the spore. The spore wall is of lesser thickness

Fig. 3. Later stages, showing enlarged vacuoles and the presence of vacuoles in either end of the spore

Fig. 4. Showing the septate condition of the lengthening and enlarged spore

Fig. 5. Early stages of the formation of primary mycelium

Fig. 6. Germination of septate individual spores. Note the different positions of the germ tube

Fig. 7. Later stage of germination of growing material

Figs. 8–10. From stained slides showing the uninucleate septate conditions of the germ tube

PLATE XLVI

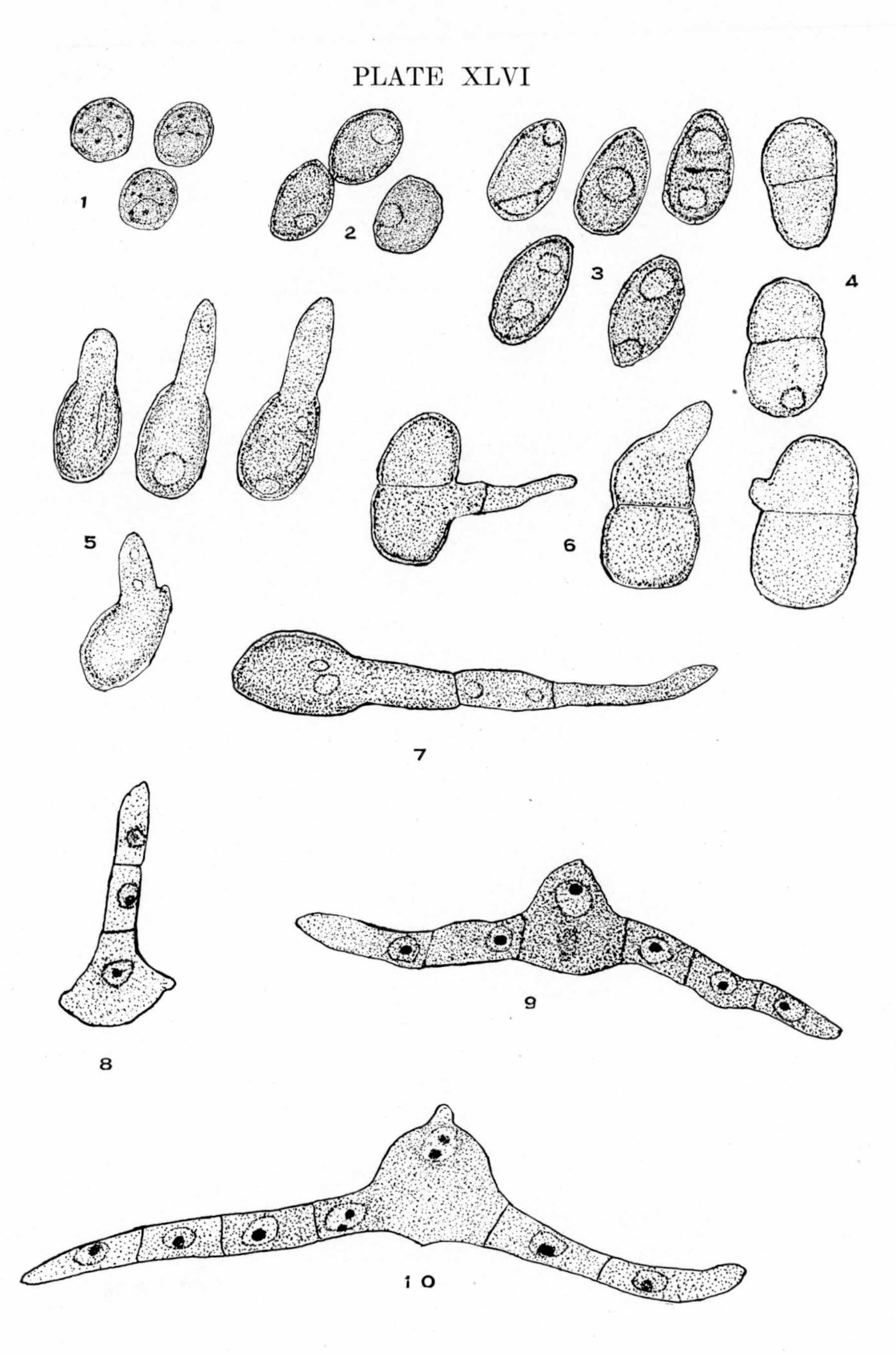

CONTRIBUTIONS TO A MONOGRAPH OF THE GENUS HELIANTHUS

ELBA EMANUEL WATSON

MY INTEREST in Helianthus, from a scientific point of view, dates from the year 1918. At that time Dr. H. A. Gleason, professor of botany in the University of Michigan, suggested that I study the genus along the lines laid down by the late S. Alexander. This very keen observer had been attracted by certain peculiarities in the root-system of plants of this genus, and had been attempting for some years to arrange a key, based entirely upon the underground parts, by means of which the major groups, if not actually all the species and varieties, could be identified. An outline key to the main subdivisions of the genus, based on the behavior of roots and rhizomes, applied to the Michigan sunflowers, was published in the *Report of the Michigan Academy of Science for 1911*, p. 191. Because of Mr. Alexander's increasingly poor health and finally his death, his work was left uncompleted. He had a very keen observation, and his problem was certainly original, and perhaps he was the only person who could have successfully carried out his ideas. After a few months of study, my attitude toward this phase of the problem underwent a change. I was unable to see the difference in the root-systems of local plants that seemed so patent to Mr. Alexander, and on the other hand I became greatly interested in the systematic study of the genus along orthodox paths. Some two or three years now intervened during which I was able to work only casually on the problem, but in August, 1922, I came to East Lansing, and have devoted myself exclusively to the systematic study of the species of Helianthus since that time.

Various American and foreign colleges and scientific institutions have loaned their collections very liberally, and these, supplemented by our own excellent herbarium and my personal collections and visits, have enabled me to examine between fifty and sixty thousand specimens. The University of Berlin sent their entire Helianthus collection of nearly seven thousand specimens, including the famous Humboldt plants from South America. The following American state universities and colleges loaned their specimens: Michigan, Iowa, Kansas, North Dakota, Ohio, Wisconsin, Mississippi, Texas, Nebraska, Wyoming, Kentucky, New Mexico, Arizona, and Minnesota. The New York Botanical Garden, the Field Museum of Natural History, the United States National Herbarium, the Gray Herbarium, the Philadelphia Academy of Science, the Missouri Botanical Garden, the California Academy of Science, Tulane University, all placed their collections at my disposal. The Reverend J. M. Bates of Red Cloud, Nebraska, and Mrs. J. Lunell of Leeds, North Dakota, sent their private specimens. I have personally made more or less extensive collections in every state east of the Mississippi except Wisconsin, Rhode Island, and Maine; west of the Mississippi, I have collected in Texas, Louisiana, Arkansas, Oklahoma, Kansas, Missouri, Nebraska, and Iowa. It will be readily seen that a very large territory has been visited, not so thoroughly as it should have been, as is obvious, of course, when it is remembered that very few sunflowers begin to bloom before the latter part of July and are mostly past the blooming stage by the early part of October. It was also necessary, especially while I was in the northeastern states, to spend a very large part of my time in the library of the New York Botanical Garden.

When I began the study of the systematic position of the species of Helianthus, my intention was to produce a complete monograph of the whole genus, but the exigencies of the problem have made it necessary to limit the scope of the study. This is due not so much to the paucity of collections as to the character of the specimens. An inadequate, incomplete herbarium specimen is of no more scientific value than someone's written record that he has found a certain plant in a certain locality. In the latter case, we cannot be certain of the observer's accuracy of identification; in the former, it is often impossible to be certain of the plant's identity. A very large number of our specimens do not have records of exact localities, and almost none have notes regarding the edaphic conditions that so profoundly influence the outward expression of the inner genetical constitution of the plant. The species, which are very incompletely treated in this paper, comprise some of our most widely distributed and individually most common sunflowers — *H. rigidus*, *H. laetiflorus*, and *H. tuberosus*. The identity of the plants grouped under the variety "*mollis*" of *H. strumosus* has not been treated at all, and cannot be treated on the evidence of any herbarium specimens now in existence. These plants are abundant in that region comprising the states of Minnesota, Wisconsin, Iowa, Missouri, Illinois, Indiana, Michigan, Ohio, and Pennsylvania. I have had abundant material from these states, and yet almost none that I could use. *Helianthus* is a genus of infinite and bewildering variability, and its individuals must be studied in their entirety. Plant collecting is not an adjunct to an afternoon stroll; it is a serious but not very well paid occupation. A safe rule in the collection of plants for herbarium purposes would be: *Each collection, with notes of the edaphic factors, should enable the student to reconstruct the entire plant,* and the locality should be stated as exactly as the situation will permit. It is also most desirable to know just *who* collected and *who* identified the plant.

The inadequacy of the herbarium material has been particularly manifest in regard to the very interesting phases of vegetative reproduction in this genus. Most of the perennial species, probably all the North American perennials, are herbaceous, but some of the South American species are apparently true shrubs.

1. *Shrubs.* — None of the South American specimens present the root-system, and none are accompanied by notes at all complete. Conclusions as to the seasonal habit are drawn entirely from the appearance of the upper stem. The following are undoubtedly shrubs, and although nothing is definitely known regarding the seasonal habit of the leaves, they are probably deciduous: *H. Jelskii*, *H. Stuebelii*, *H. subniveus*, *H. argenteus*,

and *H. rugosus*. Of these five, there can be no question about the first. The type specimen is plainly a branch of the main stem, but 10–15.0 cm. of the specimen has a well-furrowed bark, entirely without epidermis, and the basal portion of the two lowest branches of each shows five annual bud-scars. These particular stems are, therefore, at least six years old. The proof in *H. Stuebelii* is not so obvious because of the dense cauline pubescence. *H. subniveus* has every appearance, not only of the shrub habit, but also of the evergreen habit, but we have no proof of this last possibility. The two last mentioned are probably shrubs, but the evidence is not absolutely convincing.

2. *Perennials.* — Most of the perennials are herbaceous, winter annuals; only the distal portion of the more or less elongated rhizome lives throughout the winter. There is nothing particularly startling about these rhizomes, although there are specific morphological peculiarities in many cases. The diameter of the rhizome varies somewhat with the species, and the length and branching habit are also specifically variable. In some species the rhizome attains a length of more than a meter.

3. *Crown-buds.* — All species producing rhizomes produce also crown-buds, and there is perhaps no definite distinction between them, the rhizome being merely an elongated crown-bud. The tendency to produce crown-buds, however, is so much more marked and so constant in some species and so weak in others that one must conclude that it has a genetical basis. The crown-bud, properly so called, is usually from 2 to 3.0 mm. in length, or even less, and is produced on the stem base, just above, or among, the uppermost roots. In *H. tomentosus* and *H. angustifolius* this tendency is very marked, though it is also true that rhizomes occasionally occur in these species. In the former, the tendency is stable; in the latter, somewhat unstable. From my observations in the field, I should say that in the majority of plants *H. angustifolius* produces crown-buds without rhizomes, but when rhizomes are also produced, they are often 1–2.0 dm. in length. In *H. tomentosus* rhizomes are rarely produced, but the crown-buds are large and often nearly a centimeter in length. *H. giganteus* also has the crown-bud habit strongly developed,

but rhizomes are often produced with the buds, although they are normally short.

4. *Tubers.* — The tendency to form tubers is not very common in Helianthus. They occur normally in *H. tuberosus,* of course, and, as I have stated elsewhere, in certain plants that are now placed, somewhat doubtfully, in *H. laetiflorus.* The latter and *H. rigidus,* a very close relative, are among the earliest of the sunflowers to blossom, and I have never been able to be in the typical locality during the blossoming season. These plants will require frequent observation throughout the season and minute examination before their systematic position and tuber-bearing tendencies are thoroughly understood. In most of them the presence or absence of tubers can be readily determined by observation, but in others it is difficult to decide whether the enlarged distal portion of the rhizome is a true tuber or not. This is as true of *H. tuberosus* as of *H. laetiflorus.* And the variability in the form of the tuber, even when readily recognizable as such, is very great. *H. tuberosus* grows abundantly in fields in and about Grand Rapids, Michigan, and most of the tubers that I have observed there are formed by an unmistakably abrupt enlargement of the slender rhizome, resulting in a tuber about 4.0 cm. long and 2.5–3.0 cm. in diameter. This species is even more abundant in similar situations in Ann Arbor, Michigan, and many of the tubers here are long slender structures, 4–5.0 dm. in length, 2–3.0 cm. in thickness, often bent or curved and usually branched. Careful study on my part completely failed to correlate these rhizome features with either any aërial characters or edaphic conditions.

5. *Axillary-buds.* — In *H. atrorubens* the stem does not produce either crown-buds or rhizomes. This seemed so unusual to me that I took special pains to examine a large number of plants throughout the wide range of this species. I found no rhizomes or buds on any plant examined. This species invariably produces 6–8 large, long-petioled leaves at the base of the stem. In most plants the petioles of the lowermost leaves extend below the surface of the soil. In the axils of these leaves are well-developed, though rather small, but perfectly obvious buds. My first view of

these buds suggested their reproductive function, and I looked for confirmatory evidence. This I found in the occurrence, on occasional plants, of 2–3 old stems closely crowning the stem of the season. *H. atrorubens* appears, therefore, to be a true perennial, for the roots, at least, seem to remain alive more than one season.

6. *Root Buds.* — The vegetative propagation of *H. heterophyllus* is very peculiar. I dug up a large number of these plants without finding any means of reproduction other than seeds, and yet the plants of the season were always surrounded by large numbers of young plants — mere rosettes as yet. The summer of 1925, it will be remembered, was unusually dry. *H. heterophyllus* prefers a hard clay soil. The underground parts are fine and delicate, and it was extremely difficult to get the whole plant. However, I finally succeeded, and observed that four or five of the larger roots lying near the surface, and always unbranched, produced a bud 1–2 cm. back of the tip of the root, and the bud expanded and produced an aërial shoot at once. This observation was also confirmed by a large number of subsequent observations.

The leaf arrangement in Helianthus impresses the casual observer as very uncertain, and in certain species it is unstable, but the instability seems in part, at least, a response to edaphic conditions. In *H. giganteus*, for example, the leaves are almost invariably alternate; in *H. divaricatus* they are, with equal constancy, opposite, but the arrangement can readily be altered. I was attracted to a plant of *H. divaricatus* which I observed in a woods near Ann Arbor, Michigan, in 1918, on account of its small size, its pale color, and its inflorescence of a single terminal head. The height of the stem was about 5.0 dm., and it had one rhizome about 2.0 dm. long, and apparently normal. The plant grew in an open woods, in rather dry, light soil. The stem, with the rhizome, was transplanted to the Botanical Garden of the University of Michigan, placed in rich soil and kept well sprinkled during the season. The following summer the rhizome grew into a plant 1.5 m. high, profusely branched at the inflorescence, and produced over 80 heads. The leaves at and below the inflorescence were opposite; as were also the primary branches of the inflorescence, but the secondary and succeeding branches and leaves were mostly alternate. The color of the parts was also profoundly altered. The original plant was pale green with a green stem; the succeeding plant was deep green with a reddish-brown stem. The leaves of the original plant were flat with a foliar ratio of 6; those of the daughter plant were rugose, many ovate, with a foliar ratio of 2–4. Further observations on those species with a marked tendency toward opposite leaves confirmed my first conclusion that a correlation exists between leaf arrangement and vigor of growth.

In Helianthus, *all* species place the first leaves opposite, and all tend to place the last leaves alternate, and that point on the stem where the alternate arrangement begins is determined by the vigor and luxuriance of the growth. The behavior of sunflowers in the matter of leaf arrangement has led me to the conclusion that the law just stated is a generic character, and that some inhibition in certain species is a specific character, the inhibition being specifically strong in some species, as, for example, *H. hirsutus* and *H. divaricatus*, and specifically weak in others, as *H. giganteus* and *H. grosse-serratus*. *H. ambiguus* behaves in an erratic manner; the leaf arrangement is very unstable, and the correlation is not so evident. *H. annuus* normally produces most of its leaves in alternate arrangement, but small, depauperate plants will rarely have any of the leaves alternate.

The genus Helianthus has always given a great deal of trouble to amateurs in analysis and to professional botanists as well, if we may draw conclusions from the labels in herbaria. Unfortunately this is likely to continue to be the case. Related species have a most perplexing tendency to fade into one another in such a way that, while the typical extremes are readily enough recognized, there will always be a large number of plants that will not fully satisfy the definition of either of two species, and that can be as logically placed with one as with the other. This is flagrantly true with three groups that I should like to discuss very briefly.

The case of *H. glaucus* and *H. microcephalus* is fully discussed in connection with these species. Let us glance at their contrasted characters:

	H. glaucus	*H. microcephalus*
Leaves	ovate	oblong-lanceolate
	thick	thin
	scabrous above	remotely setulose above
	tomentulose beneath	thinly pubescent beneath
	very resinous beneath	rarely resinous beneath
Inflorescence	many-flowered	few-flowered
Stems	dark	light

We have here seven pairs of contrasted characters. Many plants of each group can be found with all seven characters of that group, and these two groups certainly do appear to be distinct from each other. There is also a slight geographical correlation. *H. glaucus* occurs more abundantly and in a purer form toward the west of its range, and *H. microcephalus* toward the east. But by far the larger number of specimens, as they occur in herbaria, lack one or more characters of one of these two groups, replacing it with a character from the other group. And the situation is even further complicated by the fact that each one of these characters grades into its opponent by the most gradual and imperceptible degrees, and there is almost no correlation between any of the characters. It is also very significant that there is no difference that could possibly be explained as *specific* in the floral structure of any of these plants. The only possible exception to this last statement is that possibly the floral disc of *H. glaucus* would average a little wider. The difference, however, could not be used in a key at all, and is even unwisely claimed in a description, for it could be determined only by a large number of very careful measurements. Now if we were to select *any one* of these characters, and disregard the others, it would be possible to arrange all the specimens of the two species in a regularly graduated progression. But this arrangement on the basis of *one* of these characters would not imply a graduated progression on the basis of any other character. We are, therefore, placed between two horns of a dilemma: Shall we consider them all one species? Or shall we consider them two species? And if we accept the latter alternative, what shall we do with all those plants that will not satisfy the demands of the one any more successfully or completely than they will the demands of the other? It is, as it were, a continuous curve or undulation in which *H. glaucus* is one high spot and *H. microcephalus* the other. If we knew what a species is, assuming that it is a real entity, we might perhaps answer the question, but if a species is only a convenient means to the orderly classification of our botanical knowledge, then we ought to retain both these names, and place each plant where it seems to agree with the largest number of characters.

Exactly the same situation arises with *H. grosse-serratus* and *H. instabilis*. So also with *H. mollis*, *H. doronicoides*, *H. tomentosus*, *H. resinosus*. If the leaves of *H. mollis* become somewhat elongated, and only a little less clasping, or if those of *H. doronicoides* become a little broader and shorter, it is practically impossible to tell these two species apart, yet in their extreme state they do not resemble each other. Now, when the leaves of *H. doronicoides* elongate a little and those of *H. tomentosus* decrease their pubescence, it is quite impossible to separate these two species; and the only difference between *H. tomentosus* and *H. resinosus* is a matter of size and leaf texture. Every one of these characters *may* have a genetical inception, and undoubtedly does in all the species under discussion, but it is well known to every one that each of these characters is also profoundly influenced by edaphic factors. These four species are really one species with four modes of expression. It is, of course, a matter of complete indifference whether we call them by four different names, or whether we call them one species with four varieties. The important point is to know their relationship, and especially how close that relationship is.

Of special interest are the very close relationship and the imperceptible gradations in that group comprising *H. leptocaulis*, *H. leoninus*, *H. virilis*, *H. hirsutus*, *H. chartaceus*, *H. arenicola*, and *H. divaricatus*, all of which can be seen to grade imperceptibly into one another, except possibly the last, which is by far the most stable of them all. All we can hope to accomplish here, if we are classifying plants and not herbarium specimens, is to attempt to group together genetical units and to determine the relationships of these units. The particular placement of an individual plant will very often have to remain, in this genus at least, a matter of great difficulty.

Besides the matter of leaf arrangement, with direct bearing on the relationship of species, the character of the pubescence is of considerable importance. The usual terms descriptive of the various kinds and degrees of pubescence are well understood, but the terms "scabrous-hispid," "scabrum," "seta," and its derivatives, and "struma," have been used in a very definite sense. A scabrum, in this paper, is a very coarse, short, blunt-topped structure, usually on the lower surface of a leaf. If the basal portion of an epidermal trichome is of this character, and the apex is very short and sharp, the trichome is "scabrous-setose"; if such a trichome is somewhat elongated, it is "scabrous-hispid." A seta is a short, slender, stiff hair. A struma is a conspicuous spot on the surface of a leaf, formed by a large number of very small cells, with thick walls on the surface. When a leaf in drying turns a very dark color, the struma becomes conspicuous as a rough, white spot on the dark surface of the leaf. Nearly all sunflowers have strumae on the upper surface, and a few have them also on the lower surface. The base of a seta or of a hispid trichome is frequently surrounded by a struma, but strumae may also occur without any elongated trichome in the center. Lack of time has prevented me from making the necessary microscopical examination to determine whether the struma is a modification of an ordinary epidermal cell, or whether it should be classified as a trichome. I am aware that all trichomes are modified epidermal cells. The abundance and the size of the strumae in *H. strumosus* account for the name of that species. In *H. severus*, the most resinous of all the sunflowers I have examined, the strumae are unusually large and resin-colored, and their component cells are probably filled with resin.

Frequent use of the expressions "blade decurrent on the petiole" and "winged petiole" should be understood in the sense in which I have used them. It can probably be demonstrated that the leaves of *all* the species of Helianthus are 3-nerved; that is, there are always two lateral nerves that join the midrib near the base of the blade. These are very obvious in most plants and obscure in some, particularly in *H. Maximiliani.* And in almost every plant at least a very thin line of the true blade extends down each side of the midrib or petiole, whichever it may be, to the point of its attachment to the stem. It is quite impossible in many specimens to determine definitely whether the petiole is distinct or very narrowly winged. I am not attempting to decide, from an ontological or morphological point of view, what the true petiole really is, but for descriptive purposes, the "petiole" in this paper means that portion of the midrib *between the confluence of the lateral nerves and the attachment to the stem.* The term "cyme" is restricted to an inflorescence whose main branches are opposite.

I do not feel qualified to discuss with any degree of accuracy the origin and center of distribution of sunflowers, and this, indeed, has not been the main purpose of my studies, but a bare statement of certain conditions may stimulate some investigation of the matter. In number of individuals and in breadth of distribution, the annuals precede the perennials, but they follow the perennials in the number of species. It is also true, according to our present views on evolution, that the perennial habit is more primitive than the annual habit. The wider distribution of the annuals is due, probably, to the greater efficiency of their method of reproduction. The seeds of the perennials, so far as I have observed them, are viable, but the percentage of viability is not so high as in annuals. Most of the perennials, also, blossom very late, and in the northern latitudes do not always mature their seeds. I have examined the roots of countless thousands of perennial sunflowers in their natural habitat, and have never found an unmistakable seedling. I feel, accordingly, that the annuals are younger than the perennials.

As to the place of origin of the sunflowers, the weight of evidence seems to be in favor of South America, although one must bear in mind that that continent has not been so thoroughly botanized as has North America. This conclusion is based more especially upon the very wide difference that exists in habit among the South American sunflowers and upon the greater abundance there of those genera closely allied to Helianthus:

Encelia, Flourensia, Wedelia, Viguiera, Tithonia, Verbesina. The stems of all North American sunflowers are herbaceous, but in South America we find some four or five true shrubs. It is probably true that if true shrubs, herbaceous perennials, and annuals occur in a single genus, the appearance of these groups took place in the order named.

The Key to the sunflowers is frankly artificial. The groups Rubri and Flavi do not imply any genetical connection.

KEY TO THE SPECIES

Lobes of the disc corollas red or purple..................Rubri
Lobes of the disc corollas yellow or brownish-yellow.......Flavi

Rubri

1. Rays minute, not more than 2.0 mm. long.....	1. *H. radula*
1. Rays conspicuous (2)	
2. Leaf margin toward the base with conspicuous cilia or large, white strumae (3)	
2. Leaf margin not ciliate or strumose (4)	
3. Involucral bracts about as long as the disc, obtuse, appressed; low perennial............	2. *H. ciliaris*
3. Involucral bracts longer than the disc, lanceolate, acuminate, loose; tall annual..........	3. *H. agrestis*
4. Cauline leaves linear or lanceolate, not more than 1.0 cm. wide and more than 5 times as long as wide (5)	
4. Cauline leaves lanceolate to ovate (9)	
5. Basal and cauline leaves different in form.....	4. *H. heterophyllus*
5. Basal and cauline leaves similar in form (6)	
6. Involucral bracts longer than the disc, attenuate, tips subulate (7)	
6. Involucral bracts about equal to the disc, tips not subulate (8)	
7. Leaves flat, bracts dark green................	5. *H. salicifolius*
7. Leaves revolute, filiform, bracts light green....	6. *H. filiformis*
8. Leaves flat, evenly, not densely hirsute on both sides; low annual........................	7. *H. praetermissus*
8. Leaves revolute (except in dense shade); tall perennial................................	8. *H. angustifolius*
9. Leaves conspicuously and densely white-pubescent on one or both sides (10)	

9. Leaves pubescent but not tomentose either side (13)
10. Disc normally 3.0 cm. or more wide; tall annual. 9. *H. argophyllus*
10. Disc normally less than 3.0 cm. wide (11)
11. Leaves silvery-white, appressed-pubescent on both sides; low annual.................... 10. *H. canus*
11. Leaves not equally pubescent on both sides, pubescence not appressed; robust perennials (12)
12. Involucral bracts about equal to the disc, oblong, erect.................................... 11. *H. grandiceps*
12. Involucral bracts longer than the disc, broadly lanceolate.............................. 12. *H. Lehmanni*
13. Involucral bracts glabrous (14)
13. Involucral bracts pubescent (15)
14. Bracts oblong, leaves with a long, very narrowly winged petiole......................... 13. *H. atrorubens*
14. Bracts ovate, leaves with a short, broadly winged petiole.......................... 14. *H. rigidus*
15. Stems conspicuously and densely white-hirsute, at least above........................... 15. *H. vestitus*
15. Stems pubescent or glabrous but not as above (16)
16. Chaff of the receptacle, at least in mature heads, with the middle cusp extended into a subulate awn longer than the disc................. 16. *H. Bolanderi*
16. Chaff not thus awned (17)
17. Chaff toward the center of the disc conspicuously white-bearded..................... 17. *H. petiolaris*
17. Chaff not thus bearded (18)
18. Involucral bracts ovate, disc (except in depauperate or alpine plants) more than 3.0 cm. wide.................................... 21. *H. annuus*
18. Involucral bracts lanceolate, disc 2.5 cm. or less wide (19)
19. Bracts about equal to the disc, leaves revolute and sessile; tall perennial................. 18. *H. floridanus*
19. Bracts longer than the disc, leaves flat, petiolate; annuals (20)
20. Stem weak, peduncles 1-headed.............. 19. *H. debilis*
20. Stem erect, peduncles usually 2–3-headed...... 20. *H. cucumerifolius*

N.B. — Cultivated forms of Nos. 20 and 21 frequently have yellow disc florets

FLAVI

1. Leaves verticillate in 4's..................... 22. *H. verticillatus*
1. Leaves not verticillate (2)
2. Leaves, either the basal or the cauline or both,

elongate, from filiform to linear-lanceolate and more than 10 times as long as broad (3)

2. Leaves not conspicuously elongate, less than 10 times as long as broad (6)
3. Stems scabrous-hispid, leaves revolute........ 23. *H. simulans*
3. Stems glabrous, leaves flat or conduplicate (4)
4. Involucral bracts attenuate-subulate, longer than the disc, basal and cauline leaves similar; tall plants...................... 24. *H. Kellermanni*
4. Involucral bracts acute, equal to the disc, basal leaves approximate and longer than the cauline; low plants (5)
5. Disc about 1.7 cm. wide, stems monocephalic.. 25. *H. carnosus*
5. Disc about 1.0 cm. wide, inflorescence much branched.............................. 26. *H. longifolius*
6. Lateral nerves of the leaf confluent about half-way between the apex of the blade and the base of the petiole, the latter very narrowly winged and often longer than the blade (7)
6. Lateral nerves confluent below the middle of the leaf (9)
7. Involucral bracts narrowly attenuate to subulate tips, longer than the disc, leaves usually crenate................................ 27. *H. plantagineus*
7. Involucral bracts about equal to the disc, leaves usually entire (8)
8. Basal leaves approximate, more numerous and larger than the cauline, blade broadly or narrowly elliptic......................... 28. *H. occidentalis*
8. Basal and cauline leaves nearly similar, evenly disposed on the stem, blade ovate.......... 29. *H. dowellianus*
9. Heads small to minute, the disc rarely more than 7.0 mm. wide (10)
9. Heads not conspicuously small, disc more than 7.0 mm. wide (18)
10. Rays minute or none, leaves very small (11)
10. Rays conspicuous (12)
11. Leaves broadly lanceolate, densely lanate beneath, pubescence of the stem ascending.... 30. *H. verbesinoides*
11. Leaves linear-oblong, densely hispid beneath, pubescence of the stem retrorse .... 31. *H. parviflorus*
12. Leaves and stem entirely glabrous, disc about 7.0 mm. wide........................... 32. *H. laevigatus*
12. Leaves and stem pubescent (13)
13. Leaves densely tomentose beneath (14)
13. Leaves pubescent, but not conspicuously tomentose (15)
14. Involucral bracts broadly oblong, tips abruptly acute, reflexed.......................... 33. *H. elegans*

14. Involucral bracts narrowly acute, erect........ 34. *H. Schweinitzii*
15. Leaves lanceolate, often narrowly, lower surface remotely scabrous, disc about 7.0 mm. wide... 35. *H. reindutus*
15. Leaves ovate, ovate-lanceolate, or broadly oblong (16)
16. Leaves firm, ovate-lanceolate, the lower surface conspicuously resin-dotted, the main nerves brown.................................. 36. *H. glaucus*
16. Leaves thin, ovate or oblong, the lower surface with few or no resin dots, the nerves green (17)
17. Leaves oblong, membranaceous, disc about 3.0 mm. wide.............................. 37. *H. microcephalus*
17. Leaves ovate, thinnish, disc about 7.0 mm. wide.................................... 38. *H. decapetalus*
18. Leaves sessile or apparently so, base round or subcordate (19)
18. Leaves actually or apparently petiolate (21)
19. Leaves ovate and slightly clasping............ 39. *H. mollis*
19. Leaves lanceolate, often broadly, subsessile (20)
20. Leaves and the branches of the inflorescence opposite, leaves flat, stems glabrous or rarely subglabrous.............................. 40. *H. divaricatus*
20. Upper leaves and the branches of the inflorescence alternate, leaves revolute, stems rough. 18. *H. floridanus*
21. Leaves with a conspicuously dense pubescence on the lower surface or on both surfaces, so dense as to obscure the epidermis (22)
21. Leaves pubescent but not so densely as to obscure the epidermis (31)
22. Leaves opposite (23)
22. Leaves alternate, at least the upper ones (24)
23. Leaves linear-lanceolate, small, 2–3 cm. long... 41. *H. subniveus*
23. Leaves ovate, much larger, 7–9 cm. long...... 42. *H. Jelskii*
24. Leaves lanceolate or linear-lanceolate (25)
24. Leaves ovate (27)
25. Leaves small, less than 6.0 cm. long.......... 43. *H. argenteus*
25. Leaves larger, more than 6.0 cm. long (26)
26. Leaves nearly equally pubescent on both sides, bracts longer than the disc; North American. 44. *H. Oliveri*
26. Leaves more pubescent beneath, bracts shorter than the disc; South American............ 45. *H. Matthewsii*
27. Leaves large, more than 10.0 cm. long by 5.0 cm. wide (28)
27. Leaves small, less than 10.0 cm. long by 5.0 cm. wide (29)
28. Rays short, about 7.0 mm. long, bracts ovate, shorter than the disc...................... 46. *H. imbaburensis*
28. Rays longer, about 1.5 cm., bracts lanceolate, longer than the disc...................... 47. *H. Szyszylowiczii*

29. Heads large, disc about 2.5 cm. wide, rays narrowly linear, leaves brown beneath......... 48. *H. Stuebelii*
29. Heads medium, disc not more than 1.5 cm. wide, leaves white beneath (30)
30. Involucral bracts broadly lanceolate, about equal to the disc, evenly white-tomentose; North American......................... 49. *H. niveus*
30. Involucral bracts oblong, shorter than the disc, base of bract glabrous and indurated; South American................................ 50. *H. senex*
31. Involucre subtended by a series of narrow, linear bracts extending beyond the head..... 51. *H. bracteatus*
31. Involucre not thus subtended (32)
32. Leaves lanceolate, often narrowly so, or narrowly elliptic (33)
32. Leaves prevailingly ovate, ovate-lanceolate, or broadly oblong (56)
33. Pubescence of midrib beneath retrorse or widely spreading (34)
33. Pubescence of midrib beneath appressed or ascending (39)
34. Involucral bracts erect and appressed, barely equal to the disc, the outer shorter (35)
34. Involucral bracts very loose, usually reflexed, either a little or very much longer than the disc (36)
35. Petiole short, 1–2.0 cm. long, leaves and stems densely hispid-strigose................... 52. *H. pumilus*
35. Petiole long, often more than half as long as the blade, leaves and stems sparingly hispid..................................... 53. *H. excubitor*
36. Blade decurrent to base of the petiole, leaf base acute (37)
36. Blade abruptly contracted below to a short, more or less distinct petiole (38)
37. Leaves and the branches of the inflorescence opposite, leaves light green, concolor, involucral bracts densely scabrous-setose...... 54. *H. stenophyllus*
37. Upper leaves and the branches of the inflorescence alternate, leaves paler beneath, deep green above, involucral bracts hirsute....... 55. *H. tomentosus*
38. Leaves thinnish, slightly chartaceous, dark green, hairs of the lower surface arising from a conspicuous, flat struma, involucral bracts only a little longer than the disc........... 56. *H. leptocaulis*
38. Leaves thick, firm, light green, pubescence of the lower surface hirsute, the hairs not arising from a conspicuous struma, involucral bracts longer than the disc...................... 57. *H. hirsutus*

39. Involucral bracts little, if any, longer than the disc (40)
39. Involucral bracts obviously longer than the disc (47)
40. Lower surface of leaves either glabrous or else pubescent only on the main nerves (41)
40. Lower surface of leaves evenly pubescent, either densely or sparingly (42)
41. Upper leaves alternate, blade decurrent to base of petiole, involucral bracts broadly lanceolate, inflorescence much branched.......... 58. *H. montanus*
41. Upper leaves opposite, blade not decurrent to the base of the petiole, involucral bracts narrowly lanceolate, inflorescence of 1–few heads. 59. *H. Eggertii*
42. Chaff of the receptacle entire (43)
42. Chaff of the receptacle more or less 3-cuspidate (44)
43. Branches of the inflorescence conspicuously slender and very numerous, leaves very thin and delicate in texture, obscurely pubescent on both sides; South American............ 60. *H. floribundus*
43. Branches of the inflorescence stout, not numerous, leaves thick, coarse, scabrous-setose above, hispid beneath; North American..... 61. *H. alienus*
44. Blade briefly decurrent below the confluence of the lateral nerves, the lower half of the petiole distinct (45)
44. Blade decurrent almost or quite to the base of the petiole (46)
45. Leaves copiously resin-dotted beneath, bracts densely hispidulous....................... 62. *H. vernalis*
45. Leaves sparingly or not at all resin-dotted beneath, bracts sparingly but evenly appressed-pubescent................................ 63. *H. Nuttallii*
46. Leaves broadly lanceolate................... 64. *H. validus*
46. Leaves narrowly elliptic...................... 65. *H. borealis*
47. Involucral bracts densely scabrous-setose, the pubescence short and closely appressed, leaves somewhat conduplicate, rays cupped (48)
47. Involucral bracts pubescent but not as above, leaves flat, rays not cupped (49)
48. Leaves opposite, stems single, monocephalic, small plants............................ 66. *H. Dalyi*
48. Leaves alternate, stems usually tufted, inflorescence racemose, the peduncles normally short.................................... 67. *H. Maximiliani*
49. Involucral bracts very narrow, attenuate to conspicuously long, filiform tips............ 68. *H. attenuatus*
49. Involucral bracts broad, tips not filiform (50)

50. Leaves narrow, rarely more than 1.5 cm. wide, involucre cylindrical, inflorescence, even in vigorous plants, a single, terminal head; low, tufted plants, rarely more than 8–9 dm. high.................................... 69. *H. Cusickii*
50. Leaves often broadly lanceolate, more than 1.5 cm. wide, involucre campanulate, inflorescence (except in weakly individuals) a panicle, stems not tufted; robust plants more than 1.0 m. high (51)
51. Base of blade broad and obtuse, sometimes subcordate, scarcely decurrent on the petiole, the latter distinct but short................ 70. *H. ambiguus*
51. Base of blade acute, decurrent on the petiole, often to its base (52)
52. Leaves grossly serrate-dentate, normally ample, rarely less than 15–20 cm. long, blade decurrent about half-way to base of petiole.... 71. *H. grosse-serratus*
52. Leaves entire, or if serrate, not grossly, rarely more than 15.0 cm. long, the petiole not conspicuously long (53)
53. Both leaves and involucral bracts broad at the base, with a more or less obvious constriction just above the base, bracts about 3–4 mm. wide below............................. 72. *H. californicus*
53. Neither leaves nor bracts thus constricted but tapering evenly to the apex (54)
54. The expanded apex of the peduncle, immediately below the involucre, conspicuously white-hirsute................................. 73. *H. Parishii*
54. Apex of peduncle pubescent, but not as above (55)
55. Involucral bracts narrowly lanceolate, stems always glabrous at least to the inflorescence, leaves more or less densely appressed-pubescent beneath.......................... 74. *H. instabilis*
55. Involucral bracts linear, usually abruptly acute, stem usually rough-pubescent, rarely glabrous, pubescence of the lower surface of the leaves sparing but long, consisting of somewhat remote ascending hairs............... 75. *H. giganteus*
56. Involucral bracts little, if any, longer than the disc and not conspicuously loose (57)
56. Involucral bracts longer than the disc and usually loose (64)
57. Blade broadly decurrent almost or quite to the base of the petiole, leaf base obtuse or broadly acute................................. 76. *H. cinereus*
57. Blade narrowly decurrent on the petiole, the

latter either distinct or very narrowly winged, the leaf base acute (58)

58. Chaff of the receptacle entire (59)
58. Chaff of the receptacle conspicuously or at least obviously 3-cuspidate (60)
59. Stems, leaves, and bracts coarsely spreading-hispid, usually densely so.................. 52. *H. pumilus*
59. Stems and leaves obscurely hispid, bracts at most puberulent toward the tip............ 77. *H. gracilentus*
60. Upper leaves and main branches of the inflorescence opposite (61)
60. Upper leaves and branches of the inflorescence (except in depauperate individuals) alternate (63)
61. Pubescence of stem and leaves conspicuously scabrous and strumose, very coarse......... 78. *H. severus*
61. Pubescence of stem and leaves densely hispid-hirsute, not conspicuously scabrous (62)
62. Involucral bracts and both surfaces of the leaves densely pubescent, the lower surface yellowish with resin, the rhizomes not tuber-bearing. 79. *H. Besseyi*
62. Involucral bracts pubescent but not densely, upper surface of the leaves sharply setose, the lower softly canescent, the rhizomes bearing small but perfect tubers.................. 80. *H. subcanescens*
63. Leaves and involucral bracts densely pubescent, rhizomes not tuber-bearing............... 81. *H. mollissimus*
63. Leaves softly and not very densely pubescent beneath, involucral bracts subglabrous and usually very dark green, rhizomes tuber-bearing.................................. 82. *H. tuberosus*
64. Chaff of the receptacle tipped with a long, subulate awn, extending beyond the disc florets, involucral bracts broadly oblong, abruptly reflexed; low annuals..................... 16. *H. Bolanderi*
64. Chaff either entire or 3-cuspidate, but not awned as above; tall perennials (65)
65. Blade decurrent almost or quite to the base of the petiole although often narrowly, acute at the base (66)
65. Blade decurrent on the petiole, but either so narrowly or so briefly that the leaf appears petioled (72)
66. Leaves broadly oblong, pointed at both ends (67)
66. Leaves ovate or ovate-lanceolate, but not oblong (68)
67. Leaves thin, often membranaceous, glabrous beneath, or if pubescent, then the pubescence of the midrib beneath ascending............ 83. *H. membranaceus*

67. Leaves firm, subglabrous or sparingly scabrous-hispid beneath, pubescence of the midrib beneath spreading........................ 84. *H. altissimus*
68. Pubescence of the midrib beneath spreading or retrorse (69)
68. Pubescence of the midrib beneath appressed or ascending................................ 88. *H. formosus*
69. Involucral bracts loose but not reflexed, subglabrous, peduncles long, 1-headed, pubescence of stem and leaves not dense but coarse, scabrous.......................... 85. *H. laetiflorus*
69. Involucral bracts recurved or reflexed, pubescent, peduncles not conspicuously long, often 3-headed, pubescence of stem and leaves either dense or sparing, but soft and smooth to the touch (70)
70. Leaves revolute, firm, either densely tomentose on both sides or sparingly tomentulose, in which latter case the lower surface is much paler and often glaucous; florets of the disc copiously resin-dotted..................... 55. *H. tomentosus*
70. Leaves flat, thin, concolor, pubescent both sides but not tomentose (71)
71. Florets of the disc copiously resin-dotted, lower surface of the leaves evenly but not densely pubescent, hairs rather short............... 86. *H. resinosus*
71. Florets of the disc not resin-dotted, both surfaces of the leaves softly tomentulose....... 87. *H. doronicoides*
72. Blade scarcely at all decurrent on the petiole, its base round, subcordate, or broadly acute, the lateral nerves confluent very near the base (73)
72. Blade decurrent about half-way to the base of the petiole, or if farther, then so narrowly that the leaf appears petiolate (80)
73. Lower surface of leaves glabrous or else hispid only on the main nerves.................. 89. *H. saxicola*
73. Lower surface of leaves evenly pubescent (74)
74. Leaves small, about 6–7 cm. long and widest about the middle......................... 90. *H. brevifolius*
74. Leaves ample, rarely less than 10.0 cm. long and widest below the middle (75)
75. Leaves thick, firm, not at all chartaceous (76)
75. Leaves thinnish, often chartaceous (77)
76. Involucral bracts very loose, reflexed, much longer than the disc, densely scabrous-setose, leaves rarely more than 5.0 cm. wide, hirsute-hispid beneath, main branches of the inflorescence opposite....................... 57. *H. hirsutus*

76. Involucral bracts only a little longer than the disc, sparingly hispidulous, erect or reflexed, leaves rarely less than 8.0 cm. wide, branches of the inflorescence alternate.............. 91. *H. leoninus*
77. Inflorescence contracted, peduncles short (78)
77. Inflorescence not conspicuously contracted, peduncles 10–20 cm. long (79)
78. Leaves conspicuously thin, mostly more than 5.0 cm. wide, the petiole about 1.0–1.5 cm. long.................................... 92. *H. chartaceus*
78. Leaves chartaceous but not conspicuously thin, rarely more than 5.0 cm. wide, the petiole usually more than 1.5 cm. long............. 56. *H. leptocaulis*
79. Involucral bracts broadly lanceolate, somewhat longer than the disc, loose but erect, cauline leaves with petiole less than 1.0 cm. long, branches of the inflorescence opposite....... 93. *H. virilis*
79. Involucral bracts lanceolate, much longer than the disc and reflexed at maturity, cauline leaves with petiole more than 1.0 cm. long, branches of the inflorescence alternate...... 94. *H. arenicola*
80. Leaves broadly ovate, the blade abruptly contracted just below the confluence of the lateral nerves and narrowly decurrent to the base of the petiole, the latter long (81)
80. Leaves very broadly ovate-lanceolate (83)
81. Leaves and the branches of the inflorescence alternate, leaves very coarse in texture, they and the stems very rough................. 95. *H. exasperatus*
81. Leaves opposite to the inflorescence, branches of the latter either opposite or alternate (82)
82. Leaves conspicuously thin and delicate, involucral bracts linear and much longer than the disc, branches of the inflorescence alternate.................................. 38. *H. decapetalus*
82. Leaves not conspicuously thin, bracts lanceolate, longer than, but not greatly exceeding, the disc............................... 96. *H. ambulans*
83. Blade only briefly decurrent on the petiole, the latter distinct at least toward the base (84)
83. Blade decurrent more than half-way on the petiole, but very narrowly so (88)
84. Leaves opposite at least to the inflorescence (85)
84. Leaves and the branches of the inflorescence alternate (86)
85. Leaves concolor, light green, involucral bracts narrowly lanceolate...................... 97. *H. Rydbergi*
85. Leaves paler beneath, deep green above, involucral bracts broadly lanceolate-acuminate.. 98. *H. strumosus*

86. Involucral bracts broadly linear or linear-lanceolate and much longer than the disc (87)
86. Involucral bracts narrowly linear-lanceolate and only a little longer than the disc........ 97. *H. Rydbergi*
87. Heads large, 6–10 cm. wide, including the rays, involucral bracts loose but erect, leaves firm. 99. *H. superbus*
87. Heads smaller, 3–5 cm. wide, including rays, involucral bracts irregular, curly but not reflexed, leaves thin........................ 100. *H. tracheliifolius*
88. Stems glabrous, leaves glabrous beneath except on the hispid main nerves, abruptly contracted near the base..................... 58. *H. montanus*
88. Stems hispid, at least above, leaves sparingly very short-pubescent beneath, slightly acuminate at both ends...................... 101. *H. luxurians*

See also the following Helianthi not in the key:

102. *H. australis* Phil.
103. *H. amplexicaulis* DC.
104. *H. acuminatus* Blake
105. *H. discolor* Blake
106. *H. viridior* Blake
107. *H. similis* (Brandeg.) Blake
108. *H. rugosus* Meyen

It is, as Bentham and Hooker remark, as difficult to establish definitely inclusive and exclusive limits for the genus Helianthus as it is for the species of the genus.

Generic Definition. — Heads heterogamous, radiate; rays usually conspicuous, minute in only a few species; florets of the ray in one series, ligulate, sterile, though sometimes pistillate; florets of the disc tubular, regular, 5-lobed at the apex, the limb elongate, usually pubescent at the base, constricted below the anthers to a usually short tube; the anthers without basal appendages, or at most minutely 2-lobed; the style bifid, the branches spreading, recurved; the achene obovate or rarely linear-obovate, slightly quadrangular, slightly compressed; pappus usually of two elongated awns, attached to the achene between the corolla and the achene on the long diameter of the achene, often with a small accessory palea on each side of each awn, sometimes with small intermediate paleae between the two principal awns, all paleae and awns readily caducous; the head surrounded by an involucre of 2–4 series of small bracts, varying in length, pubescence, and degree of appression; the receptacle plano-convex; the receptacular chaff conduplicate. Annual or perennial herbs, or rarely shrubs, stems simple or ramose, leaves mostly rather coarse in texture, always opposite at the base of the stem, opposite or alternate at the apex, 3-nerved, sometimes obscurely. Rays always yellow, florets of the disc yellow or red-purple.

1. H. radula (Pursh) T. & G. Fl. N. A., 2:321. 1842.

Rudbeckia radula Pursh. Fl., 2:575. 1816.
Rudbeckia apetala Nutt. Journ. Acad. Sci. Phila., 7:77. 1834.
Helianthus apetalus Le Conte, ined. ex Nutt. Trans. Am. Phil. Soc., N. S., 7:354. 1841.
Echinomeria apetala Nutt. *l.c.* 356.

Perennial, stem erect from a procumbent or ascending base, 0.5–1.5 m. high, sparingly hirsute, smooth to the touch, densely hirsute at the base, striate, simple; leaves chiefly basal and on the lowermost part of the stem, opposite, obovate, or spatulate, obtuse, coarse in texture, scabrous-hispid above, strigose-hispid beneath, often with very long hairs, not densely, blade decurrent to base of petiole, the petiole in basal leaves 1–2.0 cm. long, in the lower cauline often as long as the blade, one or two greatly reduced leaves on the upper stem, these alternate; inflorescence solitary; head large, rays wanting or minute, 1–2 mm., dark or purplish-yellow, the disc 2–3.0 cm. in diam., corollas of the disc florets deep violet-purple almost to the base, very slender, the tube unusually long; the achene slender, compressed, slightly emarginate, glabrous; pappus of two usually unequal narrow, lanceolate awns; the chaff linear with narrowly acute tips, glabrous, entire, sometimes subtricuspidate with very small lateral teeth, shining purple; the involucre broadly campanulate, deep purple; the bracts lanceolate, acute, about as long as the disc, erect, glabrous or a few short scabra on the midrib, ciliate; roots fine, fibrous, abundant, 1–2 dm. long; no rhizomes, reproducing vegetatively by crown-buds.

Low sandy barrens in the Gulf states, not abundant.

Type. — A specimen collected by Bartram, in Georgia, in Herbarium Banks. British Museum.

The most striking peculiarity of this species is the color of the head, which is a deep violet-purple. I collected some specimens near Lakeland, Florida, where it grew abundantly, but have never seen it in any other place throughout the South, and it does not often occur in herbaria. In the specimens from Lakeland, Florida, the rays were about 2.0 mm. long and less than 1.0 mm. wide. The achene is normally about 3.0 mm. long, the tube about 2.5 mm. and the corolla about 4.5 mm. The pappus of the floret from which these measurements were taken consisted of two awns, one of which was 1.0 mm., and the other 2.5 mm. long. The latter dimension is not unusual in Helianthus, but the length of the tube is.

2. H. ciliaris DC. Prod., 5:587. 1836.

H. laciniatus Gray. Mem. Am. Acad., N. S., 4:84. 1849.

Perennial, stem mostly about 6.0 dm. high, rigidly erect, rarely lax, mostly glabrous, but sometimes bristly long-hispid, mostly ramose, conspicuously glaucous, leaves mostly opposite, but quite variable in arrangement, lanceolate in outline, rarely narrowly linear, mostly deeply laciniate, but frequently entire, mostly entirely glabrous on both surfaces and conspicuously glaucous and bluish-green, rarely obscurely appressed-setulose on either or both surfaces, 2.0–6.0 cm. long by 0.5–2.0 cm. wide, sessile but very narrow at the base, bristly ciliate on the margin, rarely the marginal cilia reduced to smooth-topped, rather large scabra; inflorescence a single head, terminal on the branches which are slender, rigid; heads mostly about 1.2 cm. across the disc, rays inconspicuous, rarely more than 1.0 cm. long, corollas of the disc florets mostly with brown or reddish lobes, latter puberulent, throat pubescent at the base, the tube short and glabrous; the achene glabrous, pappus of two broadly ovate-acuminate, short scales without intermediate paleae, the chaff variable, entire or 3-cuspidate, often lacerate, the tips lanceolate, more or less hispid, not markedly carinate; the involucre hemispheric, the bracts ovate, obtuse, rarely slightly acuminate, erect, appressed, shorter than the disc, glabrous or subglabrous on the surface, more or less ciliate; roots very fine, short, fibrous, mostly at the nodes of the long, stout rhizome which apparently remains alive more than one season.

In dry, arid soil from Arizona and New Mexico south to Central Mexico.

Type. — A specimen collected by Berlandier near Reynosa de Tamaulipas, Mexico; not personally examined.

It will be observed from the description that this is an exceedingly variable plant. The involucral bracts, the short rays, the foliar marginal cilia, the invariable glaucum covering all parts, and the low stature, are all fairly constant. Perhaps it would be well to note a few of the more striking variations: (1) Palmer 616, Coahuila, Mexico, has linear leaves 5.0 cm. long by 0.2 cm. wide and a very lax stem; (2) Carleton, Moon Co., Texas; Young, Palo Duro Canyon, Texas; Tuttle, Artesia, New Mexico; and Stowell, Elida, New Mexico, have rigid, markedly ciliate, linear leaves about 2.0 cm. long by 0.5 cm. wide, hispid on the midrib beneath and scabrous-setose on the upper surface; (3) Wooton 3, Donna Ana Co., New Mexico, and Jones 4197, El Paso, Texas, have repandly serrate leaves, remotely hispid-setose on the upper surface, and a hispid midrib beneath: (4) Metcalf 134, Grant Co., New Mexico, has unusually large, nearly entire, rhomboid leaves.

Gray's *H. laciniatus* is based on three collections of Dr. Gregg from Coahuila, Mexico. I was able to examine these specimens in the Gray Herbarium and can find no distinctive character upon which specific difference can be maintained. Even the sublobed leaves are occasionally met with in the New Mexico collections. I think Gray must himself have come to this conclusion, for the species *H. laciniatus* is completely ignored in all his later writings, so far as I have been able to find out.

3. H. agrestis Pollard. Proc. Wash. Biol. Soc., 13:184. 1900.

H. Curtissii Fernald ined.
H. floridanus Gray, in part. Chap. Fl. South. U. S., Suppl. 629. 1884.

Annual; stem 1–2 m. high, ramose, glabrous, striate or sulcate, 0.5–2.0 cm. in diam. at the base, branches slender, long; leaves alternate except the lowermost, acuminate, serrate with low, regular, mucronate teeth, blade decurrent on the petiole not quite to its base, 10.0–18.0 cm. long by 1.5–5.0 cm. wide, thin, light green, shining, sharply, rather remotely strumose-setose on both sides, bristly ciliate on the margin toward the base, especially in young leaves, and conspicuously bristly on the midrib beneath; inflorescence a few-flowered panicle, the peduncles 5.0–15.0 cm. long, with spreading bristly hairs, mostly one-flowered, heads very showy, the disc about 1.0 cm. in diam.; lobes of the disc florets and nearly the whole of the throat glabrous and deep purple, tube yellow and puberulent, style branches and rays bright yellow; chaff entire, not markedly carinate, tips purple and slightly pubescent; achene glabrous, with two lanceolate awns and no other scales; involucral bracts lanceolate, with acuminate-attenuate tips a little longer than the disc, glabrous, with very short, appressed cilia, loose but not reflexed; roots fibrous, the system very shallow.

Florida, in very wet soil, frequent along ditches, especially in muck.

Type. — A. H. Curtiss 6741, Volusia Co., Florida, July 12, 1900; personally examined.

H. agrestis, in favorable soil, often attains a height of 2.0 m., and is profusely branched from the very base. The type has a stem simple to the inflorescence, and small leaves; it was collected in "rich, shelly ground," and is about 1.0 m. in height. As I have collected it, its favorite habitat seems to be the margins of ditches in black muck. Like all annuals, it is readily and profoundly influenced by its environment.

The heads are remarkable for their strong coloring; the deep yellow rays, surrounding the violet disc, and the conspicuous, long, exserted, yellow style branches, form a most attractive combination. Owing to the unusual succulence of this species, the thinness of the leaves and the laxity of the smaller branches are not apparent in the living plant. The leaves and flowers wilt almost as soon as gathered. From my own observations I think Pollard was in error when he described the involucral bracts as scabrous and the leaves as glabrous. I have seen no specimen that justifies these two items; the bracts are always glabrous and the leaves always have the same remote but sharp strumose-based setae on both surfaces.

Gray, not recognizing that this plant was an annual, had included certain specimens of it in his *H. floridanus*, a perennial. Fernald, shortly before 1900, had concluded that it was specifically distinct, and learning that Pollard in Washington was studying the same plant, turned over to the latter all his notes on the subject. Fernald had intended to call the new species *H. Curtissii*, but Pollard first published it under the name *H. agrestis*, much to the anger of Curtiss. *H. agrestis* is common throughout the lower part of Florida, but I have seen no specimen from any other state.

4. H. heterophyllus Nutt. Journ. Acad. Sci. Phila., 7:74. 1834.

H. elongatus Small. Fl. S. E. U. S., 1267. 1903.

Perennial; stem erect, slender, about 1.0 m. high, usually simple, occasionally with very long slender ascending branches, normally rough with spreading hispid hairs sometimes 2.0 cm. long, pubescence of stem extremely variable in degree, sulcate; leaves of two kinds, the basal broadly ovate to elongated oblanceolate, acute, the blade decurrent to the base of the petiole, very coarse in texture, scabrous-hispid on both surfaces but always more so above, concolor, pubescence of leaves normally long; cauline leaves narrowly linear, pubescence like that of the basal leaves, those of the upper stem and branches remote and reduced, often to mere bracts 1.0 cm. long; inflorescence a solitary large head on the stem or apex of the branches; heads very showy, disc 2.0 cm. in diam., rays numerous, narrow, bright yellow, often 3.0

cm. long; corollas of the disc florets deep purple half-way to the base, which is yellow and obscurely pubescent, lobes puberulent, the achene compressed, glabrous except the pubescent apex; pappus two narrow, lanceolate awns, sometimes with small accessory scales at each side, this character inconstant; chaff narrowly linear, compressed-conduplicate, carinate, the outer subtricuspidate, the inner entire, the tips purple, and narrowly acuminate, subglabrous, the keel ciliate; involucre hemispheric, the bracts lanceolate, acuminate, more or less attenuate, about as long as the disc, subglabrous to slightly hispidulous, loose, erect or with recurving tips; roots fibrous, abundant, woody; no rhizomes nor crown-buds, one or two of the longer and older roots produce a bud one or two centimeters from the tip of the root, which grows readily into a small plant during the season.

Wet clay soil throughout the southern states, chiefly from Florida to Louisiana.

Type. — In the Academy of Science, Philadelphia; personally examined.

While the stem and leaves of this species are very coarse and rough in texture, the large patent heads and graceful outline of the plant and its monocephalic habit render it highly decorative. Almost nothing can be affirmed of the basal leaves, so great is their variability in size and foliar ratio, but the cauline leaves are invariably narrowly lanceolate. Curtiss 6905, at least the sheet belonging to the University of Minnesota — for all specimens of that number and collector are by no means identical — has basal leaves 11.0 cm. by 4.0 cm. Pennell 4463, Mobile Co., Alabama, labeled *H. elongatus*, has basal leaves 28 cm. by 3.0 cm. There are no other distinguishing characters, and all intermediate foliar ratios between the $2\frac{3}{4}$ and $9\frac{1}{3}$ mentioned here can be found. A careful comparison of Nash 2541 from Walhalla Co., Florida, and the type of *H. heterophyllus*, and my own observation throughout the range of the species convince me that we have here a species of considerable constancy except in the single character — the foliar ratio of the basal leaves.

5. H. salicifolius A. Dietr. Otto and Dietr., Allg. Gartenz., 2:337. 1834.

H. orgyalis DC. Notul. Pl. Rar. Genev., in Mém. Soc. Phys. d'Hist. Nat. Genèv., 7:275. 1836.

Perennial; stem 1.5–2.5 m. high, mostly about 2.0 m., glabrous, glaucous, very pale green, very smooth, erect, simple to the inflorescence, slender; leaves alternate, approximate, very narrowly linear-lanceolate, appearing linear, thin, flat, light green, obscurely strumose-setulose both sides, narrowly attenuate at the apex, entire or obscurely serrulate, very narrowly attenuate at the base, sessile, normally about 15.0 cm. long and 2–3.0 mm. wide, rarely more, the lowermost leaves seldom long persistent, concolor; inflorescence a many-flowered panicle, the peduncles mostly 5–6.0 cm. long, sparingly pubescent, very slender, usually with one or two filiform leaves; heads very showy, the disc about 1.1 cm. in diam., rays numerous, light yellow, elliptic, about 2.0 cm. long, acute; corollas of the disc florets with red-purple lobes and bright yellow throat, subglabrous; the achene glabrous, slender, dark brown; the pappus two broadly lanceolate, short awns more or less lacerate; the chaff narrowly linear, the outer mostly entire, the inner 3-cuspidate, lateral cusps small, acute, the middle cusp narrowly acute, obviously pubescent; involucre campanulate; the bracts narrowly linear-lanceolate, the outermost shorter, attenuate to subulate tips longer than the disc, very loose but not reflexed, very dark green, glabrous or subglabrous, ciliate toward the base; rhizomes stout, 2–3.0 dm. long, crown-buds abundant; the roots very coarse, stout, woody, often tapering to long slender tips, root-system very shallow.

Limestone soil, chiefly in Kansas and the central plains of similar geological character.

Type. — In the Berlin Botanical Museum.

This species is the *H. orgyalis* of De Candolle, whose plants were cultivated in the Geneva Gardens from seeds sent by Pourtales. The first publication of the name *H. orgyalis* occurred in the citation above, where it is given as *H. orgyalis* DC. Prod. V. 5., ined., appearing the same year, probably later, in the Prodromus.

For some reason, which De Candolle does not state, he considered the plant in question identical with the *H. angustifolius* of Linnaeus, and he regarded Michaux's conception of *H. angustifolius* to be the same plant that we now associate with that name. So far as we can find out at the present time, this idea of De Candolle seems to have been a gratuitous assumption. It is most unlikely that Linnaeus' plant was one which is almost entirely confined to the country west of the Mississippi. At any rate the Linnaean specimen of *H. angustifolius* removes any doubt as to the identity of that species, and it certainly is the same thing as the *H. angustifolius* of the Michaux *Flora*. It is also equally plain that the plant with which De Candolle is dealing is quite distinct from *H. angustifolius*.

De Candolle makes no reference to the publication two years previously, as cited above, of *H. salicifolius*. The type of this species is in excellent condition and is identical with all the specimens I have seen, labeled according to our conception of this plant.

H. salicifolius is preëminently a plant of limestone soil. Its preference for this location is obvious to anyone who has seen it in its natural habitat. I have been informed that it does not long survive in cultivation and possibly its soil intolerance may be the explanation. The tendency of the lower leaves to wither and fall gives an otherwise delicate and handsome plant a very ragged and unsightly appearance.

The young plants of this species are remarkable for the length and close approximation of the leaves. When 3–5 dm. high, the plant resembles a dense plume of long, narrow leaves completely obscuring the stem.

6. H. filiformis Small. Fl. S. E. U. S., 1265. 1903.

Perennial; stem erect, glabrous to the inflorescence, 4–8.0 dm. high, simple or sparingly ramose above; leaves alternate, very numerous, approximate, very narrowly linear or coarsely filiform by revolute margins, 5.0–10.0 cm. long, curved, sessile, base slightly expanded; inflorescence an open panicle; heads showy, disc about 1.0 cm. in diam., rays 1–2.0 cm. long; corollas of the disc florets red or purple; achene slender, glabrous; pappus of two lanceolate awns without other scales; chaff narrow, carinate, slightly pubescent at the tips, 3-cuspidate, the lateral cusps small, middle cusp narrowly acute; the involucre campanulate, the bracts narrowly lanceolate, acuminate, attenuate into subulate tips, much longer than the disc, very loose but not reflexed, glabrous, scarcely ciliate, very light green.

Texas, in limestone soil.

Type. — Reverchon 1635, Texas, in New York Botanical Garden; personally examined.

Very close relative of *H. salicifolius*, from which it differs by its revolute, filiform leaves, lower stature, light-colored involucral bracts, and stems slightly pubescent toward the apex.

7. **H. praetermissus,** sp. nov.

(Plate XLVII)

H. petiolaris var. *foliis lineare-lanceolatis* Torrey in herb.

Annual; stem slender, erect, about 9.0 dm. high, simple, sparingly coarse-strigose; leaves opposite to the middle stem becoming alternate above, narrowly linear-lanceolate, about 6.0 cm. long by 0.6 cm. wide, acute, entire, narrowly attenuate to a sessile base, thinly appressed-hispid, both sides with hairs often 2.0 mm. long, uppermost leaves reduced to linear bracts less than 1.0 cm. long; inflorescence solitary, the head small, barely 1.0 cm. across the disc, the rays few, narrow, about 1.0 cm. long; corolla of the disc florets with reddish-brown lobes, glabrous, base obscurely pubescent; the achene villous toward the apex; pappus of two broadly lanceolate, short awns, occasionally with small, accessory paleae at their bases; chaff 3-cuspidate, subglabrous, thin, the tip dark, short-acuminate; the involucre broadly campanulate; the bracts lanceolate, acute, hispidulous, ciliate, about as long as the disc, erect.

Type. — A collection by Lorenzo Sitgreaves, on the Sitgreaves Expedition, near Rio Laguna, between the Zuñi and Little Colorado rivers, New Mexico. Gray Herbarium.

This species is represented only by the type, so far as I know, but it is very distinct from any other of the annual sunflowers.

8. H. angustifolius L. Sp. Pl., 906. 1753.

Coreopsis angustifolia L. Sp. Pl., 958. 1753.
Rudbeckia angustifolia L. Sp. Pl., ed. 2, 1281. 1763.
Leighia bicolor Cass. Dict., 25 : 436. 1826.

Stem perennial, 1–1.7 m. high, leafy, simple to the inflorescence, usually hispid, often copiously, sometimes glabrous; leaves alternate, opposite in small plants, normally narrowly linear or filiform, but varying greatly in shape and size, most frequently about 10.0 cm. long by 0.2 cm. wide, obtuse, sessile, very scabrous above, pubescent beneath, varying from subglabrous to tomentulose, often copiously resin-dotted; inflorescence usually a large, open panicle, peduncles very slender, hispid; heads very showy, disc about 1.0 cm. in diam., rays bright yellow, lobes of the disc florets purple, puberulent, the throat glabrous or pubescent, yellow, tube very short; chaff, 3-cuspidate with small or obscure lateral teeth, middle cusp short, acute, purple, slightly pubescent; the achene slender, glabrous, with two lanceolate awns without intermediate scales; involucral bracts narrowly lanceolate, slightly acuminate, usually shorter than the disc, very loose, setose or scabrous, scarcely ciliate, with one or two very small bracts on the peduncle just below the head; roots finely fibrous, abundant; the rhizomes few, very slender, 5–15 cm. long, crown-buds abundant and often more vigorous than the rhizomes.

New Jersey, south to Florida, west to Iowa, common in Texas; moist places.

Type. — In the Linnaean Herbarium, London. Photograph personally examined.

H. angustifolius is a plant of moist soil, and is found in clay, sand, or loam. It grows readily in the shade or in sunny situations, but is profoundly influenced by the amount of light, and perhaps by other less obvious conditions. The normal leaf is narrowly linear, 8–15 cm. long and about 2.5 mm. wide, and most leaves will conform pretty closely to these dimensions, but very marked and puzzling variations occur. As far as my own observations in the field are concerned, the variation in the width and texture of the leaf is invariably correlated with the amount of sunlight received. A specimen collected by Hasse in Arkansas has linear leaves, very thin, flat, 12.0 cm. long and 1.6 cm. wide, densely tomentose beneath — the label says "low thickets." Ruth 4071, Hiawassee Valley, has normal cauline leaves, except that the two lowest pair are oblanceolate, 2.0 cm. wide, with a very long, winged petiole, strikingly similar to the leaves of *H. occidentalis*. A specimen by Kearney from Waynesboro, Mississippi, also has lanceolate leaves on the lower stem, the other leaves being normal. Near Rodessa, Louisiana, I came upon a very large number of these plants in a coherent group, giving the impression that they were all the offspring of a single original plant. The plants extended from the reasonably dry roadside across a sunny meadow and on into a thicket so shaded that only occasional beams of direct light could fall upon them in the early morning. The roadside plants were of the ordinary, typical form and habit. In the wetter meadow and occasional shade, the leaves became wider and thinner, while in the densely shaded thicket, the leaves were perfectly flat, very thin, often lanceolate, tomentose beneath, and 1–2 cm. in width. There was not much difference in length. In most of the plants of my own collecting, the vegetative reproduction was by crown-buds and the stems were in tufts of three or four, but frequently there were slender rhizomes 1–2 dm. in length.

9. H. argophyllus T. & G. Fl. N. A., 2:318. 1842.

H. tephrodes Gray, the original collection, but not Syn. Fl.

Annual; stem 1–2.0 m. high, densely white tomentose, especially younger parts, profusely ramose, stout, base 1–2.0 cm. in diam.; leaves alternate except in very small individuals, ovate, obtuse, entire, rarely serrate, more or less subcordate, petiolate, petiole about as long as blade in large leaves, blade normally 2.0 dm. long and wide, densely white-tomentose both sides; inflorescence axillary from upper axils, peduncles normally one-flowered, 0.5–1.5 dm. long, densely tomentose; heads large, very showy, the disc 2–3.0 cm. in diam., corollas of the disc large, deep purple, lobes pubescent, throat glabrous or subglabrous, base of the throat villous, the tube glabrous; the achene more or less pubescent toward the apex, pappus of two lanceolate, ample awns, without other scales; the chaff ample, carinate, 3-cuspidate, all three cusps narrowly and sharply acute, the middle cusp very long, more or less villous especially toward the center of the disc, chaff red-purple; involucre flat, the bracts broadly ovate-acuminate with subulate tips, about equal to the disc, loose but not reflexed, densely tomentose, more or less ciliate, the cilia usually obscured by the tomentum. Roots fibrous, coarse, woody.

Occurs in Texas and the Gulf states, sporadically elsewhere in southeastern United States.

Type. — Drummond, Texas; not personally examined.

This species resembles *H. annuus* very closely and is a near relative. Its distinguishing feature is its silvery tomentum on all its external parts. It is a smaller, more compact plant than *H. annuus;* the leaves are less often serrate, and frequently quite entire. It is largely cultivated for ornament in the southern states and apparently maintains its escape from cultivation without difficulty. It grows in great abundance on the beach at Daytona, Florida, for several miles each side of the city. There appears to be no evidence for Gray's statement that it hybridizes freely with *H. annuus*, or that it fades into the latter species along the northern limits of its range. Specimens of *H. canus* frequently appear in herbaria labeled *H. argophyllus*, or *H. argosiphyllus*, which seems to be merely a misspelling.

For discussion of *H. tephrodes*, see No. 10, *H. canus*.

10. H. canus (Britton) Wooton & Standley. Contr. U. S. Nat. Herb., 6:190. 1913.

H. petiolaris canescens Gray. Pl. Wright., 1:108. 1852. Not *H. canescens* Michx. 1803.
H. petiolaris canus Britton. Mem. Torr. Bot. Club, 5:334. 1894.
H. tephrodes Gray. Proc. Am. Acad., N. S., 12:298. 1885. But not *H. tephrodes* Gray. Bot. Mex., Bd. 90. 1859.
Viguiera nivea Gray. Bot. Calif., 1:354. 1846. Excl. syn.
V. tephrodes Gray. Syn. Fl., 1:271. 1884.
Gymnolomia encelioides Gray. Proc. Am. Acad., 19:4. 1884.

Annual; stem stout, erect, less than 1.0 m. high, ramose, densely appressed-pubescent with coarse, stiff hairs toward the base, becoming finer and softer above, the whole stem canescent; leaves alternate except the lowermost, ovate, often deltoid, obtuse, serrulate or entire, cuneate-subcordate, distinctly petiolate, extremely variable but mature leaves mostly with blade 5–7.0 cm. long by 3–4.0 cm. wide, the petiole nearly as long as the blade, relatively shorter in small or young leaves, canescent with a dense, silvery, appressed pubescence of rather coarse, long hairs above and beneath; the inflorescence a few heads on peduncles about 1.0 dm. long from the stem and branches, these less densely pubescent than the lower stem; heads solitary on the peduncles, which usually bear one or two bract-like leaves; disc convex, 1–1.5 cm. in diam., the rays about 1.5–2.0 cm. long, very light yellow; corollas of the disc florets with brown-purple, pubescent lobes, the limb slender, glabrous, the base villous; the achene obovate, evenly but not densely villous, dark brown; the pappus two broadly lanceolate awns without other scales; the chaff ample, 3-cuspidate, the middle cusp long and narrowly acute, very hispid, tip and keel pubescent; the involucre hemispheric; the bracts lanceolate or linear-lanceolate, acute, sometimes attenuate, usually a little longer than the disc, densely hispid, usually canescent, loose but not reflexed.

Desert or arid places in southwestern United States and adjacent Mexico.

Type. — A collection by Wright, in southwestern Texas. I have seen the type in the Gray Herbarium.

This very distinctly characterized species is closely related to *H. petiolaris* Nutt., from which it differs by lower stature, marked canescence, shorter and narrower involucral bracts, though these are variable, and shorter pubescence of the receptacular chaff; this character also is variable. *H. canus* is common in Arizona and New Mexico, and frequently appears in herbaria under the name *H. argophyllus*.

The synonymy of the two varieties of *H. petiolaris* will not require discussion; the accuracy of the other names depends upon the type specimens of those species which I have not been able to examine. I am sure, however, that, provided the collections of Greene from Cape San Quentin are conspecific with *Encelia nivea* Benth., that species has no place in the synonymy of *H. canus*. I cannot, therefore, agree with Blake's treatment of *H. niveus* as given in *Contr. Gray Herb.*, N. S., 54 : 187. 1918. Blake maintains here that *H. tephrodes* and *H. dealbatus* refer to one species of great variability, and groups them with their respective synonymies under the name *H. niveus*.

H. tephrodes was first described by Gray in 1859 in the *Botany of the Mexican Boundary*, and the species was based on a collection by Schott from Mirasol del Monte in the Colorado Desert of California. I have not seen the original Schott specimen in the Gray Herbarium, but I have a specimen from the Field Columbian Museum, collected by Schott at the same date and locality, and this specimen is plainly *H. argophyllus*. It is, however, merely a small flowering branch, one or two decimeters long, bearing very small leaves and a small head whose disc is only about 1.5 cm. in diam., and does bear a superficial resemblance to *H. canus*, but is certainly not that species. The *H. tephrodes* Gray *of 1859* becomes, therefore, a synonym of *H. argophyllus*. In 1876, in the *Botany of California*, Gray reduced *H. tephrodes* to synonymy with *V. nivea* Benth., which is interesting but not to our present purpose. In 1885, *Proc. Am. Acad. N. S.*, 12 : 298, Gray amplifies his description of *H. tephrodes*, having transferred it back to *Helianthus* and suggests the synonymy: *V. nivea* Gray, *V. tephrodes* Gray, *Gymnolomia encelioides* Gray. We cannot at this time discuss the ramifications of this synonymy, but it is more to our purpose that in the same article he cites, in support of *H. tephrodes*, Pringle's specimens from northwest Sonora. I have not seen these Pringle specimens, but Lumholtz 16, from northwest Sonora, is a perfectly typical *H. canus* and matches the Wright specimen from the Colorado Desert. Also Palmer 826, from Lagoon Head, Lower California, March, 1889, although a small straggling individual, is certainly an annual, and therefore not *H. dealbatus*, as labeled, but unquestionably *H. canus*. It seems to me, accordingly, that Gray's conception of *H. tephrodes* of 1885, as based upon the synonymy and the citations of the publication of that year, was *H. canus*. An individual plant cannot, of course, be identified negatively nor by elimination, but this at least is certain — the original *H. tephrodes*, the Mirasol del Monte specimen, is *H. argophyllus*, and Gray's other cited specimens, *H. canus* and *H. dealbatus*, or more properly, *H. niveus* (Benth.) Brandegee, is a perennial; *H. tephrodes*, therefore, has no standing at all.

11. H. grandiceps Blake. Contr. U. S. Nat. Herb., 22 : 621. 1924.

Perennial; stem often 2.6 m. high, stout, ramose above, spreading-pilose, soft to the touch, pubescence fugacious, glabrescent; leaves alternate, ovate, acuminate, serrate, tapering below to a short distinct petiole, briefly winged, strigose-pilose above, very densely fine tomentose beneath, thick but not rigid in texture, blade of upper leaves 8.0 cm. long by 3.0 cm. wide, lower leaves not seen, but probably much larger; inflorescence a few heads on leafy peduncles terminating the branches, peduncles 3–8.0 cm. long; heads large with small narrow rays; the disc about 2.5 cm. in diam.; corollas of the disc florets slender-cylindrical, the lobes small, puberulent, very dark at the tip, base sparingly pubescent, the tube long, slender; the achene glabrous, dark, small for such a large head; pappus of two lanceolate awns without other scales; involucre hemispheric, the bracts very broadly oblong, abruptly acuminate, a few of the outermost broadly ovate-lanceolate, about 0.5 cm. wide and 1.5 cm. long, about as long as the disc, densely fine pilose, especially on the midrib, ciliate, erect. Lower stem and root not seen.

Huigra, Ecuador.

Type. — J. N. and Geo. Rose 22,231, in the U. S. National Herbarium.

This species is abundantly distinct, and Dr. Blake offers a very detailed description of all the parts observed. I have not seen the type, but a specimen of the type collection in the Gray Herbarium agrees with the description in all points except the pappus. I was not able to verify Blake's statement that the pappus of the sterile ray achenes consists of as many as ten short ovate scales. In the specimen examined by me the pappus of the ray achenes consisted of two lanceolate awns only, and the pappus of the disc achenes consisted also of two lanceolate awns, longer than those of the ray achenes, without any other scales. It has been my experience that the pappus of the ray achenes is most unstable, wide variations occurring in the same head. I am inclined to consider any character of the ray achenes of little importance.

12. H. Lehmanni Hieron. ex Sod., Engl. Jahrb., 29 : 39. 1900.

Perennial; stem stout, 3.0 m. high, ramose, striate, softly pilose, especially at the nodes, less densely below; leaves alternate, ovate, acuminate, sharply serrate, contracted below the confluence of the lateral nerves to a briefly winged, partly distinct, slender petiole, blade from the confluence about 8.0 cm. long by 5.5 cm. wide, the petiole from the confluence about 2–3.0 cm. long (lower leaves not shown in the specimen, probably much larger), thin, deep green and long-strigose-pilose above, lower surface villous-tomentose with long, fine hairs especially on the main nerves, where they are very long and retrorse; the inflorescence an open panicle with rather long branches; the heads large, mostly solitary, the disc about 2.0 cm. in diam., the rays few, short, about 1.5 cm. long, villous beneath, corollas of the disc florets very slender, glabrous, except the lobes which are purplish and very small, puberulent; the achene dark, glabrous; the pappus two narrowly lanceolate, pubescent awns without other scales; the chaff narrowly lanceolate, ample, 3-cuspidate, the middle cusp long, narrowly acute, the lateral cusps very small, some distance below the apex; the involucre hemispheric; the bracts broadly lanceolate, acuminate, very foliaceous, 2.5 cm. long, surpassing the disc, very loose, lax, but not reflexed, densely white-tomentose outside, villous within. Root-system not seen.

Type. — Lehmann 7966, Chapacota, Ecuador. Altitude 3000 m. Berlin Botanical Museum.

I have seen only two specimens of this species, the type and a collection by Sodiro from Ecuador.

13. H. atrorubens L. Sp. Pl., 906. 1753.

H. silphioides Nutt. Trans. Am. Phil. Soc., 7:366. 1841.
H. sparsifolius Ell. Sketch, 2:415. 1848.
H. gracilis Bertoloni. Misc. Bot., 7:41. 1848.
H. atrorubens normalis Kuntze. Rev. Gen., 1:343. 1891.
H. atrorubens pubescens Kuntze. *l. c.*

Perennial; stem erect, rarely more than 1.5 m. high, slender, very hispid-strigose, rough; leaves chiefly basal, or much more abundant on the lower part of the stem, opposite, the uppermost often alternate; blade, broadly ovate, obtuse, serrate or crenate, abruptly contracted just below the confluence of the lateral nerves, and from there broadly decurrent to the base of the petiole which is as long as or even longer than the blade, not conspicuously thick but very coarse in texture, remotely but very long-strigose-hispid on both sides, hairs of the midrib beneath long and spreading, often retrorse, 15.0–25.0 cm. long including petiole, 5.0–12.0 cm. wide, variable in size; inflorescence an open panicle with rarely more than seven or eight heads on peduncles 5–10 cm. long, bearing 2–3 very small leaves or bracts; heads with disc about 1.3 cm. in diam., rays often short, rarely more than 2.0 cm. long, deep yellow, corollas of the disc with dark red lobes, the throat usually yellow, gradually tapering to the tube, subglabrous; the achene pubescent at the apex; pappus of two thin, lanceolate awns, without other scales; the chaff linear, entire or subtricuspidate, the middle cusp narrowly acuminate, sometimes exceeding the surface of the disc; the involucre campanulate; the bracts oblong, obtuse, often mucronate, deep green, glabrous, rarely somewhat pubescent when young; roots abundant, fibrous, fine, 2–3.0 dm. long; rhizomes entirely absent, vegetative reproduction entirely from buds in the axils of the crowded basal leaves.

Common in open woods and shaded mountain sides throughout the southern states, long surviving removal of the trees.

Type. — In the Linnaean Herbarium. London. Photograph seen.

This is a very distinct and strongly marked sunflower, and yet so variable that forms of it have been described as specific by both Nuttall and Elliott. It is the only sunflower in America with distinctly oblong involucral bracts, and these are invariably glabrous except when very young, long before anthesis. Also remarkable is the constancy of the abrupt contraction of the blade and its broad decurrence to the base of the long petiole, and the retrorse pubescence of the lower side of the petiole. Most characteristic of its peculiarities is its method of reproduction. The basal leaves appear early and often attain considerable size, but they seldom persist through the season. In the axils of the lowermost of these leaves can be detected a small elongated bud, if the withered petioles are stripped off. I examined a large number of these plants throughout their entire range and failed to find any trace of a rhizome or crown-buds proper. The plant produces a great mass of tough, stringy, fibrous roots, and is distinctly a plant of not too sunny or exposed situations.

14. H. rigidus (Cass.) Desf. Cat. Hort. Par., ed. 3, 184. 1829.

Harpalium rigidum Cass. Bull. des Sci. Nat., Sept., 1818.
Helianthus crassifolius Nutt. Trans. Am. Phil. Soc., N. S., 7:367. 1841.
H. subrhomboideus Rydb. Mem. N. Y. Bot. Gard., 1:419. 1900.
H. scaberrimus Ell. Sketch, 2:423. 1824, not Benth. 1844.

Perennial; stem stout, erect, 0.5–2.0 m. high, simple or ramose, green or purple, densely scabrous-hispid, rarely nearly smooth; leaves mostly opposite, the upper often alternate, larger and more numerous toward the lower part of the stem, ovate to narrowly linear-lanceolate, extremely variable, but mostly broadly rhombic-lanceolate, acute, entire or, less often, serrate or serrulate, sessile by decurrence of the blade to the base of the petiole, the lateral nerves confluent some distance above the base, extremely variable in size, very thick, firm, rigidly coriaceous, scabrous-hispid both sides, very rough, nearly concolor, mostly dark green; the inflorescence solitary, large heads at the apex of the stem, or on the long, stout, nearly naked peduncles, which are usually sulcate; the disc 1–2.0 cm. in diam., the rays oval, often 2-dentate at the apex, about 2–2.5 cm. long; corollas of the disc florets ample, the lobes brown-purple or reddish, subglabrous, the base of the limb enlarged and very pubescent, the tube short and glabrous; the achene turgid, dark, usually more or less pubescent on the rounded apex; the pappus of the sterile ray-achenes three or four short, distorted, subulate scales, that of the fertile disc-achenes two broadly lanceolate awns, almost always with accessory shorter paleae on each side of the base, rarely with intermediate paleae; the chaff ample, entire or obscurely 3-cuspidate, the middle cusp broad and obtuse, dark, more or less pubescent on the tip and back; the involucre short-cylindrical; the bracts in 3–4 series, ovate or ovate-lanceolate, obtuse or broadly acute, the outermost shorter, glabrous, the innermost, rarely, obscurely appressed-pubescent, short-ciliate on the entire margin, deep green, usually shining, shorter than the disc, erect and closely appressed; the roots coarsely fibrous, the rhizomes stout, the terminal bud large, the rhizomes often profusely branched and often very long, producing abundant fine, fibrous rootlets at the last 3–4 nodes.

Common in plains and moist prairies from western Canada to Texas, introduced and becoming common east of the Mississippi, abundant in the vicinity of Chicago, rarely in eastern United States.

The type is, of course, the specimen from which Cassini drew his description. I am not aware of its location.

H. rigidus is a plant of remarkable characteristics, for it presents perhaps a greater range of variability than any other sunflower and yet is so constant in certain of its characters that it is readily recognizable. These constant characters are: the broad, erect, glabrous, finely ciliate bracts, the very thick, rigid, coriaceous leaves, the long, stout, naked peduncles, and the accessory paleae of the pappus. But this is the limit of its constancy. No attempt was made in the description to give foliar dimensions. The foliar ratio varies from 1 to 13 without correlation, so far as I could discover; the most frequent ratio is about 4. The length of leaves varies from 3.0 to 35.0 cm., and the width from 1.5 to 10.0 cm. in apparently normal plants.

The disc corollas are somewhat unstable in the color of the lobes, but in the vast majority of the individuals of this species the lobes are red or purple. I question the statement so often made in this connection that the lobes are at first often yellow, becoming red or purple. I have observed in a few cultivated plants that the earliest blossoms have dark lobes while those appearing toward the end of the season have an occasional floret with yellow lobes, but I have never observed any change in an individual floret. There is room here for further observation.

This species appears in herbaria under the name *H. scaberrimus* Ell. about as often as under the name *H. rigidus* Desf.; the proper form of the name must be *H. rigidus* (Cass.) Desf. The first publication was in the *Bulletin des Sciences Naturelles* for September, 1818, by Cassini, later repeated in the *Dictionnaire*, 20 : 300, 1821. Here the name appears as *Harpalium rigidum*. In 1829 it appears in the *Cat. Hort. Par.* as *Helianthus rigidus* by Desfontaines.

In 1818 Sims published *H. diffusus* in the *Botanical Magazine* with a colored plate. The description, made from a specimen grown in the garden at Chelsea, states that the disc florets are yellow, the *lobes* not being specifically mentioned, but the colored plate presents a head with purple corollas — hence the doubt regarding this synonymy. Neither does Sprengel specify the color of the disc for *H. missouricus*, nor Nuttall for *H. missouriensis*. There is, therefore, some doubt as to the identity of these two plants.

What the *H. scaberrimus* of Elliott is, no one can say. His collections of Helianthus have disappeared from the face of the earth, so far as I have been able to ascertain. Besides, Elliott specifically states in the key that the disc of his *H. scaberrimus* is yellow. During the summer of 1925 I searched the type locality of this species with great care and failed to find a single plant that could possibly be identified as his species. In fact, the identity of this plant described by him is very mysterious. The western barrens of Georgia are beyond the reasonable range of *H. rigidus* or of *H. laetiflorus.* Forms of the latter species, a very showy and handsome sunflower, have been long in cultivation, and are particularly popular in the southeastern states, and it is very possible that he had this species in mind. The disc corollas of *H. laetiflorus* are yellow.

I cannot agree with Rydberg that *H. subrhomboideus* is specifically distinct from *H. rigidus.* The type is Rydberg 1627, Grant Co., Nebraska. The differences pointed out by Rydberg in support of *H. subrhomboideus* are: (1) the leaves are broader and shorter than in *H. rigidus;* (2) the involucral bracts less acute; (3) the heads smaller; and (4) the peduncles longer. I have very carefully and laboriously endeavored to correlate these four points, but in vain. There are some marked variations in the length and breadth ratio of the involucral bracts, but they are entirely uncorrelated with the other claims for *H. subrhomboideus.*

The same thing is true of each one of the emphasized points. In consideration of the enormous variational range pointed out in the first part of the discussion, this species loses all claim to specific distinction.

15. **H. vestitus,** sp. nov.

(Plate XLVIII)

Annual, stem very lax, 6.0–7.0 dm. high, ramose, very densely hispid-hirsute, especially above; leaves alternate, deltoid-lanceolate, cuneate-subcordate, irregularly dentate, acute at the apex, dark green, concolor, long hispid-hirsute beneath, not densely, longer and more abundant on the nerves, long-appressed-hispid above, the petiole very hirsute, mostly longer than the blade, thin in texture, crowded on the stem, the blade about 6.0 cm. long by 4.0 cm. wide, inflorescence solitary, terminal on the upper branches, the peduncles very hirsute and usually with one or two small leaves; heads showy, the disc about 1.0 cm. in diam., the rays 1.5 cm. long, oval; corollas of the disc florets with purple lobes, subglabrous, the achene densely villous; pappus of two very short, subulate awns without other scales, chaff mostly entire, or abruptly acuminate with conspicuous "shoulders," tip and keel hispidulous; the involucre hemispheric, the bracts linear-lanceolate, acuminate, attenuate, longer than the disc, densely hispidulous, very loose but not reflexed.

Type. — S. M. Tracy 6919, Hog Island, western coast of Florida, determined by Greene as *H. debilis,* in the herbarium of Michigan State College.

16. *H. Bolanderi* Gray. Proc. Am. Acad., 6:544, 1865.

H. scaberrimus Benth. Bot. Voy. Sulph., 28. 1844. Not Ell., Sketch, 2:423. 1824.
H. exilis Gray. Proc. Am. Acad., 6:455. 1865.

Annual; stem ranging from a few dm. to 1.0 m. high, mostly about 0.7 m., ramose unless very small, long hirsute, not densely, often somewhat rough-scabrous in large plants; leaves alternate except in depauperate individuals, normally ovate or, in small plants, oblong-lanceolate, obtuse, contracted below to a more or less distinct petiole, the blade scarcely or not at all decurrent, entire or obscurely serrulate, especially in large leaves, pubescence extremely variable and irregular, prevailingly hirsute; obscurely scabrous or hispid, with scattering long hairs above, very long-hirsute or pilose beneath, sometimes only on the nerves, often densely all over the lower surface and petiole, the main nerves especially, with long, spreading or even retrorse hairs; the blade rarely more than 9.0 cm. long by 4.5 cm. wide, often 3.0 cm. long by 1.0 cm. wide; the petiole of stem leaves sometimes as long as the blade, more often about one third or one fourth as long, that of the upper leaves, especially of the branches, very short, mostly light green, thinnish; inflorescence solitary, at the apex of the main stem when simple, at the apices of the rather long and slender branches when ramose; heads normally large, about 2.3

cm. across the disc, rays light yellow, rarely more than 2.0 cm. long, often shorter; corollas of the disc florets either yellow throughout or with dark red-purple lobes and throat, mostly glabrous with a villous base, the tube very short and glabrous; the achene slender, dark, fulvous-villous, not densely, toward the apex; pappus of two lanceolate awns, without other scales; the chaff ample, thin, markedly carinate, glabrous or subglabrous, 3-cuspidate, the lateral cusps often very lacerate, especially in vigorous plants, and the middle cusp prolonged at maturity into a long, slender, smooth, very subulate awn far exceeding the disc florets, very conspicuous, the tips of the chaff purplish when the corollas are purple, involucral bracts conspicuously foliaceous in texture and habit, mostly oblong with very narrowly acuminate, subulate tips, in mature heads mostly much longer than the disc, always very loose, but not reflexed, light green, hirsute toward the base, with very long hairs, often densely, and very sharply, obscurely short-setose underneath the hirsute pubescence, and mostly obscured by it, in very vigorous heads, the outer bracts often longer than the rays.

California to Oregon.

Type. — Bolander, from the Geysers, Lake Co., near Clear Lake, California, in the Gray Herbarium; examined.

The peculiarities of this species are perhaps sufficiently set forth in the description, but it may be well to refer more particularly to the color of the disc florets. These corollas are either a clear yellow or an unmistakable red-purple; there seem to be no intermediate shades. This difference in color, however, constitutes the only constant difference which might serve to separate the plants assembled under the name *H. Bolanderi*. It is also noteworthy that this color difference is not correlated with any other character nor with the geographical situation. For example, Heller 6016, Lake Co., has a dark red disc, and the same collector's 12,640, Siskiyou Co., has a yellow disc; while Smith 575, Siskiyou Co., has a dark red disc in some individuals and a clear yellow disc in others of the same number. In all other particulars the specimens are identical.

The accuracy of the synonymy of *H. Bolanderi* rests upon the identity of Bentham's *H. scaberrimus*, which is based upon a collection by Hinds from River Bodegas. I have not seen the Hinds specimen, but Bentham's description is very full, and Gray, who did see the Hinds specimen, concluded that it was the same as his *H. Bolanderi*. It is true that Bentham does not specify that the middle cusp of the chaff is longer than the disc, but he does say that it is long, and he also complains of the difficulties in dealing with "dried specimens in a genus like this." From Bentham's full description of his *H. scaberrimus*, I am convinced that the only possible point of difference between it and *H. Bolanderi* is the length of the middle cusp of the chaff, and this is also the only difference between these two plants and Gray's *H. exilis*. I have examined a large number of specimens from the type locality of these three species, and have compared these with Gray's types of *H. Bolanderi* and *H. exilis*, and I fail to find any specific difference. In regard to the length of the middle cusp of the chaff, it can be seen from almost any ramose individual that the chaff continues to elongate after anthesis, becoming very conspicuous with age. Mr. Arthur Hill, director of the Royal Botanic Gardens at Kew, compared, at my request, the Hinds specimen with his specimens of *H. exilis*. Mr. Hill considers the two quite distinct, basing his opinion on the scabrous pubescence of Hinds specimen and the short middle cusp of the chaff which "scarcely reaches to the apex of the disc florets." If the head in question is anywhere near mature, it would be at least very unusual for the chaff to reach even that height, and in all cases where there were enough heads for comparison the length of this middle cusp was proportionate to the apparent age or maturity of the head. Gray himself withdrew his *H. Bolanderi*, reducing it to *H. scaberrimus* Benth., and I am convinced that *H. exilis* belongs to the same species. Besides the fact that the length of the middle cusp depends upon the maturity of the head, there is also the consideration that the leaves and bracts of both *H. exilis* and *H. Bolanderi* are scabrous-setulose underneath the long hirsute hairs, and Mr. Hill states that in the Hinds specimen, "The indumentum of the involucral and young parts is composed of a scabrid-subsetulose underlayer with a number of stiff setose hairs here and there, especially on the margin." This is a perfect description of Jepson's collection of September, 1891, from Vacaville, California, and of Heller 12,640 from Siskiyou Co., California, both of which have chaff with awns surpassing the disc by 1.0 mm.

Bentham's *H. scaberrimus* must give way to Elliott's *H. scaberrimus*, which was published in 1824. *H. Bolanderi* precedes *H. exilis*, both published in 1865, by one page; accordingly the name of the species must be *H. Bolanderi* Gray.

17. H. petiolaris Nutt. Journ. Acad. Sci. Phila., 2:115. 1821.

H. patens Lehm. Ind. Sem. Hort. Hamb., p. 8. 1828.
H. petiolaris var. *patens* Rydb. Mem. Torr. Bot. Club, 5:334. 1894.
H. integrifolius Nutt. Trans. Am. Phil. Soc., N. S., 7:366. 1841.
H. integrifolius var. *gracilis* Nutt. *l. c.*
H. petiolaris var. *phenax* Ckll. Nature, 66:174. 1902.
H. praecox Engelm. & Gray, as to type, but not as to description.

Annual; stem erect, 0.4–4.0 m. high, mostly about 0. 8 m., simple in small or crowded plants, normally profusely ramose from the base, mostly light green, densely scabrous-hispid, rough, normally stout; leaves alternate, narrowly lanceolate to deltoid-ovate, extremely variable in size and outline, mostly acute, entire or deeply serrate-dentate or dentate, cuneate, rarely cuneate-subcordate, petiolate, the lateral nerves not decurrent on the petiole, confluent by acute angles with the midrib near the cuneate base of the blade, 4.0–15.0 cm. long by 1.0–10.0 cm. wide, but mostly about 8.0 cm. long by 3–4.0 cm. wide, the petiole 1–15.0 cm. long, its length not closely correlated with the size of the leaf, but possibly with position on the stem, the lower leaves having the longer petioles, the petiole mostly about as long as the blade, hispid above and beneath, more densely and longer beneath, giving the leaf a peculiar blue-gray tint; the inflorescence paniculate, the heads solitary at the apex of the stem and the alternate branches, the peduncles being mostly about 10.0 cm. long, heads large, very handsome, the disc 1–2.5 cm. in diam., mostly about 1.4 cm., the rays bright yellow, oval, about 2.0 cm. long; corollas of the disc florets with pubescent red-purple lobes, a glabrous, very slender limb, a densely pubescent base and a short, pubescent tube, the base of the tube often conspicuously expanded; the achene turgid, oblong, rounded at the apex, normally, evenly and conspicuously villous; the pappus two broadly lanceolate awns about half as long as the corolla; the chaff ample, 3-cuspidate, the lateral cusps small, acute, some distance below the apex of the chaff, the middle cusp long, narrowly acute, hispid, especially near the center of the disc where the trichomes of the chaff are so long as to form a conspicuous white zone about the center particularly noticeable in early anthesis, the involucre hemispheric; the bracts broadly lanceolate, about as long as the disc and acute, but mostly abruptly acuminate to subulate tips a little longer than the disc, erect, somewhat appressed, with or without cilia, rarely conspicuously ciliate, densely short-hispidulous on the surface.

Very common in sandy soil on the plains west of the Mississippi, introduced and becoming common about the sandy shores of Lake Michigan; sporadically in the southern states near the Mississippi.

Type. — A collection by Nuttall, Upper Missouri River, in the herbarium of the Academy of Science, Philadelphia; examined.

The two most constant and most striking characteristics of this most variable species are its blue-gray color and the bearded middle cusp of the chaff, so conspicuous on the not too mature disc.

The *H. patens* of Lehmann and the variety of Rydberg are merely very large individuals. While I was driving along the Dixie Highway near Gary, Indiana, where for miles the road is bordered by a zone of *H. petiolaris*, with another zone of *H. annuus* just beyond, my attention was attracted to a single plant in the *H. annuus* zone which was conspicuous on account of its striking, deep, blue-gray color. This individual was 4.0 m. high, which was about the average height of the individuals of *H. annuus* about it, and except for its height and the size of its parts, was, in every detail, a perfect *H. petiolaris*, with bearded chaff, villous achenes, and blue-gray color. Such plants are occasionally met with where *H. petiolaris* grows abundantly, and it would be very interesting to know the true explanation of its gigantic size — whether it be a mutation or the result of hybridism with *H. annuus*. There is no experimental evidence at present, and size alone, especially in isolated individuals, does not justify specific distinction. These unusually large individuals sometimes appear in herbaria labeled *H. patens*.

Nuttall's *H. integrifolius* is merely one of the infinite varieties of *H. petiolaris* observable in the field, and I am very suspicious that the variety *gracilis* is a dwarf *H. annuus*.

Cockerell's *H. petiolaris* var. *phenax* I have not seen, but the description would suggest that it is an individual with yellow corollas, a mutation, or DeVriesian species.

18. H. floridanus Gray ex Chapman, Fl. S. U. S., ed. of 1884, p. 688.

H. littoralis Chapman in herb.
H. undulatus Chapman. Fl. S. U. S., ed. of 1884, p. 689.
H. variabilis Mohr. in herb.

Perennial; stem, 1–2 m. high, scabrous-hispid, erect, simple to the inflorescence, slender; leaves alternate except the lower, often opposite in small individuals, lanceolate or oblong-lanceolate, rarely ovate, mostly obtuse, the blade broadly decurrent to the base of the very short petiole, therefore sessile, the margin revolute, entire, denticulate or undulate, scabrous-setose above, glabrous to tomentose beneath, extremely variable in pubescence, 3–10.0 cm. long by 0.5 to 2.5 cm. wide, extremely variable both in size of leaves and proportion of length to width; inflorescence one to four or five heads in a loose panicle; lobes of the disc florets usually purple, but frequently yellow, glabrous, base of the throat slightly pubescent; chaff entire or subentire, the tip purplish, subglabrous, obscurely carinate; the achene glabrous, with a pappus of two lanceolate awns without other scales; involucral bracts lanceolate, acuminate, about equal to the disc, loose, rarely reflexed, glabrous or hispidulous, obscurely short-ciliate, pubescence of the bracts extremely variable; roots fibrous, rhizomes slender, usually 10.0–20.0 cm. long.

Florida, Georgia, Alabama, Louisiana.

Type. — Palmer 238, of the Florida collections of 1874, in the Gray Herbarium; personally examined.

H. floridanus is extremely variable in all its characters, particularly in the ratio of length and width and in the degree of pubescence of leaves. It is also important to note that the color of the disc florets also varies from deep purple to pure yellow. Harper 671, Coffee Co., Georgia, has leaves 6.0 cm. by 2.5 cm., while Tracy 7149 from Braidentown, Florida, has leaves 11.0 cm. long by 0.6 cm. wide. While the leaves are invariably somewhat revolute, they are irregularly so, and sometimes the difference in the inrolling of the margin gives the latter an undulating appearance not found in many other individuals. These variations undoubtedly account for the fact that Chapman considered his *H. undulatus* quite distinct from Gray's *H. floridanus*. Chapman also seems to have considered his collection No. 4, locality not stated, Sheet No. 113,976, Mo. Bot. Gard., distinct, for he labeled it *H. littoralis*. The name, however, does not appear in literature, so far as I know. Mohr also was confused by the variability of this species, for in 1891 he labeled his collection of 1886 from Mobile Co., Alabama, *H. variabilis*.

The stem is simple to the inflorescence, the upper leaves, except in depauperate individuals, are alternate and much reduced, the petiole, from the confluence of the rather obscure lateral nerves, is very short, not exceeding 0.5 cm. in any specimen that I have seen. The species is closely related to *H. angustifolius*, resembling it in the color and texture of the leaves, the variable pubescence of the stem, shape of bracts, and in habit, but it is very distinct from *H. angustifolius*, as the description of that species will show. The following are good examples of *H. floridanus:* Hale from Covington, Louisiana, Mohr, Springhill, Alabama; Watson 623, Douglas, Georgia; Curtiss 5220, 4482, 6280, 1437, Florida.

19. H. debilis Nutt. Am. Phil. Soc., N.S., 7:367. 1841.

H. praecox Engelm. & Gray. Bost. Journ. Nat. Hist., 5:221. 1847, as to description, but not as to type.

Annual, stem very lax, 1–2.0 dm. high, with prostrate branches often 1.0 m. or more in length, stem and branches subglabrous to densely hispid; leaves alternate, deltoid-ovate, acute, irregularly serrate-dentate, distinctly long-petioled, the lateral nerves confluent just above the base of the blade, petiole normally about as long as the blade, the latter setose above, hispid beneath, rather thin, 5–8.0 cm. long by 2.5–4.5 cm. wide; the inflorescence a single head terminating the stem and branches, the peduncle mostly naked, hispid; heads showy, disc about 1.5 cm. wide, rays conspicuous, light yellow, about 1.5 cm. long, oval; corollas of the disc florets with deep red-purple lobes, sharply demarcated from the yellow throat, entire corolla puberulent, the tube very short; the achene oblong, pubescent; pappus of two lanceolate, short awns; chaff of the receptable 3-cuspidate, the cusps of the outer series subequal, the middle cusp of the inner series much longer than the lateral cusps and acuminate, purplish; involucre hemispheric, the bracts lanceolate, acuminate, subglabrous to hispidulous, loose but not reflexed, usually somewhat longer than the disc.

Gulf states, in sandy soil near the coast, sporadically inland.

Type. — Baldwin, east coast of Florida, in the Academy of Science, Philadelphia.

The distinguishing characters of *H. debilis* are its prostrate habit, its long, horizontal branches, and its preference for situations very near the coast. John K. Small says that even stray plants, occasionally finding their way inland and growing side by side with the erect *H. cucumerifolius*, maintain also here their prostrate habit. Nuttall was in error when he originally described this species as a perennial.

Regarding the synonymy, Engelmann and Gray completely misinterpreted their type specimen, a collection by Lindheimer, from Galveston Island, Texas. I have examined this specimen and find it to be a small and depauperate but perfectly typical *H. petiolaris*. Evidently the authors did not recognize it at all.

It is obvious from the description, and from Gray's later reduction of it to *H. debilis*, that these authors believed they were dealing with a form or variety of the latter species. There is also, in the New York Botanical Garden, a specimen, "No. 1098, Herb. Berland. Texano-Mexicanum," locality and collector not given, labeled *H. praecox*, which is also *H. petiolaris*. This specimen is not in very good condition, but the bearded chaff in the center of the disc is still perfectly obvious, although some of the hairs have been broken off. The few leaves on the specimen are not at all characteristic of either *H. debilis* or *H. cucumerifolius*.

20. H. cucumerifolius T. & G. Fl. N. A., 2:319. 1841–43.

H. lindheimerianus Scheele. Linnaea, 22:159. 1849.
H. debilis var. *cucumerifolius* Gray. Syn. Fl. N. A., 1:273. 1884.

Annual; stem erect, 1–2.0 m. high, ramose, subglabrous to hispid, upper stem and branches usually conspicuously mottled with elongated, oval purple spots; leaves alternate, blade deltoid-lanceolate, acute, more or less cordate at the base, 3–8.0 cm. long by 2–5.0 cm. wide, irregularly serrate, deep green both sides, densely strumose-setose above, scabrous-hispid beneath, the slender scabrous-hispid petiole nearly as long as the blade; inflorescence 1–3 heads terminating the stem and branches; the disc about 2.0 cm. wide, lobes of the disc-florets deep red-purple, the throat yellow, the tube short and pubescent; the achene slender and pubescent toward the summit; the pappus of two short slender awns; chaff of the receptacle 3-cuspidate, the middle cusp of the inner series much prolonged and acuminate, purplish; the involucre hemispheric, the bracts narrowly lanceolate, attenuate to subulate tips, longer than the disc, loose but not reflexed, hispidulous, not very ciliate.

The Gulf States, in sandy soil, more abundant near the coast, but common inland.

Type. — Drummond, Texas, in the New York Botanical Garden.

H. cucumerifolius is a very close relative of *H. debilis* and of *H. vestitus*, differing from the former by its erect habit and its

1–3-headed peduncles, and from the latter by its greater size and its non-hirsute stem. The species is very showy and is frequently cultivated. Some very handsome and striking forms have been evolved, many of which have yellow disc florets. The natural species is more tolerant than *H. debilis,* and although not so common inland as near the coast, it is frequent, especially in Texas, in light woods and along roadsides, a hundred miles or more from the coast.

Scheele's *H. lindheimerianus* is probably *H. cucumerifolius.* I have not seen Scheele's type which was collected by Lindheimer at Neubraunfels, Texas, more than a hundred miles from the coast; but a specimen by the same collector from Brazos, Texas, about 200 miles north of Neubraunfels, is a typical *H. cucumerifolius.*

21. H. annuus L. Sp. Pl., 906. 1753.

H. radice annua. Vir. Cliff., 88; Hort. Cliff., 419; Hort. ups., 268; Roy. lugdb., 180.
Helenium indicum maximum. Bauh. pin. 276.
Herba maxima, Dod. pempt. 264.
Chrysis, Reneal. spec. 84. t. 83.
H. indicus L. Mant., 1 : 114. 1761.
H. tubaeformis Nutt. Gen. N. Am., Pt. 2 : 177. 1818.
H. platycephalus Cass. Dict. Sci. Nat., 22 : 352. 1821.
H. macrocarpus DC. Pl. Rar. Jard. Gen. Vme. Not., 8. 1826.
H. ovatus Lehm. Ind. Sem. Hort. Hamb., 16. 1828.
H. lenticularis Dougl. Bot. Reg., t. 1265. 1829.
H. colossus Kunze, Otto & Dietr. Allg. Gartenz., 6 : 43. 1839.
H. erythrocarpus Barth. Linnaea XIV. Litt. 125. 1840.
H. multiflorus Hook. (not L.) Fl. Bot. Am., 1 : 313. 1840.
H. aridus Rydberg. Bull. Torr. Bot. Club, 32 : 127. 1905.
H. grandiflorus Wender ex Steud. Nom., ed. 2, 1 : 737. 1841.

Annual; stem normally 1–3.0 m. high, often higher, simple or profusely ramose according to vigor and proximity of other plants, very hispid, rough, light green, often mottled, especially the branches, rarely reddish; leaves normally alternate, ovate, rarely ovate-lanceolate, obtuse, dentate, rarely entire, subcordate, petiolate, the petiole often as long as or longer than the blade, scabrous-setose above, hispid beneath, blade often 10–30.0 cm. long and wide, even larger in cultivated forms; inflorescence terminal and axillary from the upper axils of the stem and branches, often profuse, peduncles long, stout, rough; heads very large, disc normally 3–4.0 cm. in diam., low convex, lobes of the disc florets red-purple (occasionally yellow in cultivated forms), puberulent, the throat yellow, glabrous or subglabrous, base villous, the tube short, slender, glabrous; achene large, obovate, glabrous or obscurely pubescent at the apex, light gray, mottled, extremely variable in color; pappus of two broadly lanceolate awns without intermediate scales; chaff ample, 3-cuspidate, all three cusps narrowly acute, the middle cusp much longer, tips usually purplish and more or less pubescent; the involucre flat, the bracts broadly ovate or lanceolate, acuminate, often attenuate, normally about equal to the disc, sometimes much longer, normally densely hispid, occasionally hispid only in the middle, lower half of the bracts spreading-ciliate.

Middle and western North America, especially on plains and prairies, Mexico and South America. Introduced and becoming common east of the Mississippi, especially in New Jersey and about Long Island City.

Type. — In the Linnaean Herbarium, London.

H. annuus, the prairie sunflower, grows most vigorously in light, rich soil, but it is a very hardy and a very tolerant plant, and can be found, within its range, in almost any situation. Its size and appearance are profoundly influenced by its habitat, and there are many cultivated strains that are more or less constant to their particular characters. There can be no doubt that the plant which Linnaeus had in mind when he wrote his description was a cultivated sunflower with a strong tendency to produce one or only a few large heads, but the specimen preserved in his herbarium is evidently a smaller plant, the disc being about 3.0 cm. in diameter.

There is a strong tendency, observable in herbarium specimens, to reserve the name *H. annuus* for the cultivated form and *H. lenticularis* for the wild form. It is also probable that Douglas considered them distinct when he published the latter name in the *Botanical Register*. There is undeniably a difference between the native plant in its natural habitat and any or all of the cultivated races, and whether these differences are great enough and sufficiently constant to be specific or not is a matter of the species concept. My own observations in the field lead me to the conclusion that the prairie sunflower, except where very obviously influenced by its environment, is a reasonably constant entity, much more so, for example, than *H. petiolaris*. But this is not true of any of the cultivated races. Dr. E. A. Bessey informs me that he has seen in Russia large stretches of waste land, outside the cultivated sunflower fields, completely covered by a wild growth of sunflowers, self-sown from the cultivated fields. These had reverted entirely to the wild type, except that the disc corollas were uniformly yellow. The heads were small, the disc about 3.0 cm. in diam., the stems profusely branched, and the leaves much smaller. The striations of the achene, the alternate, irregular, light and dark stripes so characteristic of the cultivated plant, are frequently met with in the wild plant. The monocephalic habit of the Giant Russian sunflower does not seem to occur in the wild state, except when obviously due to crowding or depauperation. Even the cultivated monocephalic race occasionally produces an individual with two or more heads; all these differences seem to be differences in degree, and I do not feel that we are justified in regarding the wild prairie sunflower and the various cultivated races as specifically distinct.

Among the specimens I have examined are several sheets of plants collected by MacBride, No. 622, from Elmore Co., Idaho, altitude 4,500 m. These plants were identified as *H. exilis* Gray, and the identification was verified by Aven Nelson. I do not agree with this determination. The distinguishing characters of *H. exilis*, or, as we shall have to call it, *H. Bolanderi*, are the long subulate awn which forms the middle cusp of the chaff, and the *villous*, not *hispid*, bracts. In mature heads of *H. Bolanderi* the awn far exceeds the disc, and is truly subulate. In MacBride's specimens, the middle cusp of the chaff in the most mature heads is long, certainly, but not subulate, and the bracts are hispid as in *H. annuus*. These specimens of MacBride are about 4.0 dm. to perhaps 7–8.0 dm. tall. Where there is a very dense growth of *H. annuus* of normal habit, many small, depauperate plants may be found, stunted by crowding, shade, or competition for moisture, which match these collections of MacBride perfectly. In habit, size, and general appearance, these plants do suggest *H. Bolanderi*, but they lack the diagnostic characters.

I believe these considerations will also explain the *H. aridus* of Rydberg. The type of this species, Anderson 4214, is, in my opinion, *H. annuus*, although it has much the habit and general size and appearance of *H. petiolaris*. It does not belong, however, to the latter species as it lacks the bearded chaff which is the most constant character of that plant. From my observations in the states west of the Mississippi, and in the vicinity of Chicago, where *H. petiolaris* and *H. annuus* grow abundantly and in close proximity to each other, I conclude that the normally tall species are more profoundly influenced by untoward conditions than the normally low species. In favorable situations along the highway, for example, a strip several meters wide would be given up entirely to *H. petiolaris*, the plants attaining an average height of about 1.5 m. Beyond this border, sharply demarcated from it, would be found an area from 50 to 100 m. in width completely covered by *H. annuus*, these plants being on an average 3–4 m. in height. Careful observation and a little searching in such vicinities revealed isolated spots, low knolls, or small areas offering less favorable conditions, and here *H. annuus* and *H. petiolaris* could be found growing side by side, with no very marked difference in height. In this latter situation the individuals of *H. annuus* exhibited a marked tendency to simpler stems than those of *H. petiolaris*, but the outstanding and important observation here is the fact that the two species approached each other in general appearance much more closely than was the case when growing in a distinctly favorable situation. Accurate determination of depauperate individuals in so unstable a genus as *Helianthus*, particularly plants of so closely related species as are *H. petiolaris*, *H. annuus*, and *H. Bolanderi*, presents extraordinary difficulty.

Dr. T. D. A. Cockerell of Boulder, Colorado, who has devoted much study to this genus, has described and named a number of varieties of *H. annuus*. I have not seen the types of these varieties, but it must be borne in mind that the genus as a whole is exceedingly variable, and this species in particular is extremely plastic in its response to edaphic conditions, and I question the value at least to systematic botany, of the enumeration of all the varieties and peculiarities observable in the field. Following is a list of Dr. Cockerell's varieties, so far as I know them:

H. annuus lenticularis var. aridus (Rydb.) Ckll. Am. Nat., 49 : 611. 1915.
H. annuus lenticularis var. coronatus Ckll. Science, N. S., 32 : 384. 1910.
H. annuus b. macrocarpus Ckll. Am. Nat., 49 : 611. 1915.
H. annuus var. niger Ckll. Science, N. S., 40 : 708. 1914.
H. annuus var. pollescens Ckll. Gard. Chron., Ser. 3, 64 : 186. 1918.
H. annuus var. passiflora Ckll. *l. c.*
H. annuus var. primulinus Ckll. Science, N. S., 38 : 312. 1913.
H. annuus var. reversus Ckll. Gard. Chron., Ser. 3, 64 : 186. 1918.
H. annuus var. revolutus Ckll. *l. c.*
H. annuus var. scaberrimus Ckll. Science, N. S., 40 : 708. 1914.
H. annuus var. selene Ckll. Science, N. S., 40 : 284. 1914.
H. annuus var. semivinosus Ckll. Gard. Chron., Ser. 3, 64 : 186. 1918.
H. annuus var. tortuosus Ckll. Science, N. S., 38 : 313. 1913.
H. annuus var. trizonatus Ckll. Gard. Chron., Ser. 3, 64 : 186. 1918.
H. annuus var. vinosissimus Ckll. Science, N. S., 40 : 709. 1914.
H. annuus var. vinosus Ckll. Science, N. S., 38 : 313. 1913.
H. annuus var. apicalis Ckll. Gard. Chron., Ser. 3, 64 : 186. 1918.
H. annuus var. basalis Ckll. *l. c.*
H. annuus var. chrysanthemoides Ckll. Am. Nat., 49 : 617. 1915.
H. annuus var. convolutus Ckll. Gard. Chron., Ser. 3, 64 : 186. 1918.
H. annuus var. coronatus Ckll. *H. lenticularis* Dougl. Bot. Gaz., 45 : 338. 1908.
H. annuus subsp. lenticularis Ckll. Science, N. S., 40 : 284. 1914.

These varieties are DeVriesian species, or mutations of *H. annuus*, and are of interest to students of genetics, but are only incidental to our systematic study. In this connection it is of interest to note that *H. petiolaris*, *H. debilis*, and *H. cucumerifolius*, also annuals, are much given to variability, especially in the same characters that present the variations listed above by Professor Cockerell.

With regard to the ancient cultivation of *H. annuus*, Dr. Melvin R. Gilmore, of the Museum of the American Indian, has presented some interesting information. He found, in some small clay urns or vases taken from the dwellings of the Ozark Bluff Dwellers of Arkansas and Missouri, a number of sunflower seeds. On examination these proved to be seeds of the large, monocephalic sunflower, identical in every particular with the seeds of the same plant now grown extensively in Russia and the United States. Dr. Gilmore states that these seeds are at least a thousand years and probably several thousand years old. This is, therefore, the earliest existing record of the cultivation of *H. annuus*.

22. H. verticillatus Small. Bull. Torr. Bot. Club, 25:479. 1898.

Perennial; stem slender, erect, 1–1.5 m. high, glabrous, glaucous, brownish, somewhat ramose above; leaves verticillate in 4's, lanceolate, narrowly acute, sessile by decurrence of the blade to the base of the petiole, about 10.0 cm. long by 1.0 cm. wide, firm in texture, dark green, very strumose-short-setulose above, evenly fine, not densely, pubescent and paler beneath; the inflorescence a cyme; the heads with disc about 1.0 cm. in diam., the rays 1–2.0 cm. long, bright yellow; corollas of the disc florets yellow, narrowly campanulate, pubescent, especially the lobes and base; the achene linear, light brown, obscurely short-pubescent at the apex; the pappus two broadly lanceolate, rather short awns, occasionally with a very small, subulate arista at each side; the chaff linear, 3-cuspidate, the lateral cusps small, chaff pubescent on tip and keel; the involucre campanulate; the bracts narrowly lanceolate, acuminate, subglabrous, rather short-ciliate, a little longer than the disc, very loose, the outer ones with spreading but hardly reflexed tips. Root-system not seen.

Type. — A collection by Samuel M. Bain near Henderson, Tennessee, in the herbarium of the New York Botanical Garden. The type is the only specimen of this species that I have seen.

H. verticillatus is a very distinct plant. Leaves verticillate in 3's occur frequently, especially in *H. divaricatus* and *H. giganteus*, but here only by exception. In *H. verticillatus* the leaves occur in 4's and are evidently the rule. The pubescence of the upper surface is very peculiar — a short thick seta surrounded by a zone of small, white, hyaline cells, appearing like blisters to the unaided eye. The corollas are also campanulate, a character not exceptional in Helianthus, but occurring only rarely. The upper internodes are often 2.0 dm. long, and the branches closely ascending. It is evidently rare and, so far as I know, exists only in the type collection.

23. **H. simulans,** sp. nov.

(Plate XLIX)

Perennial; stem erect, 1.5–2.5 m. high, slender, sulcate, scabrous-strigose, green, simple to the inflorescence, about 0.5 cm. thick; leaves alternate, linear, acute, sessile, about 14.0 cm. long, rarely more than 0.7 cm. wide, thickish, firm, revolute, dark green, densely scabrous-setose above, tomentulose beneath, the midrib spreading hispid, abundant on the stem but not crowded; inflorescence a small, few-flowered panicle; heads very showy, the disc about 1.3 cm. in diam., the rays deeply 2–3-dentate at apex, 2–3.0 cm. long, 0.4 cm. wide; corollas of the disc florets yellow, glabrous, the tube slender; achene glabrous; pappus of two subulate awns without other scales; the chaff linear, carinate, subentire, slightly acuminate at the tip, slightly pubescent, the keel villous-ciliate; the inflorescence hemispheric, the bracts narrowly linear-lanceolate, very loose, a little longer than the disc, thinly appressed-pubescent, scarcely ciliate; the roots woody, coarsely fibrous, the rhizomes slender, rarely more than 1.0 dm. long.

Very wet black muck, Louisiana, and probably in similar situations throughout the Gulf States.

Type. — Watson 715, between Cade and St. Martinsville, Louisiana.

H. simulans is similar to *H. angustifolius*, but differs from that species by its greater constancy, less delicate habit, more scabrous and wider leaves, but more especially by its uniformly yellow corollas and woody roots. I have collected and observed it in various places in Louisiana, but its habitat was invariably wet, black muck, while *H. angustifolius* is found only occasionally in black soil and far more often in dry places. Although the latter species often produces slender rhizomes, its more usual habit of propagation is by crown-buds, but *H. simulans* always produces rhizomes. A. B. Langlois has also collected this species at St. Martinsville, and Dr. T. L. Andrews has two specimens, undoubtedly of *H. simulans*, from Louisiana, exact locality not stated.

24. H. Kellermanni Britton. Man. Fl. N. U. S., 994. 1901.

Perennial; stem tall, 2.0–3.0 m., erect, stout, glabrous, very smooth and glaucous, ramose from near the middle, branches very slender, long; leaves narrowly elongate-lanceolate or linear-lanceolate, drooping, thin, remotely serrulate, apex long acuminate, base very narrowly attenuate, sessile, or very short-petiolate, obscurely and thinly pubescent on both sides, concolor, often 20.0 cm. long, rarely more than 1.0 cm. wide; inflorescence an open panicle, the peduncles slender, thinly pubescent, rarely more than 10.0 cm. long, heads very showy, the disc about 1.2 cm. in diam., the rays narrowly elliptic, about 2.5 cm. long; corollas of the disc florets yellow, very slender, puberulent on the lobes and base, and along the principal nerves, tapering to the rather long tube; the achene glabrous, the awns broadly lanceolate, with lacerate bases; the chaff narrow, linear, subtricuspidate with very small lateral cusps, the middle cusp narrowly acute, somewhat pubescent on the tip and keel, the involucre campanulate, the bracts narrowly lanceolate, acuminate, attenuate, very loose, the outer with reflexed tips, longer than the disc, glabrous or sparingly pubescent, ciliate; the rhizomes slender, 1–2.0 dm. long, also a few crown-buds; the roots woody, coarsely fibrous.

Ohio and vicinity, rare.

This very beautiful sunflower was first collected near Columbus, Ohio, by Kellermann. Plants from the original source were long in cultivation at the Botanical Garden of Michigan State College, East Lansing, but they have gradually disappeared. There were two tall and apparently vigorous plants in 1923, but none appeared in 1924. Among the specimens I have examined is one collected by J. J. Davis at Madison, Wisconsin, which has hispidulous involucral bracts, the only one I have seen with this character.

H. Kellermanni is also described in *Ohio Nat.*, 2 : 181. 1902.

25. H. carnosus Small. Torreya, 2 : 75. 1902.

Perennial, stem 8.0–10.0 dm. high, erect from a slightly ascending, enlarged, bulboid base, bearing a large number of leaves from one side, and the stem from the other side, glabrous, very smooth, succulent, very slightly hispid and remotely strigose near the apex; leaves chiefly in a basal mass from the stem base, varying from ovate-spatulate, 4.0 cm. long by 1.3 cm. wide to narrowly linear-oblanceolate, 17.0 cm. long by 0.7 cm. wide, obscurely 3-nerved, the blade narrowly decurrent to the base of the petiole, cauline leaves alternate, smaller, glabrous both sides, succulent, obtuse; inflorescence a single terminal head, the disc mostly 1.5 cm. in diam., the rays narrow, deeply 2–3-dentate, about 2.0 cm. long; corollas of the disc florets yellow, brownish when dry, glabrous, the throat gradually tapering to the base of the tube; the achene slightly angled, glabrous; the pappus two long lanceolate awns; the chaff ample, very thick, glabrous, carinate, 3-cuspidate, the lateral cusps small but very sharply acuminate, the middle cusp broad, tapering to a narrowly acute apex; the involucre hemispheric, its bracts oblong-lanceolate, 4–5 mm. broad, acuminate, loose, erect, glabrous; roots fibrous, no rhizomes, propagation by crown-buds.

Florida, very wet soil, chiefly along banks of ponds.

Type. — Lighthipe 320, Duval Co., Florida, near San Pablo, in the New York Botanical Garden.

This species is very distinct, but apparently not widely distributed. Besides the type, a collection of Buckley from Florida, county not given, and my own collection near St. Augustine are the only examples I have seen. These three specimens are identical in all particulars. Its nearest relative is the *H. longifolius* of Pursh, although Dr. Small considers it more closely related to *H. heterophyllus*. Probably all the species of this group with basal leaves are closely related.

26. H. longifolius Pursh. Fl. Am. Sept., 2 : 57. 1814.

Leighia longifolia Nutt. Trans. Am. Phil. Soc., N. S., 7 : 365. 1841.

Perennial; stem erect, slender, glabrous, very smooth, light green, purplish, simple to inflorescence, about 0.8 m. high; leaves chiefly basal, these approximate, those of the stem remote, linear-oblanceolate, obtuse, the largest about 25.0 cm. long, 1.5 cm. wide, the lateral nerves confluent near the middle and the blade decurrent to the base of the petiole, basal leaves extremely variable in length, entire, glabrous both sides, light green, firm, flat or conduplicate, not revolute, nerves obscure, opposite except the uppermost, apparently sheathing the base of the stem; inflorescence a very open panicle; the heads rather small, scarcely 1.0 cm. across the disc, which is convex; rays 1.5–2.0 cm. long, light yellow, corollas of the disc light yellow, glabrous, scarcely 3.0 mm. long, the tube very short; the achene about as long as the corolla, very plump, almost black, villous at the apex and on the two principal angles; pappus of two broadly lanceolate, spreading awns with enlarged bases, nearly as long as the achene; the chaff very thin, 3-cuspidate, glabrous, the middle cusp narrowly acute; the involucre hemispheric, the bracts lanceolate, acute, about as long as the disc or a little shorter, glabrous, not ciliate, erect with very loose tips; roots fibrous, abundant.

Very wet soil, Georgia and Alabama.

This species rests upon a collection of Lyon from Georgia, but Pursh does not say anything more about it. It is very distinct but evidently rare. I looked for it in the type locality in vain, and the only specimens I have seen are Harper 2237, two miles west of Paschal, Talbot Co., Georgia, and a very excellent specimen from the Biltmore Herbarium, No. 9405d, cultivated at Biltmore from plants originally collected at Albertville, Alabama.

27. **H. plantagineus** (T. & G.), stat. nov.

(Plate L)

H. occidentalis var. *plantagineus* T. &. G. Fl. N. A., 2: 323 and 504. 1842.

Perennial; stem slender, erect, 1.5 m. high, finely appressed-pubescent, simple to the inflorescence; leaves chiefly basal, these persistent, and on the lower stem, ovate, obtuse, crenate-dentate, coriaceous, blade, from the confluence of the lateral nerves, about 10.0 cm. long by 5.0 cm. wide, the petiole about the same length in mature leaves, the blade very narrowly decurrent to the base of the petiole, remotely appressed-pubescent above with very short hairs, and smooth to the touch, lower surface the same, but densely so on the nerves, strictly opposite except sometimes the greatly reduced upper leaves; inflorescence a small panicle at the apex of the stem, 4–5 heads on short, slender, alternate peduncles; heads about 1.0 cm. across the disc; corollas of the disc florets yellow, puberulent at the base; achene villous at the apex and on the angles; pappus of two broadly lanceolate awns; the chaff lanceolate, subglabrous; involucre subcampanulate, the bracts narrowly lanceolate, subulate-attenuate, very loose but not reflexed, longer than the disc, obscurely and very finely appressed-pubescent, roots abundant, fine, fibrous, the rhizome very slender, the terminal bud growing in the season.

Known only in Texas and Mexico.

Type. — Drummond, Texas.

Other specimens of this species have been collected by Lindheimer, twenty miles south of Houston, Texas; also by Wright. The crenate-dentate leaves, the long, loose subulate bracts, the very villous apex of the achene, and the very short, appressed pubescence of the leaves serve to render this species quite distinct from *H. occidentalis* and *H. dowellianus,* its closest relatives.

28. H. occidentalis Riddell. Suppl. Cat. O. Pl., 13. 1836.

H. illinoensis Gleason. Ohio Nat., 5: 214. 1904.
H. occidentalis var. *illinoensis* (Gleason) Gates. Bull. Torr. Bot. Club, 37: 79. 1910.

Perennial; stem erect, slender, 0.5–1.5 m. high, usually simple, but branching freely in optimum situations, hispid-hirsute, the pubescence spreading or retrorse and often very dense toward the base, less dense and appressed toward the apex, light green, rarely reddish; leaves opposite, approximate at the base, the first few internodes barely 1.0 cm. long, the succeeding internodes much longer, the form varying from narrowly oblanceolate or spatulate to very broadly obovate, the lateral nerves confluent near the base of the blade proper, the blade narrowly decurrent to the base of the petiole which varies in length from a little less than the blade proper to three or four times its length, obtuse, entire or serrulate, thinnish, somewhat remotely strumose-setose above, and hispid beneath; inflorescence varying from a solitary head to an open panicle of 30–40 heads, branches of the panicle alternate, sparingly leafy with very small, almost sessile leaves; heads medium on slender, hispid peduncles, extremely variable in length; disc about 1.0 cm. in diam., convex, rays 1–2.0 cm. in length, bright yellow; corollas of the disc florets yellow, the lobes glabrous or puberulent, remainder of the corolla increasingly fine pubescent toward the base, the tube short; the achene not much compressed, villous at the apex and on the two principal angles, very dark brown; pappus of two broadly lanceolate, rather short awns without other scales; pappus of the ray achenes usually two very short, spreading subulate awns, often obsolete or obscure; chaff subtricuspidate, lateral cusps very small, middle cusp narrowly acute, subglabrous; the involucre hemispheric; the bracts lanceolate, narrowly acuminate, attenuate, loose but not recurved, about as long as the disc, sparingly appressed-pubescent, densely ciliate, roots fibrous, very fine, often long; rhizomes slender, 0.5 to 2–3 dm. long, almost always producing a flat rosette of leaves toward the end of the season, the parent plant surviving two or more seasons.

Wisconsin to Arkansas, Georgia and New England. Locally abundant, but not evenly distributed throughout its range.

Type. — The type is, of course, Riddell's original specimen. I am not aware of its location.

While *H. occidentalis* is a species of gratifying floral constancy, its foliar variability is well-nigh infinite. Beyond a mere statement of the extremes, as far as they have been recorded, any attempt to give the dimensions or proportions of the leaves is futile. Equally futile is any statement of stem height, stem pubescence, or of size of inflorescence. It grows abundantly in the vicinity of Grand Rapids, Michigan, in light, dry, sandy, very poor soil, and equally abundantly in Illinois in low, wet, black muck. It is profoundly influenced by its environment. A small plant, less than 0.5 m. in height, with an inflorescence of three heads, with two rhizomes, each about 15.0 cm. long, was transplanted from Old St. Andrews Cemetery, Grand Rapids, Michigan, where it grew in thick turf, to a well-cultivated spot in the Botanical Garden of Michigan State College, at East Lansing. The parent plant did not survive, but the two rhizomes grew, one of them becoming 1.5 m. in height with an inflorescence of over 40 heads. The original plant had been slightly hispid at the base of the stem, but the daughter plants were both densely long-hirsute below. A specimen in the M. E. Jones herbarium, from Champaign Co., Illinois, has leaves with blade 16.0 cm. long from the confluence of the lateral nerves and 5.0 cm. wide, and the petiole, measured from the same place, 19 cm. long. As an antithesis, we would mention Gates 2437, collected early in June, in Kankakee Co., Illinois, which has leaves with blade 14.0 cm. long and 9.5 cm. wide, and petiole 15.0 cm. long, very broadly winged. The latter specimen was identified by Gates as var. *illinoensis*. One of the basal leaves of the plant mentioned above in the Botanical Garden of Michigan State College measures 12.0 cm. from the confluence, with a petiole of only 4.0 cm. A very remarkable collection of this species is A. J. Pieters' specimen from High Island, a small island in the northern part of Lake Michigan, near Beaver Island. The stem is 9.0 dm. high, absolutely glabrous, the leaves with blade 7.0 cm. long by 2.0 cm. wide, the petiole, from the confluence, 2.0 cm. long. In all other details it is a typical *H. occidentalis*. It is evident, therefore, from experiment and observation, that nothing can be stated definitely concerning the size and foliar ratio in this species.

The views of Dr. Gates are clearly set forth in his article in *Bulletin of the Torrey Botanical Club*. In view of the fact that the variations I have emphasized above have not, according to my observations, been so clearly correlated with edaphic factors as to lead me to believe that they can always be so explained, I cannot see that anything is to be gained by retaining the name of the variety. It ought to be noted here, also, that Gleason's type in the Gray Herbarium is, in my opinion, a perfectly typical *H. occidentalis*, and does not at all resemble Gate's collection.

29. H. dowellianus M. A. Curtis. Am. Journ. Sci., 44: 82. 1843.

Perennial; stem slender, erect, 1.0–2.5 m. high, simple or less frequently, ramose, appressed-pubescent with short, soft hairs, leafy below the middle; leaves opposite on the middle and lower stem, upper leaves alternate and much reduced, lower internodes about 5.0 cm., upper ones often 1–2 dm., blade broadly ovate, acute, mostly about 8.0 cm. long from the confluence of the lateral nerves, by 5–6.0 cm. wide, petiole from the confluence of lateral nerves more than 8.0 cm. in lower leaves, a little less in upper leaves, variable in petiolar length, the blade narrowly decurrent to the base of the petiole, obscurely short-hispid above, evenly, but not densely hispid beneath, concolor, entire or obscurely serrulate, inflorescence 4–5 heads on alternate peduncles terminating the main stem and branches, rarely one or two heads some distance below the apex, peduncles very hispid, 4.0–10.0 cm. long, very slender; heads normally about 1.0 cm. in diam., rays light yellow about 2.0 cm. long or less, corollas of the disc florets yellow, broadly cylindrical, lobes ample, base puberulent, tube short; the achene slightly angled, pubescent at the apex and somewhat so on the angles; pappus of two awns without other scales; chaff thin, obscurely 3-cuspidate, the lateral cusps short and sharp, not very pubescent; involucre hemispheric, the bracts lanceolate, very acuminate, about equal to the disc, finely appressed-pubescent, with short, fine cilia; roots fine, fibrous, the rhizomes very slender, 1–3.0 dm. long, buds small.

Illinois to North Carolina and south, particularly in mountains and drier woods, not abundant.

Type. — M. A. Curtis, Macon Co., North Carolina, New York Botanical Garden; personally examined.

This species differs from *H. occidentalis*, to which it is closely related, by its greater height, its tendency to branch, its leafy stem, fugacious basal leaves, and particularly by the failure of the terminal bud to sprout during the season. In *H. occidentalis* the rhizomes are more abundant and produce small plants late in the summer and fall, a tendency that careful search failed to reveal in *H. dowellianus*. Torrey and Gray reduce this species to a variety of *H. occidentalis*, which is a matter of opinion, but the plant seems to me to be a very distinct entity and is reasonably constant. It is by no means abundant. Gates' specimen, 851, from Cass Co., Illinois, labeled *H. atrorubens* is a ramose individual and quite typical.

30. H. verbesinoides H. B. K. Nov. Gen. et Sp., 4: 221. 1820.

H. pseudoverbesinoides var. *gracilis* Hieron. ex Sod., Engl. Jahrb., 29: 40. 1900.

Perennial; stem slender, erect, ramose, softly appressed-strigose, brownish; leaves alternate, elliptic, acute at both ends, entire, slightly revolute, blade briefly decurrent on the short, partly distinct petiole, thin, about 4.0 cm. long by 0.7 cm. wide, appressed strigose-villous above, densely fine-lanate beneath; inflorescence an open panicle; heads on peduncles about 2.0 cm. long, small, the disc convex, about 0.7 cm. in diam., rays none or minute; corollas of the disc florets brownish-yellow, slender, pubescent, the lobes small, acute; the achene very slightly villous at apex and on the angles; the pappus two subulate, plumose awns without other scales; the involucre hemispheric; the bracts ovate, obtuse, shorter than the disc, tomentulose, erect with slightly recurving tips, purplish-green, finely short ciliate. Root-system not seen.

Peru, temperate places between Guancabamba and Paramo de Guamani. Altitude 2,400 m.

Type. — Humboldt 3534, Peru, in Paris, probably at the Jardin des Plantes.

The Berlin specimen, which is a topotype, and the type specimen of *H. pseudoverbesinoides* var. *gracilis*, also in Berlin, are the only specimens I have seen. The plant is evidently a small, rather delicate, suffruticose sunflower.

31. H. parviflorus H. B. K. Nov. Gen. et Sp., 4: 222, t. 378. 1820, not *H. parviflorus* Bernh. in Spreng., Syst., 3: 617. 1826.

H. micranthus Spreng. Syst., 3: 618. 1826.

Probably perennial; stem herbaceous, slender, about 0.5 m. high, simple, retrorsely short-hispid, rough to the touch; leaves alternate, sessile, linear-oblong, obtuse, subentire, very small, 1–2.0 cm. long by about 0.5 cm. wide or less, thickish, coarse in texture, densely scabrous-hispid above, densely hispid beneath, the upper leaves reduced to minute scales; the inflorescence in the type specimen a solitary, minute, sessile head, with an abortive head in the axil of the bract-like leaf just below it; the head about 0.5 cm. across the disc, the rays minute, 0.5 cm. long, pubescent beneath, corollas of the disc florets yellow, glabrous, the base and tube villous; the achene slightly pubescent at apex and on the angles, otherwise glabrous; the pappus two very minute, subulate awns without other scales; the chaff thin, acute, subentire, the margin being slightly fimbriate, tip dark, glabrous; the involucre hemispheric; the bracts lanceolate, acute, hispid, barely 0.5 cm. long, about equal to the disc. Root-system not seen.

Type. — Humboldt 4275, Santa Rosa Mexicanorum, Mexico, in Paris, probably at the Jardin des Plantes.

The only specimen I have seen is one of the original Humboldt specimens in the Berlin Botanical Museum.

Springel states in *Systema* that his *H. micranthus* is founded on the *H. parviflorus* of H. B. & K. The *H. parviflorus* of Bernhardi, published in *Systema* in 1826, has, therefore, no standing and is, moreover, the *H. microcephalus* of Torrey and Gray — an entirely different plant.

32. H. laevigatus T. & G. Fl. N. A., 2: 330. 1842.

Perennial; stem slender, erect, glabrous, 1–2.0 m. high, simple to the inflorescence or in vigorous individuals, somewhat ramose above, very smooth, slightly glaucous; leaves mostly opposite, the uppermost, especially in large plants, becoming alternate, mostly narrowly, but often broadly lanceolate, acuminate, obscurely, often remotely serrulate, blade decurrent quite or almost to the base of petiole, 12–20.0 cm. long, including petiole, by 2.5–4.5 cm. wide, the lateral nerves confluent 1–3.0 cm. above base of petiole, glabrous both sides, slightly paler beneath, not conspicuously glaucous, very graceful in outline; the inflorescence a small, very open panicle with slender, glabrous branches 1–3.0 dm. long; heads very small, 0.5–0.9 cm. across the disc, the rays 1.5–2.0 cm. long; corollas of the disc florets yellow, the lobes and base puberulent, the tube short; the achene linear, glabrous except for a few very short hairs at the apex; the pappus two broadly lanceolate awns, shorter than the achene, with enlarged, lacerate bases, and rarely a very small accessory palea on either side of each awn; the chaff obscurely 3-cuspidate, lateral cusps very small, middle cusp acute, slightly pubescent on tip and keel; the involucre campanulate; the bracts lanceolate, acuminate, about equal to the disc, glabrous, ciliate, loose but erect; the roots coarse, often 2.0 cm. in diam.; the stem base producing crown-buds and rarely very short rhizomes 1–3.0 cm. long.

Mountains of Virginia, West Virginia, and Pennsylvania.

Type. — A specimen without date, locality or name of collector, in the herbarium of the New York Botanical Garden; examined.

H. laevigatus is readily recognized by its perfect smoothness and its gracefully outlined leaves. In very vigorous specimens one or two trichomes may be discovered on the lower surface of the leaves, but this only rarely; I have never discovered anything on the upper surface. Examination of the type specimen reveals its similarity to the collections of this species by A. H. Curtiss in Virginia. The locality and collector of the type are unknown. The plant grows abundantly on the slopes and summits of mountains, but its range is restricted. I have seen no specimens from Kentucky or Tennessee, but I feel sure that it might be found there.

H. laevigatus is related to *H. strumosus*, *H. Eggertii*, and *H. microcephalus*. I question Gray's remark about a form of this species with long and narrow leaves being *H. longifolius*. There is no very close relationship between these species and *H. longifolius*, the later being sharply demarcated by its basal-leaf habit, and its low, swampy habitat, while *H. laevigatus* confines itself exclusively to the mountains.

33. **H. elegans,** sp. nov.

(Plate LI)

Perennial; stem erect, herbaceous, probably 2.0 m. or more tall, rather slender, sulcate, with a fine, closely appressed pubescence, especially above, evidently somewhat glabrescent below, smooth to the touch, somewhat short-hispid above and on the branches and peduncles, probably ramose; leaves opposite except the uppermost, elongated lanceolate, acute, obscurely serrulate or entire, attenuate below to a partly distinct petiole, blade from the confluence of the lateral nerves, about 16–17.0 cm. long by 2.5 cm. wide, the petiole, from the confluence 2–3.0 cm. long, winged a little less than half-way; upper surface of leaves rugose, shining, sharply hispid, the hairs on the nerves longer but closely appressed, the lower surface with a dense, fine, short tomentum, all the veins prominent and spreading-hispid; the inflorescence an open, compound panicle, each branch from the upper axils 8–10.0 cm. long, bearing a small panicle of 8–9 heads on short, hispid peduncles; the heads small, the disc plane, 6–8.0 mm. in diam., rays about 1.3 cm. long; corollas of the disc florets yellow, very slender, about 6.0 mm. long, including the tube which is 1.5 mm. long, lobes and base puberulent; the achene compressed, pubescent toward the apex, 3.5 mm. long; the pappus two subulate awns 2.5 mm. long, each with a small, accessory scale on each side of the base; the chaff glabrous, linear, thin, the outer subentire, broadly acute, the inner 3-cuspidate, lateral cusps narrowly acute, short, the middle cusp long and very narrowly acute; the involucre short-cylindrical, the bracts very dark green, broadly oblong, obtuse or acute, the outer much shorter, the longest not longer than the disc, obscurely pubescent, ciliate, abruptly reflexed. Root-system not seen.

Type. — Schiede 1576, Mexico, in the Berlin Botanical Museum.

The date and exact locality of the type collection are not stated, and it is also impossible to say anything about the habit of this plant beyond what appears in the description. The species is very distinct, and undoubtedly Helianthus, although the leaves and especially the involucral bracts are very different from most of the species in this genus.

34. H. Schweinitzii T. & G. Fl. N. A., 2: 330. 1841.

(Plate LII)

Perennial; stem erect, ramose, 1–2.0 m. high, strigose, or glabrous, apparently becoming so with age, purple, shining when old; leaves opposite below, becoming alternate above, or, in depauperate individuals all opposite, lanceolate, acuminate, revolute, entire or obscurely serrulate, blade narrowly decurrent to the base of the petiole, 14.0 cm. long, including petiole, by 1.7 cm. wide, the petiole rarely more than 3.0 cm. long, densely scabrous-setose and dark green above, densely tomentose beneath, thick, firm; the inflorescence a few heads on very short, slender, tomentose peduncles at the apex of stem and the long, slender branches; heads very small, rarely more than 7–8.0 mm. across the disc, rays 1–1.5 cm. long; corollas of the disc florets deep yellow, glabrous except the villous base; the achene glabrous; the pappus two broadly lanceolate awns without other scales; the chaff 3-cuspidate, pubescent on tip and keel; the involucre campanulate, the bracts lanceolate, acuminate, pubescent, ciliate, erect, shorter than the disc. Root-system not seen.

North Carolina.

Type. — A collection by Schweinitz from Salem, North Carolina.

I have seen in the herbarium of the Academy of Science, Philadelphia, a specimen of this species bearing the name "Salem." On the label is the name *H. strumosus* var. *leptophyllus*, obviously incorrect. If this is the original specimen collected by Schweinitz, it is the type. I have also seen in the Gray Herbarium a sheet containing a collection by Schweinitz from North Carolina, and another by Dr. Boykin, locality not stated. Both of these are *H. Schweinitzii*. The Philadelphia Academy also has another sheet containing a typical specimen of this species collected by Dr. Boykin in North Carolina.

H. Schweinitzii is evidently rare. I failed to find it in the vicinity of Salem, North Carolina, during the summer of 1925, and the specimens noted above are the only ones I have seen. It is, nevertheless, a very distinct species characterized by narrow leaves, densely tomentose beneath.

35. **H. reindutus** (Steele), comb. nov.

H. laevigatus subsp. *reindutus* Steele. Contr. U. S. Nat. Herb., 13: 374. 1911.

Perennial; stem slender, erect, 1–2.0 m. high, reddish, especially above, glabrous, striate-sulcate, ramose, the branches long and very slender; leaves opposite, becoming alternate above, lanceolate, acuminate or very narrowly acute, serrulate, the blade decurrent below the confluence of the lateral nerves to the base of the petiole, 10–14.0 cm. long by 1.5–3.5 cm. wide, the length and width not correlated, thickish, firm in texture, very remotely setose above but often quite glabrous, very remotely scabrous beneath, the scabra widely removed, broad, very short and blunt, the margin appressed-hispid-ciliate, somewhat remotely; the inflorescence a very open panicle; heads often large, the disc 1–1.2 cm. in diam., the rays about 1.7 cm. long, light yellow; corollas of the disc florets yellow, narrowly campanulate, lobes puberulent, base pubescent; the achene linear, slightly pubescent at the apex and on the angles; the pappus two broadly lanceolate awns without other scales; the chaff entire or subentire, carinate, obtuse, pubescent on tip and keel; the involucre campanulate; the bracts lanceolate, acuminate, attenuate to subulate tips, longer than the disc, loose, spreading, sometimes reflexed, glabrous, scarcely ciliate; roots slender, fibrous, often very long; rhizomes stout, short, often reduced to large crown-buds.

The mountains of Virginia.

Type. — A collection by Steele, vicinity of Millboro, Bath Co., Virginia. Altitude 500 m. Sheet No. 494,565 in the United States National Herbarium. Type seen.

H. reindutus is certainly closely related to *H. laevigatus*, but its characters seem to me to entitle it to specific rank. Not only are the leaves pubescent, even though remotely, but the heads are large, while in *H. laevigatus* they are very small. Also the involucral bracts are much longer than the disc, which is not characteristic of *H. laevigatus*.

36. H. glaucus Small. Bull. Torr. Bot. Club, 25: 480. 1898.

Perennial; stem stout, erect, 1–2.5 m. high, purple, glabrous, glaucous, very smooth, ramose; leaves alternate or opposite, ovate, or ovate-lanceolate, acuminate, serrate, often deeply, mostly broad at the base, abruptly contracted to the partly distinct petiole which may be long or short, the blade 7–14.0 cm. long by 2–6.0 cm. wide, the petiole 1–4.0 cm. long, its length by no means correlated with the size of the leaf, thick, firm in texture, densely scabrous-setose above, evenly, more or less densely pubescent beneath and copiously brown-resin-dotted, the main nerves beneath prominent and conspicuously brownish, quite variable; the inflorescence an open panicle with long and slender, obscurely pubescent branches; heads small, the disc about 6–7.0 mm. in diam., the rays 1.5 cm. long or less, not showy; corollas of the disc florets yellow, the lobes and base pubescent; the achene glabrous; the pappus two lanceolate awns without other scales; the chaff linear, 3-cuspidate, lateral cusps small, middle cusp short-acute, pubescent on tip and keel; the involucre cylindrical-campanulate; the bracts lanceolate, acuminate, not longer than the disc, hispidulous toward the tip, very loose, often reflexed; roots coarse, woody; the rhizomes very short, 2–5.0 cm. long.

Low altitudes, rarely on low mountains, in rich soil, generally throughout the southern states.

Type. — A collection by J. K. Small on Dennis Mt., Rowan Co., North Carolina, in the herbarium of the New York Botanical Garden. I have compared the type with various other collections.

H. glaucus, as well as *H. microcephalus*, is a species of bewildering variability. This fact probably accounts for Torrey and Gray's varieties *Beta* and *Gamma* of *H. microcephalus*. The *H. divaricatus* var. *ferrugineus* of Elliott, *Sketch*, 2 : 420, undoubtedly belongs here, although I strongly suspect that the brown color noted by Elliott was due, not to the pubescence, but to the brown nerves, and the very copious deposits of brown resin on the lower surface of the leaves. If I am right in this interpretation of this variety of Elliott's, here, too, would belong the variety *Beta* of Torrey and Gray. In *H. glaucus* the uppermost leaves are always small and usually ovate, and although I do not remember having seen the Drummond specimen, cited by Torrey and Gray in support of the variety *Gamma*, I do not hesitate to place that variety in *H. glaucus*. Here also would belong, on the authority of Torrey and Gray, *H. tracheliifolius* as understood by Hooker, but not the Miller species.

H. glaucus is very abundant in the southern states, except possibly in Florida and Texas, and while not rare in mountains prefers the lower altitudes.

37. H. microcephalus T. & G. Fl. N. A., 2: 329. 1842.

H. parviflorus Bernh. ex Spreng., Syst., 3 : 617. 1826, not H.B.K. 1825.

Perennial; stem slender, erect, 1–2.0 m. high, glabrous, light green, not glaucous, simple to the inflorescence; leaves prevailingly opposite, rarely, in very vigorous plants, the uppermost alternate and greatly reduced, oblong-lanceolate, acuminate, serrate-dentate above the entire base, distinctly petiolate, the blade scarcely or not at all decurrent below the confluence of the lateral nerves, 10–20.0 cm. long by 4–8.0 cm. wide, the petiole

1–4.0 cm. long and very slender, the blade membranaceous, dark green, finely short-hispid above, thinly, evenly short-pubescent beneath; the inflorescence a very small, open, few-flowered panicle with filiform branches, these mostly alternate; the heads very small, the disc rarely more than 0.5 cm. in diam., the rays narrowly oblanceolate, about 1.5 cm. long and light yellow; corollas of the disc florets yellow, slender, puberulent, the lobes and base short-villous; the achene glabrous; the pappus two lanceolate awns without other scales; the chaff linear, carinate, 3-cuspidate, the middle cusp short, acute, the laterals small, chaff pubescent on tip and keel; the involucre campanulate; the bracts narrowly lanceolate, acuminate, subglabrous, ciliate toward the base with fine, rather long cilia; the roots fibrous, abundant; the rhizomes slender, about 1.0 dm. long; crown-buds abundant.

Chiefly the mountainous regions of Pennsylvania, Virginia, and North Carolina.

Type. — The first citation by Torrey and Gray is a specimen collected by Goldie in Upper Canada, now in Herbarium Hooker, Royal Botanic Gardens at Kew, England; Goldie's specimen not seen.

The range of this species is perhaps Upper Canada to Georgia, west to Ohio, but it is not very abundant, and is exceedingly variable. Its chief character, aside from the microcephalic heads, is the great delicacy and fine texture of the leaves, resembling the same items in *H. decapetalus* to which, in spite of the small heads, it seems to be closely related. The anastomosings of the veinlets on the lower surface are larger than in the closely related group of *H. glaucus*. In typical plants the resin deposits on the lower surfaces of the leaves are very few or entirely wanting. Small and Heller's collections in Caldwell Co., North Carolina, have only a single head and the leaves are entirely glabrous beneath. The most perfect specimens I have seen are those of Small, collected in Smyth Co., Virginia, and Habersham Co., Georgia. Typical specimens have also been collected by Stair, in Cuyahogo Co., Ohio, and by Kellermann and Fullmer in Jackson Co. in the same state. Although not justified by any notes on these collections, I believe the extreme and typical form of *H. microcephalus* to be a shade-loving plant — another item, if true, in its similarity to *H. decapetalus*.

On the authority of Gray, the following are also to be referred to *H. microcephalus: H. divaricatus* as understood by Michaux and Elliott, not the Linnaean species; *H. strumosus* var. *pallidus* Ell., *Sketch*, 2: 420.

38. H. decapetalus L. Sp. Pl., 905. 1753.

H. frondosus L. Amoen. Acad., 4: 290. 1759.
H. tenuifolius Ell. Sketch, 2: 420. 1824.
H. scrophulariaefolius Britton. Man. Fl. N. U. S., 1901.
H. grandiflorus Juss. ex Pers., Syn., 2: 475. 1807.

Perennial; stem erect, simple to the inflorescence, rarely more than 1.5 m. high, slender, smooth, glabrous or subglabrous, slightly pubescent above, green; leaves normally ovate, acuminate, serrate-dentate, often deeply, extremely variable in form and proportion, usually ample, thin, often large, often membranaceous, dark green and strumose-setulose above, subglabrous to remotely and somewhat unevenly scabrous or hispid beneath; the petiole, always more or less winged by the decurrence of the blade below the confluence of the lateral nerves, mostly about one fourth or one fifth as long as the blade, but occasionally either longer or shorter, opposite to the inflorescence, rarely alternate below it; inflorescence axillary on the slender, alternate branches of the upper stem, these branches leafy, the peduncles hispid and often bracteate; heads showy, the disc usually small, the rays, about ten, 2.5 cm. long; corollas of the disc yellow, mostly densely puberulent throughout; the achene glabrous; the two awns of the pappus short and narrowly lanceolate; the chaff lanceolate, long acuminate, with two very small, obscure lateral teeth, the tip and keel normally pubescent; the involucre somewhat campanulate, the bracts linear-lanceolate, rather broad, normally very much longer than the disc, often glabrous, never more than slightly pubescent, ciliate, exceedingly loose, with tendency to curve about, but rarely truly reflexed, except in very small plants; rhizomes stout, very long, commonly about 5–6 dm., roots woody, coarsely fibrous, not abundant.

Found most abundantly in New England, New York, west to Michigan, Ohio, Kentucky, and Tennessee, occasional in the states bordering on this range; rich, open woodlands.

Type. — *H. decapetalus* in the Linnaean Herbarium; photograph examined.

H. decapetalus is typically a plant of not too densely shaded places and is probably the most common sunflower, next to *H. divaricatus* and *H. giganteus,* of the northeastern part of the United States. It is a woodland plant, and can be found along the borders of woods, in copses, thickets, but not in swampy places.

The leaves are invariably extremely thin, and in very shaded copses often membranaceous. The shapes vary from broadly lanceolate or oblong-lanceolate to broadly ovate, the latter being the normal or most usual shape. They are invariably acuminate, often deeply and saliently serrate-dentate and the petiole is always winged. The regularity with which the leaves are opposite to the inflorescence and the inflorescence branches alternate is very marked. The lower surface of the leaves is often somewhat lustrous and is only a little paler than the upper surface. Perhaps the most constant characteristics of this species are the long, loose, curly bracts, much longer than the disc.

I have frequently collected specimens in rather dry woods that differed from the normal *H. decapetalus* in smaller stature and leaves, and these opposite, the stem terminating in a single very small head, nearly as small as the normal *H. microcephalus.* I thought at first that here was a race or variety or possibly a species. However, these were the only differences, and individuals could be found with more than one head, on alternate branches, which seems negative to specific distinction.

39. H. mollis Lam. Encyc. 3 : 85. 1789.

H. canescens Michx. Fl. Am. Bor., 2 : 140. 1803.
H. mollis var. *cordatus* S. Wats. Gard. and For., 2 : 136, F. 100. 1889.

Perennial; stems often tufted, erect, 0.5–1.0 m. high, scabrous-hirsute, simple in medium or small plants, often branched above in large individuals, the branches closely ascending, often parallel, or nearly so, to the main stem, pubescence of stem mostly of two kinds, fine, short, appressed hairs, and long scabrous-hispid hairs, spreading or often retrorse; leaves opposite, or opposite below, becoming alternate and gradually smaller above, ovate, acute, entire or serrulate, sessile, clasping, sometimes cordate-clasping, mostly 9.0 cm. long by 4.5 cm. wide, variable in size, densely scabrous-hispid both sides; inflorescence often a solitary terminal head, or racemose on the main stem or the branches, peduncles stout; heads very showy, disc 2–3.0 cm. wide; corollas of the disc yellow, cylindrical, the lobes and base pubescent, the tube short, glabrous; the achene slightly villous at the apex; pappus of two broadly lanceolate awns, without other scales; the chaff linear, entire, rarely with small lateral lobes half-way below the apex, the tip villous; the involucre hemispheric; the bracts broadly linear-lanceolate, acute, often abruptly acuminate, not much longer than the disc, erect, densely hispid or scabrous-tomentose; roots very fine, fibrous, very abundant, 1–3.0 dm. long; the rhizomes, 2–3 to each stem, very stout, rarely more than 15.0 cm. long, with abundant rootlets, and a large terminal bud; crown-buds are also produced, resulting in tufted stems, often 3–5 stems from a single root.

Michigan to Alabama, Virginia to Oklahoma, Texas. Locally abundant in rather poor, sandy soil, in Illinois, Tennessee, and Kentucky.

Type. — The species was described by Lamarck; possibly in Paris.

This is a very strongly marked and a very handsome plant. The color from a distance is a soft gray-green; the heads are very large and are held very erect; the color is a bright vivid yellow. The plant is readily cultivated; I saw it in many commercial nurseries in the East and South. In cultivation it is often very large and rather coarse, not nearly so attractive as the less blatant wild form.

H. mollis is a close relative of *H. doronicoides* and it is often difficult to be certain unless one has the whole plant. The method of branching in *H. mollis* is very characteristic.

Willdenow's interpretation of *H. pubescens* Vahl is *H. mollis.*

40. H. divaricatus L. Sp. Pl., 906. 1753.

H. truncatus Schwein. ex Ell., Sketch, 2 : 416. 1824.

Perennial; stem slender, normally 0.5 to 1.5 m. high, simple to inflorescence, glabrous or subglabrous, somewhat glaucous, rarely, especially in the southeastern mountains of the United States, stout, 2.0 m. high, purplish and very glaucous; leaves vary from rarely narrowly lanceolate to broadly ovate-lanceolate, subsessile, the petiole being merely the expanded base of the midrib, never more than 1–3 mm. long, the lateral nerves always confluent at the base of the blade, broadest at the base and often slightly subcordate, scabrous-setose above, with remote, long, curving hairs beneath, light green in shade plants, often dark green in sunny situations, papery but not conspicuously thin in texture, opposite throughout except occasionally those of the branches in very vigorous individuals, 4.0–12.0 cm. long by 0.7–6.0 cm. wide; inflorescence a cyme with all branches opposite, rarely one or two alternate in very ramose plants; heads medium, the disc about 1.0 cm. in diam., rays narrow, 2 cm. long; corollas of the disc florets yellow, glabrous or obscurely puberulent at the base, the tube very short; pappus of two broadly lanceolate rather short awns; achene glabrous; chaff 3-cuspidate, the lateral cusps small, middle cusp acuminate, tips slightly pubescent, carinate; the involucre hemispheric, the bracts lanceolate, about as long as the disc, loose, tips usually reflexed, subglabrous to pubescent, variable in this character, ciliate toward the base; stem base under the surface of the soil often greatly enlarged, woody and irregular, the roots also woody and coarse; rhizomes abundant, 1.0–7.0 dm. long, terminal bud large.

Very abundant in drier situations from Wisconsin to New England, south to the Carolinas, west to Missouri, sporadically outside this range.

Type. — In the Linnaean Herbarium; photograph examined.

This is perhaps the most abundant sunflower in northeastern United States, very tolerant of soil and very hardy. Its favorite habitats seem to be hillsides and very open woods in soil not too moist. The leaves are almost invariably opposite; in fact the tendency to opposite leaves is more marked in this species than in any other sunflower; only the ultimate branches of the inflorescence in very large and vigorous individuals are rarely alternate. A collection by R. S. Cocks from Louisiana is the only one of all the thousands I have seen in which the upper leaves of the main stem are alternate. *H. divaricatus* maintains its characters with rare constancy, the only marked variability being in the proportions of the leaves. A specimen of my own from the vicinity of East Lansing, Michigan, has leaves 11.0 cm. long by 6.0 cm. wide, which is an unusually low foliar ratio; Small's collection from Dennis Mt., Rowan Co., North Carolina, has leaves 6.0 cm. long by 1.0 cm. wide, and Morong, from Martha's Vineyard Island, has leaves 9.5 cm. long by 0.7 cm. wide, an extremely large foliar ratio. Perhaps the most usual dimensions are 13.0 cm. by 4.0 cm. The leaves present only rarely an exception to the statement that the lateral nerves are confluent at the base of the blade, the petiole, therefore, not at all winged. In my collection No. 530 from Albemarle, North Carolina, the confluence of the lateral nerves is about 0.7 cm. from the base and the bracts are unusually broad, short and glabrous, but these are the only variations. The pubescence of the lower surface of the leaves is unusually spreading and long in *H. divaricatus*, but never dense, often very remote. This species is the earliest blossomer of the northeastern sunflowers.

41. H. subniveus Blake. Contr. U. S. Nat. Herb., 22 : 621. 1924.

H. niveus Hieron. Engl. Jahrb., 21: 350. 1895, not Brandegee. 1889.

Perennial; stem ramose, densely white-lanate, branches short, 8–10.0 cm. long; leaves opposite, narrowly linear-lanceolate, 1–2.0 cm. long by 2–3.0 mm. wide, entire, obtuse, revolute, sessile, upper surface rugose, pilose with very fine tuberculate-based hairs, deep green, lower surface densely white-lanate, crowded on the stem, the internodes 5–6.0 mm. long, thick, firm, drooping; inflorescence a solitary sessile, rather large head, the disc 1.5 cm. in diam., the rays about 1.0 cm. long, villous beneath, conspicuously veined, puberulent above; corollas of the disc florets slender, villous, the lobes narrowly linear-lanceolate with spreading tips, the tube short; the achene glabrous; pappus of two very slender, subulate awns without other scales, the awns pubescent; chaff narrowly lanceolate, acute, not 3-cuspidate, but the margin lacerate-dentate, the acute tip somewhat galeate; pubescent on tip and keel; the involucre hemispheric; the bracts rather broadly linear, or oblong-lanceolate, about as long as the disc, loose, erect, obtuse, densely white-lanate.

Type. — Stuebel 34, collected in 1875 near Moyabamba, Peru. Altitude 3,200.0 m., Berlin Botanical Museum; personally examined.

The type specimen is in very good condition, but unfortunately is only a fragment about 15.0 cm. in length. Its sessile heads and short, crowded leaves are sufficient to identify it. Nothing further is known concerning the size and habit of the entire plant.

42. H. Jelskii Hieron. Engl. Jahrb., 36 : 490. 1904.

Perennial; stem stout, erect, probably tall, profusely ramose, fruticose, young parts densely lanate, soon glabrate, leaves opposite, ovate, acute, entire, subcordate, distinctly petiolate, the blade 6–8.0 cm. long by 3–4.0 cm. wide, the petiole 1–3.0 cm. long, the blade thick, deep green and rather long-hispid above, very densely lanate-tomentose beneath; the inflorescence cymose, the peduncles very short, 2–3.0 cm., stout, lanate; heads crowded, very large, the disc about 3.0 cm. in diam., rays about 1.5 cm. long, few, pubescent beneath; corollas of the disc florets yellow with large brownish-yellow lobes and base, the whole corolla pubescent; the achene glabrous; the pappus two plumose, subulate awns without other scales; the chaff ample, broadly lanceolate, thin, entire, glabrous, the carinate keel obscurely pubescent; the involucre hemispheric; the bracts linear-oblong, about 1.5 cm. long and 0.5 cm. wide, about as long as the disc, abruptly acuminate, loose but not reflexed, firm, tomentose. Root parts not seen.

Peru, near Chala.

Type. — Jelski 713 in the Berlin Botanical Museum.

I have examined the two specimens in the Berlin Botanical Museum. They are evidently portions of a large woody shrub, probably not at all herbaceous. The older portions of the stem have a well-developed corky bark, rough and full of fine fissures like the bark of a tree. The thickness and density of the tomentum of the lower surface of the leaves are remarkable. Evidently the arrangement of the leaves is exclusively opposite.

43. H. argenteus H. B. K. Nov. Gen. et Spec., 4 : 221. t. 376. 1820.

Stem perennial, somewhat shrubby, up to 4.0 m. high, ramose, branches slender, leafy, younger stems densely fine, appressed sericeous-villous; leaves alternate, lanceolate, attenuate-acuminate, 4.0 cm. long by 0.7 cm. wide, entire, gradually tapering to a short petiole, the latter very shortly winged, finely sericeous-villous, green above, very densely white, woolly-tomentose beneath, thin, approximate; inflorescence one or two heads from the upper axils of the branches, on peduncles about 10.0 cm. long, appressed sericeous-villous; head medium, the disc about 1.5 cm. in diam., rays short, 1.5 cm. long, tomentose beneath; corollas of the disc slender, yellow, the lobes and the tube pubescent, the throat glabrous; the achene sparingly pubescent; pappus of two long aristiform, somewhat plumose awns; chaff lanceolate, slender, entire, carinate, tip and keel pubescent, very thin; involucral bracts broadly lanceolate, acuminate, about equal to the disc or a little longer, very dark green, lanate-tomentose.

Type. — Humboldt 3267, Summits of the Andes, Ecuador; in Paris.

The type, which I have not seen, was collected near Los Paredones, Province of Azuay, Ecuador. Altitude about 4,000 m. Topotype seen.

44. H. Oliveri Gray. Proc. Am. Acad., 20 : 299. 1885.

H. Parishii f. *Oliveri* Ckll.

Perennial; stem stout, 2–4.0 m. high, often ramose above, sulcate, glaucous, purplish-brown, with obsolete scabra below, the upper part densely strigose-tomentose; leaves alternate, lanceolate, obscurely serrulate, or entire, acute, tapering below to a partly distinct petiole, the blade from the confluence of the lateral nerves about 12.0 cm. long and 2–2.5 cm. wide, the petiole from the confluence 3–4.0 cm. long, thick in texture, densely white tomentose on both sides, pubescence of the midrib beneath markedly retrorse; inflorescence 3–4 heads on short peduncles, 1–2.0 cm. at the apex of the short flowering branches; heads conspicuous, disc 1.5–2.5 cm. in diam., rays about 2.5 cm. long, on the very densely tomentose short peduncles; corollas of the disc florets yellow, the lobes and base villous, the tube glabrous; achene of the ray sterile, with two long, lanceolate awns, achene of the disc glabrous; the pappus two lanceolate awns without other scales; the chaff linear, 3-cuspidate, the lateral cusps small, narrowly acute, the middle cusp broadly acute, all three densely long, strigose-villous at the apex, keel pubescent; the involucre hemispheric; the bracts narrowly linear-lanceolate, attenuate, loose but not reflexed, longer than the disc, densely villous-tomentose. Root-system not seen.

Swampy ground, vicinity of Los Angeles, California.

Type. — J. C. Oliver, Cienega, between Los Angeles and Santa Monica, California, in the Gray Herbarium; examined.

H. Oliveri is evidently a rare plant, as it has not found its way into herbaria from many different collectors. It grows in the type locality of *H. californicus* and *H. Parishii*, and is considered by Cockerell as a form of the latter species. I have compared several specimens by Hasse and by Braunton with the type, and find them identical. This plant is related to *H. Parishii*, but not more closely than to *H. californicus*. I do not agree with Cockerell's reduction to a form of *H. Parishii*. The two plants are certainly more widely separated than *H. strumosus* and *H. decapetalus*. *H. Oliveri* is remarkable for its very short peduncles, the shortness of the branches, its dense tomentum, especially on the involucral bracts, and the glabrescent lower stem.

45. H. Matthewsii Hochr. Bull. N. Y. Bot. Gard., 6 : 296. 1910.

Perennial; stem shrubby, minutely striate, somewhat canescent-tomentose, branches slightly scabrous, 0.15–0.3 cm. thick; leaves alternate, spirally placed, but probably opposite at the bases of the branches, lanceolate or ovate-lanceolate, apex attenuate, acute or acuminate, entire, base contracted into the petiole, blade 7–9.0 cm. long by 1.8–2.1 cm. wide, the petiole 0.5–0.7 cm. long; upper surface deep green, subscabrous and thinly tuberculate-pilose, lower surface appressed-canescent-tomentose, lanate, the nerves prominent; the inflorescence corymbose, its branches long, alternate, with small, almost subulate leaves, the peduncles canescent-pilose, subscabrous; heads small, the disc 0.8–1.3 cm. in diam., the rays with the sterile achenes, 1.0–1.2 cm. long; the outer achenes mostly glabrous, the inner mostly pubescent; the pappus one or two awns, about 0.4 long; chaff pubescent at the apex; bracts of the involucre lanceolate, green, appressed-canescent-villous, ciliate. Root-system not seen.

Type. — An unnumbered specimen collected by Matthews, in 1862, in Peru, in the herbarium of the New York Botanical Garden. I have seen no specimen of this species. The description is abridged from the cited publication.

46. H. imbaburensis Hieron. Engl. Jahrb., 21 : 348. 1895.

H. pseudoverbesinoides Hieron. ex. Sod., Engl. Jahrb., 29 : 40. 1900 (excl. var. *gracilis*).
H. hypargyreus Blake. Bot. Gaz., 74 : 421. 1922.

Perennial; stem stout, evidently tall and ramose, deep green, often brownish, somewhat thinly short-tomentose, soft to the touch, leafy; leaves alternate, ovate, upper ones ovate-lanceolate, narrowly acute or slightly acuminate, thickish but not rigid, serrate, the blade abruptly narrowed below the confluence of the lateral nerves, and partly decurrent on the petiole, blade from the confluence 11.0 cm. long by 7.0 cm. wide, petiole from the confluence about 4.0 cm. long, densely sericeous-pilose and deep green above, densely sericeous-tomentose, often shagreen, canescent beneath, inflorescence an open panicle, often with rather long and slender branches, the heads very small and somewhat conglomerate at the apex of the branches, the peduncles mostly less than 1.0 cm. long and densely sericeous-tomentose; disc rarely more than 1.5 cm. in diam. at maturity, the rays very small, about 0.7 cm. long by 0.3 cm. wide, oval, puberulent above, villous beneath; corollas of the disc florets yellow, slender, the lobes small, acute, recurved, base of the corolla very villous, the tube glabrous; the achene glabrous; the pappus two long, subulate, plumose awns without other scales; the chaff narrowly lanceolate, acute, integral, but somewhat lacerate, carinate, glabrous, but slightly villous on the keel; the involucre subglobose; the bracts ovate, acute, shorter than the disc, erect, but the tips slightly recurved, densely sericeous-tomentose both sides. Root-system not seen. Common local name "poto."

Province of Imbabura, Ecuador. Altitude 2,300 m.

Type. — Stuebel 135, collected in 1841, in the Berlin Botanical Museum; examined.

A very careful comparison of the type specimen of *H. imbaburensis* with the type of *H. hypargyreus* Blake leaves no doubt that these two are conspecific. The type of the latter species is E. W. D. and M. M. Holway 815, in the United States National Herbarium. Rose and Rose 22,171 and 22,568, Huigra, Ecuador, are cited by the author.

The type of *H. pseudoverbesinoides* Hieron. is Sodiro 3613 (?), near Tumbaco, Ecuador, in the Berlin Botanical Museum. The sheet contains three slender branches which are lettered *alpha*, *beta*, *gamma*, and the label states that *alpha* and *beta* are "*forma typica*." These are perfectly typical specimens of *H. imbaburensis* and what possible difference Hieronymus thought he saw between these plants and his type specimen of that species I cannot understand. Equally impossible is it to explain his failure to recognize that the third fragment on the sheet, lettered *gamma*, and called var. *gracilis*, is in every way a typical *H. verbesinoides*. One is certainly almost inclined to think that that author wished to discard his *H. imbaburensis*, for Lehmann's collection No. 5215 from Ambato, Ecuador, is labeled *H. pseudoverbesinoides* Hieron.

"*forma robusta,*" and is merely an unusually good specimen of *H. imbaburensis.*

47. H. Szyszylowiczii Hieron. Engl. Jahrb., 36 : 491. 1904.

Perennial; stem stout, herbaceous, probably 1–2.0 m. high, ramose, softly spreading pilose, striate-sulcate; leaves alternate, broadly ovate-acuminate, sharply serrulate above the entire base, abruptly contracted to cuneate base, the blade very narrowly decurrent on the petiole about one third of its length, blade from the confluence of the lateral nerves, about 13.0 cm. long by 8.0 cm. wide, petiole from the confluence about 3.0 cm. long, the upper leaves of the inflorescence greatly reduced; the upper surface deep green, pilose, the lower surface very pale, densely pilose-tomentose and copiously resin-dotted, the midrib and main nerves densely and retrorsely pilose; the blade thin, delicate in texture, very soft to the touch on both sides; a few small heads on very slender, short peduncles at the apex of the flowering branches; the disc about 1.0 cm. in diam., the rays very narrow, about 1.5 cm. in length; corollas of the disc florets very slender, the lobes small, acute, slightly brownish, puberulent, the limb glabrous, the base pubescent, the tube long and glabrous; the achene linear, slender, glabrous; the pappus two very slender, subulate awns without other scales; the chaff glabrous, thin, the margin lacerate, tip acute, the keel obscurely villous; the involucre hemispheric; the bracts lanceolate, acuminate, a little longer than the disc, densely villous. Lower stem and root-system not seen.

Type. — Jelski 732, collected in May, 1879, at Callacate, Peru; in the Berlin Botanical Museum.

I have seen no other specimen of this species than the type, which is in good condition and adequate for the upper portion of the plant. The smoothness of the pubescence of the stem and leaves is remarkable.

48. H. Stuebeli Hieron. Engl. Jahrb., 21 : 349. 1895.

Perennial; stem very stout, fruticose, ramose, densely brown-lanate-tomentose; leaves crowded, alternate, ovate, acuminate, abruptly contracted to a short distinct petiole, blade 5.5 cm. long by 2.5 cm. wide, base of blade roundish, the petiole about 0.7 cm. long, very coarse in texture, very thick, densely scabrous-setose above, the setae coarse and sharp, the short, lower surface very densely fulvous lanate-tomentose; the inflorescence a single, large, sessile head terminating stem and branches; the disc 2–3.0 cm. in diam., the rays very numerous, narrowly linear, 2–3.0 cm. long, 2–3-dentate at the apex, pubescent beneath; corollas of the disc florets yellow, somewhat campanulate, the lobes with brownish tips, subglabrous; the achene sparingly pubescent, small; the pappus two narrowly lanceolate, puberulent awns; chaff ample, linear-lanceolate, entire, acute, glabrous, or slightly and obscurely puberulent on tip and keel; the involucre hemispheric; the bracts broadly lanceolate, acuminate, somewhat longer than the disc, so densely brown-lanate as to obscure the outline of the bract. Root parts not seen.

Rocky places in the mountains, Peru.

Type. — Stuebel 34e, Moyabamba, Peru. Altitude 3,200 m.

The only specimens I have seen are the type and a collection by Weberbauer No. 4241, near Celendin, Peru. The species is remarkable for the dense wool on the stem and lower surface of the leaves, the very numerous narrow rays, the sessile heads, and the small crowded leaves.

49. H. niveus (Benth.) Brandegee. Proc. Calif. Acad., Ser. 2, 2 : 173. 1889.

H. dealbatus Gray. Syn. Fl. N. A., 1: 280. 1884.
Encelia nivea Benth. Bot. Voyage Sulph., 27. 1844.

Perennial; stem stout, 0.4 cm. in diam., 3–5.0 dm. high, ramose, densely appressed-sericeous-villous, snow-white; leaves alternate, only the lowermost opposite, the blade ovate, obtuse, entire, the margins somewhat fluted, contracted below to a long, distinct petiole, the lateral nerves confluent at base of the blade, the latter, therefore, not decurrent on the petiole, blade mostly 3–4.0 cm. long by 1.5–2.0 cm. wide, the petiole 1–3.0 cm. long, not correlated with the size of the leaf, appressed-sericeous-villous on both sides, more densely beneath, snow-white, approximated toward the base of the stem and of the branches; the inflorescence a solitary head terminating the almost naked upper stem which bears at most only 1–2 very small, bract-like leaves; the disc about 1.5 cm. in diam., the rays numerous but not more than 1.2 cm. long, short-pubescent on the nerves beneath; corollas of the disc florets very slender, campanulate from just below the lobes which are brownish and very short-pubescent, the limb glabrous, the base pubescent, the tube short and also pubescent; the achene dark, linear-obovate, thinly but evenly villous over the entire surface; the pappus two very short, subulate awns without other scales; the involucre hemispheric, the bracts in 3–4 series, broadly lanceolate, acute, the outer shorter and more or less reflexed, the inner erect, less than 1.0 cm. long, about equal to the disc, densely white-tomentose, the trichomes coarser than those of the leaves and stems. Root-system not seen.

Type. — *Encelia nivea* Benth. in herbarium of the Royal Botanic Gardens, Kew, England, which I have not seen. The type of *H. dealbatus* Gray is Belding, Lower California, 1875, in the Gray Herbarium.

In the original description Gray cites also a collection by Parry, in 1883, from All Saints Bay and he does not suggest any synonymy. In the collected edition of 1888 Gray cites the collections of E. L. Greene at Cape San Quentin in 1885, and states that *H. dealbatus* and *Encelia nivea* Benth. are the same thing. His opinion is based upon the agreement of his specimens, presumably the Greene specimens, with the description of *Encelia nivea* Benth. On p. 271 of the *Syn. Fl.* of 1888, under *V. tephrodes*, Gray states that *V. nivea* Gray, *Bot. Calif.*, 1: 354, is the same as *H. tephrodes*. Reference to this citation reveals that *V. nivea* Gray is based on *E. nivea* Benth.; on p. 450 he evidently changes his mind and here maintains that *V. nivea* Gray, excluding the synonymy, which is *E. nivea* Benth., is really a Helianthus and is synonymous with *H. tephrodes*. This final arrangement of the juggled names thus leaves the excluded *E. nivea* as a possible synonym for *H. dealbatus*. If this is true, the name of the species, as Brandegee points out, will have to be *H. niveus* (Benth.) Brandegee.

See also discussion of *H. canus*.

50. Helianthus senex Blake. Journ. Wash. Acad. Sci., 16, No. 8 : 220. 1926.

Stems perennial, growing in clumps, shrub, about 1.0 m. high, glabrate, striatulate, canescently long-villous, the hairs reflexed and 2–3 mm. long; leaves opposite below, alternate above, broadly ovate, serrulate-crenate above the entire, rounded base, acute, scarcely decurrent on the petiole, thick cinereous-pilose above, densely white-tomentose beneath, 5–6.0 cm. long by 3–4.0 cm. wide; the petiole stout, 5–7.0 mm. long, densely white-tomentose; the inflorescence 2–5 heads on the main stem and branches on mostly 1-flowered peduncles which are naked or few-bracted and 2–8.0 cm. long; the disc about 8–15.0 mm. in diameter; the rays about 8, small, 5–10.0 mm. long, 2–4.0 mm. wide, 2–4 denticulate, pilose beneath on the nerves, with basal appendages suggestive of abortive stamens; corollas of the disc florets yellow, the nerves and lobes hispidulous; bracts of the involucre oblong or oblong-ovate, 7–8.0 mm. long, appressed except the recurved tips, pilose-tomentose except on the glabrate, indurated base; chaff acutish, callous-apiculate, not keeled, pilose and ciliate toward the apex, about 11.0 mm. long; the achene dark, glabrous; awns 2, linear-lanceolate, hispidulous-ciliate, about 3.0 mm. long.

Huanuco, Peru, mountain sides.

Type. — MacBride and Featherstone 1572, sheet No. 518,077 in the Field Columbian Museum; also a duplicate, sheet No. 1,198,884 in the United States National Herbarium; collected on a canyon slope at Milo, Huanuco, Peru, July 8–22, 1922. Altitude 2,745 m.

I have seen no specimen of *H. senex.*

51. **H. bracteatus,** sp. nov.

(Plate LIII)

Perennial; stem probably 1–2.0 m. high, stout, erect, slightly sinuous above, glabrous below, striate or sulcate, sparingly strigose toward the apex, purplish, ramose above; leaves, at least the upper ones, alternate, very narrowly linear, slightly oblanceolate, 13–14.0

cm. long, less than 1.0 cm. wide, scabrous-setulose above, hispid beneath, thickish, light green, concolor, narrowly acute at the apex, narrowly attenuate at the base; inflorescence racemose from the upper axils, the heads solitary on slender, bracteate peduncles 1–2.0 dm. long, the peduncular bracts about 1.0 cm. below the head, filiform, 3–5.0 cm. long, erect; heads large, the disc about 1.6 cm. in diam., the rays 1.5–2.0 cm. long and very narrow, apex of the peduncles densely strigose; corollas of the disc florets yellow, the lobes puberulent, the throat tapering to the rather long tube; the achene glabrous; the pappus two long, narrowly lanceolate, carinate awns; the chaff narrow, sharply carinate, 3-cuspidate, the lateral cusps small, the middle cusp acute, villous, the keel ciliate-villous; the involucre hemispheric; the bracts broadly linear-lanceolate, attenuate, not much longer than the disc, loose, not reflexed, strigose on the surface and very strigose-ciliate. Lower stem and root parts not seen.

Type. — A. Isabel Mulford 177. Logan, Utah, sheet No. 113,971, Missouri Botanical Garden.

This very distinct sunflower from Utah is known to me only from Miss Mulford's collection. It is clearly a close relative of *H. Nuttallii.* It is very unfortunate that the type shows only about 45.0 cm. of the upper stem. The constancy of the long, filiform bracts produced on the peduncle just under the head is very striking, also the ciliate keel of the chaff. The specimen was collected on July 18, 1898, and was apparently just coming into bloom. It is to be hoped that further collections of this species will confirm the diagnosis, and afford further information concerning the habitat and the root-system.

52. H. pumilus Nutt. Trans. Am. Phil. Soc., N. S., 7 : 366. 1841.

Perennial; stems erect, mostly tufted, less than 1.0 m. high, simple, rarely at all ramose, scabrous-hispid, pubescence spreading, often retrorse, usually very dense and long; leaves opposite, ovate, acute, with a distinct short petiole, thick, very coarse in texture, very rough, densely strigose-hispid on both sides, mostly about 6.0 cm. long by 2.0 cm. wide, but extremely variable in size and outline; 1–3 heads on short peduncles terminating the stem; heads about 1.3 cm. across the disc, rays 1.0–1.5 cm. long; corollas of the disc florets yellow, the lobes and base puberulent, tube very short; the achene glabrous, somewhat angular; pappus of two broadly lanceolate awns with small, lacerate paleae close to or half attached to the bases of the awns; chaff lanceolate, entire, hispid on the tip; involucre hemispheric, the bracts ovate-lanceolate, acute, erect, a little shorter than the disc, normally densely hispid; the root very coarse, woody, producing crown-buds, no rhizomes.

Colorado, Wyoming and vicinity.

I have not seen Nuttall's type of this species, which was described from a specimen from "plains of the Platte." The species is, however, strongly marked and there can be little doubt of its identity. The most striking and constant difference between it and its near relative *H. gracilentus* of California is the character of the pubescence of the involucral bracts and the tip of the chaff; in *H. gracilentus* the pubescence is puberulent, in *H. pumilus* it is coarsely hispid. This species presents very unusual variation in leaf outline and four of these should be especially noted:

(1) Patterson, from Boulder, Colorado, July, 1892, has ovate leaves, very regular in outline, entire, 6.0 cm. by 2.0 cm.

(2) A specimen by C. F. Baker, Larimer Co., Colorado, 1895, has deltoid-subcordate leaves, the blade 6.0 cm. long by 4.0 cm. wide, margin slightly repand, petiole 1.0 cm. long, less densely pubescent.

(3) Clements 240, Cañon City, Colorado, has narrowly lanceolate leaves 4.0 cm. by 0.8 cm., the upper alternate and stem branched above. This may prove to be specifically distinct, though the floral structure is typical.

(4) Daniels 59, Boulder, Colorado, has oblong-lanceolate leaves 9.0 cm. long, including petiole, by 3.2 cm. wide, margin repandly dentate. This seems to be the most usual form of this species and the form that most closely resembles *H. gracilentus*.

53. **H. excubitor,** sp. nov.

(Plate LIV)

Perennial; stem erect, tall, 1.0–2.0 m. high, strigose-hispid, light green, ramose at least above; leaves opposite, lanceolate, acute, entire blade very narrowly decurrent upon the long and slender petiole, blade from confluence of lateral nerves 15.0 cm. long by 3.4 cm. wide, the petiole from the confluence 6.0 cm. long, remotely strigose-hispid above, scabrous-hispid beneath, concolor, chartaceous; inflorescence a few small heads on slender peduncles from apex and upper axils; disc about 1.0 cm. in diam., rays 2.5 cm. long; corollas of the disc florets yellow, the lobes brownish and puberulent, base of corolla puberulent; the achene of the ray with three very long lanceolate awns, sterile; of the disc, fertile, slightly angular, slightly pubescent at apex and on angles; pappus of two long lanceolate awns with one or two accessory awns sometimes nearly as long as the principal awn, and one or two small paleae, all crowded together at the two principal angles of the achene; chaff entire, lanceolate, hispid; involucre subcampanulate, the bracts narrowly ovate, obtusish, equal to or shorter than the disc, puberulent-hispidulous with longer coarsely hispid hairs especially on the midrib, the cilia long and very coarse. Lower stem and root parts not seen.

Type. — M. E. Jones 530, Idaho Springs, Colorado, altitude 7,500 ft., in Field Columbian Museum, Chicago.

This species is closely allied to *H. pumilus* and *H. gracilentus*, more closely to the former, but very distinct from both. It has smaller heads, is much taller than *H. pumilus*, the stem is less pubescent, the leaves conspicuously thin and chartaceous, but its most marked character is the petiole which is nearly half as long as the blade.

54. **H. stenophyllus** (T. & G.), comb. nov.

H. hirsutus var. *stenophyllus* T. & G. Fl. N. A., 2:329. 1842.

Perennial; stem slender, erect, 0.5–1.0 m. high, simple to the inflorescence, scabrous-hispid, light green; leaves opposite, narrowly lanceolate, narrowly acute, entire or obscurely serrulate, revolute, tapering below to winged petiole, the blade decurrent below the confluence of the lateral nerves nearly or quite to the base of the petiole, 10–15.0 cm. long, including petiole, by 1.5–2.5 cm. wide, rather thick, firm, densely strumose-setose above, scabrous-hispid beneath, the trichomes being often long; the inflorescence cymose, the heads large, the disc 1–2.0 cm. in diam., convex, the rays few, 2.5 cm. long, narrow, acute, deep yellow; corollas of the disc yellow, the lobes puberulent, the limb pubescent on the five main nerves, base and the tube pubescent; the achene glabrous, turgid; the pappus two broadly lanceolate awns, usually with intermediate paleae; the involucre hemispheric; the bracts broadly linear-lanceolate, attenuate, longer than the disc, densely hispid or hispidulous, very loose, recurved; roots coarsely fibrous, woody; the rhizomes stout, ramose, 1–3.0 dm. long.

Texas, Oklahoma, Louisiana.

Type. — A collection from Louisiana by Dr. Hale, in the New York Botanical Garden. Type examined.

The chief claim of this group for specific distinction lies in the leaves which are narrow, elongate, broad below, but gradually tapering to the base of the petiole, in sharp distinction from those of *H. hirsutus*, which are always distinctly petioled and rounded or subcordate at the base. In *H. stenophyllus* the leaves are thicker and firmer and revolute. As I have observed it in the field in Texas and Louisiana, in the vicinity of the true *H. hirsutus*, there seems to be no tendency to hybridization, at least no intermediate forms could be found. Good examples of *H. stenophyllus* are Lindheimer, Dixon 198 and 398, Hall 360, from Texas, ranging from Houston to the northern limits of the state. In Louisiana it has been collected by Steinhauer, by R. S. Cocks at Ruston, by E. J. Palmer, 8891, at Natchitoches; and I have collected it near Atlanta, Texas, and between Shreveport and Odessa, Louisiana.

55. H. tomentosus Michx. Fl. Bor. Am., 2 : 141. 1803.

H. spathulatus Ell. Sketch, 2 : 421. 1824.
H. squarrosus Nutt. Trans. Am. Phil. Soc., N. S., 7 : 367. 1841. Not *H. squarrosus* H.B.K. Nov. Gen. et Sp., 4 : 222. t. 377. 1820.

(Plates LV–LVI)

Perennial; stem stout, erect, 1–2.0 m. high, simple to the inflorescence, often very ramose above, usually red-purple, pubescence of the stem varying from glabrous toward the base and somewhat hispid toward the summit to densely strigose-hispid above and below, the pubescence always at least spreading and in most individuals conspicuously retrorse; leaves always alternate on the upper stem, usually so from a little below the middle, rarely only the lowermost opposite; extremely variable in outline, narrowly lanceolate to very broadly so, or even ovate-lanceolate, always narrowly acute or a little acuminate at the apex, entire or serrulate, rarely in very large and vigorous plants more or less serrate, the blade decurrent below the confluence of the lateral nerves to the base of the petiole, or rarely, in exceptionally vigorous plants, the lower third of the petiole distinct, usually the upper leaves conspicuously reduced in width, and somewhat also in length, extremely variable in size, the most usual dimensions 15–25.0 cm. long, including petiole, by 2–8.0 cm. wide, length and breadth rarely correlated, the upper surface deep green, scabrous-hispid, seldom densely, the trichomes short, the lower surface thinly or very densely tomentose, in most cases rather thinly, almost always conspicuously resin-dotted, the pubescence of the midrib *always* conspicuously spreading or retrorse; the inflorescence racemose or paniculate, the heads mostly on short, leafy, rough peduncles; heads variable in size, the disc 1–2.5 cm. in diam., the rays about 2.0 cm. long, often shorter, pubescent beneath on the nerves, and usually very resin-dotted, bright yellow; corollas of the disc yellow, the lobes and base very pubescent, the tube short; the achene glabrous; the pappus two broadly lanceolate awns with enlarged bases, the base often laciniate, rarely with accessory paleae at the bases of the principal awns; the chaff deeply 3-cuspidate, the middle cusp larger and acute, the chaff ample, very pubescent on tip and keel; the involucre hemispheric; the bracts linear-lanceolate, attenuate, very hispid, resin-dotted, in mature heads very abruptly reflexed, variable in length, evidently continuing to elongate after anthesis, but in most heads longer than the disc and often much longer; the roots long, thick, gradually tapering, very woody; rhizomes very rare, short if any; elongated crown-buds very abundant.

Common generally in the lower mountains and drier plains throughout the southern states, rarely north of Ohio and Pennsylvania.

I have not seen the type of *H. tomentosus* and do not know where it is. My conception of the species is based upon the traditional view, modified by my observations in the field.

The illustration in the *Botanical Register*, No. 524, is labeled *H. pubescens*, but is unquestionably *H. tomentosus* Michx. The species is extremely variable, but the following characters are fairly constant: (1) except in very rare individuals, and these of most vigorous growth, the petioles are winged by the decurrent blade to the very base, but very narrowly so near the stem; (2) the pubescence of the midrib is always spreading and usually more or less retrorse; (3) the lower surface of the leaves and rays, the chaff, the involucral bracts, the apices of the stamens and frequently the disc florets are copiously resin-dotted; (4) the involucral bracts are abruptly reflexed by the time the head is in full anthesis; (5) the roots are invariably coarse, woody and long, often gnarled, and the stem base produces innumerable buds 0.5–1.0 cm. in length, and only rarely a short rhizome.

At Rock Mart, Georgia, on a limestone cliff near the extensive stone-works, these plants grew in great abundance, covering a considerable area. My attention was attracted to one individual about 2.5 m. high and very stout and vigorous. The stem was practically glabrous throughout the lower two thirds, but rough above. The maximum leaves were 25.0 cm. long, including petiole, 7.0 cm. wide, very thick, saliently dentate, and the lower half of the petiole was quite distinct. Not more than three meters distant grew another individual, nearly as tall, on which the maximum leaves were 20.0 cm. long and 2.0 cm. wide, entire, and whose petioles were winged by the decurrence of the blade to the very base. This foliar difference was so striking that I examined the two plants with great minuteness and found absolutely no other differences. The root-systems were identical. Further search made it possible to find leaves with all the intervening foliar ratios between these two — the first with a foliar ratio of $3\frac{4}{7}$ and the other of 10, certainly a wide variation. *H. tomentosus* was the only sunflower that I detected the rest of that afternoon, and all exhibited the same foliar variations and the same constancy of the root-system.

At Bat Cave, North Carolina, I obtained an extreme state of this species with a racemose inflorescence and all parts so densely tomentose as to give the plant a conspicuous pale green color. The difference proved, however, to be merely a difference of degree.

See also discussion of *H. resinosus* Small.

56. H. leptocaulis (S. Wats.) Blake. Proc. Am. Acad., 51: 519. 1916.

Viguiera leptocaulis S. Wats. Proc. Am. Acad., 26: 140. 1891.

(Plates LVII–LVIII)

Perennial; stem slender, erect, simple to the inflorescence, sulcate, usually light green, pubescence of the stem varying from that of the type, which is glabrescent below, with evidences of the obsolete trichomes, and sparingly scabrous-short-hispid toward the apex, to densely long-scabrous-hispid above and below, with all intergrades; leaves prevailingly opposite, extremely variable in size and foliar ratio, lanceolate, ovate-lanceolate or ovate, acuminate serrulate, rarely serrate, abruptly contracted below to a short, more or less distinct petiole, those of the type 11.0 cm. long, including petiole, by 2.5 cm. wide, more often 15.0 cm. long by 5.0 cm. wide, sometimes even larger; thin, very chartaceous, blade rounded at the base, densely strumose-setose above, strumose-hispid beneath, especially on the nerves, a little paler beneath; the inflorescence cymose; the heads showy, mostly on rather short, hispid peduncles, occasionally solitary on the main stem, the disc about 1–1.5 cm. in diam., rarely much larger, the rays 2–2.5 cm. long; corollas of the disc florets yellow, subglabrous, except the slightly pubescent base; the achene glabrous; the pappus two broadly lanceolate, rather long awns without other scales; the chaff linear, 3-cuspidate, the tip and keel pubescent; the involucre campanulate; the bracts narrowly lanceolate, acuminate, attenuate, longer than the disc, hispidulous, ciliate, very loose, often reflexed; the roots fibrous; the rhizomes slender, 1–2.0 dm. long.

Mexico, north to Nebraska, chiefly the plains on both sides of the Mississippi, more abundant on the western plains.

Type. — Pringle 2247, from Nuevo León, Mexico, in the Gray Herbarium; examined.

H. leptocaulis is a slender sunflower with papery leaves, this chartaceous character being especially conspicuous in the dried specimen. It is extremely variable in leaf characters and especially in the pubescence of the stem. In regard to the latter character, individuals with smooth stems always give evidence of the former presence of trichomes. My attention was attracted to this group before I had seen the type, and I intended to recognize its specific identity; the examination, however, of the Pringle specimen made the position of the group clear. The leaves are always rounded at the base, sometimes somewhat cuneate, rarely subcordate, and the petiole is always relatively short and at least partly distinct.

Closely resembling the type are: Eggert, Anderson Co., Texas; Bush 6100, Missouri; Gattinger, Tennessee. The following are undoubtedly *H. leptocaulis*, but have larger leaves and a rougher stem: Thornber, Nebraska; Bates 6223, Nemaha, Nebraska; E. A. Bessey, South Bend, Nebraska; Pound and Saunders, 3132, Nebraska; Stanfield, San Marcos, Texas; Kimball, Pottawatamie Co., Kansas; Norton 275, Kansas., many other collections from Riley Co., Kansas. A Biltmore Herbarium specimen, No. 498-k from Fort Smith, Arkansas, is remarkable for its densely hispid-strigose stem and rather narrow leaves; it is labeled *H. hirsutus*, which is indeed closely related but quite distinct.

The nearest familiar species to *H. leptocaulis* is *H. hirsutus*.

57. H. hirsutus Raf. Ann. Nat., p. 14. 1820.

H. diversifolius Ell. Sketch, 2:423. 1824.
H. hispidulus Ell. *l. c.*, p. 419.
H. hirsutus var. *trachyphyllus* T. & G. Fl. N. A., 2:324. 1842, and var. *diversifolius* T. & G. *l. c.*

Perennial; stem erect, stout, 0.5–1.7 m. high, usually simple to the inflorescence, sometimes profusely branched above, densely scabrous-hispid or scabrous-hirsute, often glabrescent below, rough, the trichomes spreading, often more or less retrorse; leaves opposite, ovate or ovate-lanceolate, acuminate, serrate, rarely entire, rounded or abruptly contracted at the broad base, sometimes subcordate, distinctly, but short, petiolate, densely strumose-hispid above, the strumae bearing sometimes very long trichomes, sometimes merely a scabrum, scabrous-hispid beneath the blade, 6–15.0 cm. long by 1.5–8.0 cm. wide, the petiole 0.5–2.0 cm. long, the lateral nerves confluent near the base of the blade which is scarcely at all decurrent on the petiole; the inflorescence solitary in small individuals or cymose, often many-flowered; the heads showy, the disc 1–2.0 cm. in diam., low convex, the rays 1.5–2.0 cm. long, oval; corollas of the disc florets yellow, cylindrical, ample, puberulent on the lobes, pubescent at the base and tube and on the fine main nerves of the limb; the achene broadly oboval, turgid, dark, glabrous; the pappus two broadly lanceolate, rather short, pubescent awns without other scales; the chaff 3-cuspidate, carinate, the cusps short acute, pubescent on tip and keel; the involucre hemispheric; the bracts broadly linear-lanceolate, a little, sometimes very much, longer than the disc, ciliate, hispid, very loose, recurved; the roots coarse, woody, the rhizomes very stout, abundant, profusely ramose, 1–3.0 dm. long.

Abundant in rich, rather dry soil throughout the southeastern quarter of the United States, on both sides of the Mississippi, especially in Kentucky and Tennessee and the southern adjacent states.

Type. — A collection by Rafinesque from Kentucky. I have seen in the herbarium of the New York Botanical Garden a specimen labeled *H. hirsutus*, collected by Rafinesque in Kentucky.

If this is not original type, it is one of his collection and may serve as such.

This species is, as Gray remarks, truly polymorphous, but, except for the variety *stenophyllus*, which seems to me distinct, any attempt to recognize genetical groups within the species is bound to prove futile. I have carefully examined Dr. Pitcher's specimen from Arkansas, type of the variety *trachyphyllus*, and a specimen labeled var. *diversifolius*, which Gray compared with Elliott's type of his *H. diversifolius*, and it is my opinion that they are variations well within the species, but the cause we are at present unable to explain. In fact, as I have observed this species throughout its entire range, it is almost impossible to find two plants that closely resemble each other. For example, a collection of my own from Glasgow Junction, Kentucky, has leaves with a large and prominent, salient serrature on each side, like a lobe, and involucral bracts nearly 3.0 cm. long; Curtiss 1448, collected by Gattinger near Nashville, Tennessee, has almost sessile leaves; the specimen by R. S. Cocks, Ruston, Louisiana, has leaves very hispid on the nerves beneath, but glabrous between the nerves, a very unusual form.

The synonymy Elliott is offered on the authority of Gray.

H. hirsutus is a very close relative of *H. leptocaulis*.

58. **H. montanus,** nom. nov.

H. australis Small. Fl. S. E. U. S., p. 1268. 1903, not Phil. 1895.

Perennial; stem 1–2.0 m. high, erect, glabrous, purple, striate, more or less glaucous, ramose above; leaves alternate, lanceolate, acuminate, serrate, slightly revolute, at least when dry, tapering below to a petiole narrowly winged almost to its base, strumose-scabrous above, paler and glabrous beneath, except on the hispid nerves, 12.0 cm. long by 2.3 cm. wide; inflorescence an open panicle, 2–3 heads on slender, somewhat hispid, leafy branches from the upper axils of the main stem; heads small, disc about 1.0 cm. in diam., rays about 2.0 cm. or less long; corollas of the disc yellow, the lobes puberulent, throat subglabrous, more or less pubescent on the main nerves, base small and pubescent, the tube short and glabrous; the achene slender, glabrous; pappus of two broadly lanceolate awns without other scales; the chaff 3-cuspidate, middle cusp and keel pubescent, narrowly acute; involucre subcampanulate, the bracts lanceolate, slightly acuminate, glabrous or with a few short hispid hairs along the midrib, loose but erect, about equal to the disc. Underground parts not seen.

Stony or sandy soil, Georgia, Florida.

Type. — A collection by Small from Currahee Mt., Habersham Co., Georgia, Sept. 1–3, 1894.

This is a clearly marked, distinct species, allied to *H. strumosus*, from which it differs by its alternate leaves which are narrower and less distinctly petioled, and firmer than those of *H. strumosus*. It appears to be somewhat rare. I have never seen it in the field myself, and the only specimen other than the type collection that has come to my attention is a collection by Hitchcock in July, 1898, from Jefferson Co., Florida, labeled *H. strumosus*.

The new name *H. montanus* is made necessary by the preëmption of *australis* by Philippi, for a Chilean sunflower.

59. H. Eggertii Small. Fl. S. E. U. S., 1267. 1903.

Perennial; stem slender, erect, striate, simple, purplish, glaucous, glabrous, about 1–2 m. high; leaves opposite, the uppermost alternate in vigorous plants, lanceolate, acute, thinnish, glaucous on both sides, more so beneath, very remotely strumose-setose above, glabrous beneath, light green, obscurely and remotely serrulate, sessile, the blade being broadly decurrent to the base of the petiole, about 12.0 cm. long by 3.0 cm. wide, the lateral nerves confluent about 1.3 cm. from the base; inflorescence a few heads on short, alternate peduncles at apex of stem; heads medium, disc about 1.2 cm. in diam., rays 1.5 cm. long; corollas of disc florets yellow, puberulent, tube very short; achene glabrous; pappus of two broadly lanceolate awns without other scales; chaff ample, carinate, slightly pubescent at the tip, 3-cuspidate with very small lateral cusps, the middle cusp short, acute; involucre cylindrical, the bracts rather broadly lanceolate, acuminate, not very loose, erect, glabrous, short-ciliate, about equal to the disc or a little more; root parts not seen.

Mountains of Tennessee.

Type. — Eggert, White Bluff, Dickson Co., Tennessee; in the New York Botanical Garden.

This species, although apparently very restricted in its range, is abundantly distinct. It is closely related to *H. laevigatus*, from which it differs by its larger heads and occasional trichomes on the leaves. I have seen it only in the type collection, of which there are many specimens.

60. **H. floribundus**, sp. nov.

(Plate LIX)

Perennial; stem slender, erect, probably 1–2.0 m. high, herbaceous, red-purple, glabrous, glaucous, ramose, the branches long and very slender; leaves alternate, narrowly lanceolate, acuminate, denticulate above the middle, tapering below to a short, partly distinct, slender petiole, about 10.0 cm. long by 1.5 cm. wide, those of the branches smaller, thin, delicate in texture, obscurely pubescent on both sides with very short fine hairs, smooth to the touch; the inflorescence a very large, open panicle; the heads numerous, disc convex, about 1.0 cm. in diam., rays obtuse, oval, light yellow, glabrous, nearly 2.0 cm. long; corollas of the disc yellow, lobes glabrous, base pubescent, the tube rather long; the achene dark brown, sparingly villous; the pappus two lanceolate awns without other scales; the chaff linear, obtuse, entire, thin, glabrous, scarcely carinate; the involucre hemispheric; the bracts narrowly lanceolate, acuminate, about as long as the disc, loose, the tips spreading but not reflexed. Root-system not seen.

Type. — K. Fiebrig 2758, San Luis, Bolivia. Altitude 2,000 m. Berlin Botanical Museum.

H. floribundus is a very handsome, graceful, perennial herb, its large panicle bearing 50–100 heads. The collector states that it grows on the rocky cliffs of mountains and in cultivated fields.

61. **H. alienus,** sp. nov.

(Plate LX)

Perennial; stem stout, erect, 1–1.8 m. high, 0.8 cm. in diam. at the base, simple to the inflorescence or slightly ramose above, densely scabrous-hispid on middle and upper stem, pubescence spreading, glabrescent toward the base, brown-purple, sulcate; leaves alternate, lanceolate, abruptly acuminate, entire or obscurely denticulate, tapering below to the base of the petiole, very narrowly sessile, 11–15.0 cm. long by 2–2.5 cm. wide, the upper leaves obscurely 3-nerved, if at all, densely strumose-setose, very rough above, evenly, not densely, coarsely scabrous-hispid and a little paler beneath, the lower surface more or less resin-dotted and the veins very prominent, thick and firm in texture; the inflorescence a few-flowered panicle, the branches with greatly reduced leaves, the peduncles slender; heads 1–1.3 cm. across the disc, the rays 1.5–2.0 cm. long; corollas of the disc florets yellow, the lobes a little darker yellow or brownish, lobes and base puberulent; the achene ample, glabrous, mottled; the pappus two broadly lanceolate, rather short awns without other scales; the chaff broadly linear, entire, obtuse, pubescent on the tip and keel, and on the margin of the tip; the involucre hemispheric; the bracts linear-lanceolate, attenuate, about as long as the disc, densely hispidulous, with spreading cilia; the roots coarsely fibrous, woody; rhizomes probably very short.

Type. — Biltmore Herbarium, No. 2482-a, sheet No. 113,903 in the herbarium of the Missouri Botanical Garden, St. Louis, Missouri. Type collected in moist soil near Biltmore, Buncombe Co., North Carolina, Sept. 12, 1898.

The type specimen is labeled *H. giganteus*, and is plainly related to that species, but differs from it in certain important characters. These differences are: (1) the roots are coarsely fibrous, not resembling elongated tubers; (2) the leaves are thick and firm, and either entire or very obscurely denticulate; (3) the chaff is entire; (4) the involucral bracts are much shorter and not nearly so loose as in *H. giganteus*.

Specimens of lanceolate-leaved sunflowers from the southern

states frequently appear in herbaria labeled *H. giganteus*, but I have yet to see a good, typical specimen of that species from any locality south of a line from Kentucky to Virginia. There are, no doubt, duplicates of the type collection in herbaria generally. The specific distinction of the plant was not decided until after visiting most of the larger herbaria. I have seen, however, an identical specimen in the herbarium of the Berlin Botanical Museum.

62. **H. vernalis,** sp. nov.

(Plate LXI)

Perennial; stem slender, erect, 1–1.5 m. high, simple, light green, glabrous below, remotely scabrous-setose toward the apex, not glaucous, finely striate-sulcate; leaves opposite, lanceolate, narrowly acute, serrulate, tapering below to a short, partly distinct, very slender petiole, the lateral nerves briefly decurrent about half-way down the petiole, the blade from the confluence of the lateral nerves about 12.0 cm. long by 2.5 cm. wide, the petiole 1–2.0 cm. long, thin, somewhat chartaceous, evenly, rather short-hispid above, evenly, a little longer and less abundantly hispid, resin-dotted and somewhat paler beneath, the upper leaves not much reduced; the inflorescence normally a few-flowered cyme, or a solitary terminal head, the peduncles short, very slender and hispid; heads showy, the disc about 1.2 cm. in diam., the rays about 2.5 cm. long, broadly oval, copiously resin-dotted beneath; corollas of the disc florets yellow, puberulent throughout, the base pubescent, the tube glabrous; the achene linear-oboval, light brown, glabrous; the pappus two broadly lanceolate awns with small accessory paleae on each side of their broad bases; the chaff ample, linear, conspicuously 3-cuspidate, the lateral cusps shorter but very acute, the middle cusp narrowly acute, the keel and tip slightly pubescent; the involucre broadly campanulate; the bracts linear-lanceolate, narrowly attenuate, densely short-hispid and resin-dotted, scabrid-ciliate, very loose but not reflexed; the roots finely fibrous, the rhizomes slender, few, 1–2.0 dm. long.

Type. — Reverchon 2582, "sandy woods," Gladewater, Texas. Sheet No. 113,865 in the herbarium of the Missouri Botanical Garden, St. Louis, Missouri.

63. H. Nuttallii T. & G. Fl. N. A., 2 : 324. 1842.

H. giganteus var. *utahensis* D. C. Eaton. Bot. King Exped., 169. 1871.
H. californicus var. *utahensis* Gray. Syn. Fl., 2 : 277. 1884.
H. fascicularis Greene. Pl. Bak., 3 : 28. 1901.
H. utahensis A. Nels. Bull. Torr. Bot. Club, 29 : 405. 1902.

Perennial; stem 1–2.0 m. high, simple or ramose, mostly glabrous, sometimes remotely scabrous, light green, rarely purplish; leaves lanceolate, narrowly acute, serrulate or serrate, tapering to a rather long petiole, winged, but often so narrowly as to appear distinct, mostly about 16.0 cm. long, including petiole, and 1.5–3.0 cm. wide, extremely variable, opposite below, alternate above, arrangement unstable, evenly, often densely very short-setulose above, hispid and veiny beneath, light green, concolor; inflorescence a solitary head in small plants, or a cyme or panicle in larger plants; heads medium large, the disc 1.5–2.0 cm. in diam., convex; corollas of the disc florets yellow, mostly glabrous; the achene glabrous; the pappus two narrowly lanceolate long awns, rarely with intermediate paleae; the chaff linear, subentire, acuminate, carinate, tip and keel pubescent; the involucre hemispheric; the bracts narrowly linear-lanceolate, appressed-pubescent on the surface, mostly not very ciliate, loose but not reflexed, longer than the disc; roots thick, tuber-like, usually fascicled; rhizomes slender, rarely more than 2.0 dm. long, mostly short.

Chiefly in the eastern slopes of the Rocky Mts., occasionally on the plains.

Type. — *H. californicus* Nutt. (not DC.) in the herbarium of the Academy of Science, Phila.; personally examined.

Nuttall's original collection, the type of the species, was found on the "plains of Lewis River," Wyoming. It is a small and delicate specimen, originally described as "apparently strict and simple." In more favorable situations it is ramose and taller. All specimens showing the root-system give evidence of the constancy of the fascicled roots. These are for the most part 3–4 cm. in length and 4–5 mm. in diameter, and usually distinctly fascicled. In view of the wide range of this species, it exists under many varying aspects, and I have thought it advisable to mention a few of the more common collections that I place in *H. Nuttallii* and to point out some of the more striking variations. Cusick 1000, Union Co., Oregon, cited by Gray; Baker 816, Colorado; Burglehaus, Mammoth Hot Springs, Wyoming; Jones 1334, Utah, with larger leaves and ramose stem; Tracy 400, Utah; C. P. Smith 2023, Cache Co., Utah, a very peculiar form with opposite leaves 20 cm. long, by 1.8 cm. wide; Jones 5980, Utah, an individual with very scabrous stems; Buffum 1841, Wyoming; A. and E. Nelson 6757, Wyoming, with scabrous and ramose stems; Buffum 2496, Wyoming, with leaves 17.0 cm. long by 4.0 cm. wide, a very stout stem, evidently a vigorous plant; A. Nelson 8135, Wyoming, a very vigorous, ramose plant; Gooding 344, Wyoming; Gooding 547, same state, a very virgate plant; Tweedy 4929, Brandegee 529, Baker 289, Ramaley 923, Osterhout, New Windsor, a form with very large leaves and long internodes, Jones 553 — all from Colorado; Bates 7124, Loveland, Colorado, with very wide, rather thin leaves; Clements 240, labeled *H. pumilus*, Canyon City, Colorado, with scabrous stems and unusually pubescent bracts, Crandall, near Ft. Collins, Colorado. Among the Utah specimens are: MacBride 1683, 1632, Nelson and MacBride 1395, Jones 6405, with a purple stem, Clokey 3947, Colorado, with a conspicuously mottled stem. From New Mexico, Standley 4998, Metcalf 1270, Wooton 2610, 375. Bates 5370, Nebraska, near Valentine, has a scabrous stem; Murdock, South Dakota; Bell, Hankinson, North Dakota; Jones, Panaca, Nevada, have very narrow leaves; Jones 2949, Wells, Nevada, has very narrow leaves, virgate; Bergman, Fargo, North Dakota. From Montana: Kelsey, near Helena, and Blankinship, near Bozeman, have sharply scabrous stems and leaves prevailingly opposite; T. W. Anderson; M. E. Jones 8686, Flathead Lake. Here also belong Moody 29 *bis*, Rosedale, and Macoun 22,731, from Alberta.

There is a distinct tendency in the larger and more vigorous forms of this species to produce very long internodes and widely spreading long branches on the upper part of the stem. I have never seen the living plant, but the prevailing light straw-color of the stems, branches and the receptacular chaff is, in the dried plant at least, very striking. The specimens from Utah exhibit a marked tendency to produce red stems. In normal individuals the short, sharp setae of the upper surface of the leaves, obscurely surrounded by an often umbilicate struma, are also very characteristic.

H. Nuttallii is very closely related to *H. californicus* DC., from which it differs chiefly in involucral bracts, which are narrowly linear-lanceolate, erect though loose in *H. Nuttallii*, and broadly lanceolate, acuminate, abruptly reflexed in *H. californicus*. To the same group belong *H. Maximiliani*, *H. Parishii*, *H. grosse-serratus*, *H. borealis*, *H. giganteus*, *H. membranaceus*, *H. Rydbergi*, *H. instabilis*, as the more important members of the family group.

64. **H. validus,** sp. nov.

(Plate LXII)

Perennial; stem slender, erect, 1–2.0 m. high, light green, sparingly, rather finely scabrous, ramose above, the branches long, slender, hispid; leaves alternate, broadly lanceolate, acute, obscurely serrulate, the blade decurrent nearly to the base of the petiole, about 10.0 cm. long by 2.5 cm. wide, scabrous-setose above, not densely, very sparingly hispid, paler and slightly resinous beneath; the internodes about 1.0 dm.; the inflorescence three or four rather large heads, solitary on leafy peduncles 0.5–2.0 dm. long, the disc normally 1.8 cm. in diam., the rays about 1.5 cm. long; corollas of the disc florets yellow, the lobes and base pubescent; the achene glabrous; the pappus two broadly lanceolate awns without other scales; the chaff very thin, ample, 3-cuspidate, the lateral cusps small, the middle cusp short, acute, tip and keel dark, short-pubescent; the involucre hemispheric; the bracts linear-lanceolate, sparingly short-pubescent or puberulent, scarcely ciliate, longer than the disc, loose but not reflexed. Root-system not seen.

Type. — A collection by T. G. Harbison, from Richland Creek Valley, North Carolina, Oct. 1, 1897, in the Gray Herbarium.

H. validus is unquestionably distinct, but the type specimen, although in excellent condition, is very inadequate, and it is to be hoped that further collections of the species will be made.

The label indicates that the specimen came from the Sherwood Herbarium.

65. **H. borealis,** sp. nov.

(Plate LXIII)

H. giganteus var. *subtuberosus* (Bourgeau) Britton. Ill. Fl. N. States and Can., 3 : 425. 1898 as to description but not as to type specimen.
H. subtuberosus Bourgeau in herb. Hooker., as to description in Man. Fl. N. States and Can., p. 993. 1901.

Perennial; stem slender, erect, 1–2.0 m. high, simple or rarely somewhat ramose above, especially in large individuals, more or less hispid, at least above, often quite smooth below, the apex of the stem and the branches always hispid; leaves normally alternate, readily opposite in small or depauperate individuals, lanceolate-elliptic, acuminate, serrate, rarely entire, obscurely 3-nerved, the blade decurrent on the petiole about two thirds of its length, rarely to its base, therefore in most cases, the petiole partly distinct, 6–12.0 cm. long by 1.5–3.0 cm. wide, very evenly hispid on both sides, the pubescence longer and finer beneath, nearly concolor; the inflorescence a few-flowered panicle or often a solitary head; the disc 1–1.5 cm. in diam., the rays 1.5–2.0 cm. long; corollas of the disc florets yellow, glabrous; the tube short; the achene dark brown, linear-oblanceolate, glabrous; the pappus two short, broadly lanceolate awns, little more than twice as long as the tube, occasionally each awn double, and rarely very small accessory paleae at the base of the awn; the chaff subentire or entire, pubescent, the apex acute; the involucre broadly campanulate; the bracts linear-lanceolate, rather sparingly appressed-pubescent, ciliate with spreading cilia, very loose but not reflexed, a little longer than the disc; roots of two kinds, the one long, slender, fibrous, not very abundant, the other one or more succulent tuber-like roots, 3–5.0 cm. long, constricted at the proximal end and tapering at the distal end into a long, slender, fine root, these often in fascicles; the rhizomes, three or four, slender, less than 1.0 dm. long.

Common in low or swampy places from Minnesota and adjacent Canada to Maine, especially in Minnesota, Wisconsin, and Michigan.

Type. — A specimen in the herbarium of the University of Minnesota, collected in that state by George B. Aiton, Sept., 1890.

H. borealis is probably the plant that represents the current conception of *H. giganteus* var. *subtuberosus.* I have shown under *H. Maximiliani* that the name "*subtuberosus*" cannot be applied to any plant other than *H. Maximiliani* and is a synonym of that species, and it is my opinion that our type is quite distinct from *H. giganteus,* although it is a close relative. *H. borealis* differs from *H. giganteus* by its smaller stature, its frequently opposite leaves, its smaller inflorescence, its partly distinct petioles, shorter involucral bracts, and most constantly of all, by the pubescence of the lower surface of the leaves. In *H. giganteus* this pubescence is long, and confined to the nerves, at most scattering on the surface; in *H. borealis* it is more dense, very even, shorter, somewhat tomentulose in character. The tuber-like roots are also very distinctive. These are excellently presented by the type and also by several other collections at our disposal, but unfortunately only a very small fraction of all the specimens that I have grouped under the name *H. borealis* present the root-system.

This species stands about midway between *H. giganteus* and *H. Nuttallii.* The relation is both geographic and phylogenetic, as will be observed.

66. H. Dalyi Britton. Journ. N. Y. Bot. Gard., 2 : 89. 1901.

Perennial; stem slender, simple, roughish, appressed-hispidulous, 6–10.0 dm. high; leaves opposite or the upper sometimes alternate, narrowly lanceolate-acuminate remotely serrate with low teeth, petiole winged to the base, conduplicate, scabrous-setose both sides, about 10.0 cm. long, 1.0 cm. wide or less; inflorescence a single terminal head, rarely one or two more, the disc 1.5 cm. in diam., the rays 3–4 cm. long, numerous; corollas of the disc florets yellow, the lobes and base puberulent; pappus of two subulate awns without other scales; chaff lanceolate, acute, subentire, pubescent at apex; involucre campanulate, the bracts narrowly lanceolate, attenuate, acuminate, longer than the disc, densely hispid; roots coarse, woody, rhizomes short.

Sag Harbor, New York.

Type. — In the New York Botanical Garden.

This plant was first brought to the attention of Dr. Britton by Judge Daly. It grew in coarse, gravelly soil near the beach at Sag Harbor, New York. Many attempts were made to propagate it at the New York Botanical Garden, but unsuccessfully, and it has apparently disappeared from its original locality. A collection by Aiton from Minneapolis bears a very close resemblance to the type, and a number of specimens of my own, collected on a gravelly hill-side near Grand Rapids, Michigan, are also inseparable from the type specimen. It cannot be denied that there is at least a very close relationship between this species and *H. Maximiliani*. Indeed, it has the small stature, the opposite leaves, and the reduced inflorescence that one would expect in a depauperate *H. Maximiliani*. Dr. Britton does not state whether the latter species was found in close proximity to the *H. Dalyi* at Sag Harbor, but as far as I have myself collected it, careful search failed to reveal any individuals of *H. Maximiliani* within several miles. Farwell, in fact, has reduced the species to a variety of *H. Maximiliani*. I see Mr. Farwell's point of view, but I do not see the logic of the reduction to a variety. If the plant is a depauperate *H. Maximiliani*, then it is not *Dalyi*, either variety or species, and if it is not a depauperate plant, it is certainly sufficiently striking to deserve specific rank.

67. H. Maximiliani Schrad. Ind. Sem. Hort. Götting. 1835.

H. subtuberosus Bourgeau, in herb. Hooker, in Royal Bot. Gard. Kew, Eng.
H. Maximiliani var. *iubaris* Lunell. Am. Mid. Nat., 5:63. 1917.

Perennial; stem stout, erect when solitary, ascending or divergent when tufted, as they often are, 0.5–2.8 m. high, mostly about 2.0 m., simple, normally rough hispid, more so above, often glabrescent toward the base, pubescence mostly appressed; leaves alternate, or, in small or depauperate individuals, opposite, linear-elliptic, attenuate at both ends, apex acute, the blade narrowly decurrent to the base of the petiole, entire or serrate, mostly serrulate, falcate, strongly conduplicate, 10–15.0 cm. long by 1–2.0 cm.

wide, scabrous-setose and light gray-green both sides, the color residing in the leaf, not in the pubescence; the inflorescence racemose from the upper axils, the peduncles normally very short, 1–3–4 cm., very villous, the heads very showy, mostly large, the disc 2–3.0 cm. in diam., the rays 2.5–4.0 cm. long and conspicuously "cupped"; corollas of the disc florets yellow, subglabrous, slender, the tube short; the achene linear-oblanceolate, slender but turgid, dark brown, longitudinally striate, glabrous; the pappus two broadly lanceolate, rather short awns without other scales; the sterile ray-achenes, inane, very flat, the pappus as above but with conspicuous accessory paleae; the chaff linear, acute, entire, very pubescent; the involucre flat-campanulate; the bracts linear-lanceolate, very attenuate, longer than the disc, often 3.0 cm. long, conspicuously appressed-pubescent, almost always canescent, very loose and spreading but not reflexed; the roots very thick and woody, tapering to a long slender tip, numerous; the stem base below the ground surface, normally much enlarged, bearing numerous crown-buds and very short rhizomes, rarely 1.0 dm. long.

Common in rich, not too dry, ground from middle Canada to Texas, both sides of the Mississippi, especially west.

Type. — I have not been able to locate one type; it is probably in the herbarium of the University of Göttingen, Germany.

H. Maximiliani is one of the most distinctive and readily recognized of our perennial sunflowers, and next to *H. grosse-serratus* is a decorative and ornamental plant. Owing to the liberal production of crown-buds, the stems are frequently tufted, four or five or more from a single root. The rays are always conspicuously cupped, no other sunflower that I have seen having this character. The plant grows readily from seed, the seedlings attaining a height of 1.5 m., and producing mature flowers the first season. The leaves of seedlings are usually opposite to the inflorescence, much larger, less conduplicate, and the internodes longer, and the stem produces abundant branches from even the lower axils. In older plants, however, the stem, as far as my observations extend, is always simple unless injured. The peduncles are normally not more than 3–4 cm. long. One of two stems from the same root, in our garden at East Lansing, became broken and lay prostrate on the ground during the entire season. On this broken stem the peduncles grew to a length of 25.0 cm. while those of the erect stem were normal.

I was permitted to examine Bourgeau's original specimen, which he labeled *H. subtuberosus*. The specimen was collected on the "prairie de la rivière," Assouri, wherever that may be. This specimen is plainly a perfectly typical *H. Maximiliani*, and presents no peculiarities whatever. The current belief that *H. subtuberosus* is a variety of *H. giganteus* is patently incorrect. The earliest reference that I find in literature to *H. subtuberosus* Bourgeau is in Gray's *Synoptical Flora*, 1 : 276, 1884, where that author includes it in the synonymy of *H. giganteus*, suggesting it as a race or strain of the latter species.

One of Lindheimer's collections from Texas, No. 261, near the Brazos, in the Berlin Botanical Museum, bears the words in Lindheimer's hand, "var. *asperrimus*." This plant differs from the typical form only in the greater roughness of the leaves. It is possibly a race or strain, but is not, in my opinion, entitled to varietal rank. S. P. Rixford's collection from San Antonio, Texas, is the same thing, but is obviously a stunted plant, barely 0.5 m. high.

In the Missouri Botanical Garden are two sheets of a cultivated form of *H. Maximiliani* that deserve some attention. The leaves are unusually large and apparently not conduplicate, the peduncles are about 1.0 dm. long and slender, and 1–3-flowered. No information was obtainable at the Missouri Botanical Garden in regard to the original source of these plants, but they are more entitled to special attention than the form "*asperrimus*" above referred to. These sheets are No. 877,198, collected by J. H. Kellogg, and No. 113,877, collected by C. H. Thompson. These two sheets both bear the word "Mexico," but I was unable to ascertain if this means the country of that name or the town in northern Missouri. The plants are very unlike anything I have seen from the country of Mexico.

H. Maximiliani is related to *H. Rydbergi* most closely, and is not distantly related to *H. grosse-serratus*, *H. giganteus*, and *H. Nuttallii*.

68. **H. attenuatus,** sp. nov.

(Plate LXIV)

Perennial; stem light green, subappressed-hispid, ramose, height not apparent from the specimen, but evidently a tall plant; leaves alternate, narrowly lanceolate, attenuate at both ends, the blade very narrowly decurrent to the base of the petiole, 8–15.0 cm. long by barely 1.0 cm. wide, scabrous-hispid on both sides, the pubescence of the lower surface a little longer, somewhat resin-dotted beneath, thin, chartaceous; the inflorescence racemose, the peduncles hispid, 1–3.0 dm. long, internodes of the inflorescence 3–10.0 cm. long, the flowering branches with a few very narrow leaves; heads showy, the disc 1.5–2.0 cm. in diam., the rays about 2.5 cm. long, narrowly acute at the apex; corollas of the disc florets yellow, cylindrical, glabrous except the pubescent base; achenes of the ray inane, with a pappus of two broadly lanceolate short awns with accessory fimbriate paleae at each side of their bases; achenes of the disc fertile, linear, glabrous, with a pappus of two very broadly lanceolate awns as long as the limb of the disc corollas, without other scales; chaff subentire, acute, densely pubescent on tip and keel; the involucre hemispheric; the bracts lanceolate, abruptly acuminate and very long-attenuate to subulate tips, 1.5–3.0 cm. long, much longer than the disc, densely appressed-pubescent, scarcely ciliate, very loose and spreading or reflexed. Lower stem and root-system not seen.

Type. — A collection by A. Fendler, "cult. ex sem. N. Mex. Oct. 16, 1852." Accession No. 113,942, in the herbarium of the Missouri Botanical Garden.

It is very unfortunate that the type presents only four or five decimeters of the inflorescence, but the characters of the plant are very marked. The very long, loose involucral bracts, attenuate to filiform tips, the large heads, the narrow leaves broadest about the middle, with a similar pubescence on both surfaces, the racemose inflorescence, and the narrowly acute rays sharply identify this species. As the label states, the specimen was grown in Tennessee from seeds from New Mexico, and it is to be hoped that further collections either from Memphis or New Mexico may add to our knowledge of this interesting plant.

It is difficult, without a more complete specimen, to estimate its relationships. Its racemose inflorescence suggests *H. Maximiliani*, its leaves and color suggest *H. Cusickii* and *H. Nuttallii*, its bracts and sinuous inflorescence *H. grosse-serratus*.

69. H. Cusickii Gray. Proc. Am. Acad., 21 : 413. 1886.

Perennial; stems 1.0 m. or less high, tufted from a large thick root, glabrous, rarely hispid, light green, simple or ramose, slightly ascending; leaves narrowly linear-elliptic, or linear-lanceolate, acute, entire, the blade decurrent to the base of the petiole, thin, remotely appressed-hispid on both sides, smooth to the touch, rarely the pubescence less appressed and leaves rough, mostly alternate, concolor, the lateral nerves extending nearly to the apex of the leaf, parallel to the midrib, angle of confluence with the midrib very acute, 10.0 cm. long by 1.4 cm. wide, rarely larger, often smaller; inflorescence a single head terminal on stem and branches; heads normally large and showy, the disc often 2.0 cm. in diam., the rays up to 3.0 cm. long, elliptic, deeply bidentate at apex; corollas of the disc florets yellow, 1.0 cm. long, slender, glabrous except the puberulent base of the throat; achene glabrous, light brown; pappus two broadly lanceolate awns, sometimes short and 3-cuspidate, usually about 3 mm. long; the chaff narrowly lanceolate, tip narrowly acute, pubescent, entire or with minute lateral teeth; abruptly broad campanulate, dark green; the bracts broadly linear-lanceolate, loose, not reflexed, longer than the disc, thinly appressed-pubescent, rarely ciliate; the root a large, resinous, woody structure 3–4.0 cm. in diam., irregular in shape; no rhizomes, propagation from crown-buds.

Oregon, Idaho, Washington, Nevada. In desert regions.

Type. — Cusick, dry hills near Malheur River, southeastern Oregon; not examined.

70. H. ambiguus (T. & G.) Britton. Man. Fl. N. States and Can., 993. 1901.

H. giganteus var. *ambiguus* T. & G. Fl. N. A., 2:325. 1842.

Perennial; stem glabrous or hispid, never densely, erect, 0.7 m. to 3.0 m. or more in height, simple or usually profusely ramose from the base, very stout; leaves opposite or alternate, leaf arrangement in this species exceedingly unstable, lanceolate, often very broadly lanceolate or ovate-lanceolate, acuminate, serrate, often obscurely, nearly sessile by the broadly winged short petiole, very broad and round as in *H. divaricatus*, slightly chartaceous, nearly concolor, strumose-setose above, evenly hispid beneath, not densely, 8.0–17.0 cm. long by 2–4.5 cm. wide; inflorescence a very loose, open panicle, the peduncles 10.0–25.0 cm. long, usually bearing one or two, rarely more, small leaves; heads with light yellow rays, the disc about 1.5 cm. in diam., corollas of the disc light yellow, the lobes rather large, puberulent; chaff 3-cuspidate, the lateral cusps small, the middle cusp acute, tips pubescent, carinate, very light green or straw color, the achene glabrous, pappus of two lanceolate awns without other scales; involucral bracts linear-lanceolate or lanceolate, longer than the disc, very loose, but firm, rarely recurved, surface hispidulous, spreading-ciliate below the middle with long cilia; the roots coarsely fibrous, very woody, rhizomes and crown-buds abundant, the former 2.0–25.0 cm. long, and rather stout.

Long Island to Wisconsin, Indiana.

Type in the New York Botanical Garden; personally examined.

Britton says of this species that it "appears to be a hybrid with *H. giganteus* as one of its parents." So far as I know, there is no experimental proof that this plant is a hybrid. If it is, and if *H. giganteus* is one parent, the other is *H. divaricatus*, and it is a fact that wherever I have collected it both these supposititious parents were found close by. However, it does not appear to me to be a hybrid. One of its most marked peculiarities is its tendency to branch from the base, a character not found in either of the other two species. The original collection from which the variety was described came from Long Island. Among the specimens in the herbarium of the Berlin Botanical Museum are several collections by Heuser from St. Ronan's Well, near Flushing, Long Island. These plants are small in comparison with many others that I have seen, and the leaves are opposite except the uppermost. The species grows abundantly in the vicinity of East Lansing, Michigan, and great instability is observable in the leaf arrangement. Of two large plants, equal in size and vigor, one may have all leaves opposite and the other only the lowermost opposite. In fact, the most distinguishing character is the shape of the leaf, with its broad base, nearly sessile. *H. ambiguus* is readily distinguished from *H. divaricatus* by the fact that in the former the blade is decurrent below the confluence of the lateral nerves, and in the latter, the lateral nerves are confluent at the very base of the leaf. It is also readily distinguished from *H. giganteus* by its larger, opposite leaves, broader at the base, and its broadly winged petiole. Besides the specimens already cited, the following also belong here: Lansing 681, Hyde Park, Chicago, Illinois; Gates 741, Clark Junction, Indiana; Watson 393, Angola, Indiana.

71. H. grosse-serratus Martens. Sel. Sem. Hort. Lov. ex Linnaea XIV. Litt. 133. 1840.

Perennial; stem stout, erect, tall, 1–4.0 m., normally simple to the inflorescence, glabrous, glaucous, very smooth, sulcate, light green, often purplish; leaves very broadly linear-lanceolate, acuminate only at the apex, grossly and saliently serrate, contracted below to a long, stout petiole, the blade briefly decurrent, dark, shining green and very finely strumose-setulose above, with very fine, short, even, rather dense hispid hairs beneath; alternate, the blade in average cauline leaves 20.0–25.0 cm. long, from the confluence of the lateral nerves, and 5–6.0 cm. wide toward the base, the petiole from the confluence, about 8.0 cm. long, the upper leaves reduced, lanceolate or oblong-lanceolate, and less deeply serrate; the inflorescence a large panicle with slender, sinuous branches; heads very showy, disc 1–2.0 cm. in diam., the rays 2.5–4.0 cm. long, obovate, bright yellow; corollas of the disc florets yellow, very slender, glabrous, about 0.7 cm. long, tube very slender; achene, slender glabrous, light brown, sometimes mottled, about 0.5 cm. long; pappus of two slender, narrowly lanceolate awns without other scales; the chaff linear, very slender, mostly entire, rarely subtricuspidate, light green, tip dark, narrowly acuminate, somewhat pubescent, carinate; involucre hemispheric, the bracts narrowly lanceolate, acuminate, attenuate to long, subulate tips, very dark green, mostly glabrous toward the base, finely appressed-pubescent toward the tip, softly appressed-ciliate, very loose but not recurving, longer than the disc; rhizomes abundant, often very long, often branched; roots very thick and woody, often 1–2.0 cm. in diam. near the stem, with numerous fine fibrous rootlets.

In wet or moist humus soil, in open sunny places, Maine to North Dakota, Oklahoma to Virginia; common within the range.

I am not familiar with the type.

This is undoubtedly the handsomest and most graceful of all the sunflowers, rising to a height of from 4 to 5 m., the stem with its large and graceful leaves surmounted by a large panicle of flowers often nearly a meter in diameter. The normal cauline leaf is most distinctive in outline, resembling a narrow isosceles triangle, with only the tip acuminate. The leaves are firm in texture.

H. grosse-serratus belongs in a very large group of which the more conspicuous members are *H. giganteus, H. instabilis, H. Maximiliani, H. borealis* and *H. Nuttallii*. It is probable also that *H. californicus* and *H. Parishii* and *H. Oliveri* are not far removed from the same group.

Wherever collections of this species present the maximum cauline leaves, the identification is a very simple matter. Unfortunately, however, most collections exhibit only the inflorescence and the reduced upper leaves, which are often only mildly serrate. In such cases the deciding factor will be the fine, soft, short, not too dense pubescence of the lower surface of the leaves.

The variety *Beta* of Torrey and Gray I am not able to identify, and Gray ignores it in his *Synoptical Flora*. The leaves in this variety are supposed to be less canescent, and the stem scabrous toward the summit. The stem is always more pubescent toward the summit in this genus, and the leaves in this species are not canescent except as an individual peculiarity. The variety *Gamma* of Torrey and Gray becomes in part var. *hypoleucus* of Gray's *Synoptical Flora*. Gray does not state what becomes of the other part of *Gamma*. The citations for this variety are "Texas — Drummond, Lindheimer, Wright." Of these I have seen only the Lindheimer specimen from Industry, Texas. In this specimen the pubescence of the lower surface of the leaves is very dense, but the specimen is typical in all other respects. The Sullivan specimen from Ohio has leaves somewhat thicker than the typical form and rather reticulate beneath. In fact, the specimen impresses me as being somewhat abnormal. At any rate, the various differences here enumerated are all, in my opinion, well within the specific limits.

72. H. californicus DC. Prod., 5 : 589. 1836.

H. californicus var. *mariposianus* Gray. Syn. Fl. N. A., Vol. I, Part II, 277. 1884.

Perennial; stem tall, 1–3.0 m., ramose above, glabrous, very smooth, sulcate, often purplish; leaves alternate except the lowermost, lanceolate, acuminate, entire or serrate, lateral nerves obscure, blade decurrent to the base of the petiole, very narrowly below, the blade slightly enlarged near the base, then tapering to the acute or acuminate apex, short setulose above, hispid beneath and a little paler, pubescence not dense, 12.0–18.0 cm. long by 3–5.0 cm. wide, deep green; inflorescence 1–3 heads at the apices of the leafy upper branches of the stem, the peduncles somewhat hispid near the heads; heads rather large, the disc about 1.5 cm. in diam., the rays about 2.0 cm. long, often deeply 2–3-dentate at the tip; corollas of the disc florets yellow, very slender, the lobes lanceolate, lobes and upper part of the throat puberulent, base villous, the tube rather long, 1.5 mm., glabrous; achene large, glabrous; pappus of two awns without other scales, the awns broadly lanceolate; chaff ample, carinate, entire, the tip acuminate or narrowly acute, the tip and keel very dark and pubescent, otherwise very light in color and glabrous; the involucre campanulate, the bracts broadly lanceolate, dilated at the base, narrowly acuminate but not attenuate, very dark, hispidulous toward the tip and near the margin, subglabrous below, obscurely, very short appressed-ciliate, much longer than the disc, very loose and reflexed. Root parts not seen.

California, along streams, chiefly south of San Francisco Bay.

Type. — A collection by Douglas from California, sent to De Candolle by the London Horticultural Society; not seen.

This species is apparently confined to California, and possibly to the type locality. Its involucral bracts and the leaves as well, though to a lesser degree, have a slight bulge or dilation near the base.

H. californicus var. *mariposianus* Gray is based upon a collection of Bolander from Mariposa Co. I have not seen the type, but the description, in view of the plasticity of the genus, does not seem to me to represent a sufficiently distinct plant to deserve varietal mention. A collection of Alice Eastwood from Tuolumne Co. seems to fit the description of the variety, but does not verify the 4-awned pappus.

73. H. Parishii Gray. Proc. Am. Acad., 19 : 7. 1883.

Perennial; stem stout, erect, 1.5–2.5 m. high, simple to the inflorescence, glabrous, very smooth, very sulcate, leafy; leaves alternate, lanceolate or broadly linear-lanceolate, narrowly acute, serrate, tapering below to the partly distinct, partly winged, slender petiole, 10–20.0 cm. long, including petiole, 1.5–2.5 cm. wide, the petiole from the confluence of the lateral nerves 2–4.0 cm. long, the blade very narrowly decurrent about half-way; rather densely hispid above, thinly tomentose beneath, deep green; nearly concolor, thinnish in texture; the inflorescence racemose-paniculate, the lowermost flowering branches 1–2.5 dm. long usually bearing a single head, and one or two pairs of small leaves with abortive buds in the axils, the succeeding flowering branches shorter, the apex of the peduncle densely pubescent; heads showy, the disc about 1.5 cm. in diam., the rays 2.5 cm. long, usually 2–3-dentate at the apex; corollas of the disc florets yellow, slender, subglabrous, tapering somewhat to the rather long and glabrous tube; the achene glabrous; the pappus two lanceolate awns without other scales; the chaff linear, 3-cuspidate, cusps acute, pubescent on the tips; the involucre broadly campanulate; the bracts linear-lanceolate, attenuate to long slender tips, densely pubescent with long-appressed hispid-villous hairs, ciliate, and conspicuously villous toward the base. Root-system not seen.

California, chiefly San Bernardino Co. and vicinity, in low places, swamps, and the margins of streams.

Type. — S. B. and W. F. Parish 1025, in the Gray Herbarium; examined.

H. Parishii is closely related to *H. californicus*, *H. Nuttallii*, and *H. instabilis*.

74. **H. instabilis,** sp. nov.

(Plate LXV)

Perennial; stem slender, erect, 0.5–2.0 m. high, mostly about 1.7 m., glabrous except toward the apex, never scabrous, usually green, simple to the inflorescence; leaves alternate, opposite in very small individuals only and then rarely, acuminate, mostly serrulate, rarely entire, the base tapering to a rather long, partly distinct petiole, the blade narrowly decurrent from one third to one half the length of the petiole, extremely variable in size, 8.0–25.0 cm. long by 1–4.5 cm. wide, prevailingly about 17.0 cm. long, including petiole, by 2.0 cm. wide, the petiole, from the confluence of the lateral nerves, about one fifth of the entire length, scabrous-setulose and deep green above, evenly and copiously pubescent below with long hairs, not tomentose, slightly paler beneath; the inflorescence paniculate, the branches more or less sinuous, the peduncles mildly hispid, the size of the inflorescence correlated with the size of the plant, and sometimes consisting of a single terminal head, the cauline leaves then being mostly opposite; the heads showy, the disc about 1.0 cm. in diam., the rays 1.5–2.5 long, oval, bright yellow; corollas of the disc florets yellow, mostly pubescent from lobes to the glabrous tube, this character variable, but the lower half of the disc corollas at least always short-pubescent; the achene elongated oboval, often as long as the corolla, glabrous, mottled when mature, the pappus two broadly lanceolate awns without other scales; the chaff narrow, linear, acute, subentire, very pubescent on tip and keel; the involucre flat-campanulate; the bracts linear-lanceolate, narrowly acuminate, a very little longer than the disc, thinly appressed-pubescent, somewhat ciliate, loose but not recurved; roots woody, coarsely fibrous, often thick near the attachment to the stem base; rhizomes and crown-buds abundant but short, varying from the crown-bud to 3.0 dm.

Moist prairies, abundant about the southern shores of the Great Lakes, particularly in the vicinity of Chicago, sporadically toward the east, west, and south.

Type. — Watson 147, Old Trails Highway, near Casey, Illinois, in the herbarium of Michigan State College, East Lansing, Michigan.

H. instabilis, so named on account of the great dimensional variation of the foliage and stature, is a close relative of *H. grosse-serratus*, and frequently appears so labeled in herbaria, but it is abundantly distinct. Its chief points of departure are as follows: (1) the pubescence of the lower surface of the leaves differs both in character and degree from that of *H. grosse-serratus* — it is much more dense, imparting a conspicuous pallor to the leaf, and consists of long, subappressed hairs instead of short, straight hairs as in the related species; (2) the leaves are much less abruptly contracted into the petiole; (3) the involucral bracts are shorter, and the heads not so showy; (4) the stem is rarely so tall as in *H. grosse-serratus;* and (5) the inflorescence, though a panicle, is more contracted. *H. instabilis* is by far the most frequent sunflower in the vicinity of Chicago, great areas of moist prairie in and about Burnside and Pullman being covered by it. It is also abundant from Chicago to Missouri, and occurs in Ohio, Indiana, and Michigan.

75. H. giganteus. Sp. Pl., 905. 1753.

H. virgatus Lam. Encyc., 3: 85. 1789.
H. crinitus Nutt. fide Steud. Nomen, ed. 1, 1: 737. 1841.
H. giganteus var. *oppositifolius* Farwell. Rept. Mich. Acad. Sci., 17: 180. 1917.
H. giganteus var. *virgatus* Farwell. *l. c.*

Perennial; stem stout, erect, 1–3.0 m. high, mostly glabrous but often hispid, purplish, rarely green, simp le to the inflorescence; leaves lanceolate, acuminate, serrate, almost sessile by decurrence of the blade to the base of the petiole, but narrowly pointed at the base, normally 9–25.0 cm. long by 2–3.0 cm. wide, mostly deep green, thinnish and somewhat chartaceous in texture, with very short, sharp, often remote setae above, and a pubescence beneath variable in degree but never dense, consisting of long, curving, spreading hairs, chiefly on the main nerves, but also scattered about the surface; inflorescence a corymbose panicle, large or small, according to the size and vigor of the individual; heads showy, the disc about 2.0 cm. in diam., low convex, the rays 1.5–2.0 cm. long, oval, light yellow; corollas of the disc florets yellow, the lobes and base pubescent, the tube very short; the achene glabrous; the pappus two lanceolate awns without other scales; the chaff 3-cuspidate, pubescent, the cusps short, acute; the involucre hemispheric, the bracts linear-lanceolate, longer than the disc, very loose but not reflexed, subglabrous on the surface, ciliate with long cilia almost always at right angles with the margin of the bract; rhizomes short and stout, 1–2.0 dm. long, crown-buds very abundant; the roots elongated — fusiform, woody, often with shorter, thicker, very fleshy, edible roots, 5–15.0 cm. long and 1–2.0 cm. thick, not tubers but resembling them.

Abundant in wet soil throughout the northeastern quarter of the United States and adjacent Canada.

Type. — *H. giganteus* in the Linnaean Herbarium.

H. giganteus is very common within its range, and occurs only sporadically outside it. I question its occurrence south of a line drawn from North Carolina to southern Missouri. The *H. giganteus* var. *subtuberosus,* based upon Bourgeau's specimen, is an error, for the Bourgeau specimen is a perfectly typical *H. Maximiliani.*

The leaves in this species are normally alternate, but their arrangement is profoundly influenced by edaphic conditions. Depauperation, due to drought, competition, accident, the short season, or an unusually cold season in northern latitudes, readily results in a small plant with all leaves oppoite and an inflorescence of a single head. This is very evidently the explanation of Bourgeau's specimen from Saskatchewan, 1858, labeled *H. rigidus.* Similar instances also are readily found in places that have not been too profoundly disturbed. Four or five miles southeast of Grand Rapids, Michigan, tall normal plants grow abundantly by the roadside, but where they fade into the woods, they become small, delicate, with opposite leaves and a contracted inflorescence of from one to three or four heads. I have seen specimens that readily fit the varieties mentioned by Farwell, and could add many more, notably Bebb's specimen from Rock Creek, Washington, D. C., but I fail to see any purpose served by the drawing of such fine distinctions. These plants are all plainly *H. giganteus,* and no one expects them to be exactly identical.

76. H. cinereus T. & G. Fl. N. A., 2 : 243. 1842.

Perennial; stem erect, about 1.5 m. high, strigose-hispid, densely so toward the base, more leafy below, leaves remote above, simple to the inflorescence; leaves oblong-ovate, acute, the lowermost obtuse, serrulate, sessile, the blade broadly decurrent below the confluence of the lateral nerves to the base of the petiole, amplexicaulent, pointed at both ends, long scabrous-hispid above, ashy-strigose beneath, very spreading or retrorsely and densely strigose on the midrib, prevailingly opposite, larger and more approximate below, about 12.0 cm. long by 3.0 cm. wide, lateral nerves confluent a little below the middle, firm in texture, ashy-green in color, little, if any, paler beneath; inflorescence a few heads on short alternate peduncles at apex of the stem, the peduncles very hispid; heads about 1.0 cm. across the disc, rays conspicuous; corollas of the disc florets yellow, pubescent from lobes to base, the base villous; the achene villous toward the apex and on the angles; pappus of two broadly lanceolate awns; the chaff entire, lanceolate, the tip narrowly acute, keel and tip pubescent; the involucre hemispheric, the bracts lanceolate, narrowly acuminate, loose but erect, equal to or only a little longer than the disc, densely scabrous-hispid, dark and ciliate below; the rhizome slender, 1-2.0 dm. long; roots not seen.

Texas to Illinois.

Type. — A collection by Drummond, from Texas, exact locality not stated; in the New York Botanical Garden; personally examined.

This species seems to be rare; the only specimens I have seen are the type and a collection C. A. Geyer, from Beardstown, Illinois. In habit it resembles *H. rigidus;* the leaves resemble those of a small *H. occidentalis*, which is perhaps its nearest relative.

77. H. gracilentus Gray. Proc. Am. Acad., 11 : 77. 1876.

Perennial; stem erect, 1–2 m. high, slender, green or purplish, normally strigose-hispid, rough; often tufted; leaves opposite, becoming alternate near the inflorescence, lanceolate, narrowly acute, often somewhat dilated near the base, denticulate, or saliently dentate near the base, the petiole narrowly winged by the decurrent blade, distinct toward the base, 15.0 cm. long by 2–3 cm. wide, coarsely but not densely hispid on both sides, internodes very long; inflorescence a few-flowered panicle on long nearly naked peduncles; mature heads 2.0 cm. across the disc, rays 2–3 cm. long; corollas of the disc florets yellow, entire corolla puberulent; the achene glabrous, somewhat angled; pappus two broadly lanceolate puberulent awns; the chaff entire, lanceolate, acute, the tip and keel dark, coarsely puberulent; the involucre hemispheric, the bracts lanceolate, acuminate, often abruptly so, puberulent or finely short-pubescent, often resinous, about equal to or shorter than the disc, erect; the root large, perennial, forming crown-buds, no rhizomes.

California.

Type. — Palmer's collection from San Diego Co., California, in 1875.

This species is very closely related to *H. pumilus*, from which it is distinguished by its larger size, lanceolate leaves, broadest near the base, its smoother stem, acuminate bracts, and the salient dentations of the lower part of the leaf.

78. **H. severus,** sp. nov.

(Plate LXVI)

Perennial; stem stout, erect 1–1.5 m. high, mostly simple to the inflorescence, sulcate, very rough, scabrous-hispid, the trichomes with conspicuously large bulbous bases; leaves opposite, large, ovate, acute, saliently serrate, the teeth more or less incurved, abruptly contracted below to a very narrowly winged petiole, maximum cauline leaves with blade 18.0 cm. wide, the petiole, from the confluence, 5.0 cm. long, leaves of the inflorescence abruptly reduced; the upper surface very densely and coarsely strumose-setose, the strumae unusually large, the lower surface very densely scabrous-hispid, with erect, sharp trichomes with a very conspicuous bulbous base, texture of the leaf exceedingly coarse, thick, rigid; the inflorescence a cyme, usually 3–5 heads; the disc about 1.5 cm. in diam., rays not seen; corollas of the disc yellow, cylindrical, the lobes slightly pubescent, the limb subglabrous, the base and the tube pubescent with short, comparatively coarse hairs; the achene ample, dark brown, brown-villous on the upper half; the pappus two narrowly lanceolate awns without other scales; the chaff ample, subentire, the margin slightly and shallowly lacerate, the tip narrowly acute, it and the keel thinly pubescent; the involucre hemispheric, very compact; the bracts broadly ovate, acuminate, subglabrous, the outer with a few very short hispid trichomes on the midrib, but often quite naked, the inner usually thinly short-pubescent toward the base, somewhat ciliate below, erect, appressed; the roots coarse, woody, not numerous; the rhizomes slender, numerous, profusely branched, often 1.0 m. or more in length, the distal portion enlarged, the terminal producing one or more well-developed buds.

Common on rocky hillsides in Kansas, probably also elsewhere in that vicinity, in similar situations.

Type. — Watson 744, highway between Garrison and Cleborne, Kansas.

H. severus is as plainly a relative of *H. rigidus* and *H. laetiflorus* as it is plainly distinct from those species. Its exceedingly harsh, coarse pubescence, acuminate bracts, broadly ovate saliently serrate leaves, and yellow disc are its chief claims to distinction.

79. H. Besseyi J. M. Bates. Am. Bot., 20 : 16. 1914.

(Plate LXVII)

Perennial; stem 1–1.5 m. high, densely scabrous-hispid, especially below the nodes, simple to the inflorescence, light green, about 0.5 cm. in diam. at the base; leaves prevailingly opposite, sometimes the upper ones alternate, ovate, thick, firm, acute or slightly acuminate, entire or serrate, densely and so profusely resin-dotted as to give the lower surface a yellowish tint, abruptly contracted to a short, very narrowly winged petiole, usually about 14.0 cm. long, including petiole, and 5.0 cm. wide, but variable in size and texture, light green; inflorescence 3–5 heads on short, stout, densely hispid peduncles 2–3.0 cm. long, the inflorescence appearing condensed; heads medium, about 1.5 cm. across the rather convex disc; corollas of the disc bright yellow, the lobes puberulent, base of the throat villous, the tube glabrous and very short; the achene pubescent above; the pappus two lanceolate awns without intermediate scales; the chaff ample, obscurely 3-cuspidate, the tips and keel villous, and densely resin-dotted; the involucral bracts lanceolate-acuminate, about equal to the disc, or a little longer, densely, usually canescently, hispid and resin-dotted, very loose, the tips more or less recurved.

Nebraska.

Type. — Bates 5816½ and 5382, Red Cloud, Nebraska; personally examined.

This species is, as Bates says, closely related to *H. subcanescens*, but I cannot help wishing that I knew exactly how close this relationship is. Those specimens that present root parts seem to have been pulled up bodily, breaking off the tips of roots and rhizomes, and the author's statement of the root parts is purely negative, "not strongly tuberous." *H. Besseyi* differs from *H. subcanescens,* its nearest relative, in its thicker leaves, the densely resinous lower surface of the leaves, its more uniformly rough stem, its denser pubescence, and its contracted inflorescence.

80. **H. subcanescens** (Gray), comb. nov.

H. tuberosus var. *subcanescens* Gray. Syn. Fl., 1:280. 1884.

Perennial; stem stout, erect, 1–1.5 m. high, simple to the inflorescence, or in vigorous plants somewhat ramose above, scabrous-hispid, often densely, very rough; leaves opposite, very rarely the uppermost alternate, ovate-lanceolate, sometimes ovate, acute, rarely a little acuminate, serrate or serrulate, sometimes obscurely, the blade tapering below to a more or less winged petiole, 12–20.0 cm. long, including petiole, by 4–7.0 cm. wide, the petiole from the confluence of the lateral nerves 2–4.0 cm. long; texture of leaf normally thick, firm, the upper surface densely scabrous-setose, the lower surface densely, spreading, strigose-hispid, paler, subcanescent; the inflorescence cymose, usually few-flowered, often only one; heads 1–1.5 cm. across the disc, the rays 2–2.5 cm. long; corollas of the disc florets yellow, cylindrical, the lobes and limb puberulent, the base densely, and the tube obviously, pubescent, the tube comparatively long; the achene slightly villous at the summit; the pappus two slender awns with greatly enlarged and laciniate bases, rarely narrow accessory paleae at the sides of the principal awns; the chaff 3-cuspidate, the lateral cusps small and very acute, the middle cusp acute, tips and keel pubescent; the involucre broadly campanulate; the bracts somewhat narrowly lanceolate, very dark green, a little longer than the disc, loose but reflexed only in age, slightly hispidulous toward the tip, ciliate; the roots coarsely fibrous; the rhizomes very slender, numerous, normally short, 1–2.0 dm. long, terminating abruptly in a well-defined tuber 2–5.0 cm. thick, the rhizomes frequently branched.

Abundant in moist ground, chiefly in rich soil, Wisconsin, northern Illinois, and westward.

Type. — A specimen collected in Minnesota by Kennicot. I have not seen the type, which is, I believe, in the Gray Herbarium.

H. subcanescens is, of course, very closely related to *H. tuberosus*, and Gray considered it a variety of that species, but it is at least a very distinct variety, and in my judgment is entitled to specific rank. Its leaves are almost invariably opposite, the lower surface densely pubescent, the texture thick and somewhat coarse, while those of *H. tuberosus* are normally alternate, thinly pubescent beneath, and much thinner. The latter species also has a large, many-flowered paniculate inflorescence, while that of *H. subcanescens* is small, cymose, and few-flowered. *H. subcanescens* is also a near relative of *H. Besseyi*, which has coarser leaves, very short petiole, and is much more densely pubescent, especially on the involucral bracts.

Our description of *H. subcanescens* was taken from Ward's specimen, cited by Gray in his original description. It was collected at Ft. Stevenson, North Dakota. Other excellent specimens are: Sheldon, Ottertail Co., Minnesota; Hapeman, Minden, Nebraska; Baker 42, Scotts Bluff Co., Nebraska.

It is very difficult to be absolutely certain of one's indentification of the tuber-bearing sunflowers, and it is so much easier simply to yank up the plant than to dig it up, that most of our specimens do not present the root-system. However, I believe Wheeler 576 and 566, from Houston Co., Minnesota, belong here, although the stems are glabrescent toward the base and the leaves very round and distinctly petioled. Here also I would place a specimen from Decorah, Iowa, collector not named, and two specimens collected by M. E. Jones, Aug. 7 and Aug. 22, 1877, from Grinnell, Iowa, Thornber, from Brookings, South Dakota; R. A. Harper, Neligh, Nebraska; Sandberg 942, and Geo. B. Aiton, both from Hennepin Co., Minnesota. B. C. Taylor's specimens from Center City, Minnesota, Nos. 1586 and 4593, both collected in August, 1892, apparently belong here in spite of the very short petiole.

The collections of J. H. Schuette, vicinity of Benderville, Brown Co., Wisconsin, are of very great interest, and apparently belong under *H. subcanescens*. The stem is a bright red-purple in most of these plants, and the roots are very similar to those of the type, and the broken rhizomes also suggest this species, but not one specimen has an entire rhizome. The Schuette specimens are numbered 70, 56, 18, and 70, 56, 20, and are all from Brown Co., Wisconsin. I believe these plants are *H. subcanescens;* if they are not, they are an unrecognized species. Reference has already been made to the unusual richness of Helianthus forms in Wisconsin, Minnesota, Iowa, and vicinity.

81. **H. mollissimus,** sp. nov.

H. tuberosus var. *subcanescens* Gray. Syn. Fl., 1: 280. 1884, in part.
H. doronicoides lancifolius Engelm. in herb.

(Plate LXVIII)

Perennial; stem stout, erect, probably 2–3.0 m. high, ramose, the branches often long, scabrous-hispid with spreading, strigose hairs; lower cauline leaves very large, ovate, acuminate, serrate, abruptly contracted below to a scarcely winged, partly distinct petiole, blade, from the confluence of the lateral, nerves 20–24.0 cm. long by 11.5 cm. wide, the petiole 4–6.0 cm. from the confluence; becoming narrower above, the blade more broadly decurrent, less abruptly contracted, these 20–23.0 cm. long, including petiole, by 7–8.0 cm. wide; those of the branches oblong-lanceolate, about 15.0 cm. long, including petiole, by 3.0 cm. wide, upper surface densely scabrous-setose, deep green, the lower surface pale with dense, rather coarse tomentum, soft to the touch; opposite below, alternate above, those of the branches mostly opposite; inflorescence loosely paniculate from the apices of the stem and branches, peduncles rather short, 4–7.0 cm., mostly with one or two small leaves; heads showy, disc 1–1.5 cm. in diam., the rays 3–4.0 cm. long; corollas of the disc florets yellow, cylindrical, glabrous except the very pubescent base; the achenes obovate, conspicuously narrowed toward the base, very villous at the apex, otherwise glabrous; the pappus two broadly lanceolate awns without other scales; chaff 3-cuspidate, pubescent on tip and keel; acute, lateral cusps small; the involucre hemispheric; the bracts lanceolate, acuminate, attenuate, equal to or a little longer than the disc, densely hispid, loose but not reflexed. Root-system not seen.

Kansas, Missouri, Ohio, Illinois.

Type. — Glattfelter, in the herbarium of the Missouri Botanical

Garden, No. 113,893. Another identical specimen, No. 113,892, is dated 1890; No, 113,893 is dated Sept. 11, 1892. The exact locality is not stated on either sheet.

In habit and leaf-shape, *H. mollissimus* resembles *H. tuberosus*, but it seems to be a more generally ramose plant than the latter. The absence of root parts on any of the collections makes it impossible to say how close its relationship to *H. tuberosus* is, but it is evidently close. The most conspicuous feature of *H. mollissimus* is the dense tomentum of the lower surface of the leaves. The opposite arrangement and the oblong character of the leaves of the branches are also characteristic. The recognition of this species in herbaria is made difficult by the fact that most of the collections consist merely of a branch with its inflorescence, and narrow oblong leaves. This is the case with the Engelmann specimen, cited by Gray and mentioned in synonymy, which was collected near St. Louis in 1843. The following are good examples of *H. mollissimus:* Hall, Athens, Illinois, two collections, unnumbered and therefore impossible of specification, one labeled *H. rigidus*, re-identified by Sherff as *H. giganteus*, the other labeled *H. doronicoides;* Baker, Nos. 15,318.1 and 15,277, St. Louis in Forest Park; and Baker 15,291, labeled *H. Maximiliani*, collected in St. Louis; a collection from Paola, Kansas, by Dr. J. H. Oyster; Rev. John Davis 3,811, Mainland Park, Hannibal, Missouri; a specimen from Dayton, Ohio, collector not stated.

This species differs from the specimens cited by Gray in support of his *H. tuberosus subcanescens* as widely as, perhaps even more widely than, it does from the well-known *H. tuberosus*. I looked for specimens in the type locality in 1923, but failed to find them. It would be of interest to know whether this plant is or is not a tuber-bearer.

82. H. tuberosus L. Sp. Pl., 905. 1753.

H. esculentus Warcz. Allg. Gartenz., 20 : 293. 1852.
H. vicetinus Turra ex Zang., Atti Soc. Sci. Nat. Milan, 11 : 389. 1868.
H. serotinus Tausch. Flora, 11 : 504. 1828.

Perennial; stem stout, erect, 1.5–2.5 m. high, ramose, sulcate, scabrous-hispid, rarely subglabrous, sometimes glabrescent toward the base; leaves normally opposite on the lower one fourth to one third of the stem and alternate above, occasionally all opposite, especially when plants are crowded or in unfavorable habitats; normally ovate or broadly ovate-lanceolate, sometimes broadly oblong-lanceolate, always acuminate, dentate or serrate-dentate, abruptly contracted below the confluence of the lateral nerves and very narrowly decurrent on the petiole usually to its base, though often so narrowly as to be obscure; extremely variable in size but usually large, the blade from the confluence of the lateral nerves 10–20.0 cm. long by 7–15.0 cm. wide, the petiole from the confluence 4–9.0 cm. long; texture of the leaves about normal, thinnish, not at all coarse; the upper surface bright green, scabrous-setose, the lower surface more or less densely pubescent with rather softly hispid hairs, not rough to the touch; the inflorescence paniculate, the heads normally numerous and very handsome, characterized, in general terms, by a small disc and long, broad, bright yellow rays; the disc usually about 1.0 cm. in diam., rarely more than 1.5 cm., the rays 2.5–4.0 cm. long, often 1.0 cm. wide, numerous; corollas of the disc florets yellow, broadly cylindrical, glabrous except the very pubescent base, the tube short; the achene turgid, usually dark, either glabrous or a little pubescent at the summit; the pappus two narrowly lanceolate awns without other scales; the chaff 3-cuspidate, all three cusps narrowly acute, or the middle cusp slightly acuminate, all pubescent on tip and keel; the involucre hemispheric or sometimes broadly campanulate; the bracts linear-lanceolate, often attenuate, usually more or less short-appressed-pubescent, ciliate, very dark green unless the color is obscured by the pubescence, extremely variable in length, but usually from a little to a great deal longer than the disc, usually loose, the tips somewhat reflexed when they are only a *little* longer than the disc, but loosely erect when they are much longer; the roots coarsely fibrous, woody, abundant; the rhizomes very slender at the proximal end, bearing tubers at the distal end, which are of greatly varying form and size, both rhizomes and tubers usually branched, the tubers more often simple.

Chiefly along water courses and in old fields and open woods, in almost any soil, throughout North America at least east of the Rocky Mts. Usually abundant, frequently cultivated.

Type. — In the Linnaean Herbarium. I have not seen the type specimen, but I have an excellent photograph of it.

H. tuberosus has been in cultivation since before the discovery of America. The tubers are abundant, often large, agreeable in flavor to most people, readily digested, of doubtful nutritive value to the human race, but of great nutritive value to herbivorous animals. Its wide distribution is explained by its ancient cultivation.

I have never failed to find *H. tuberosus* in any part of the country that I have visited, and while the range of its variability is considerable, it can usually be recognized without difficulty. The disc is unusually narrow for the length of the rays, and the latter are a deep, golden yellow. The upper leaves and the branches of the inflorescence are normally alternate. In any group of *H. tuberosus* not more than one plant in perhaps fifty would have opposite leaves. The pubescence of the lower surface of the leaves is always soft to the touch, and usually very evenly distributed, but there is some variation in degree. The presence of resin dots on the lower surface is too variable to be significant from the standpoint of classification.

The tuber-bearing sunflowers form a small but very interesting group, and are well worth intensive study. The more usual forms of *H. tuberosus* are readily recognizable from the aërial parts of the plant, but so great are the variations and possibly also the response to edaphic conditions, that it is difficult to place many specimens with certainty. Dr. Lucy has apparently made large collections in Chemung Co., New York, and along the headwaters of the Susquehanna River. Most of his specimens are labeled *H. strumosus* which they plainly are not — I think they are *H. tuberosus*. But it seems very unlikely that a man would collect *H. tuberosus* over a considerable area, and during a considerable length of time, under the impression that it was *H. strumosus* without sometime discovering, if only by accident, that the plant bore tubers. Thus psychology here plays havoc with systematic botany. Why cannot collectors understand that the underground parts of a plant are just as truly an integral part of the individual as the flower! I had intended on my eastern trip to search the fields of Chemung Co., New York, and to find out what the roots of these plants are like, but lack of time made it necessary to omit this part of my trip.

I am quite conscious that my treatment of *H. tuberosus* is very inadequate, and I intend to devote my spare time to the preparation of a paper on the tuber-bearers of this genus, from the standpoint of their systematic position. In the meantime it must suffice if I mention a few of the forms that seem to me as possibly worthy of specific rank, reserving the right, however, to reverse myself, if necessary, after further study:

(1) The first of these is a specimen taken from a country dooryard near Raceland, Louisiana. The leaves are obscurely denticulate, scabrous-hispid beneath, and the involucral bracts ovate, acute, none of which characters are typical of *H. tuberosus*.

(2) A specimen from North Carolina, between Greensboro and Beedsville, has rhombic leaves, acute at both ends, the confluence of the lateral nerves very low and the angles of the confluence very acute, and a markedly campanulate involucre, the tubers slender and much branched.

(3) A specimen from Chester, South Carolina, taken from a very sunny flood-plain of the river, a tall, very vigorous plant with well-developed tubers, has a perfectly glabrous stem, as did all the individuals of this group.

It is also of great interest that large and well-developed tubers occur on plants plainly identifiable as *H. laetiflorus*. My own are the only collections that I have seen with this peculiarity, although it is impossible to tell how many of the specimens of *H. laetiflorus* at my disposal would have shown that they were tuber-bearing, had the *whole* plant been collected. It is also true that many other specimens of *H. laetiflorus* do not bear tubers. I can offer no explanation at the present time, but hope to be able to do so soon. Specimens of *H. laetiflorus*, or at least, plants so identifiable at present but bearing well-developed tubers, have been collected in Nebraska, between Humbolt and Auburn; in Iowa, near Creston; in Michigan, at Paw Paw, here plainly a horticultural form; in

Kansas, at Arkansas City. These plants seem to have nothing in common with *H. tuberosus* except the tuber-habit, and their relation to the non-tuber-bearing plants of their own group and to the typical *H. tuberosus* is still undetermined.

An even more perplexing problem is raised by a specimen collected by Dr. E. A. Bessey near Jefferson, Iowa. This is a tall, vigorous plant, whose aërial parts are all perfectly typical of *H. tuberosus.* The leaves are somewhat densely pubescent beneath, as in *H. subcanescens,* but alternate and very large. The roots are as might be expected in *H. tuberosus,* but the rhizomes are very slender, up to 1.0 m. in length, with a small terminal bud not at all enlarged. Externally this plant bears a close resemblance to Dr. Lucy's specimens of Chemung Co., New York. There is just a possibility that this is the *H. strumosus* var. *mollis* T. & G., *Fl. N. A.*, 2 : 327, 1843. The actual facts in regard to this variety cannot be settled by reference to the type, unless one is fortunate enough to secure a plant from the type locality, identical with the type and presenting the root-system in its entirety. *H. strumosus* var. *mollis* is first described in the *Flora of North America* cited above. No collection nor specimen is cited, and I suppose there is accordingly no type. In the *Synoptical Flora,* also, no specimens are cited. I have seen, however, in the Gray Herbarium, a specimen collected by Wolff, Aug. 30, 1880, at Canton, Illinois, which was used by Gray in the preparation of the *Synoptical Flora,* and which is labeled by him *H. strumosus* var. *mollis.* This specimen resembles the Bessey specimen in pubescence and floral characters, but not in leaf shape nor in the cauline characters, and it also presents only the upper stem. In view of the possible relation of this specimen to *H. tuberosus,* nothing can be said about it expect that it is "different." It is unquestionably nearer to *H. tuberosus* than to *H. strumosus,* whether it is a tuber-bearer or not. The identity of this variety of *H. strumosus* must, therefore, be determined only after further study, and observations in the field.

Professor T. D. A. Cockerell has published a number of varieties of *H. tuberosus,* based principally on tuber characters, which are of horticultural interest, but not necessary in a systematic study.

83. **H. membranaceus,** sp. nov.

(Plate LXIX)

Perennial; stem slender, erect, 1–2.0 m. high, mostly simple to the inflorescence, sometimes ramose above, glabrous or rarely obscurely and remotely strigose-hispid, rarely scabrous-hispid; leaves mostly alternate, in medium or small plants frequently opposite, broadly oblong-lanceolate, acuminate, serrate, tapering below, the blade decurrent almost or quite to the base of the petiole, 8–17.0 cm. long by 2–5.0 cm. wide; the upper surface thinly strumose-setulose, the lower surface glabrous or evenly, long hirsute-hispid, pubescence of the lower surface extremely variable, thin, almost membranaceous in texture, mostly concolor, often a little paler beneath; inflorescence open-paniculate, the peduncles rather long, the heads usually few, often only one; the disc 1–2.0 cm. in diam., the rays 2–3.0 cm. long; corollas of the disc florets yellow, the lobes and limb slightly pubescent, the base more so, the tube short and glabrous; the achene glabrous, the pappus two broadly lanceolate awns without other scales; the chaff 3-cuspidate, the lateral cusps small, pubescent on tip and keel; the involucre hemispheric; the bracts linear-lanceolate, sparingly pubescent, very ciliate with long, spreading cilia; the roots slender, elongated fusiform, often fascicled; no rhizomes, crown-buds abundant.

Minnesota and Wisconsin to Missouri.

Type. — A specimen collected in Itasca Co., Minnesota, by J. H. Sandberg, Aug., 1891, in the herbarium of the University of Minnesota.

H. membranaceus is similar to *H. borealis*, especially in the root-system, and is a close relative also of *H. giganteus*. It differs from these by its larger leaves, the thinner texture of the leaf, the greater smoothness of lower surface, the greater part of which is almost glabrous. In those individuals with the lower surface of the leaves pubescent, the surface is smooth to the touch, and occasional leaves are shining. The inflorescence is small, very often only four or five heads, and the rays are longer than those of *H. giganteus*.

84. H. altissimus L. Sp. Pl., ed. 2, 1278. 1763.

(Plate LXX)

H. giganteus var. *altissimus* (L.) Farwell. Rept. Mich. Acad. Sci., p. 180. 1915.

Perennial; stem erect, 1–2.5 m. high, simple to the inflorescence, rarely ramose from the base, spreading strigose-hispid at least above, usually glabrescent below, often very smooth, stout, often 1.5 cm. in diam. at the base, usually dark red-purple, extremely variable in stem color; leaves oblong or sometimes oblong-lanceolate, pointed at both ends, rather firm but papery in texture, short-acuminate at both ends, the blade broadly decurrent to the base of the petiole, usually dark green, not much paler beneath, sharply strumose-setose above, somewhat remotely strigose-hispid beneath with long hairs, principally on the nerves, spreading, never appressed, never dense, serrate-dentate, rarely subentire, alternate; inflorescence a large open panicle, except in small plants; heads showy, the disc about 1.5 cm. in diam., rays and disc florets light yellow, the rays rarely more than 2 or 2.5 cm. long; chaff 3-cuspidate, carinate, somewhat pubescent at the tip and on the keel; the achene glabrous, with a pappus of two lanceolate awns without intermediate scales; involucral bracts lanceolate, a little longer than the disc, loose, often reflexed, appressed-pubescent on the surface, not densely, the margin ciliate with long, spreading cilia; roots very thick, coarse, woody, abruptly contracted to a long tapering tip; the rhizomes very short, rarely more than 5–6 cm. long, crown-buds very abundant.

Wet, rich soil in sunny situations, normal range, the northern states east of the Mississippi; sporadically elsewhere.

Type. — In the Linnaean Herbarium in London. Photograph examined.

This species is a very close relative of *H. giganteus* L. and is considered by most botanists as conspecific with it. Mr. Farwell, in 1915, reduced the Linnaean species to a variety of *H. giganteus*. My own observations in the field, however, have led me to consider it a separate species, rather than a variety or state of *H. giganteus*. The two species are frequently found in close proximity, which renders it improbable that their differences are environmental responses, and it does not appear that there is any gain in clearness or consistency by recognizing the group as a variety rather than a species.

In *H. altissimus* the leaves are invariably oblong, and the ratio of length to width is smaller. The most usual dimensions of the leaves might be stated as about 12.0 cm. long by 4.0 cm. wide. This plant grows abundantly in the prairies north of Dowagiac, Michigan, and most of the leaves would answer to the dimensions just suggested, but I found one plant with cauline leaves 18.0 cm. long and 5.0 cm. wide. I have seen no specimen of *H. giganteus* with so small a foliar ratio, nor with leaves so large. Another significant difference between *H. giganteus* and *H. altissimus* is the tendency of the latter to branch below the inflorescence proper, and in very vigorous plants, from the very base of the stem. My own collections of this species have been made at Edwardsburg, Michigan, three miles north of Dowagiac, Michigan; east of Grand Rapids, Michigan, on the Ada road; at Oceanside, Long Island; and Danbury, Connecticut. Here, also, I would place Topping, from Tennallytown, D. C.; Topping, Maryland Agricultural College; McFarland, Urbana, Ohio.

85. H. laetiflorus Pers. Syn., 2 : 476. 1807.

H. tricuspis Ell. Sketch, 2 : 422. 1824.
H. scaberrimus Ell. Sketch 2 : 423. 1824, not Benth. 1844.
H. diffusus Sims. Bot. Mag., 45 : t. 2020. 1818.
H. missouricus Spreng. Nov. Prov., p. 21. 1819.
H. missouriensis Schwein. ex Nutt., Trans. Am. Phil. Soc., N. S., 4 : 368. 1841.

Perennial; stem stout, erect, 1–2.0 m. high, simple rarely ramose, purplish, scabrous-hispid, the pubescence usually spreading or retrorse; leaves opposite, the uppermost sometimes alternate, broadly lanceolate, acute, serrate or serrate-dentate, the blade narrowed below and very narrowly decurrent on the petiole usually to the base of the petiole, in unusually large leaves, decurrent only part way and the petiole distinct near the stem, 18–28.0 cm. long, including petiole, by 4–7.0 cm. wide, thick and firm in texture, strumose-scabrous above, strumose-hispid beneath, the pubescence of the midrib beneath normally somewhat retrorse; the inflorescence normally a few large heads, solitary on very long subnaked peduncles, rarely paniculate; the heads very showy, the disc 1.5–2.0 cm. in diam., the rays 2–3.0 cm. long, very deep yellow; corollas of the disc florets yellow, the base villous, the tube glabrous; the achene pubescent above; the pappus of the sterile ray achenes normally three long, broadly lanceolate awns, of the fertile disc achenes, two broadly lanceolate, pubescent awns, with accessory awns at each side of the principal awns; the chaff ample, 3-cuspidate, the lateral cusps small, the middle cusp acute, tip and keel pubescent; the involucre cylindrical, slightly campanulate; the bracts broadly linear-lanceolate, acute, slightly pubescent, very rarely glabrous, ciliate, the lower cilia normally longer; the roots woody, coarsely fibrous; the rhizomes remarkable for the length and the enormous number produced, normally slender, frequently bearing tubers.

Illinois and Missouri east to Georgia, not common.

Type. — I have no information concerning the type; it is probably either at Paris or Geneva.

This very handsome sunflower is rare in its native habitat, and does not often appear in herbaria, but several horticultural forms have been evolved. It is a close relative of *H. rigidus*, but is in my opinion abundantly distinct. Its chief departures from *H. rigidus* are: (1) the disc corollas have yellow lobes; (2) the leaves are less rigid, more deeply serrate, less variable, and the pubescence of the midrib beneath is retrorse, not appressed as in *H. rigidus;* (3) the ray achenes have large and conspicuous awns; and (4) its rhizomes are far more abundant.

See also discussion of *H. rigidus.*

86. H. resinosus Small. Fl. S. E. U. S., p. 1269. 1903.

Perennial; stem slender, erect, 1–2.0 m. high, mostly about 1.2 m. retrorsely hispid, ramose; leaves opposite below, alternate above, in small plants all opposite, ovate, or oblong-ovate, acuminate, or narrowly acute, narrowly sessile by decurrence of the blade upon the petiole, hispid above with rather long hairs, or in large plants, strumose-setose, tomentose beneath, not densely, and copiously resin-dotted, thin in texture, not much paler beneath, 6–8.0 cm. long, including petiole, by 2–3.5 cm. wide; the inflorescence a few heads on rather long, slender peduncles, either cymose or paniculate; heads 1–1.6 cm. across the disc, the rays 2–2.5 cm. long, light yellow, resin-dotted beneath, and pubescent on the nerves; corollas of the disc florets yellow, the lobes and base conspicuously pubescent, the tube short and glabrous; the achene glabrous; the pappus two broadly lanceolate awns without other scales; the chaff ample, 3-cuspidate, the middle cusp larger, the chaff very pubescent on the tip and keel; the involucre hemispheric; the bracts linear-lanceolate, hispid, ciliate, very loose, a little longer than the disc in young flowers, becoming greatly elongated and abruptly reflexed at full anthesis; roots coarsely fibrous, rather long; crown-buds produced at the stem base, rhizomes uncertain.

Northern Florida, Apalachicola, Gadsden.

Type. — Nash 2581, Gadsden Co., Florida; in the herbarium of the New York Botanical Garden; examined.

After a very minute comparison of *H. resinosus* and the various specimens of *H. tomentosus*, my final opinion is that they are distinct, but they are unquestionably very closely related. In fact, an almost continuous line of intergrades can be formed leading from the extreme of *H. tomentosus*, as exemplified by the Bat Cave specimen, to the other end, at which stands Small's type of *H. resinosus*. The latter species, however, is readily recognized by the characters that lead me to judge that it is a distinct genetical entity, to wit: the thin leaves, the long pubescence of the upper surface of the leaves, the marked tendency toward opposite arrangement of the leaves, the longer peduncles, the more abrupt reflexion of the involucral bracts, the tendency to the ovate or oblong shape in the leaf.

Besides the type collection, there are several sheets of this species collected by Chapman at "Apalago," which I take to be Apalachicola. I have not been able to locate "Apalago."

87. H. doronicoides Lam. Encyc., 3 : 84. 1789.

(Plate LXXI)

H. pubescens Vahl. Symb., 2 : 92. 1791.
H. Hookeri G. Don. Lond. Hort. Brit., 358. 1827.
H. pilosus Tausch. Fl., 11 : 502. 1828.
H. cinereus var. *Sullivanti* T. & G. Fl. N. A., 2 : 324. 1842.

Perennial; stem tall, stout, erect, 1–2 m. high, softly often densely hirsute-pubescent, simple to the inflorescence; leaves opposite to or a little above the middle stem, rarely all opposite, the upper leaves and branches of the inflorescence alternate, broadly oval-lanceolate, acuminate, rather finely serrate, rarely entire, the lateral nerves confluent a little below the middle, and the blade broadly decurrent to the base of the petiole, mostly slightly acuminate below, scabrous-setose or hispid above, softly and usually densely subtomentose beneath, pubescence of the midrib spreading or even retrorse, mostly 12–15.0 cm. long by 5–6.0 cm. wide, frequently smaller; inflorescence an open, lax panicle, branches ascending, peduncles leafy, 1–4-flowered, usually densely-softly pubescent; heads showy, the disc about 1.7 cm. in diam., rays oval, 2–3 cm. long, bright yellow; corollas of the disc yellow, the lobes puberulent, base villous; the achene glabrous; pappus of two broadly lanceolate awns with lacerate bases, and often an accessory palea on either side of the awn; chaff ample, carinate, very pubescent, 3-cuspidate, lateral cusps small; involucre hemispheric, the bracts linear-lanceolate, often narrowly, densely hispid-hirsute and spreading ciliate, mostly reflexed, usually longer than the disc; roots woody, coarse; rhizomes short, stout.

Illinois to New Jersey, evidently rare.

I have not been able to locate the type with certainty.

H. doronicoides is a very close relative of *H. tomentosus,* and is distinguished from that species chiefly by its sessile leaves, longer rhizomes, and softer pubescence. Its tendency to produce resin on the under surface of the leaves is also much less constant.

I have frequently seen races or strains of *H. doronicoides* in cultivated gardens and in nurseries, but I have never collected it in its natural habitat, and conclude, therefore, that it is rare.

It grows in a garden opposite the Wayside Inn at Sudbury, Massachusetts, and in the Harvard Botanical Garden, where it is labeled *H. hirsutus.* I have also seen a specimen from the Kew Gardens. C. A. Gross has collected it in an "old field" at Victoria, Gloucester Co., New Jersey. Of the specimens collected in their native habitat, the following may be mentioned: E. Hall, Barrens, near Spring Creek, Sangamon Co., Illinois; Mosely, near Kimball, Erie Co., Ohio; Sturtevant, Nonquit, Massachusetts.

The Mosely specimen satisfies Torrey and Gray's description of their *H. cinereus* var. *Sullivanti,* the type of which is Sullivant's collection from Columbus, Ohio, about 150 miles south of Erie Co., Ohio.

H. mollis and *H. tomentosus* are the closest relatives of *H. doronicoides* and the relation is very close indeed. They form a continuous line in which these three species, in their extreme forms, are the high points. In *mollis* and *doronicoides* the leaves are always sessile, in *tomentosus,* the petiole is, in some cases, so narrowly winged as to appear distinct; *mollis* has longer peduncles, and more densely pubescent and usually shorter, erect bracts; *tomentosus* is resin-dotted and its pubescence coarser, more hispid; *mollis* is lower, less ramose, frequently tufted. All have very short, stout rhizomes.

The synonymy of *H. doronicoides,* as suggested above, represents the author's opinion gathered from illustrations and descriptions. To unravel all the manifold misinterpretations of the post-Linnaean authors would constitute a thesis in itself.

I have not seen Vahl's specimen of his *pubescens,* but the illustration No. 2778 in the *Botanical Magazine,* referred to by De Candolle, is a typical *H. doronicoides,* although I have never seen one with leaves so large. The variations suggested by Torrey and Gray on p. 327 can all be identified, and no doubt many more added, but they are unquestionably nothing more than evidences that no two things in the world are exactly alike.

88. **H. formosus,** sp. nov.

(Plate LXXII)

Perennial; stem stout, erect, 1–2.5 m. high, somewhat ramose above, light green, sulcate, glaucous, but scabrous or scabrous-hispid, especially at the nodes; leaves large, mostly opposite, the upper often alternate, ovate, ovate-lanceolate, or broadly lanceolate, very narrowly acute, rarely slightly acuminate, mostly entire, rarely serrulate, thick, firm, the blade narrowly decurrent to the base of the petiole, rarely the petiole distinct toward the base, bright green and strumose-setulose above, not densely, lower surface conspicuously paler and glaucous, the veins very prominent and copiously spreading-hispid, otherwise glabrous or subglabrous, rarely a few coarse scabra scattered about, mostly 17.0 cm. long, including petiole, by 4–5.0 cm. wide, somewhat variable in size, but never small; inflorescence a few heads, solitary on long stout peduncles from the upper axils; heads showy, the disc 1–2.0 cm. in diam., the rays deep yellow, about 2.0 cm. long; corollas of the disc florets yellow, base pubescent; the achene brown, pubescent toward the apex; the pappus two very large, lanceolate awns, enlarged and fimbriate at the base, acuminate; the chaff 3-cuspidate, the lateral cusps small, the middle cusp acute, hispid-pubescent on the tip and keel; the involucre hemispheric; the bracts broadly lanceolate-acuminate, a little longer than the disc, subglabrous, more or less reflexed. Lower stem and root-system not seen.

Missouri, Oklahoma, Illinois, probably also toward the east.

Type. — Rev. John Davis 3274, Mississippi Bluffs, south of Hannibal, Missouri, sheet No. 887,689, in the Missouri Botanical Garden.

This is a very well marked species, with thick, elegantly formed, large leaves. The glaucous lower surface, very pale green, glabrous except on the very hispid nerves, and the few-flowered but elegant inflorescence combine to give it its distinctive character. Its nearest relative is, perhaps, *H. strumosus*.

Very similar to the type are: J. Davis 3018, 6440, 23, 29, Sherff 1043 — all from near St. Louis, Missouri; and E. J. Hill

105, Oak Lawn, Illinois. In the Hill specimen the leaves are opposite and the inflorescence cymose. G. W. Stevens 2390 and 2391, Ottawa Co., Oklahoma, has the primary branches of the inflorescence cymose, the secondary alternate. Rev. John Davis 3355, Adams Co., Illinois, has crowded leaves, opposite, and a cymose inflorescence; the leaves are broadly lanceolate. Here also belongs Engelmann's specimen 1843 (or is it 63?) from Riehl's, southwest of St. Louis; the stem is nearly glabrous. Bush 7869, Morton, Missouri, is an unusually fine specimen. C. F. Baker 15,291, St. Louis, has rather thin leaves, but seems well within the species.

89. H. saxicola Small. Fl. S. E. U. S., p. 1268. 1903.

(Plate LXXIII)

Perennial; stem slender, 0.8–1.5 m. high, rarely up to 2.0 m., glabrous, usually glaucous, often deep red-purple, sulcate, simple to the inflorescence or rarely ramose above; leaves usually alternate above, but arrangement unstable, ovate or broadly ovate-lanceolate, acuminate, serrulate (in the type) or serrate, blade rounded below to a partly distinct petiole, sparingly strumose-setose above, many of the strumae *not* bearing setae, deep green, the lower surface essentially glabrous and much paler, the principal nerves slightly hispid, 10–18.0 cm. long, including petiole, by 3–7.0 cm. wide; texture of the blade somewhat chartaceous, rather thin but firm; the inflorescence solitary or loosely paniculate; heads showy, the disc about 1.5 cm. in diam., the rays 2–2.5 cm. long, oval, acute; corollas of the disc florets yellow, broadly cylindrical, the lobes ample, deltoid-ovate, pubescent, the limb somewhat pubescent on the principal nerves, the broad base densely short-pubescent, the tube glabrous; the achene slender, dark brown, glabrous; the pappus two narrowly lanceolate awns, with expanded, lacerate bases without other scales; the chaff ample, carinate, the tip entire in outline, but lacerate a little below the apex on each side, tip acute, it and the keel pubescent; the involucre broadly campanulate, the bracts broadly lanceolate, somewhat acuminate, dull green, glabrous, rarely subglabrous, ciliate, somewhat longer than the disc, very loose, usually spreading or reflexed. The type specimen does not present the root-system, but some collections of my own, that I believe belong in the species, have fibrous roots, very long and slender, woody at the base; the rhizomes slender, 3–5.0 dm. long, usually more or less branched, with very small terminal buds.

Rocky places in and about low mountains, Virginia, North Carolina, Georgia.

Type. — A specimen collected by J. K. Small, on the summit of "Thomas Bald" near the North Carolina-Georgia Boundary, Aug. 19, 1893, in the herbarium of the New York Botanical Garden. I have compared my own collections with the type.

H. saxicola is, as the name indicates, a plant of rocky places and moderately high altitudes. The type is unquestionably distinct, and the collections that I have placed with it seem to me to possess the diagnostic characters of the species, although differing somewhat from the type in their morphological expression. Along the banks of the Etowa River, near Canton, Georgia, this species grows abundantly, and frequently attains a height of 2.0 m., and, except where densely crowded, is ramose above the middle. It is significant that the larger cauline leaves of these plants agree with the type in the matter of pubescence, but the upper leaves of the inflorescence are somewhat more pubescent beneath. This is also true of the type, although here the lower surface is, at most, very remotely pubescent. The achene and pappus of the Etowa River specimens are typical, but the chaff seems to be definitely 3-cuspidate. In this connection it must be remembered that in the type the margin of the chaff is conspicuously lacerate, and it is difficult to draw a line between a "lacerate" and a "cuspidate" margin. I also collected specimens that readily arrange themselves with *H. saxicola*, five miles south of Atlanta, Georgia; near Indian Springs, Georgia; near Franklinton, North Carolina; and near La Crosse, Virginia. There is also in the herbarium of the Missouri Botanical Garden, sheet No. 791,354, a specimen collected near Rome, Georgia, by Dr. Chapman, and labeled by him, *H. strumosus* var. *humilis*, which is unquestionably conspecific with the type.

Although this species seems to have a reasonably wide range, and was published twenty years ago, and is locally abundant, it is strange that the name appears in herbaria associated only with the original type collections, which apparently have been widely distributed.

H. saxicola is a close relative of that division of *H. strumosus* which is characterized by leaves, glabrous beneath, except on the nerves. It is sharply demarcated from the latter group by its alternate upper leaves, paniculate inflorescence, shorter petiole, and by the low degree of pubescence on the nerves beneath.

90. **H. brevifolius,** sp. nov.

(Plate LXXIV)

Perennial; stem stout, erect, 1–2.0 m. high, ramose above, sparingly scabrous, light green, striate; leaves mostly opposite, the uppermost and branches of the inflorescence alternate, ovate or oblong-ovate, acute, serrate, distinctly petiolate, the lateral nerves confluent very near the base of the blade, the latter about 8.0 cm. long by 3.0 cm. wide, the petiole 1.5–3.0 cm. long, texture of blade firm, thickish, short-strumose-setose above, evenly hispid and a little paler beneath, the upper cauline leaves not much reduced; the inflorescence a very open panicle, the branches long, the peduncles short, the latter 5.5–1.0 dm.; heads about 1.2 cm. across the disc, the rays about 2.0 cm. long; corollas of the disc florets yellow, subglabrous; the achene glabrous; the pappus two narrowly lanceolate awns without other scales; the chaff linear, subentire, the lateral cusps very obscure, the middle cusp acute, carinate, the outer pubescent on tip and keel, the inner subglabrous; the involucre hemispheric; the bracts linear-lanceolate, about as long as, or a little longer than, the disc, hispidulous, ciliate at the base. Root-system not seen.

Type. — A collection by Otto Hacker, near Richmond, Lake Co., Ohio, 1894, in the herbarium of Ohio State University.

The type is adequate except that it does not exhibit the root system. The two most striking characters are the small, distinctly petioled, evenly placed leaves, which are not reduced toward the apex, although smaller on the branches, and the inflorescence, with ascending branches 3–4.0 dm. long, bearing toward the apex 3–5 heads on peduncles of uneven length. Lake Co., Ohio, is readily accessible, and the species ought to be easily verifiable.

91. **H. leoninus,** sp. nov.

(Plate LXXV)

Perennial; stem stout, probably up to 3.0 m. high, sulcate, light green; glabrous, at least above, ramose; leaves opposite, the cauline leaves very large, deltoid-ovate, distinctly petiolate, 22.0 cm. long, excluding petiole, by 10.5 cm. wide, the petiole 2.5 cm. long, the lateral nerves confluent near the base of the blade; those of the branches smaller and somewhat narrower, about 7.5 cm. by 3.5 cm., the petiole distinct, 0.5 cm. long; the blade very thick, firm, coarse in texture, densely and coarsely scabrous above, and deep green; lower surface sparingly, unevenly, short-hispid, the pubescence very coarse but mostly short, the trichomes occasionally long, with a strumose base; concolor; the inflorescence cymose-paniculate, the branches very long, the peduncles slender, hispid; heads medium, about 1.6 cm. across the convex disc, the rays 2–3.0 cm. long; corollas of the disc florets yellow, subglabrous, the tube very short; the achene ample, turgid, brown, dull, glabrous; the pappus two lanceolate awns with a very expanded, fimbriate, but scarcely laciniate, base, without other scales; the chaff ample, linear, conspicuously 3-cuspidate, the lateral cusps long and acute, the middle cusp longer, narrowly acute, not conspicuously carinate, softly, rather short-pubescent on the back of all three cusps and on the keel; the involucre hemispheric; the bracts broadly lanceolate, slightly acuminate, sparingly hispidulous above the middle, sometimes also on the midrib, sparingly ciliate, a little longer than the disc, very loose, often reflexed, especially in age. Lower stem and root-system not seen.

Illinois, Kansas, and Missouri, evidently not common.

Type. — A specimen collected by M. C. Jensen, at Lake Forest,

Lake Co., Illinois, Sept., 1896, sheet No. 113,874, in the herbarium of the Missouri Botanical Garden.

H. leoninus is also represented by a specimen collected in Swope Park, Jackson Co., Missouri, Aug. 23, 1896, by K. K. Mackenzie, and by another specimen of the same collector, with smaller leaves, but characteristic pubescence, from Wyandotte Co., Kansas, Aug. 30, 1896. It is evidently a plant of drier ground or hillsides. It is especially unfortunate that none of our specimens present the root-system. This species is closely related to *H. divaricatus*, *H. chartaceus*, *H. hirsutus*, and *H. leptocaulis*. The conspicuously large, thick leaves, the 3-cuspidate chaff, the pubescence of the lower surface of the leaves, and its smooth stem constitute its chief claims for specific distinction.

92. **H. chartaceus,** sp. nov.

(Plate LXXVI)

Perennial; stem slender, erect, 1–2.5 m. high, very sparingly scabrous, more so toward the apex, mostly smooth below, apparently glabrescent; leaves opposite, ample, ovate, or broadly ovate-lanceolate, acuminate, serrate, abruptly contracted at the wide, rounded or cuneate base to distinct, relatively short petioles, the lateral nerves normally confluent at the base of the blade, maximum cauline leaves about 20.0 cm. long, excluding petiole, by 8.0 cm. wide, the petiole about 3.0 cm. long, the blade thin, chartaceous, light green, inclined to be shining, sharply strumose-setulose above, not densely, remotely hispid beneath with long, erect hairs from a more or less strumose base, the nerves very prominent on the lower surface, but not much more hispid than the surface, the petiole scabrous; the inflorescence solitary or cymose, 3–5 heads, rarely more, on short, hispid peduncles; heads not very showy, the disc about 1.5 cm. in diam., the rays rarely more than 2.0 cm. long, the peduncles proper 0.5–3–5.0 cm. long, heads often sessile; corollas of the disc florets yellow, the lobes slightly pubescent, the limb and the very short tube glabrous; the achene glabrous; the pappus two very acuminate, pubescent, lanceolate awns with a much enlarged, laciniate base, rarely with accessory paleae at the base of the awns; the chaff ample, carinate, 3-cuspidate, narrowly acute, pubescent on the tip and keel; the involucre hemispheric; the bracts somewhat broadly linear-lanceolate or lanceolate-acuminate, hispidulous, somewhat ciliate, a little longer than the disc, very loose, often spreading or recurved. Root-system not seen.

Copses and open woods, rather dry soil, Nebraska and Minnesota.

Type. — J. M. Bates 5247, collected near Weeping Water, Nebraska, Aug. 8, 1910. The type specimen is in the private herbarium of the Rev. J. M. Bates, Red Cloud, Nebraska.

H. chartaceus is a tall, shade-loving sunflower with large, thin leaves and a very contracted, cymose inflorescence. In many of its superficial characters it is suggestive of *H. divaricatus;* it is sharply demarcated by its ample, petiolate leaves. The specimen of the same number as the type in the New York Botanical Garden is perfectly typical and is to be considered a cotype. Other collections of this species are Sandberg, Hennepin Co., Minnesota, 1890, which is identical except that the leaves are somewhat cuneate-pointed below; and Geo. B. Aiton, Minnesota, locality not stated.

93. **H. virilis**, sp. nov.

(Plate LXXVII)

Perennial; stem stout, erect, tall, probably 1–2.0 m. high, ramose above, the branches closely ascending, stems and branches light green, very scabrous-hispid, with coarse, spreading or retrorse hairs; leaves prevailingly opposite, those of the upper stem, especially above the first branches, often alternate, mostly large, ovate, acuminate, serrate or serrulate, abruptly contracted below to a short, nearly distinct, stout petiole, the lateral nerves confluent very near the base of the blade, the latter 10–15.0 cm. long, excluding petiole, by 4–8.0 cm. wide, the petiole 0.5–2.5 cm. long and very scabrous, the upper surface very coarsely scabrous-setose, the lower surface strumose-hispid, the trichomes rather long and spreading, with a very conspicuous strumose base, the leaves nearly or quite concolor, and usually very thick and coarse in texture; the inflorescence cymose-paniculate, the peduncles very rough hispid and extremely variable in length, mostly long; the heads often large, the disc 1.5–2.0 cm. in diam., the rays 2–3.0 cm. long, oval, bright yellow; corollas of the disc florets yellow, the limb subglabrous, the lobes, base and the short tube more or less pubescent; the achene glabrous; the pappus two narrowly lanceolate awns with expanded very laciniate bases without other scales; the involucre hemispheric, the bracts broadly linear-lanceolate, hispidulous, ciliate, very loose, spreading and at length recurved, from a little to very much longer than the disc; the roots very coarse and woody; the rhizomes short, 1–2.0 dm. in length, very stout, light colored or white, the terminal bud ample.

Northern Texas, Kansas, Missouri, and Indiana.

Type. — A specimen collected in Wyandotte Co., Kansas, on Aug. 30, 1896, by Kenneth K. Mackenzie, sheet No. 64,398, in the herbarium of Kansas State Agricultural College, Manhattan, Kansas.

H. virilis represents the extreme development of that group of plants to which belong its near relatives *H. hirsutus*, *H. vernalis*, *H. chartaceus*, *H. leoninus*, and that morphologically variable species, *H. leptocaulis*. Closely resembling the type are Popenoe, from Topeka, Kansas; Hitchcock, from Anderson Co., Kansas; Kellermann, from Riley Co., Kansas; and Bergman, from the same locality. So, also, are several specimens collected near Dallas, Texas, by Reverchon, No. 3970, and a specimen by Rev. John Davis, No. 6129, collected near Mark Twain's Cave, Marion Co., Missouri. K. K. Mackenzie's specimen from Wyandotte Co., Kansas, June 18, 1895, in the herbarium of the Kansas State Agricultural College, is a smaller and smoother plant, but plainly belonging to this species, and is a very valuable adjunct to the type, as it illustrates the form assumed by plants of this species which for some reason or other, most probably shade, fail to attain their full stature. It is worthy of attention that this specimen of Mackenzie's, though small, does not resemble specimens of *H. leptocaulis* which are normally about the size of the plant under discussion. My own collection, No. 167, is an excellent example of this species, and was obtained about five miles north of Terre Haute, Indiana, in thick turf, over rich black soil by a roadside fence.

94. **H. arenicola,** sp. nov.

(Plates LXXVIII–LXXIX)

Perennial; stem stout, erect; 0.5–2.0 m. high, profusely ramose except when very small, very sparingly scabrous, often, in fact usually, glabrous, light green, striate-sulcate; leaves mostly opposite, the uppermost sometimes alternate in very vigorous plants, mostly ample, ovate or broadly ovate-lanceolate, acuminate, mostly serrate with low teeth, very small leaves entire, very large ones dentate, abruptly contracted below to a cuneate base and a partly distinct petiole, the blade often very rounded at the base, and rarely, in very large leaves, slightly subcordate, 10–25.0 cm. long, excluding petiole, 3–9.0 cm. wide, the petiole 0.5–2.0 cm. long and stout, nearly concolor, scabrous-setose above, somewhat copiously and evenly hispid beneath with rather fine, erect, curving trichomes, thinnish and slightly chartaceous in texture; solitary on the flowering branches or cymose-paniculate, according to the leaf arrangement, the inflorescence small for the size of the plant, peduncles leafy; heads medium, the disc 1–1.5 cm. in diam., the rays about 2.0 cm. long; corollas of the disc florets yellow, stout, cylindrical, lobes ample, glabrous, the base slightly pubescent, the tube short; the achene brown, finely mottled, turgid, oboval, very obscurely and sparingly pubescent at the summit; the pappus two broadly lanceolate awns; the chaff ample, firm, 3-cuspidate, acute, the tip sparingly pubescent; the involucre hemispheric; the bracts broadly lanceolate, acuminate, loose, only a little longer than the disc and erect in early anthesis, but elongating and becoming much recurved in age, slightly pubescent; the roots very coarsely fibrous, woody, and stout at the base; the rhizomes abundant, very stout and profusely ramose, 1–8.0 dm. long, producing abundant fibrous roots at the ultimate nodes and particularly just behind the stout terminal bud.

Sandy loam soil, Illinois to Michigan.

Type. — Watson 767, roadside near Princeton, Illinois, in the herbarium of Michigan State College, East Lansing, Michigan.

My attention was first attracted to this plant in the summer of 1923, when I collected several specimens of it along the fence around Mt. Olivet Cemetery in Chicago, Illinois. The general outline of the leaf suggested that of *H. divaricatus*, but the leaf base and the presence of a definite petiole excluded that species. The variation in the leaf bases in this first group was very great, some of the leaves being subcordate and others acute at the base. Further observation indicated that the younger leaves were acute at the base, while the more mature became rounded. There was evidence that the period of growth in the leaf was considerable, the leaf apparently increasing in width after it had ceased to elongate. *H. arenicola* grows abundantly in the vicinity of Mt. Olivet Cemetery.

In October, 1925, while driving east from Princeton, Illinois, I came upon a very large number of these plants some three or four miles from the town. The sandy hills here have been cut through to make way for the road, and along the gullies at the side of the road the plants grew very luxuriantly. They were naturally well supplied with moisture, and the result was a profusely ramose plant, 2.0 m. high, with large leaves. It was very noticeable, however, that the leaves of all the plants in the group were by no means identical. In one large plant the maximum leaves measured 17 by 8.5 cm., the base of the leaf was nearly straight, the petiole 1.8 cm. long, and the lateral nerves were confluent at the base of the blade, that is, the petiole was quite distinct. Less than three meters distant grew another plant of equal height and ramosity, with maximum leaves 23.0 cm. from apex to the confluence of the lateral nerves, and the petiole from the confluence 4.5 cm. long, the blade cuneately decurrent about two thirds of the length. There was no evidence of any edaphic factor that would account for the difference.

The cut in the hill east of Princeton, Illinois, where the type was collected, is about 25.0 m. deep or more. On the top near the cut and along the sides of the hill the species grew abundantly, but the plants were very small, evidently owing to lack of moisture and the shade of the trees. These small plants were typical except in size. Their stems were always simple, the leaves opposite, and the inflorescence either solitary or a small cyme. The stem measured about 0.5 m. in height, and the leaves 8.0 cm. long by 2.0 cm. wide, the petiole distinct and about 0.5 cm. long. All gradations between the extremes given above could be found. It is also significant that the roots and rhizomes of these small plants were identical with those of the large plants, perhaps less ramose, but not smaller, nor less abundantly supplied with the long, fibrous rootlets at the nodes.

The nearest relatives of *H. arenicola* are *H. divaricatus* and *H. chartaceus*. *H. hirsutus* and *H. leptocaulis* are not distant relatives.

Besides the two collections mentioned above, good specimens have also been collected on the Dixie Highway near Michigan City, Indiana.

95. **H. exasperatus,** sp. nov.

(Plate LXXX)

Perennial; stem stout, erect, 1–1.5 m. high, simple to the inflorescence, very rough, scabrous, hispid, sulcate; leaves prevailingly opposite, sometimes alternate above, arrangement unstable, broadly lanceolate to ovate, acuminate, abruptly narrowed to a short, winged petiole, very irregularly serrate, densely scabrous-setose above, and densely hispid beneath, very rough, thick and coarse in texture, concolor, 8–12.0 cm. long, including petiole, by 3–6.5 cm. wide; the inflorescence cymose or paniculate according to leaf arrangement; heads 1–1.7 cm. across the disc, convex, the rays about 1.7 cm. long, about 0.4 cm. wide; corollas of the disc florets yellow, the lobes, base and tube slightly pubescent; the achene light brown, glabrous, the pappus two narrowly lanceolate awns without other scales; the chaff 3-cuspidate, hispid on tip and keel; the involucre hemispheric; the bracts linear-lanceolate, hispidulous, ciliate toward the base, very loose, a little longer than the disc; the roots narrowly fusiform, very coarse, woody, often 1.0 cm. thick, 6–8.0 cm. long, tapering to a long, slender tip, two or more in a fascicle; no rhizomes, numerous crown-buds.

Rich soil, Wisconsin to Minnesota, possibly Nebraska.

Type. — A specimen collected by J. H. Schuette, in Brown Co., Wisconsin, Sept. 13, 1886, sheet No. 377,704 in the Field Columbian Museum, Chicago, Illinois.

Schuette's collections of Helianthus from Brown Co., Wisconsin, and vicinity, are extraordinarily interesting, and deserve very careful study. In fact, the flora of this state is remarkably rich in this genus. The species which I have called *H. exasperatus* is a very well defined group. Its nearest relative is *H. giganteus;* in fact, Schuette called his specimen *H. giganteus foliosus,* but the name was never published, so far as I have been able to find out. The type has somewhat narrow leaves. Another specimen by the same collector, numbered 70.56.19 — whatever those figures mean — from Elkhart, Wisconsin, Aug. 28, 1887, has the larger ovate leaves. This is sheet No. 377,673, and the two should be used in conjunction. The type specimen was selected because the root-system is most excellently presented.

H. exasperatus is a very coarse unlovely "weed," but is a true Helianthus and a very distinct species.

96. **H. ambulans,** sp. nov.

(Plates LXXXI–LXXXII)

Perennial; stem slender, erect, 1–2.0 m. high, simple to the inflorescence, light green, glabrous, except a little hispid toward the apex; leaves opposite, large, lanceolate or ovate-lanceolate, the upper cauline leaves much narrower, but not much shorter, attenuate-acute at the apex, remotely crenate-denticulate, the lower with blade abruptly contracted at the base, decurrent on the long petiole about half-way, the upper with blade broadly decurrent to the base of the relatively long petiole; the lower 22.0 cm. long from the confluence of the lateral nerves, by 8.0 cm. wide, the petiole from the confluence about 6.0 cm. long, the entire length, accordingly, nearly 3.0 dm., the upper cauline leaves, 20.0 cm. long from the confluence, by 5.5 cm. wide, the petiole about 6.0

cm. long; the upper surface sharply but minutely somewhat remotely setulose, lower surface evenly, not densely, very short-subhispid; light green on both sides, somewhat shining, thin, delicate in texture; the principal nerves prominent beneath, very inconspicuous above; the inflorescence cymose, with long rather lax branches, the inflorescence subtended by two much reduced, drooping leaves, and the leaves of the flowering branches also reduced and drooping; the heads medium large, 1.5–2.0 cm. across the convex disc, the rays 2–2.5 cm. long; corollas of disc florets yellow, cylindrical-campanulate, the lobes narrowly acute, obscurely pubescent, the limb glabrous, the base pubescent, the tube glabrous; the achene ample, turgid, mottled, glabrous; the pappus two narrowly lanceolate awns, without other scales; the chaff ample, 3-cuspidate, the cusps narrowly acute, pubescent, the keel sparingly pubescent; the involucre hemispheric; the bracts broadly linear-lanceolate, acute, glabrous, finely short-ciliate, somewhat loose, but erect, reflexed only in the fully mature and fading head, about as long as the disc; the roots fine, fibrous, not abundant; the rhizomes slender, remarkable for their great length, often 1.5 m. long, usually about 0.9 m. long, sometimes branched, the ultimate 3–4.0 cm. somewhat enlarged, the internodes of the rhizomes often 1.5 dm. long, rootlets abundant at and near the tip.

Very plentiful in woods and fields, in light soil, in the vicinity of South Bend and Notre Dame, Indiana.

Type. — Watson 170, in the herbarium of Michigan State College, East Lansing, Michigan.

H. ambulans is clearly specific by reason of the three foliar forms: (1) the broad lower leaves with their half-distinct petioles; (2) the narrow upper leaves with petioles broadly winged to the base; and (3) the small leaves that subtend the inflorescence and occur on its branches and are conspicuously drooping. I observed this latter character in all specimens of the species noted over a radius of more than three miles. The pubescence is also distinctive, obscure, and short, but very sharp on the upper side, even and not very dense, and also short on the lower surface. The species is typically a plant of open woods and light soil, but was a common relict in cleared fields where it usually was not quite so tall, and its rhizomes were shorter and stouter, but even here of extraordinary length. My specimens were secured late in the season and I cannot write in detail regarding the rays.

97. H. Rydbergi Britton. Man. Fl. N. U. S., p. 993. 1901.

H. apricus Lunell. Am. Mid. Nat., 1: 237. 1910.
H. apricus var. *camporum* Lunell. *l. c.*
H. nitidus Lunell. Am. Mid. Nat., 1: 236. 1910.
H. nitidus var. *trifoliatus* Lunell. Am. Mid. Nat., 5: 64. 1917.

Perennial; stem stout, erect, 0.7–1.5 m. high, often ramose above, often reddish, usually scabrous-hispid, especially above, sometimes quite glabrous; leaves prevailingly opposite, or the upper ones alternate, much reduced, ovate, ovate- or oblong-lanceolate, the upper ones narrowly oblong-lanceolate, narrowly acute, mostly serrulate, often serrate, abruptly contracted below the confluence of the lateral nerves to a short, stout, partly distinct petiole, thick, firm in texture, densely scabrous-setose above, coarsely hispid beneath, rough, pale-green both sides; the inflorescence often solitary or in vigorous plants subpaniculate; head with disc 1–1.5 cm. in diam., the rays 2–3.0 cm. long; corollas of the disc florets yellow, glabrous except the obscurely puberulent base, the lobes unusually long, lanceolate; the achene light brown, glabrous, shining; the pappus two broadly lanceolate, rather long, carinate awns usually with small accessory paleae at their base; the chaff 3-cuspidate, the lateral cusps very small, very pubescent on tip and keel; the involucre hemispheric; the bracts linear-lanceolate, hispid, ciliate; the roots several narrowly fusiform, very stout, short, tuber-like structures, usually in a fascicle, and several coarsely fibrous roots intermingled with them; rhizomes few, short, slender, less than 1.0 dm. long.

Sandy, arid soil, Nebraska, the Dakotas and vicinity.

Type. — Rydberg 1767, from Hooker Co., Nebraska, in the herbarium of the New York Botanical Garden. I have compared the type with a large number of other collections of this species.

The synonymy suggested under *H. Rydbergi* is the result of my effort to classify the Lunell species. The result of these efforts is the opinion that *H. Rydbergi* is not one of the more characteristic or strongly marked species, though abundantly distinct, and is also extremely variable, making it an exceptionally difficult species to handle; and that the Lunell species are merely divergent forms of *H. Rydbergi*. I have studied the type of *H. apricus* var. *camporum*, and have seen several specimens identified by Lunell as *H. nitidus*, and the result of very careful study upon them is the suggested synonymy.

98. H. strumosus L. Sp. Pl., 905. 1753

(Plate LXXXIII)

H. macrophyllus Willd. Hort. Berol., t. 70. 1816.

Perennial; stem erect, mostly slender, 1–3.0 m. high, glabrous or subglabrous, sometimes a little pubescent toward the inflorescence, mostly simple, but, in large, isolated individuals, often ramose; leaves prevailingly opposite, broadly lanceolate, or sometimes broadly oval, or ovate-lanceolate; the apex acuminate, the margin serrate or serrulate, rarely subentire; the blade decurrent upon the partly distinct petiole; leaves mostly 10–15.0 cm. long, including petiole, by 2–7.0 cm. wide, extremely variable in size; usually thinnish in texture; the upper surface strumose-setulose, the lower surface either (1) glabrous, except on the more or less hispid main nerves and often conspicuously glaucous, or else (2) evenly, not densely, rather softly pubescent over the whole lower surface; the inflorescence cymose, the secondary branches often alternate, or, in very small plants, the head solitary, the branches and peduncles usually somewhat pubescent; heads showy, the disc 1–2.0 cm. in diam., the rays 2–3.0 cm. long; corollas of the disc florets yellow, the lobes and base somewhat pubescent, the limb glabrous or obscurely pubescent on the main nerves, the tube glabrous; the achene glabrous, ample; the pappus two broadly lanceolate awns without other scales; the chaff 3-cuspidate, the lateral cusps small, pubescent on the tip and keel; the involucre hemispheric; the bracts broadly lanceolate, acuminate, glabrous or sometimes slightly pubescent, ciliate, loose but not reflexed, a little longer than the disc; the roots few, coarse, woody; the rhizomes stout, sometimes branched, often very long, usually only two or three, but in vigorous plants often numerous.

Abundant in the northeastern states, west to Wisconsin, south to the Gulf of Mexico, sporadically west of the Mississippi, probably also in Canada.

Type. — In the Linnaean Herbarium, London. I have an excellent photograph of the type.

The precise interpretation of *H. strumosus* is more uncertain than that of any other of our sunflowers, and it is beyond doubt that no specific name has been more generally misapplied than this. My own conception of *H. strumosus* is based upon the photograph of the type and upon a specimen collected by Thomas A. Greene near New Bedford, Massachusetts, which very closely resembles the photograph of the type. This specimen is the property of the University of Wisconsin. It presents the upper 3.0 dm. of the stem, three pairs of leaves and a cyme of three heads, one of the lateral branches bearing also an abortive head. The leaves are of normal texture, neither very thick nor very thin, broadly lanceolate, and acuminate, 13.0 cm. long, including petiole, by 3.5 cm. wide, the petiole, from the confluence of the lateral nerves, about 1.0 cm. long, the blade decurrent about half-way. The stem was probably about 1.0 m. high. The pubescence of the upper surface resembles that of the photograph in detail. The strumose character of the trichomes is very noticeable, the dark surface of the leaf being covered by conspicuous white dots, which, on closer examination, are seen to consist of a group of small, thick-walled cells, bearing a seta in their midst. It was undoubtedly this character which led to the choice of the name "strumosus." It is true that the "strumose-setose" pubescence just described is more or less characteristic of the upper surface of the vast majority of sunflower leaves, but it is more conspicuous in *H. strumosus* than in any other sunflower with which Linneaus was acquainted, and it evidently attracted his attention at once.

The specimens that I have included in the species under discussion all have this character, though, to be sure, like every other character in the genus, in varying degree. The whole group, however, is sharply divided into two subgroups by the character of the pubescence of the lower leaf-surface, as indicated in the description. Unfortunately, the Linnaean specimen presents only the upper surface of the leaves, and Dr. B. D. Jackson, director of the Linnaean Herbarium, was not able to inform me with certainty in regard to this particular peculiarity. I have decided, therefore, to include both groups in the species. The habitat, as given by Linnaeus, is Canada, which to him meant everything north of Virginia, and this would include Massachusetts, the locality of the Greene specimen mentioned above. The lower surface of the leaves in this specimen is practically glabrous except the hispid nerves, and this seems to be the form which is commonest in the Atlantic and Gulf states. The other group, with leaves evenly though not densely pubescent on the lower surface and of thicker texture, is the form more frequently met with farther inland. However, there is no reliably close geographical correlation of these groups.

It is also of interest to observe that the specimens of *H. strumosus* from the southern states, and particularly from the southeastern states, are often conspicuously glaucous on the lower surface.

The *H. macrophyllus* Willd. is a large-leaved plant, from the Berlin Botanical Garden. I have examined Willdenow's original specimens, and I believe they are of this species. The leaves are evenly pubescent beneath and the bracts are somewhat hispidulous.

I am not satisfied as to the identity of *H. strumosus* var. *mollis* of Torrey and Gray, which I strongly suspect is *H. tuberosus*. And the *H. strumosus* var. *leptophyllus* of the same authors, marked questionable by them, is no doubt a small individual, but as I have seen no guaranteed specimen, I do not feel qualified to decide.

99. **H. superbus,** sp. nov.

(Plate LXXXIV)

Perennial; stem stout, erect, 1–2.0 m. high, ramose above, sulcate, sharply scabrous-hispid; leaves mostly opposite, but arrangement unstable, ovate-lanceolate, narrowly acute, serrulate, blade contracted below to a cuneate base very briefly decurrent on the long petiole, normally 12–14 cm. from apex to the confluence of the lateral nerves by 5.5 cm. wide, the petiole from the confluence 4–6.0 cm. long, winged about one fifth of its length, very deep green and strumose-setose above, paler and copiously rather softly pubescent beneath; the inflorescence cymose when the leaves are opposite, the branches very leafy, the cyme often compound, or solitary at the apex of the long branches when the leaves are alternate; the heads large and very showy, the disc 1.5–2.5 cm. in diam., the rays up to 5.0 cm. long; corollas of the disc florets yellow, 1.0 cm. long, exclusive of achene, the lobes, base and tube pubescent, the limb pubescent on the main nerves; the achene ample, turgid, obovate, mottled, pubescent, especially above; the pappus two lanceolate awns without other scales; the chaff ample, 3-cuspidate, all cusps narrowly acute, the laterals small, the middle cusp long, sparingly pubescent at the tip; the involucre hemispheric, the bracts linear-lanceolate, long-attenuate, very loose but not conspicuously reflexed, hispidulous, sometime subglabrous in smaller plants, ciliate below, normally longer than the disc, sometimes 2.0 cm. long, dark green; the roots fibrous, the rootlets unusually numerous and fine; the rhizomes numerous, stout, 2–6.0 dm. long, the main rhizome often branching near the base, rarely if ever beyond the middle.

Type. — Watson 363, Jamaica Plain, Massachusetts.

A very handsome and showy plant. My best specimens were taken from a group growing in turf in the corner of a garden belonging to Mr. R. March, 11 Goldsmith St., Jamaica Plain, Massachusetts. Several other smaller plants with shorter petioles grew in and about the village. From the fact that these first collections were made in a village and in a very old part of the United States, there is a suspicion that the plant is a horticultural form, but it is apparently not referable to any of the known wild species, and seems to be well defined by its long-petioled leaves and by the size and beauty of the heads. These measure fully 1.0 dm. in full anthesis. The flowering branches are often 4–5.0 dm. long and bear a single terminal flower. This method of inflorescence and the great size of the heads are unusual in perennial sunflowers.

100. H. tracheliifolius Miller. Gard. Dict., ed. 8, No. 7. 1768.

H. prostratus Willd. Sp. Pl., ed. 4, 3 : 2242. 1797.

Perennial; stem slender, erect, apparently about 1.5 m. high, simple or ramose above, reddish, striate-sulcate, glabrous; leaves opposite or alternate, arrangement apparently unstable, rather broadly lanceolate, slightly acuminate, serrate-dentate, rounded below, with a very short, partly distinct petiole, 8–11.0 cm. long, including petiole, by 3.0 cm. wide, the petiole from the confluence of the lateral nerves less than 1.0 cm. long, rather thin in texture, copiously strumose-setose above, rather unevenly hispid beneath, more so on the main nerves, the anastomosings of the veinlets small and fine, the petioles somewhat ciliate near the base; the inflorescence cymose or paniculate, according to the arrangement of the leaves; heads medium, showy; the disc 1–1.5 cm. in diam., the rays about 2.5 cm. long, broadly oval; corollas of the disc florets yellow, slender, tapering to the tube, puberulent on lobes and base; the achene glabrous, dark, linear; the chaff linear, subtricuspidate or entire, the tip narrowly acute, slightly villous; the involucre broadly campanulate; the bracts narrowly linear-lanceolate, very loose, longer than the disc, the tips spreading, sparingly hispidulous, often subglabrous, spreading ciliate. Lower stem and root-system not seen.

Type. — *H. tracheliifolius* Miller, in the British Museum; photograph seen.

Perhaps no sunflower is so little known in America, at least, as *H. tracheliifolius*, and the reason is probably twofold. In the first place, I have grave suspicions that the plant is a horticultural form, and very probably a mutant or a variation of *H. decapetalus*, very possibly a hybrid — a most convenient explanation. In the second place, if the specimens at my disposal be truly *H. tracheliifolius*, the species is a very colorless, poorly defined entity.

Among the specimens submitted by the Berlin Botanical Museum are several labeled *H. tracheliifolius*, collected in the Paris and Berlin Botanical Gardens, and others with origin not stated. These are all conspecific, and closely resemble the photograph of the original Miller type, except that the leaves in the Miller specimen are longer. As indicated in the photograph, the leaves are 12.5 cm. long by 5.0 cm. wide, but the contour of the leaves, particularly of the base, is similar to that of the specimens.

The plant is very close to *H. decapetalus*, its points of departure from that species being: (1) the leaves are coarser in texture, and the anastomosings of the veinlets on the lower surface much smaller; (2) the bracts are narrower and more pubescent; (3) the petiole, from the confluence of the lateral nerves, is very short and scarcely winged, while in *H. decapetalus* the broadly winged, long petiole is very conspicuous; and (4) the leaves are truly lanceolate whereas they are rarely so in *H. decapetalus*, being at most oblong-lanceolate, and usually broadly ovate. The range of *H. tracheliifolius* is stated by various authors to be Ohio, Pennsylvania, and vicinity. I have seen no native specimen that I would classify as *H. tracheliifolius*, although it is perfectly true that I have not seen all the specimens there are.

The synonymy is on the authority of Gray. There are several specimens in the Berlin Herbarium, collected in northern United States and labeled *H. prostratus*, but they are plainly *H. divaricatus*.

101. **H. luxurians**, sp. nov.

(Plates LXXXV–LXXXVI)

Perennial; stem stout, erect, 1–2.0 m. high, ramose from above the middle, sharply scabrous-hispid, not densely, glabrescent at the base and deeply sulcate, red-purple toward the apex; leaves alternate, often very large, very broadly elliptic-lanceolate in large plants, oblong-elliptic in smaller plants, acuminate at both ends, denticulate, the blade decurrent below the confluence of the lateral nerves about three fourths of the length of the petiole, 15–23.0 cm. long, including petiole, by 3–5.0 cm. wide, the petiole from the confluence of the lateral nerves 3–6.0 cm. long, sparingly strumose-setulose above, the setae very short and sharp, evenly, not densely hispid beneath, and the nerves not more hispid than the surface of the leaf, concolor, very deep green; the inflorescence loosely paniculate, a few heads on short peduncles at the apex of the main stem, and 1–3 heads on very short peduncles at the apex of the flowering branches; heads showy, the disc 1–1.5 cm. in diam., the rays bright yellow 2–3.0 cm. long; corollas of the disc florets yellow, the lobes and base pubescent, the tube slender and glabrous; the achene dark brown, glabrous; the pappus two narrowly lanceolate, carinate awns without other scales; the chaff linear, 3-cuspidate, the tip pubescent; the involucre hemispheric; the bracts linear-lanceolate, very dark, mostly subglabrous, with abundant spreading cilia; the roots narrowly fusiform, very coarse and woody, often 1.3 cm. thick for a distance of 5–15.0 cm., then gradually tapering to a long, slender tip, the whole with abundant rootlets; rhizomes very short, 3–4.0 cm., crown-buds numerous.

Chiefly in wet muck, northern Ohio.

Type. — Watson 387, vicinity of Cedar Point, Ohio, in the herbarium of Michigan State College, East Lansing, Michigan.

H. luxurians is a close relative of *H. giganteus*, but differs in these points: (1) the size and shape of the leaves; (2) the smaller disc, but the longer rays; (3) the pubescence of the lower surface evenly hispid and not denser on the nerves, while in *H. giganteus* it is long and usually confined to the nerves; and (4) the margin of the leaf at most denticulate, while in *H. giganteus*, although variable, it is usually deeply serrate.

102. H. australis Phil. Anal. Univ. Chile, 90 : 36. 1895.

Perennial; stem very glabrous, ramose; leaves narrowly oblong, blade of the lower leaves decurrent on the petiole, serrate from the middle toward apex, one-nerved, crowded at the base, 10.0 cm. long by 1.2 cm. wide, acute; inflorescence of solitary heads terminal on the branches, the disc 1.0 cm. in diam., rays about 1.2 cm. long; involucral bracts very loose, linear-lanceolate, the inner twice as long as the outer, glutinous, cartilaginous at the base but foliaceous toward the tip, resin-dotted; the achene glabrous.

The Andes of Valdivia, Chile.

I have seen no specimen of this species.

103. H. amplexicaulis DC. Prod., 5 : 589. 1836.

Stem herbaceous, ramose, subscabrous; leaves semi-amplexicaulent, dentate, the lower opposite, the base obtuse, auricled, the lateral nerves confluent far above the base, narrowed above the auricles, from there on ovate-lanceolate, almost lyrate, in the middle stem, opposite, entire, the upper alternate. Panicle lax, the peduncles a little rough; involucral bracts in 2–3 series, linear-lanceolate, acute, bases rough, appressed-ciliate; chaff entire, acuminate.

Type. — Mendez from Guanaxuata, Leonina, Mexico.

Habit of Viguiera, but receptacle convex, and pappus of two awns only.

I have not seen any specimen of this species, and have merely quoted De Candolle's description. However, I consider the species very doubtful; auricled leaves in *Helianthus* would be most unusual, and the author does not state whether the two awns of the pappus are persistent or caducous.

104. Helianthus acuminatus Blake. Journ. Wash. Acad. Sci., 16, No. 8 : 219. 1926.

Stem perennial, shrub, stout, about 0.6 cm. thick, apparently tall, glabrous or glabrate, the young branches densely griseous-pilose or tomentose, the hairs white, spreading, from tuberculate bases; leaves opposite except those of the inflorescence, ovate, acuminate, rounded or truncate at the base, or often subcordate, 4–7.0 cm. long by 2.8–4.3 cm. wide, obscurely serrulate, dark green and densely short pilose above, the hairs from tuberculate bases, densely griseous-pilose beneath, the blade scarcely decurrent on the slender, densely pilose-tomentose, distinct petiole, which is 0.8–1.8 cm. long; the inflorescence terminal and axillary, 1–5 heads toward the tips of the branches on stout peduncles, 1–14 cm. long; the disc 1.2–2.0 cm. wide, the rays about 2.0 cm. long by 0.6 cm. wide; corollas of the disc florets yellow, about 7.5 cm. long, the tube 2.0 mm. long, the chaff acute, mucronulate, 1.1 cm. long, pilose on the keel; the awns 2 only, 3.0 mm. long, ciliate;

the achenes dark, glabrous; the involucre about 1.3 cm. high, its bracts oblong, acute or acuminate, ashy-puberulent-pilose to sparsely pilose, 4-seriate, 1.2–1.4 cm. long by 2.8–5.5 mm. wide, dark green, appressed-puberulent-pilose, the hairs short, glabrescent in age, 3-nerved.

Huanuco, Peru, mountain sides.

Type. — MacBride and Featherstone 2429, sheet No. 518,863 in the Field Columbian Museum, a duplicate in the United States National Herbarium, sheet No. 1,198,894. Collected on an open, moist, rocky slope at Tomaiquichua, Peru, about three miles south of Ambo, Huanuco, Peru, altitude 2590 m., Sept. 19, 1922.

I have seen no specimen of this species. The description is strikingly suggestive of *H. Jelskii*.

105. Helianthus discolor Blake. Journ. Wash. Acad. Sci., 16, No. 8 : 220. 1926.

Stem perennial, a shrub, in clumps or tufts from a caudex, about 40.0 cm. long, slender, about 2.5 mm. thick, older parts with gray bark, glabrate, somewhat hispid at the nodes, the branches alternate, thinly appressed-pilose, more or less glandular; leaves opposite below, soon becoming alternate, linear or linear-lanceolate, 2.3–3.8 cm. long by 4–6.0 mm. wide, dull green and strigose or hispid-strigose above, the hairs with tuberculate bases, glabrescent, the lower surface white tomentose, somewhat falcate, apex acuminate to an obtuse tip, base cuneate, entire or subentire, revolute, subcoriaceous, with fascicles of small linear leaves in the axils, the petiole very short, about 1.5 mm. long, pilose; the inflorescence a solitary head terminal on the main stems and the branches on peduncles 3–7.0 cm. long and naked or few-bracted, sordid-pilose and somewhat hispid below the head; disc 1–2.0 cm. in diam.; the disc corollas yellow with fuscescent lobes, the tuber 1.0 mm. long and puberulent, the florets puberulent on the nerves and lobes; the chaff acuminate, mucronulate, blackish on the costa, hispidulous on the keel, ciliolate and 9.0 mm. long; the achene small, glabrous; the awns two, linear-subulate, hispidulous; the involucral bracts about 9.0 mm. long, 3–4 seriate, lanceolate or oblong-lanceolate, appressed with recurved tips, the outer bracts loose, the margins hirsute-ciliate, the bracts cinereous appressed-pubescent.

Huanuco, Peru.

Type.—MacBride and Featherstone 2240, sheet No. 518,724 in the Field Columbian Museum, a duplicate, sheet No. 1,198,892 in the United States National Herbarium. Collected on the eastern side of the cañon at Llata, Huanuco, Peru, altitude about 2135 m., Aug. 21, 1922. I have seen no specimen of this species.

106. Helianthus viridior Blake. Journ. Wash. Acad. Sci., 16, No. 8 : 221. 1926.

Stem perennial, a shrub, very ramose, slender, about 0.5 cm. in diam., gray-barked, lenticellate, glabrate, apparently somewhat procumbent, about 30.0 cm. high, the branches numerous and almost as long, the younger branches appressed-pilose, warty, soon glabrescent; leaves alternate except the lowermost, on short petioles 3–8.0 mm. long, lanceolate, acuminate or acutish, callous-apiculate, cuneate at the base, 3–4.3 cm. long by 0.5–1.3 cm. wide, entire or obscurely serrulate above the middle, thin, upper surface subsericeous-pilose when young, soon glabrescent, lower surface densely, appressed subsericeous-pilose, soon antrorse-pilose and green, glabrescent; inflorescence a solitary head terminal on main stem and branches, the peduncles about 3–5.0 cm. long, naked or with a few bracts; the disc 1–1.3 cm. in diam.; florets of the disc numerous, the corollas yellow with brownish tips, the tube and lobes pilose; the rays about 9, linear-elliptic, the tube of the ray pilose, less so on the nerves of the ray which is about 1.5 cm. long and 3–4.0 mm. wide; the achene dark, glabrous; the awns 2, lanceolate, acuminate, about 3.0 mm. long, the awns of the ray achenes, 2–3 lacerate squamellae; the chaff acuminate, blackish above, somewhat pilose toward the tip and glandular on the sides, about 0.8 cm. long; the involucral bracts in 3–4 series, about 8–11.0 mm. long, linear-lanceolate, the outer broader, the apex acuminate callous-apiculate, ciliate, appressed, the tips loose.

Junin, Peru, limestone cliffs.

Type. — MacBride and Featherstone 1070, sheet No. 517,591, in the Field Columbian Museum; also a duplicate, sheet No. 1,198,869 in the United States National Herbarium, collected at Tarma, Junin, Peru, altitude about 3965 m., June 1–6, 1922.

I have seen no specimen of this species.

107. H. similis (Brandegee) Blake. Contr. Gray Herb., N. S., 54 : 189. 1918.

Viguiera similis Brandeg., Zoe, 5 : 260. 1908.

Perennial; stem suffruticose, slightly tomentose, 1.0 m. high; leaves opposite, cordate, long acuminate, sharply serrate, tomentose on both sides, white beneath, 12.0 cm. long by 8.0 cm. wide; petiole 1–2.0 cm. long, white tomentose; heads few, terminal, peduncles 3–7.0 cm. long, involucral bracts about equal to the disc, 1–1.5 cm. long, lanceolate, white, rays 2–2.5 cm. long by 0.5 cm. wide, acuminate; achenes almost glabrous, black; pappus of two awns and sometimes intermediate scales, deciduous.

Cape region of Baja, California.

I have not seen the type nor any specimen of this species, which, with the synonymy, is quoted on the authority of Blake. He points out that *H. similis* has the habit and nearly the involucre of the Dentatae of Viguiera and a viguieroid pappus of two awns and several intermediate squamellae. The whole pappus is deciduous and the achene glabrous and it seems, therefore, more consistent to place it with Helianthus than with Viguiera. Blake suggests that it is probably a late derivative of Viguiera.

108. Helianthus rugosus Meyen. Reise, 2 : 45. 1835.

Stem perennial, low, lax, prostrate, ramose, hispid, powdery below, less so above; leaves alternate, subsessile, the blade decurrent to the base of the petiole, ovate-oblong, acute, upper surface sparingly scabrous-setose, lower surface sparingly pubescent, but hispid on the main nerves, both sides white-powdery, obcurely denticulate, slightly revolute, 4.0 cm. long by 1.3 cm. wide, thickish, firm, rugose, the nerves prominent beneath; heads solitary, terminal on the branches; the involucral bracts ovate or slightly obovate, acute, erect, 2–3.0 mm. wide, and about as long as the disc, pubescent, ciliate, white-powdery; chaff narrow, obtuse, somewhat galeate, mucronulate, entire, thin, puberulent at tips, otherwise glabrous; the achene glabrous, slender, the base very narrow, the shoulder angular, light colored; the pappus two slender, subulate aristae with expanded, lacerate bases, no intermediate squamellae; corollas of the disc florets yellow with brownish lobes, at least in the dried specimen, glabrous.

Type. — A specimen collected by Meyen in Peru on mountain sides, in the Berlin Botanical Museum.

The type presents a small terminal portion of a stem, with two heads. The most puzzling feature of the specimen is the powdery substance which occurs abundantly on stem and leaves. The collector describes it as "calcareus." Under the microscope it has the appearance of amorphous particles of wax, but it did not give the reactions of lime, wax, or resin, and Mr. Nelson of the Department of Pathology of Michigan State College says that it is not mildew. The specimen looks unhealthy, as though it had been injured either by disease or drought or by some other condition. Besides the type, Dr. Brehmer of Lübeck also collected a specimen of this species at Quibra de la Cuesta, Peru.

Summary

The following observations are important:

1. *Phyllotaxy.* — In all sunflowers, at least the first four or more leaves are opposite, and from here on they tend, more or less strongly according to the species, to become alternate. Vigor and luxuriance of growth are conducive to the alternate arrangement, and depauperation, even to a very slight degree, is favorable to the opposite arrangement. Drought, crowding, shade, poor soil, and mechanical injury are all favorable to opposite leaves.

2. *Specific intergrades.* — Typical or extreme specimens of the various species in an obviously related group are sharply demarcated by their diagnostic characters, but intergrading forms are to be found in large numbers which can be arranged in a regular and gradual progression, from any one of the related species to any

other one, and this progression can be arranged according to any one of the various diagnostic characters, and the varying characters are not correlated.

3. The annual species are more responsive to edaphic conditions than the perennials; and normally tall species are more responsive than normally low species.

4. Depauperate individuals of a related group tend to resemble one another to such a degree that their identification, beyond the group to which they belong, is often impossible.

5. *Vegetative propagation.* — There are five distinct methods of vegetative propagation in sunflowers: (1) by rhizomes, (2) by crown-buds, (3) by tubers, (4) by axillary buds, and (5) by radical buds formed near the root tip.

6. Radical buds (produced only in *H. atrorubens*) do not undergo a resting period, but grow immediately, producing plants and often flowers in the first season. The rhizomes of two species produce plants but not flowers in the first season. These are *H. occidentalis* and *H. rigidus*.

Subjects for Further Study

1. *H. strumosus.* — This species, as treated in this monograph, comprises plants with leaves evenly pubescent over the whole lower surface, and those with leaves pubescent only on the nerves. It also includes those with very thick firm leaves and with very thin leaves. Within its limits are also very tall plants with large, ovate-lanceolate leaves, and short ones with merely lanceolate leaves. The author feels that these are possibly differences of specific rank, and was inclined to separate this group accordingly, but he has not been able to examine the Linnaean type and is not in position to say which of these groups conforms to the type.

2. *H. rigidus.* — There can be no question as to the identity of the true *H. rigidus.* There still remains to be determined the status of the plants whose yellow disc corollas exclude them from *H. rigidus,* but whose bract characters exclude them from *H. laetiflorus.*

Also, what is the status of those plants, mostly large, ramose individuals, very similar to *H. rigidus* but bearing well-developed tubers, and yet not conforming to the other characters of *H. tuberosus?* Some effort should be made here to detect any correlation between disc color and root characters.

The author is inclined to think that those plants in this group, with yellow disc and without tubers, may prove to be *H. missouricus* Spreng., and that the tuber-bearing group is specifically distinct. The most favorable area for collecting the former is between Chicago and St. Louis, and for the latter between Chicago and Iowa.

All the plants of this group blossom early, and repeated observations should be made looking toward a possible correlation between corolla color and either age of individual flower or time of blossoming in the season.

3. *H. laetiflorus.* — Our view of this species is largely the traditional view, since it has been impossible to examine Persoon's type. It is usually described as similar to *H. rigidus*, but with yellow disc corollas. It is, however, quite different in habit, both above and below ground. Its leaves, while thick in texture and coarse, are not rigid, and the flowering branches are shorter. The rays are distinctly a deeper yellow and the bracts narrower, more acute, longer, not so closely appressed, and often pubescent. The species seems to be very rare, the author never having collected it in its natural state, and it is found but rarely in herbaria. The most perfect of these specimens is one collected by Patterson in the vicinity of Mt. Carmel, Wabash Co., Illinois. The relation between this species and the plants with yellow disc, mentioned above, should be carefully determined.

4. The whole group of tuber-bearing sunflowers will have to be minutely studied. This will necessitate much original collecting on account of the fact that herbarium material rarely presents root parts. Certain collections from Chemung Co., New York, and along the Susquehanna River suggest *H. tuberosus*, but the root parts are not shown. A collection by Dr. E. A. Bessey from Jefferson, Iowa, has all the characters of *H. tuberosus*, but no tubers. The position of these plants cannot be determined without the root parts, and even then it is a very obscure matter.

In this connection the author believes that *H. strumosus mollis* of Gray is, in reality, a shade form of *H. tuberosus*. The type does not present root parts, and the aërial parts definitely exclude it from *H. strumosus*. Only thorough collecting in the vicinity of the type locality can establish the identity of this variety. Tbe type locality is the vicinity of Canton, Illinois.

5. All the vast region from the Bemiji Lakes of Minnesota, through the Green Bay district of Wisconsin, particularly, Brown Co., to Indiana, Ohio, and Pennsylvania, contains specimens of very great interest and bewildering variability, which the author has not been able to determine or dispose of. Thorough collections should be made here. I believe that many or at least a few new species would result from a study of this district.

HELIANTHI NOT MENTIONED IN THE TEXT

I. Transferred to other genera

H. araucana Phil. = Flourensia corymbosa var. araucana Reiche.
H. aureus H.B.K. = Viguiera aurea (H.B.K.) Hieron.
H. atacamensis Phil. = F. atacamensis (Phil.) Reiche.
H. baillonianus Gomez = V. dentata var. helianthoides Blake.
H. besserianus B & H. = F. besseriana Meyen & Walp.
H. buddleiaeformis DC. = V. buddleiaeformis B & H.
H. buphthalmoides Hort. ex DC. = Heliopsis buphthalmoides Dun.
H. calvus Sch. Bip. = V. calva (Sch.Bip.) Britton.
H. campestris Kuntze = F. campestris Grieseb.
H. cernuus B & H. = F. cernua DC.
H. copiapinus Phil. = Wedelia copiapina (Phil.) Reiche.
H. cordatus Lamb. = Heliopsis canescens Don.
H. cornifolius H.B.K. = V. cornifolia (H.B.K.) Blake.
H. corymbosus Poeppg. = F. corymbosa (Poeppg.) Reiche.
H. excelsus Willd. = V. excelsa DC. var. genuina Blake.
H. gayanus Phil. = F. gayana (Phil.) Reiche.
H. giganteus Cav. = V. excelsa DC.
H. glutinosus Hook & Arn. = F. corymbosa Reiche.
H. grosse-serratus Pohl. = Wulffia stenoglossa DC.
H. hookerianus DC. = Wyethia angustifolia Nutt.
H. invenustus Greene = Balsamorrhiza invenusta Coville.
H. laevis L. = Bidens laevis (L.) Brit. Stearns. & Pogg.
H. lanceolatus Meyen = F. corymbosa var. lanceolata Reiche.

H. Navarri Phil. = F. Navarri (Phil.) Reiche.
H. oaxacanus Greenm. = V. oaxacana (Greenm.) Blake.
H. oleifer Wall. = Guizotia abyssinica Cass.
H. quinquenervis Hook = Helianthella quinquenervis (Hook.) Gray.
H. revolutus Meyen = V. revoluta (Meyen) Blake.
H. rivularis Poeppg. = Leptocarpha rivularis (Poeppg.) DC.
H. rugosus Schau. = V. rugosa B & H. (according to Hemsley).
H. sarmentosus Rich. = Wulffia stenoglossa DC.
H. speciosus Hook. = Tithonia speciosa (Hook.) Griesch.
H. squarrosus H.B.K. = V. linearis.
H. Thurifer Molina = F. thurifer (Molina) DC.
H. trinervis Hort. Madr. = Tithonia excelsa.
H. truxillensis H.B.K. = V. truxillensis (H.B.K.) Blake.
H. tubaeformis Orteg. = Tithonia tubaeformis.
H. uniflorus Nutt. = Helianthella uniflora T. & G.

II. Excluded names

H. brasilicus Vellosa — undetermined, but certainly not Helianthus. The description presents a four-parted disc corolla, and a pappus not at all like that of Helianthus.

H. herbaceus Vellosa — undetermined, but not Helianthus. The description presents a duplex disc corolla, and an involucre of bracts united below the middle.

H. longiradiatus Bertol — undetermined, but not Helianthus; the achene has no pappus.

III. Unknown or doubtful species

H. cirrhoides Lehm. — grown from seeds sent from Utrecht under name *H. patens;* probably either *H. petiolaris* or *H. annuus.*

H. cochinchinensis Pers. — having been introduced into Asia, it is probably not a valid species; possibly *H. annuus* or *H. tuberosus.*

H. diffusus Moench. — source and habitat not given; description inadequate; type not seen.

H. esculentus Rottb. — source given as India, text gives medicinal properties only; validity very doubtful.

H. fulgidus (Ait.) Sturm — in the *Flora Deutschlands*, Sturm transfers Aiton's *Rudbeckia fulgida* to Helianthus. I am unable to verify the transfer without seeing the type.

H. giganteus Lour. — a plant from Cochin China; have seen no specimen; validity doubtful.

H. grandiflorus Wood — unknown.

H. Kentuckiensis M'Farl. & Anderson in *Am. Mid. Nat.*, 9:136, 1924. — not Helianthus.

H. Mandonii Sch. Bip. — undescribed.

H. membranifolius Poir. — type is in Herb. Desfont. I have seen no specimen; I suspect it is *H. decapetalus.*

H. mexicanus (Walp.) Hemsl. — originally described as a *Harpalium*, and transferred to *Helianthus* by Hemsley. If this is correct, it is probably *H. rigidus*, or *H. laetiflorus*, at least in that group. (See "Subjects for further study," p. 471.)

H. neomexicanus W. & S. — I have seen neither the type nor any specimen. From the description I suspect that it is *H. canus*.

H. pauciflorus Nutt. — No one seems to know anything about this species.

H. peruvianus Klotsch. — I have not seen the type, but the brief description suggests *H. annuus*.

H. polycephalus Cass. — certainly not *H. decapetalus*.

H. procumbens Pers. — unknown to me.

H. procumbens Raf. — *Quid?* I suspect that it is *H. debilis*.

H. pumilus Pers. — probably *H. annuus*.

H. quinqueradiatus Cav. — the description is curiously suggestive of Blake's *H. senex*.

H. ramosissimus Mill. — I have not seen the type nor any specimen; validity doubtful.

H. striatus Raf. — nothing is known of this species.

H. tenellus Raf. — this and the preceding species are unknown, owing to the loss of Rafinesque's herbarium, and are likely to remain unknown.

H. trilobatus Link — so far as I know, lobate leaves do not occur in Helianthus; perhaps a Rudbeckia?

H. trinervis Noronha — founded on a Javan plant; I have seen no specimen; validity very doubtful.

IV. Hybrid

H. orgyaloides Ckll., *Bot Gaz.*, 67 : 264, a hybrid.

Michigan State College
East Lansing Michigan

PLATES XLVII–LXXXVI

PLATE XLVII

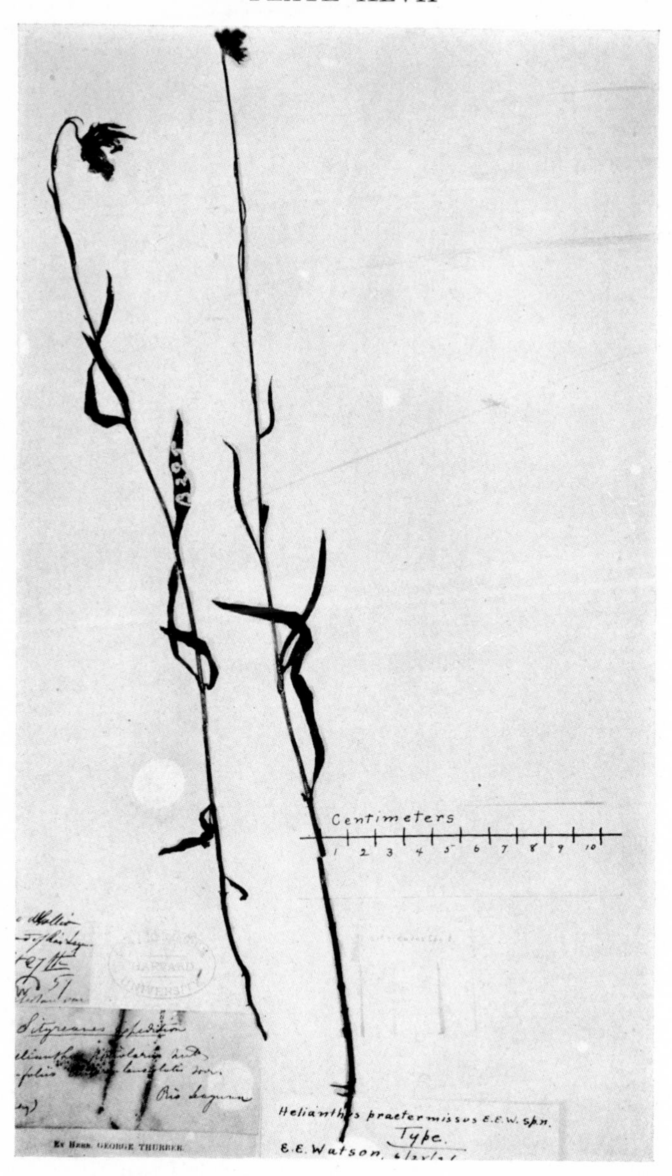

H. praetermissus E. E. Wats., sp. nov. Type

PLATE XLVIII

H. vestitus E. E. Wats., sp. nov. Type. Note hirsute stem

PLATE XLIX

H. simulans E. E. Wats., sp. nov. Type

PLATE L

H. plantagineus (T. & G.) E. E. Wats. Not the type, but a typical specimen

PLATE LI

H. elegans E. E. Wats., sp. nov. Type

PLATE LII

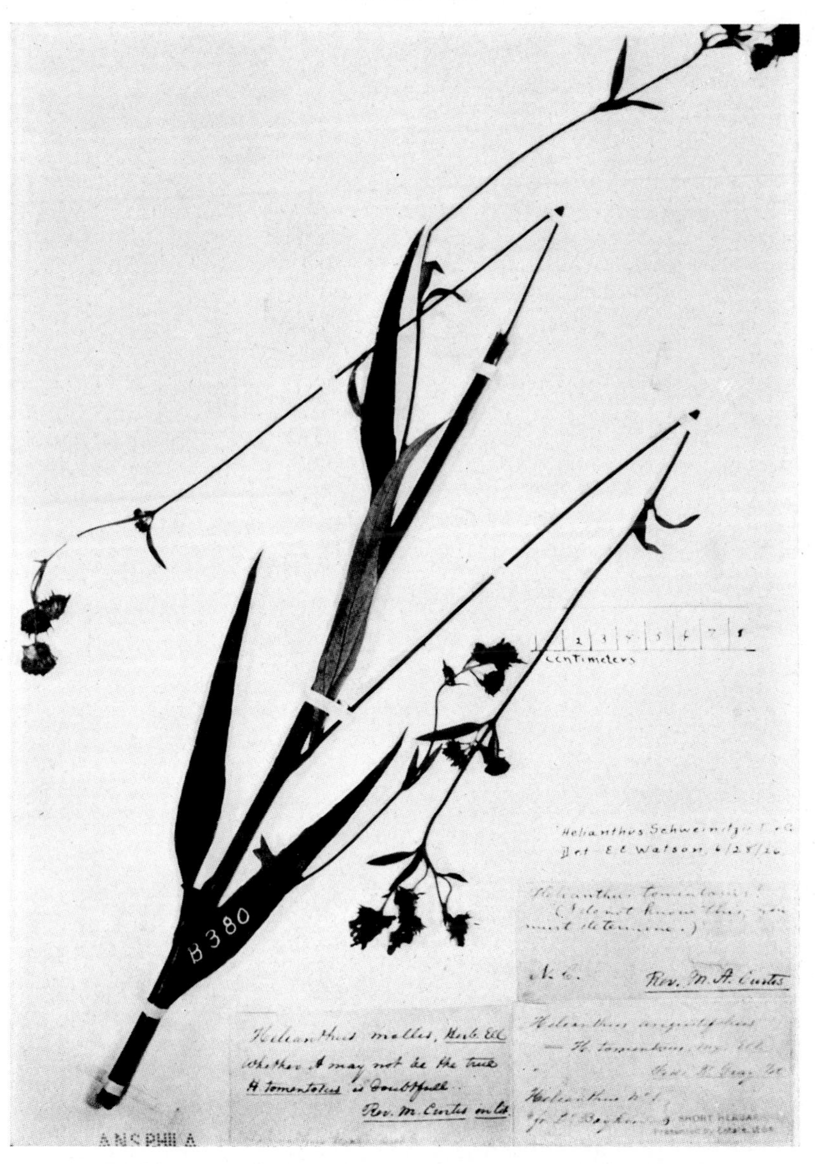

H. Schweinitzii T. & G. Not the type, but a typical specimen

PLATE LIII

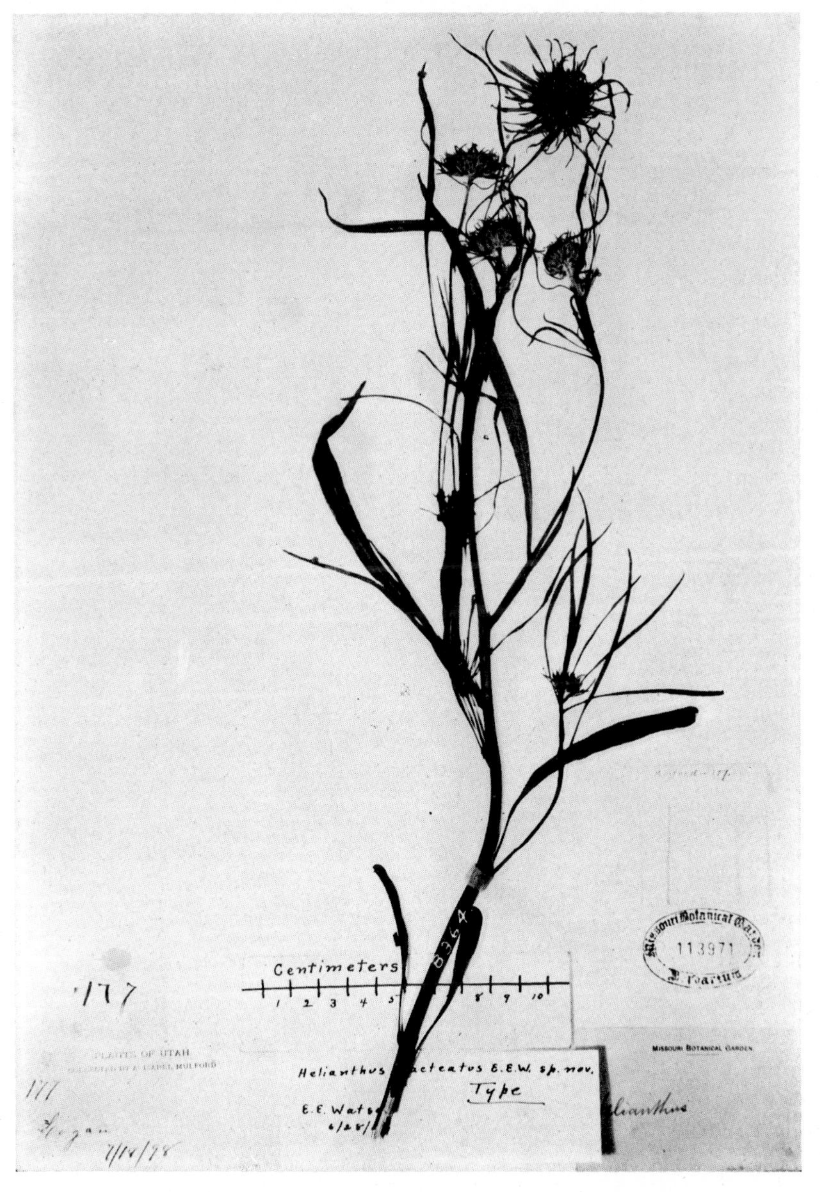

H. bracteatus E. E. Wats., sp. nov. Type. The characteristic bracts are especially obvious in the head at the lower right

PLATE LIV

H. excubitor E. E. Wats., sp. nov. Type

PLATE LV

H. tomentosus Michx. Form with very narrow leaves

PLATE LVI

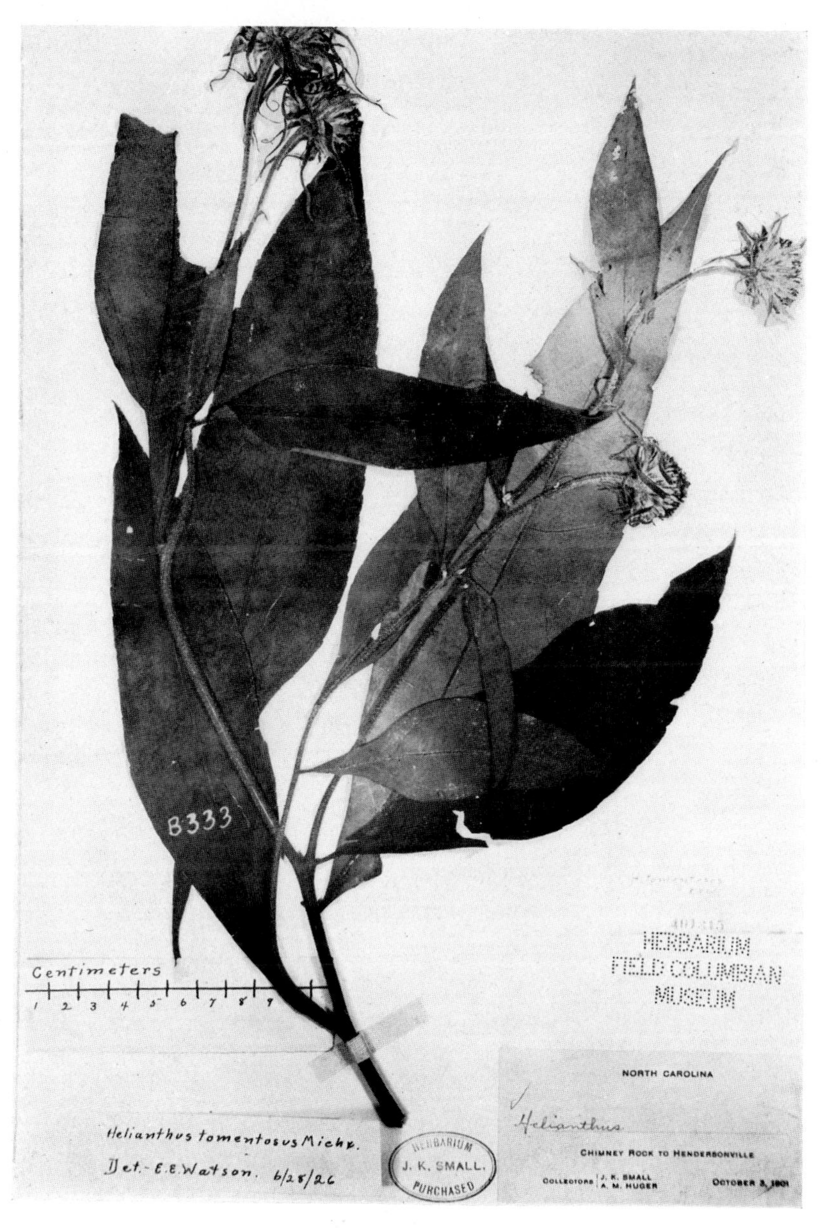

H. tomentosus Michx. Form with broad leaves

PLATE LVII

H. leptocaulis (S. Wats.) Blake. Type. Southern and Mexican form

PLATE LVIII

H. leptocaulis (S. Wats.) Blake, as it appears from Texas north

PLATE LIX

H. floribundus E. E. Wats., sp. nov. Type

PLATE LX

H. alienus E. E. Wats., sp. nov. Type

PLATE LXI

H. vernalis E. E. Wats., sp. nov. Type

PLATE LXII

H. validus E. E. Wats., sp. nov. Type

PLATE LXIII

H. borealis E. E. Wats., sp. nov. Type

PLATE LXIV

H. attenuatus E. E. Wats., sp. nov. Type

PLATE LXV

H. instabilis E. E. Wats., sp. nov. Type

PLATE LXVI

H. severus E. E. Wats., sp. nov. Type

PLATE LXVII

H. Besseyi Bates. Type

PLATE LXVIII

H. mollissimus E. E. Wats., sp. nov. Type

PLATE LXIX

H. membranaceus E. E. Wats., sp. nov. Type

PLATE LXX

H. altissimus L. Type

PLATE LXXI

H. doronicoides Lam. Not the type, but a typical specimen

PLATE LXXII

H. formosus E. E. Wats., sp. nov. Type

PLATE LXXIII

H. saxicola Small. Not the type, but part of the original collection and perfectly typical

PLATE LXXIV

H. brevifolius E. E. Wats., sp. nov. Type

PLATE LXXV

H. leoninus E. E. Wats., sp. nov. Type

PLATE LXXVI

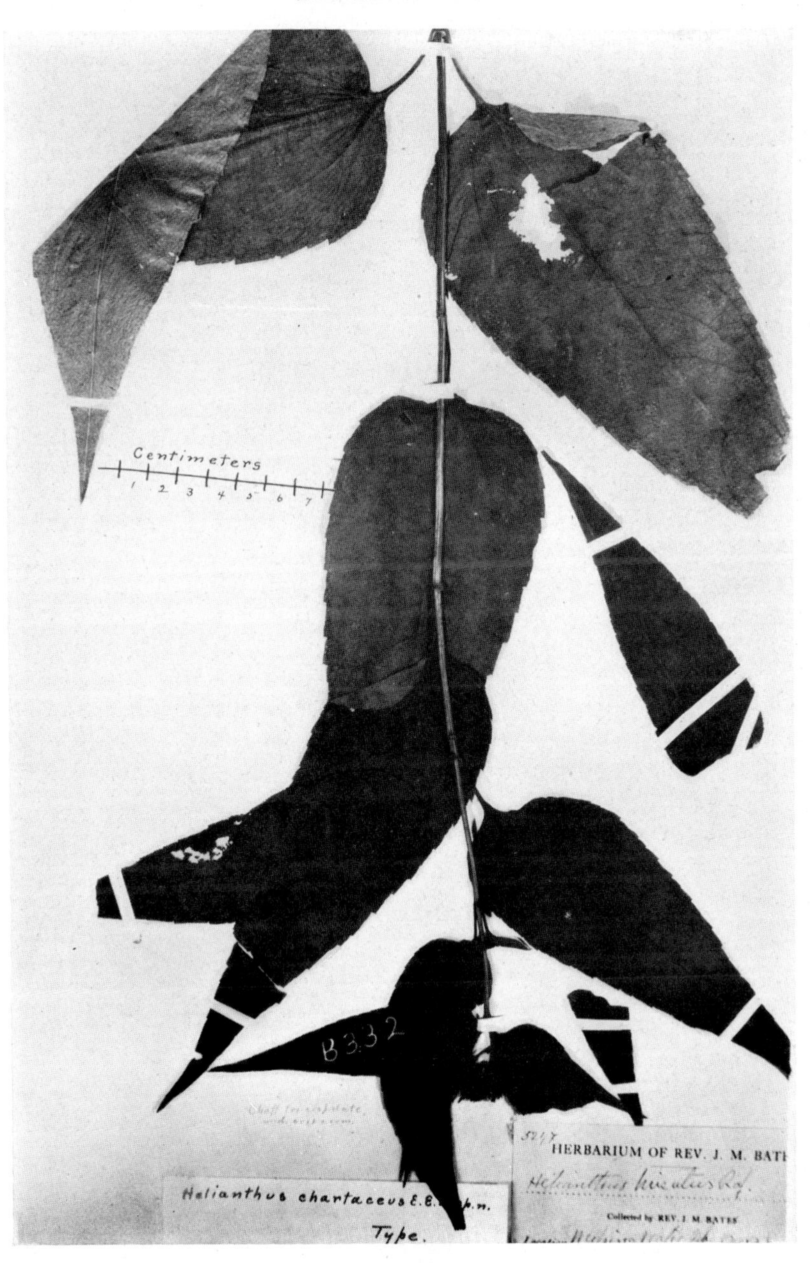

H. chartaceus E. E. Wats., sp. nov. Type

PLATE LXXVII

H. virilis E. E. Wats., sp. nov. Type

PLATE LXXVIII

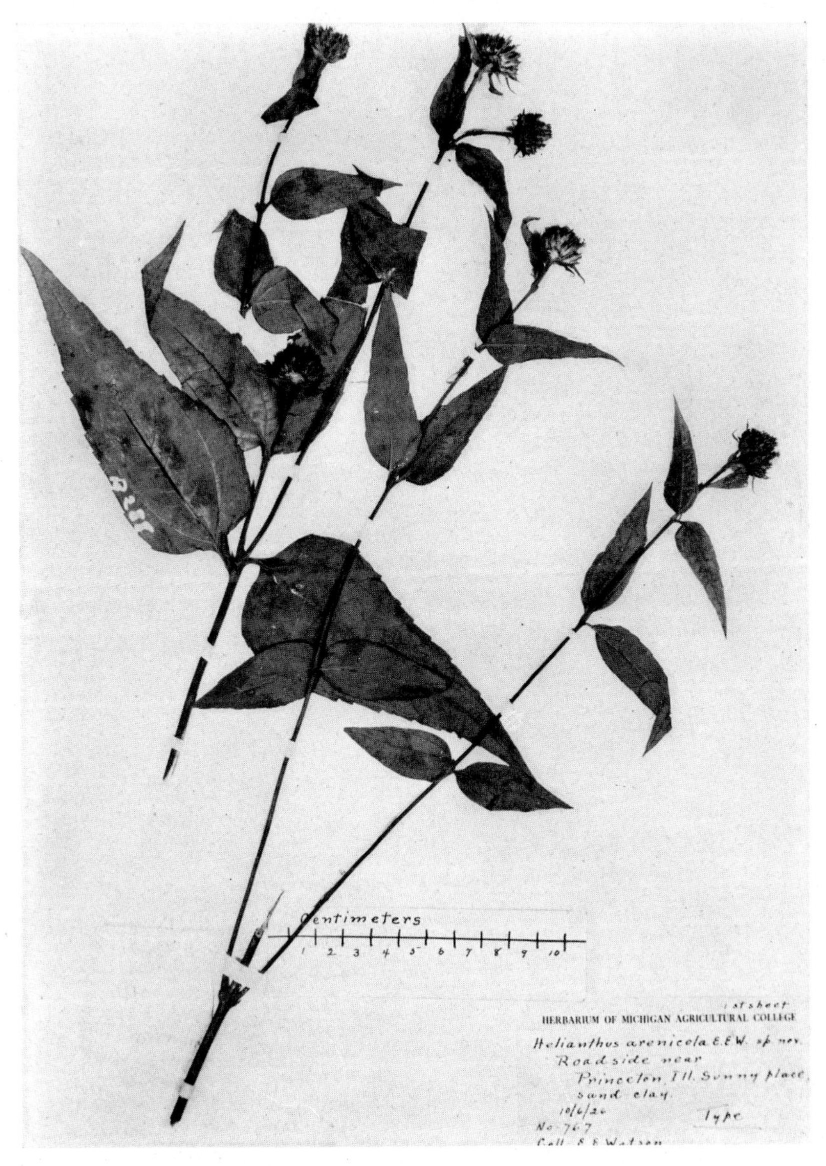

H. arenicola E. E. Wats., sp. nov. Type. Upper portion of main stem and inflorescence

PLATE LXXIX

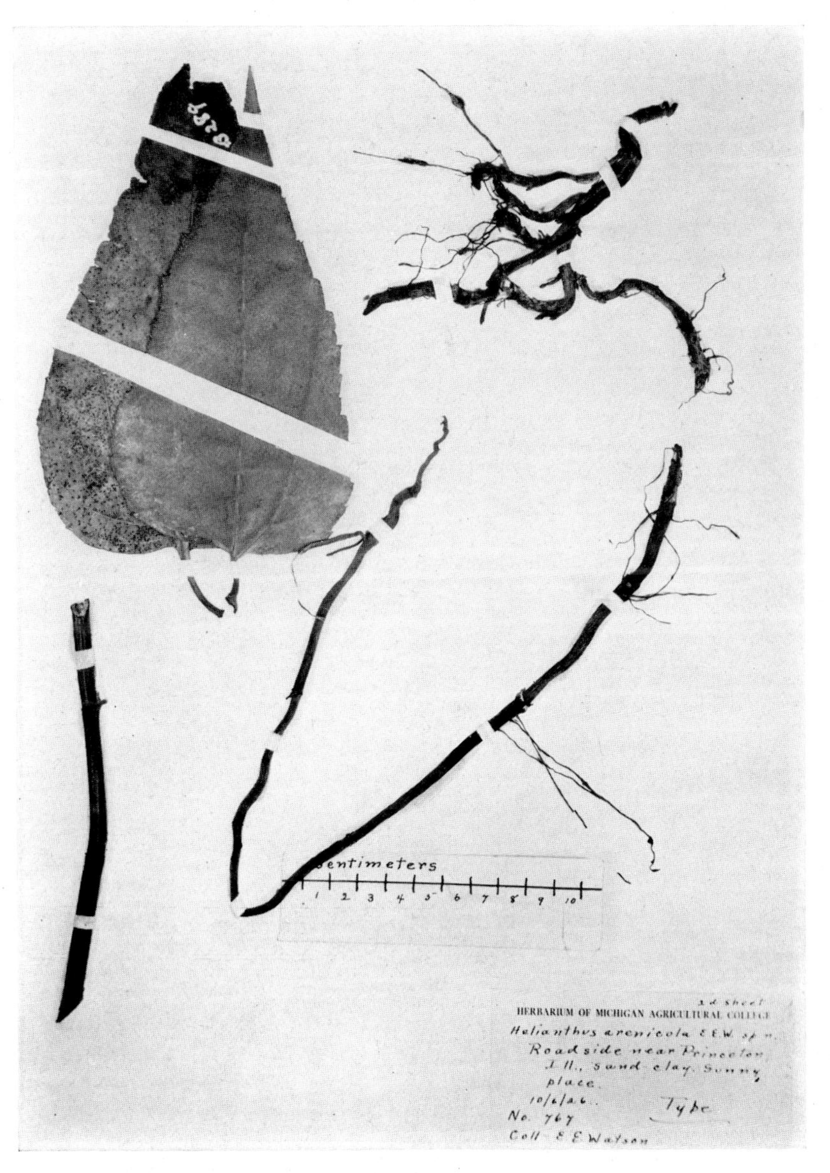

H. arenicola E. E. Wats., sp. nov. Lower stem, maximum leaf, and root-system

PLATE LXXX

H. exasperatus E. E. Wats., sp. nov. Type. Note root-system

PLATE LXXXI

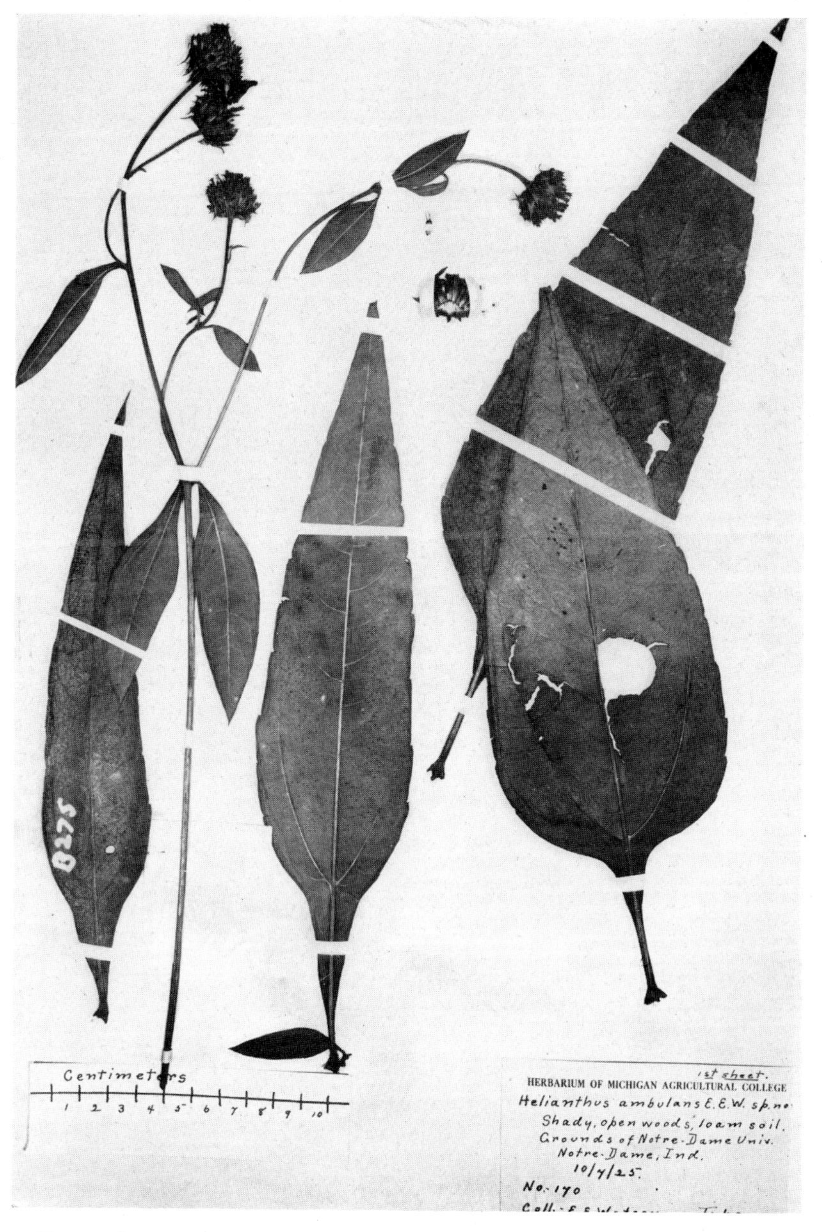

H. ambulans E. E. Wats., sp. nov. Type. Upper stem and inflorescence, maximum leaves to the right, leaves of middle stem to the left. Note drooping leaves at the inflorescence

PLATE LXXXII

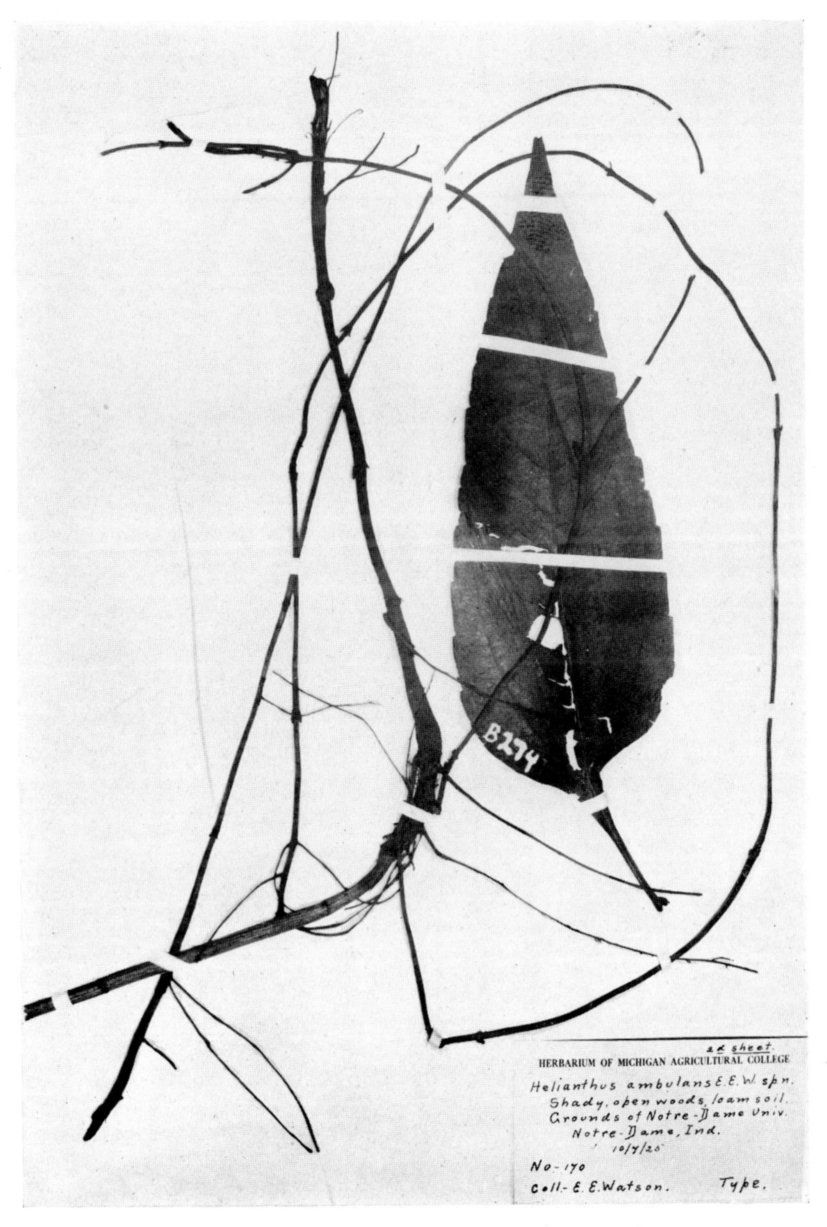

H. ambulans E. E. Wats., sp. nov. Type. Lower stem and root-system. Note long rhizomes

PLATE LXXXIII

H. strumosus L. Type. Note strumose leaves

PLATE LXXXIV

H. superbus E. E. Wats., sp. nov. Type. Portion of main stem, branch of the inflorescence, a root and a rhizome

PLATE LXXXV

H. luxurians E. E. Wats., sp. nov. Type. Lower stem, maximum leaves and a branch of the inflorescence

PLATE LXXXVI

H. luxurians E. E. Wats., sp. nov. Tip of main stem, upper cauline leaves, portion of middle stem, typical root

CULTURAL LIFE-HISTORIES OF DIAPORTHE IV*

LEWIS E. WEHMEYER

THE conidial connections of the following species of Diaporthe give further evidence of a correlation between the morphological characters of the perfect and imperfect stages of this genus. Three of these species, *Diaporthe detrusa* (Fr.) Fck., *D. ampelopsidis* (Ell.) E. & E., and *D. impulsa* (Cke. & Pk.) Sacc., are typical of the genus, since they have blackened zones in the substratum and produce the Phomopsis type of conidial stage in culture. *Diaporthe leiphaemia* (Fr.) Sacc. is somewhat atypical in having a rather strong entostromatic and ectostromatic development, but only an irregular blackening of the bark surface, and gives rise to conidial fruit-bodies somewhat intermediate between Phomopsis and Fusicoccum in structure. *Diaporthe spicata* E. & E., finally, shows no blackened zones in the substratum and produces Phoma-like pycnidia with only one type of conidium.

Diaporthe detrusa (Fr.) Fck.

Material of this species collected on *Berberis vulgaris* L. near Milton, Massachusetts, and used as a source of cultures agrees in all respects with the type (Fries' Scler. Suec. No. 6) of *Sphaeria detrusa*, except that this collection shows a definite ventral zone within the wood, which is unusual in this species. The fungus appears on the surface as small ectostromatic discs, or small dense clusters of cylindrical ostioles. The discs are 0.3–1.5 mm. in diameter. The perithecia (Pl. LXXXVII, Fig. 1) are definitely clustered and collectively erumpent through the rather well-developed ectostroma. A dorsal blackened zone, which is pustulate in charac-

*The work reported in this paper was carried out at Harvard University under the grant of a National Research Fellowship in the Biological Sciences.

ter, is present, dipping into the bark between the perithecial clusters. The ventral zone is usually absent or present only at the margins of the fruiting areas. The asci (Pl. LXXXVIII, Fig. 2) are clavate with a refractive ring in the apex and 60–80 $\times$ 9–12 μ. The spores (Pl. LXXXVIII, Fig. 3) are biseriate to obliquely uniseriate, oblong-elliptic to fusoid-elliptic, obtuse, scarcely constricted, 14–16 $\times$ 4.5–5.5 μ when young, becoming 15–17 $\times$ 5–7 μ when fully mature.

This species was placed in the genus Valsa by Fries (7, p. 411); was given out in Fuckel's Fung. Rhen. No. 588 as *Wuestneia aquilineariformis* Awd.; again in Wart. & Schenk, Schweiz. Krypt. No. 531, as *Mamiana detrusa* (Fr.) Sollm.; and was placed by Traverso (27, p. 195) in the genus Chorostate. Although *Diaporthe crassiuscula* Sacc. & Bizz. (23, p. 378) on Mahonia is given with spores 18–20 $\times$ 6–7.5 μ, type material (Myc. Ven. No. 1456) of this species shows the typical structure of *D. detrusa*, and immature spores. *Diaporthe mahoniae* Speg. (25, p. 456) is also apparently this same species on Mahonia as indicated by the description and Roum. Fung. Gall. No. 5840. *Diaporthe pycnostoma* Otth (14, p. 99) on Berberis is also the same as *D. detrusa*, as is shown by the type material under V*alsa pycnostoma* Otth in Nitschke's Herbarium.

Ascospores of this species were sprayed on agar on October 17, 1926, after the twigs had been in a damp chamber for two days. The next day the spores were germinating by means of a single germ tube 2.5–3 μ in diameter.

Single-spore cultures on oat agar produced grayish, erumpent, pycnidial stromata, 0.7–1.3 mm. in diameter. These pycnidial stromata arose as a proliferation of the vegetative hyphae just beneath the surface of the agar. There was often a slight superficial growth of hyphae which also proliferated and fused with the immersed stroma to form the somewhat erumpent fruit-body. There were no blackened zones in the agar. One or several conidial locules were initiated within each stroma. The locules were often confluent, more or less irregular in shape, and the older locules were bounded by a zone of darkened hyphae. Two types of conidia were formed, often intermixed within the same locule. The beta conidia (Pl. LXXXVIII, Fig. 5) were long cylindric, hyaline, one-celled, strongly bent or curved and 14–33 × 1–1.5 μ. The alpha conidia (Pl. LXXXVIII, Fig. 4) were elliptic-fusoid to elongate-fusoid, one-celled, hyaline and 8–13.5 × 2.5–3 μ. The alpha conidia were borne on short stout conidiophores, or on long filiform ones identical with the beta type of conidium (beta conidia were often seen with a terminal or intercalary swelling, while the alpha conidia were occasionally somewhat elongate and curved, representing intermediate growth forms). The spore horns composed of beta conidia were white, while those consisting mostly of alpha conidia were orange-yellow.

On May 24, 1927, steam-sterilized twigs of *Berberis vulgaris* were inoculated from a single-spore culture. A few weeks later numerous, small, grayish, erumpent-superficial stromata, which exuded white to yellowish spore horns, appeared on these twigs. A small ectostroma composed of greenish hyphae was formed on the bark surface, and at the same time there was a rapid proliferation of entostromatic hyphae in the surface bark layers beneath. The conidial locules (Pl. LXXXVIII, Fig. 1) usually originated in the entostromatic portion of the pycnidium, but where the ectostroma was well developed the cavities often arose in this tissue. On Berberis, the alpha conidia measured (8) 9.5–17 × 2–3 (5) μ, and the beta conidia 11–32 × 1–1.3 μ.

The conidia of *D. detrusa* are given by Fuckel (8, p. 205) as being 8–10 × 2.5 μ. Saccardo (20, p. 96) described this conidial stage as *Phoma detrusa* and gave the "basidia" as 20 × 1 μ. In his Fl. Boh. & Mor. No. 2001, Petrak has issued a *Phomopsis berberidis* (West.) Pet. which he considers (18, p. 19) the conidial stage of *D. detrusa* and the same as *Phoma detrusa* and *Phyllosticta Westendorpii* Thüm. (*P. berberidis* West.). Petrak's fungus produces spots on the leaves of Berberis, often about the aecia of *Puccinia graminis*. The conidia are given as 7–12.5 × 3–5 μ and the conidiophores as 10–20 × 2–2.75 μ. Its connection with *D. detrusa* is extremely doubtful and the conidial stage of this Diaporthe should stand as *Phomopsis detrusa* (Sacc.) Died. (Krypt.-Fl. d. Mark Brandenburg. Pilze VII, 9, 247).

DIAPORTHE AMPELOPSIDIS (Ell.) E. & E.

Material of this species collected on *Psedera quinquefolia* (L.) Greene near Waverley, Massachusetts, is identical with Ellis' type material (N. A. F. No. 881) of *Valsa ampelopsidis* Ell. (3, p. 112). It appears on the surface as minute black discs, 0.1–0.5 mm. in diameter, consisting of a compact cluster of cylindrical ostioles erumpent through a rather well-developed ectostroma. The perithecia (Pl. LXXXVII, Fig. 2) are clustered and cause a slight swelling of the bark. The entostroma is effuse, the dorsal blackened zone being on the bark surface, and the ventral zone more or less irregular deep in the wood or in the pith. The asci (Pl. LXXXVIII, Fig. 7) are broad clavate with a refractive ring in the apex and $67–80 \times 14–16\ \mu$. The spores (Pl. LXXXVIII, Fig. 8) are biseriate, broad, blunt, fusoid-elliptic, two-celled, hyaline, constricted at the septum and measure $15–19 \times 5–8\ \mu$.

On June 2, 1927, ascospores from this material were sprayed on agar after the twigs had been kept in a damp chamber for three days. The following day these spores were germinating freely by means of a single germ tube 3–4 μ in diameter. The germ tube nearly always arose from the under side of the spore and penetrated deeply into the agar.

Single-spore cultures on oat agar produced numerous, pulvinate, partially immersed, pycnidial stromata, $160–480 \times 160–240\ \mu$, after two weeks' growth. The pycnidial stromata were formed, as in *D. detrusa*, by the increase of the vegetative mycelium in the surface layers of the agar. A somewhat compact layer of darkened hyphae extended outward from the pycnidia along the agar surface. The surface layers of hyphae of this zone were heavily blackened, affecting the surface of the agar in a manner corresponding to the dorsal zone formed on twigs. Elliptical or irregularly shaped pycnidial locules, bounded by a zone of greenish hyphae, were formed in these stromata. Two types of conidia were produced. The first formed were of the beta type (Pl. LXXXVIII, Fig. 10), long cylindric, somewhat curved or slightly hamate, one-celled, hyaline and $16–27 \times 1\ \mu$, and were emitted as whitish spore horns. The later conidia were of the alpha type (Pl. LXXXVIII, Fig. 9), elliptic-fusoid, one-celled, hyaline, 9.5–13 (14) × 3–4 μ, and formed yellowish to orange spore horns.

On July 6, steam-sterilized twigs of *Psedera quinquefolia* were inoculated from single-spore cultures. A grayish to olive-green superficial mycelium appeared upon the surface of these twigs and numerous, small, spherical, erumpent-superficial, pycnidial stromata, 350–700 μ in diameter were formed. The outer layers of these stromata were heavily blackened, and the elliptic or irregular locules (Pl. LXXXVIII, Fig. 6) formed within them contained conidia which were mostly of the beta type and 15–20 × 1.3 μ. A few alpha conidia, 9–12 × 2.5–3 μ, were seen. No perithecia were formed on twigs. Pycnidial locules found in the ectostromata of the material collected at Waverley contained alpha conidia measuring 11–16 × 2.5–4 μ, and beta conidia measuring 15–19 × 1–1.5 μ.

Petrak (16, p. 441) reports a *Phomopsis ampelopsidis* Pet. on *Psedera quinquefolia* with conidia bacilliform to fusoid and 6–11 × 2–3 μ. Since *D. ampelopsidis* has not been reported from Europe, however, and since the conidia mentioned resemble more those of one of the forms of *D. eres,* which does occur on Psedera in Europe, it is probable that this Phomopsis is the conidial stage of *D. eres* on Psedera rather than of *D. ampelopsidis.*

Diaporthe spicata E. & E.

Material of *Diaporthe spicata* E. & E. was collected on *Acer saccharum* Marsh in Randolph Township, New Hampshire, on July 17, 1927. It appears on the surface of the twigs as numerous, angular, pustulate ruptures of the periderm, through which there are erumpent loose clusters of conical to fine cylindrical, or somewhat elongated ostioles. The perithecia (Pl. LXXXVII, Fig. 3) are 300–400 μ in diameter and grouped in loose clusters. A small light-colored ectostroma is formed above the perithecia, but soon crumbles away. There are no blackened zones formed in the substratum. The asci (Pl. LXXXVIII, Fig. 12) are clavate, have a refractive ring in the apex and are 47–55 × 12–13 μ. The spores (Pl. LXXXVIII, Fig. 13) are biseriate, elliptic-fusoid, straight or somewhat curved, two-celled, hyaline, constricted at the septum and 13–17 × 3.5–4.5 μ.

The material collected agrees with Ellis' type (N. A. F. No. 3330) of *Diaporthe spicata* (5, p. 143), and is very similar to *Diaporthe densissima* Ell. (4, p. 316) on Quercus, and should probably be considered as a variety of that species.

Sprays of ascospores were made from this material on July 22, 1927, after having been in a damp chamber for four days. After twenty-four hours a few spores were germinating, and after sixty-five hours nearly all the spores had produced 1–3 broad irregular germ tubes (Pl. LXXXIX, Fig. 1) some 4 μ in diameter. The germinating spores were swollen and measured 15–17 × 6–7 μ.

Single-spore cultures on oat agar produced numerous, hemispherical, white to grayish stromata, 480–800 μ in diameter. These consist of a stromatic proliferation of hyphae within the surface layers of the agar, together with a small, more compact superficial cushion of mycelium. The conidial locules are formed in this erumpent portion of the stroma. They arise as spherical to ellipsoidal masses of closely interwoven meristematic hyphae which break up in their entirety into conidia without forming any definite hymenium. The locules thus formed are entirely enclosed and usually surrounded by a wall-like layer of dark-walled hyphae. The conidia are of one type only, but are variable and irregular in shape (Pl. LXXXVIII, Fig. 14), being elliptic-fusoid to fusoid or cylindric, straight, inequilateral or somewhat curved, and often tapered toward one end. They measure 6.5–12 × 3–4 μ and form spore masses which are pinkish in color. Perithecia were formed in the looser stromatic area within the agar, but the contents of these fruit-bodies disintegrated and no mature ascospores were formed. Elongated cylindrical ostioles were formed which were collectively erumpent through the conidial ectostromata.

On August 16, steam-sterilized twigs of *Acer saccharum* were inoculated from single-spore cultures. When examined on September 29, these twigs showed numerous minute ectostromata, 300–480 μ in diameter, consisting of pulvinate masses of upright parallel hyphae arising upon the bark surface or within the periderm. Conidial locules (Pl. LXXXVIII, Fig. 11) similar to those described on agar were formed in some of these ectostromata. The conidia were identical with those formed on agar. Later these twigs showed numerous long, thread-like ostioles. Perithecia which failed to mature ascospores were formed in groups beneath the ectostromata.

The structure of *D. spicata* is very similar to those species which Petrak (17, p. 117) has placed in his genus Cryptodiaporthe, which are characterized by the entire lack of any blackened zones in the substratum and a very slight stromatic development. Petrak gives the form genus Septomyxa as the conidial stage of these forms. This conclusion, however, was drawn from a single observational connection, and it is more likely that these simpler forms present various types of conidial stages, as they appear to be a heterogeneous group from which several lines of development have arisen.

The pycnidia of *D. spicata* resemble somewhat those already reported by the writer (29; 31) for the genus Apioporthe, in both their structure and development, and the conidial fruit-bodies of both these genera can be considered as primitive forms derived from the Gloeosporium type of fruit-body of the genera Gnomonia and Apiognomonia merely by the increase in stromatic development due perhaps to the firmer tissue of a twig substrate.

Diaporthe impulsa (Cke. & Pk.) Sacc.

In a previous paper (30), under a discussion of the cultural connection of the perfect and imperfect stages of *Diaporthe pruni* E. & E., the writer has pointed out that a similar species (*D. impulsa*) occurs on species of Sorbus, differing only in the somewhat smaller non-appendaged ascospores. It was there suggested that this species on Sorbus might be found to differ also in the somewhat longer alpha conidia. The following cultural connection confirms this suggestion.

Material of *Diaporthe impulsa* (Cke. & Pk.) Sacc. was collected on twigs of *Pyrus* (*Sorbus*) *americana* (Marsh) DC. on Mt. Adams, New Hampshire, on June 23, 1927. The fungus appears on the surface as circular discs 1.5 mm. in diameter and consisting of a cluster of stout cylindric ostioles erumpent through a grayish ectostromatic disc. There is a dorsal blackened zone which dips to the wood about the perithecial clusters, cutting out pustulate entostromatic areas (Pl. LXXXVII, Fig. 5). There is an effuse ventral zone well within the wood or along the pith. The asci (Pl. LXXXIX, Fig. 3) are clavate-cylindric and 60–70 × 7–10 μ. The spores (Pl. LXXXIX, Fig. 4) are biseriate, elliptic-fusoid, two-celled, hyaline, constricted at the septum and 13–18 × 2.5–5.5 μ.

The material collected on Mt. Adams is identical with the type (Herb. N. Y. Mus., Upper Ausable & Edmond's Pond, by Peck) of *Valsa impulsa* Cke. & Pk. (15, p. 109). Von Höhnel (12, p. 387) distinguishes two species of Diaporthe on Sorbus. One of these, *D. sorbicola* (Nit.) v. H., is based on *Valsa sorbicola* Nit., and according to material from Nitschke's herbarium differs from *D. impulsa* in the somewhat smaller ascospores (12–14 × 2.5–3.5 μ) and the lack of any definite well-developed ectostroma. Brefeld (2, p. 236) cultured what he considered to be this species and published it as *D. sorbicola* (Nit.) Bref. Von Höhnel (12, pp. 338–339), on the bare evidence of an ascus figured (2, Pl. 8, Fig. 10), decides that Brefeld's fungus was the same as *Diaporthe patria* Speg. (22, p. 250), which according to von Höhnel's description and most European exsiccati is the same as *D. impulsa.* Jaczewski (13, p. 72) points out, however, that the description of *D. patria,* with spores 12–15 × 3–4 μ, shows it to be the same as *Valsa sorbicola* Nit., which, in the absence of authentic material, is the writer's opinion. Von Höhnel (12, p. 389) states that *Dioporthe aucupariae* Hazsl. (10, p. 193) and *D. Woroniniae* Jacz. (13, p. 72) are the same as *D. patria.* Through the kindness of Dr. Filarszkey of the Hungarian National Museum, the type of *D. aucupariae* has been examined and proves to be the same as *D. impulsa.* Material of *D. Woroniniae,* kindly sent to the writer by Dr. Jaczewski, shows only decayed pustules, but from this material and the original description it appears to be the same as *D. impulsa.* The types of *Diaporthe congesta* E. & E. (Ellis Herb. Myc. 8.12 [6, p. 165]) and *D. strumelloides* Rehm (Fung. Eur. No.

3753) are the same as *D. impulsa*. Under Syd. Myc. March. No. 1654 there is a label, *Diaporthe expatriata* Rehm, with no accompanying specimen. A second packet labeled *Valsa sorbi* (Alb. & Schw.) contains typical material of *D. impulsa*.

Ascospores of the Mt. Adams material were sprayed on agar after being kept in a damp chamber for four days, and germinated within twenty-four hours. The germinating ascospores measured 15–17 × 4–5 μ and produced one or sometimes two germ tubes, 2–3 μ in diameter.

Single-spore cultures on oat agar produced, within two weeks, numerous, small, pulvinate, partially superficial, pycnidial stromata, 320–560 × 160–320 μ, from which there were exuded whitish to pinkish-yellow spore horns. Only one type of conidium was produced on agar. This was of the alpha type (Pl. LXXXIX, Fig. 5) and was long fusoid, one-celled, hyaline and (15) 17–24 × 2.5–3 μ. The stromata were composed of prosenchymatous masses of hyphae within which one, or sometimes several, flattened, irregular locules were formed.

On August 13, steam-sterilized twigs of *Pyrus americana* and of *Prunus sp.* were inoculated from single-spore cultures. By September 27, a number of large, grayish, strongly erumpent, pulvinate ectostromata, 1–2 mm. in diameter, were formed on the twigs of *Pyrus americana*. Most of these stromata remained sterile, but a few exuded spore masses containing two types of conidia. Entostromatic areas were formed beneath these ectostromata and were outlined by a blackened ventral zone in the bark or wood. In a few cases mature perithecia, with ascospores measuring 12–15 × 3.5–4.5 and asci 67–75 × 7–8 μ, were formed in these areas beneath the ectostromata.

On Prunus the growth was much more limited and the stromata were usually smaller, but more often containing pycnidial locules. The beta type of conidium (Pl. LXXXIX, Fig. 7) was most abundant on Prunus, but alpha conidia were also present. The variation in the size of the conidia covered the same range on both host substrata. The alpha conidia measured (13) 16–27 × 2.5–5 μ. On Sorbus the alpha conidia occasionally showed abnormal swellings, while on Prunus such swellings (Pl. LXXXIX,

Fig. 6) were the rule and quite characteristic. The beta conidia (Pl. LXXXIX, Fig. 7) were long cylindric, allantoid or hamate, one-celled, hyaline and 10–19 × 1–1.3 μ. These conidia it will be noted are very similar to, but distinctly longer than, those of *Diaporthe pruni* (alpha 10–19 × 2.5–3; beta 10–15 × 1–1.5 μ.)

Brefeld (2) in his cultures of *D. sorbicola* (Nit.) Bref. obtained fusoid hyaline conidia 11–16 × 2–3 μ, which are smaller than those obtained by the writer. It is interesting to note that his figures (2, Pl. 8, Fig. 13) of germinating conidia are identical with the abnormal alpha conidia found on Prunus, which may be the initial stages of germination occurring within the spore mass. Dr. Jaczewski has pointed out to the writer that the imperfect stage of his *Diaporthe Woroniniae* has been described from *Caragana arborescens* Lam. as *Phomopsis caraganae* Bond. by Bondarzew (1). The alpha conidia of this species are given as 13–18 × 3–3.5 μ and the beta conidia as 14–20 × 1.5 μ. These alpha conidia are somewhat shorter than those of *D. impulsa*, and as there has been described on Caragana another species of Diaporthe (*D. caraganae* Jacz.) which is very similar to *D. impulsa*, it seems more probable that this Phomopsis is the conidial stage of that species.

Diaporthe leiphaemia (Fr.) Sacc. var. **Raveneliana** (Thüm. & Rehm), comb. nov.

Material of this species was collected on *Quercus alba* L. near Canton, Massachusetts, on July 23, 1927. The fungus appears on the surface as prominent conical or pulvinate pustules 0.5–1.2 mm. in diameter with a central, yellow-brown, ectostromatic disc erumpent through an angular rupture of the periderm and containing the scattered slightly erumpent ostioles. The perithecia (Pl. LXXXVII, Fig. 4) are 240–480 × 320–640 μ, clustered beneath the yellow ectostromatic disc and surrounded by more or less of a development of entostromatic mycelium. The surface of the bark is usually more or less blackened above the perithecia and this blackening may extend laterally between the pustules. There are no ventral zones in the substratum. The asci (Pl. LXXXIX, Fig. 11) are clavate with a refractive ring in the apex and 55–65 × 6–9 μ. The spores (Pl. LXXXIX, Fig. 9) are biseriate, broad fusoid-elliptic, two-celled, hyaline, slightly constricted at the septum, straight to inequilateral or somewhat curved and measure 12–15 (16) × 4–6 (7) μ.

The true *Diaporthe leiphaemia* (Fr.) Sacc. is a European species and has a lengthy synonymy which need not be considered here. The variety here considered occurs only in America and has generally been called *D. leiphaemia* by American mycologists. It was described by de Thümen (26, p. 178), however, as *Diaporthe Raveneliana* Thüm. & Rehm from material collected by Ravenel, and the type of this species (Myc. Univ. No. 865) is typical of all American collections seen by the writer. The spores (Pl. LXXXIX, Fig. 8) of the European *D. leiphaemia* are longer and narrower (15–20 × 3.5–5.5 μ), and are more strongly constricted and curved than those (Pl. LXXXIX, Fig. 9) of the American variety. *D. leiphaemia* of Europe also tends to have a stronger stromatic development, with a more widely ruptured periderm, a more prominent disc and a heavier blackening of the bark surface.

Ascospores from the twigs of *Quercus alba* collected near Canton, Massachusetts, were sprayed on agar on August 1, 1927. The following day these spores had thrown out a single germ tube 4–5.5 μ in diameter.

Single-spore cultures on oat agar produced a white to tan cottony, superficial growth. Numerous, hemispherical, superficial stromata 1–2.5 mm. in diameter were formed in these cultures as a result of a local proliferation of the hyphae just within and on the surface of the agar. Most of these stromata remained sterile, but a few produced numerous irregular and finally confluent locules in their interior. These locules on agar, although irregular and confluent, were entirely enclosed and had a well-defined layer of conidiophores. Two types of conidia were found in these pycnidia. The alpha type (Pl. LXXXIX, Fig. 12) of conidium was long cylindric-fusoid, one-celled, hyaline and 13–20 × 2–3 μ. The beta conidia (Pl. LXXXIX, Fig. 13) were short cylindric to somewhat allantoid, one-celled, hyaline and measured 5.5–10 × 1.5–2 μ. The spore horns were yellowish.

On August 12, 1927, steam-sterilized twigs of *Quercus alba*

L. and *Castanea dentata* (Marsh) Borkh. were inoculated from single-spore cultures. When examined on September 27, these twigs showed numerous conical to pulvinate ectostromata, 0.3–1.0 mm. in diameter. These ectostromata were formed on the surface of the bark and conidial locules (Pl. LXXXIX, Fig. 10) arose in the upper and lateral peripheral portions of the stroma in the form of one or more irregular flattened cavities. These marginal locules increased in size, became confluent, and often broke open to the exterior. There was no definite wall formed about these locules, although there were a few layers of subhymenial cells beneath the conidiophore layer. Both types of conidia were found in either the same or separate fruit-bodies. There was no constant difference in the size of the conidia formed on Quercus and Castanea. The beta conidia were (6.5) 8–11 × 1–1.5 μ, and were whitish to yellow in mass. The alpha conidia measured 11–20 × 2.5–5.5 μ and were yellow-brown in mass.

The imperfect stage of *Diaporthe leiphaemia* has been variously reported and interpreted. The Tulasnes (28, p. 197) gave *Cytispora leucosperma* Desm. as the imperfect stage of their *Valsa leiphaemia.* They gave the "stylospores" as 10 μ long, linear and straight. Their figures of the conidial fruit-bodies show ectostromata with peripherally placed locules opening to the exterior which are typical of the pycnidia obtained in cultures of the var. *Raveneliana.* Fuckel (8, p. 64) gives the conidia of his *Cryptospora leiphaemia* as lanceolate-cylindric, continuous and 10 × 2 μ. In 1878, Saccardo (19, p. 261) gave *Cytispora quercina* West. with "spermatia" 10–12 × 2–3 μ and slightly curved as the imperfect stage of *D. leiphaemia.* In 1880, he (21, p. 345) gives this conidial stage as *Fusicoccum quercinum* Sacc., with conidia fusoid and 15–18 × 3–3.5 μ. Von Höhnel (12, p. 395) gives *Myxosporium lanceola* Sacc. & Roum. (24, p. 36), with conidia fusoid and 20–22 × 4 μ, as being the same as *Fusicoccum quercinum.* He places the conidial stage of *D. leiphaemia* as *Phomopsis quercinum* (Sacc.) v. H. (11, p. 681), and mentions two types of fusiform conidia, one 6–10 × 2 μ, and the other 16–22 × 2–3 μ. He also reports filiform hamate conidia 20 × 1 μ from Krieger's Fung. Sax. No. 1782, but these must belong with some other fungus, as such conidia have not occurred in culture nor been previously reported for *D. leiphaemia*. Grove (9, p. 62) gives the conidia of *Phomopsis quercinum* as 7–10 × 1.5–2 μ and says that larger (15–16 × 3–3.5 μ) and intermediate (10–14 × 3–3.5 μ) forms of conidia seem to exist. He considers the fruit-body as intermediate between Fusicoccum and Phomopsis in structure.

From these descriptions, two types of conidia, one cylindric, more or less curved and 6–12 × 1.5–2 μ, the other fusiform and 14–22 × 3–4 μ, can be distinguished. These agree very well with the conidia obtained in cultures of the var. *Raveneliana*. The laterally placed, rather indefinite, often apically exposed locules and the elongate fusiform alpha conidia, as well as the short cylindric beta conidia, suggest the form genus Fusicoccum rather than Phomopsis.

The perithecial stroma is also somewhat atypical for the group of species having a Phomopsis conidial stage. There is no ventral blackened zone within the substratum, and although there is a dorsal blackening of the bark surface, this is often indefinite or interrupted. There is a rather copious development of entostromatic mycelium about the distinctly clustered perithecia, but no definitely outlined or differentiated entostromatic area. There is also a well-developed ectostromatic disc. All these characters, together with the Fusicoccum-like conidial fruit-body, point to this species as an advanced form lying on the border line of the genus.

SUMMARY

The production of the imperfect stage in single ascospore cultures of five species of Diaporthe has presented further evidence of a correlation between the characters of the perithecial and conidial stages of this genus, as previously indicated by the writer.

Diaporthe detrusa (Fr.) Fck., *Diaporthe ampelopsidis* (Ell.) E. & E. and *Diaporthe impulsa* (Cke. & Pk.) Sacc., all species showing definite blackened zones within the substratum, produced the Phomopsis type of conidial stage typically associated with such species.

Diaporthe Raveneliana Thüm. & Rehm is given as *Diaporthe leiphaemia* (Fr.) Sacc. var. *Raveneliana* (Thüm. & Rehm), comb. nov. The true *D. leiphaemia* is shown to occur only in Europe while the variety *Raveneliana* is found in America only. The perithecial stromata of this species and variety show an advanced type of development in the definitely clustered perithecia, well-developed entostromatic and ectostromatic mycelium, lack of any ventral zone and often indefinite dorsal blackening of the bark surface. In correspondence with this the conidial stage is somewhat atypical, having laterally placed locules often open to the exterior as in the form genus Fusicoccum.

Diaporthe spicata E. & E., a species without any blackened zones in the substratum and resembling the species placed in Petrak's genus Cryptodiaporthe, produced only one type of conidium in a Phoma-like pycnidium, in a manner similar to that previously described by the writer for the genus Apioporthe.

HARVARD UNIVERSITY

BIBLIOGRAPHY

1. Bondarzew, A. S. 1922. De fungo novo in ramis Caraganae arborescentis (Not. syst. Inst. Crypt. Hort., Petropol.), 1 : 84–86. In Russian with Latin diagnosis.

2. Brefeld, O. 1891. Untersuchungen aus dem Gesammtgebiete der Mykologie, 10 : 158–351. Münster.

3. Ellis, J. B. 1882. New Species of North American Fungi. Bull. Torr. Bot. Club, 9 : 98–99; 111–112.

4. —— 1883. New Species of North American Fungi. Am. Nat., 17 : 316–319.

5. —— and Everhart, B. M. 1893. New Species of North American Fungi from Various Localities. Proc. Acad. Nat. Sci. Phil., 1893 : 128–172.

6. —— —— 1903. New Species of Fungi from Various Localities. Journ. Myc., 9 : 164–168.

7. Fries, E. 1846. Summa Vegetabilium Scandinaviae. 1–572. Holmiae et Lipsiae.

8. Fuckel, L. 1869. Symbolae Mycologicae. Pp. 1–459. Wiesbaden.

9. Grove, W. B. 1917. The British Species of Phomopsis. Bull. Misc. Inf., Kew, 1917 : 49–73.

10. Hazslinsky, F. 1892. Magyarország S társorszagainak Sphaeriái. Math. es term. Közlem., 25 : 3–333.

11. Höhnel, F. von. 1906. Fragmente zur Mykologie. Mittheil. II. Sitzungsb. Kais. Akad. Wiss. Wien. Math.-naturw. Kl., Abt. 1, 115 : 649–695.

12. —— 1917. Fragmente zur Mykologie. Mittheil. XX. Sitzungsb. Kais. Akad. Wiss. Wien. Math.-naturw. Kl., Abt. 1, 126 : 353–399.

13. Jaczewski, A. 1896. III série de matériaux la flore mycologique du gouvernement de Smolensk. Bull. Soc. Imp. Nat. d. Moscou, 10 : 65–94.

14. Otth, G. 1870. Siebenter Nachtrag zu dem in den Mittheilungen vom Jahr 1844 enthaltenen Verzeichnisse schweizerischer Pilze, und Fortsetzung der Nachträge vom Jahr 1846, 1850, 1857, 1863, 1865 und 1868. Mittheil. d. naturforsch. Gesell. in Bern, 1870 : 88–115.

15. Peck, C. H. 1875. Report of the Botanist. N. Y. St. Mus. Rep., 27 : 73–116.

16. Petrak, F. 1916. Beiträge zur Pilzflora von Mähren und Österreich-Schlesien.

17. —— 1921. Mykologische Notizen. II. Ann. Myc., 19 : 17–128.

18. —— 1925. Mykologische Notizen. VIII. Ann. Myc., 23 : 1–143.

19. SACCARDO, P. A. 1878. Fungi Veneti novi vel critici. Ser. VIII. Mich., 1 : 237–275.

20. —— 1880. Fungi Gallici. Ser. II. Mich., 2 : 40–135.

21. —— 1880. Fungi Gallici. Ser. III. Mich., 2 : 302–371.

22. —— 1881. Fungi Veneti novi vel critici v. Mycologigiae Venetae addendi. Ser. XII. Mich., 2 : 241–301.

23. —— 1881. Appendix ad seriem XII Fungorum Venetorum Mich., 2 : 377–383.

24. —— AND ROUMEGUÉRE, C. 1884. Reliquiae Mycologicae Libertianae. Ser. IV (1). Rev. Myc., 6 : 26–39.

25. SPEGAZZINI, C. 1879. Nova addenda ad Mycologiam Venetam, Mich., 1 : 453–487.

26. THÜMEN, F. DE. 1878. Fungorum Americanorum triginta species nova. Flora, 61 : 177–184.

27. TRAVERSO, J. B. 1906. Flora Italica Cryptogamia. Pt. I, 2 : 1–352. Rocca S. Casciano.

28. TULASNES, L. R. AND C. 1863. Selecta Fungorum Carpologia, II : 1–319. Paris.

29. WEHMEYER, L. E. 1926. Further Cultural Life Histories of the Stromatic Sphaeriales. Journ. Bot., 13 : 231–247.

30. —— 1927. Cultural Life-Histories of Diaporthe I. Papers Mich. Acad. Sci., Arts and Letters, 6 : 377–396.

31. —— 1928. Cultural Life-Histories of Diaporthe III. Papers Mich. Acad. Sci., Arts and Letters, 8 : 215–232.

EXPLANATION OF PLATES

PLATE LXXXVII

FIG. 1. Vertical section through perithecial stroma of *Diaporthe detrusa* (Fr.) Fck. on *Berberis vulgaris* L.

FIG. 2. Vertical section through perithecial stroma of *Diaporthe ampelopsidis* (Ell.) E. & E. on *Psedera quinquefolia* (L.) Greene

FIG. 3. Vertical section through perithecial stroma of *Diaporthe spicata* E. & E. on *Acer saccharum* Marsh

FIG. 4. Vertical section through perithecial stroma of *Diaporthe leiphaemia* (Fr.) Sacc. var. *Raveneliana* (Thüm. & Rehm), comb. nov. on *Quercus alba* L.

FIG. 5. Vertical section through perithecial stroma of *Diaporthe impulsa* (Cke. & Pk.) Sacc. on *Pyrus americana* (Marsh) DC.

PLATE LXXXVIII

Diaporthe detrusa (Fr.) Fck.

FIG. 1. Vertical section of pycnidial locule as formed in culture on *Berberis vulgaris* L.

FIG. 2. Ascus with ascospores

FIG. 3. Ascospores

FIG. 4. Alpha type of conidia obtained in culture

FIG. 5. Beta type of conidia obtained in culture

Diaporthe ampelopsidis (Ell.) E. & E.

FIG. 6. Vertical section of conidial locule as formed in culture on *Psedera quinquefolia* (L.) Greene

FIG. 7. Ascus with ascospores

FIG. 8. Ascospores

FIG. 9. Alpha type of conidia produced in culture

FIG. 10. Beta type of conidia produced in culture

Diaporthe spicata E. & E.

FIG. 11. Vertical section of pycnidial locule as formed in culture on *Acer saccharum* Marsh

FIG. 12. Ascus with ascospores

FIG. 13. Ascospores

FIG. 14. Type of conidia obtained in cultures

PLATE LXXXIX

FIG. 1. Germinating ascospores of *Diaporthe spicata* E. & E.

Diaporthe impulsa (Cke. & Pk.) Sacc.

FIG. 2. Vertical section of conidial locule as formed in culture on *Prunus sp.*

FIG. 3. Ascus with ascospores

FIG. 4. Ascospores

FIG. 5. Alpha type of conidia formed in cultures

FIG. 6. Irregularly swollen type of conidia formed in cultures on *Prunus sp.*

FIG. 7. Beta type of conidia obtained in culture

Diaporthe leiphaemia (Fr.) Sacc. var. *Raveneliana* (Thüm. & Rehm), comb. nov.

FIG. 8. Ascospores of *D. leiphaemia* (Fr.) Sacc. (from Syd. Myc. March. No. 471. and Roum. Fung. Gall. No. 5635)

FIG. 9. Ascospores of *D. leiphaemia* var. *Raveneliana* (from material cultured)

FIG. 10. Vertical section of conidial fruit-body as formed in culture on *Quercus alba* L.

FIG. 11. Ascus with ascospores

FIG. 12. Alpha type of conidia obtained in culture

FIG. 13. Beta type of conidia obtained in culture

PLATE LXXXVII

PLATE LXXXVIII

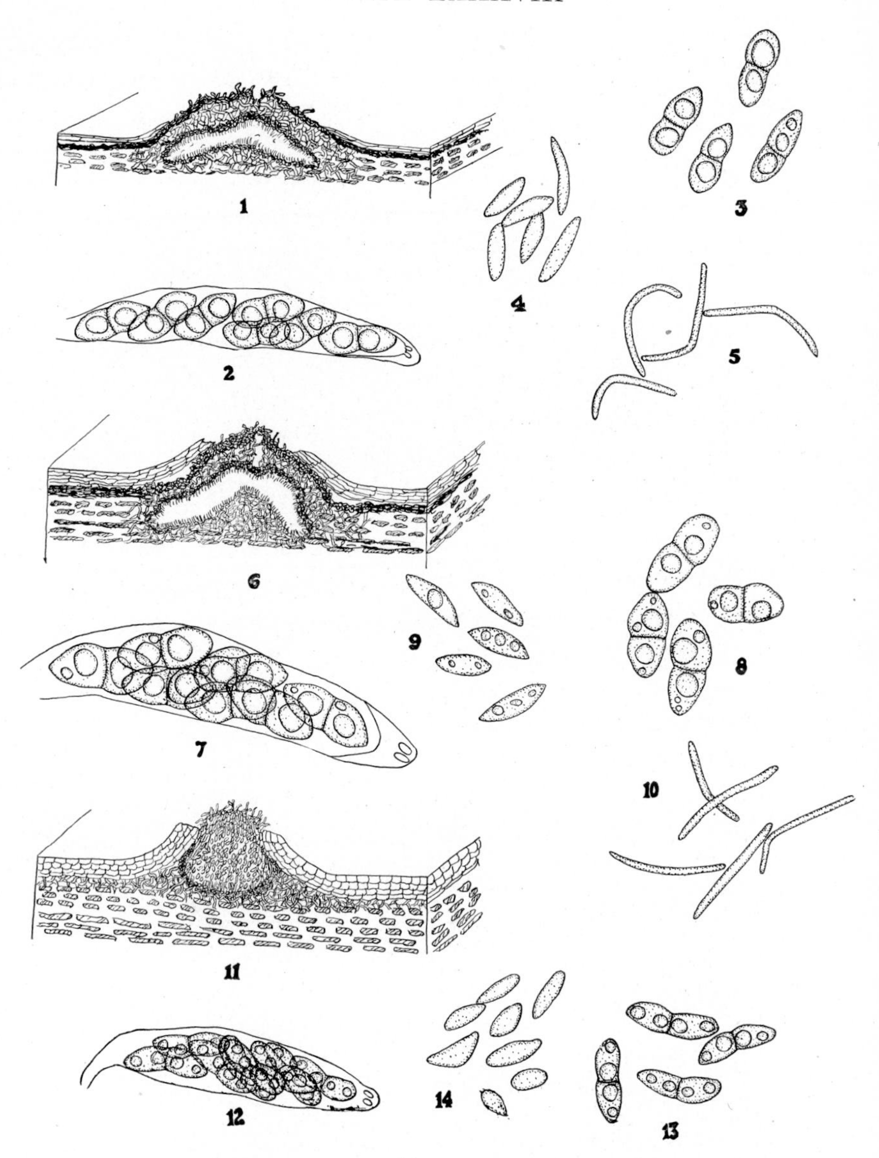

PLATE LXXXIX

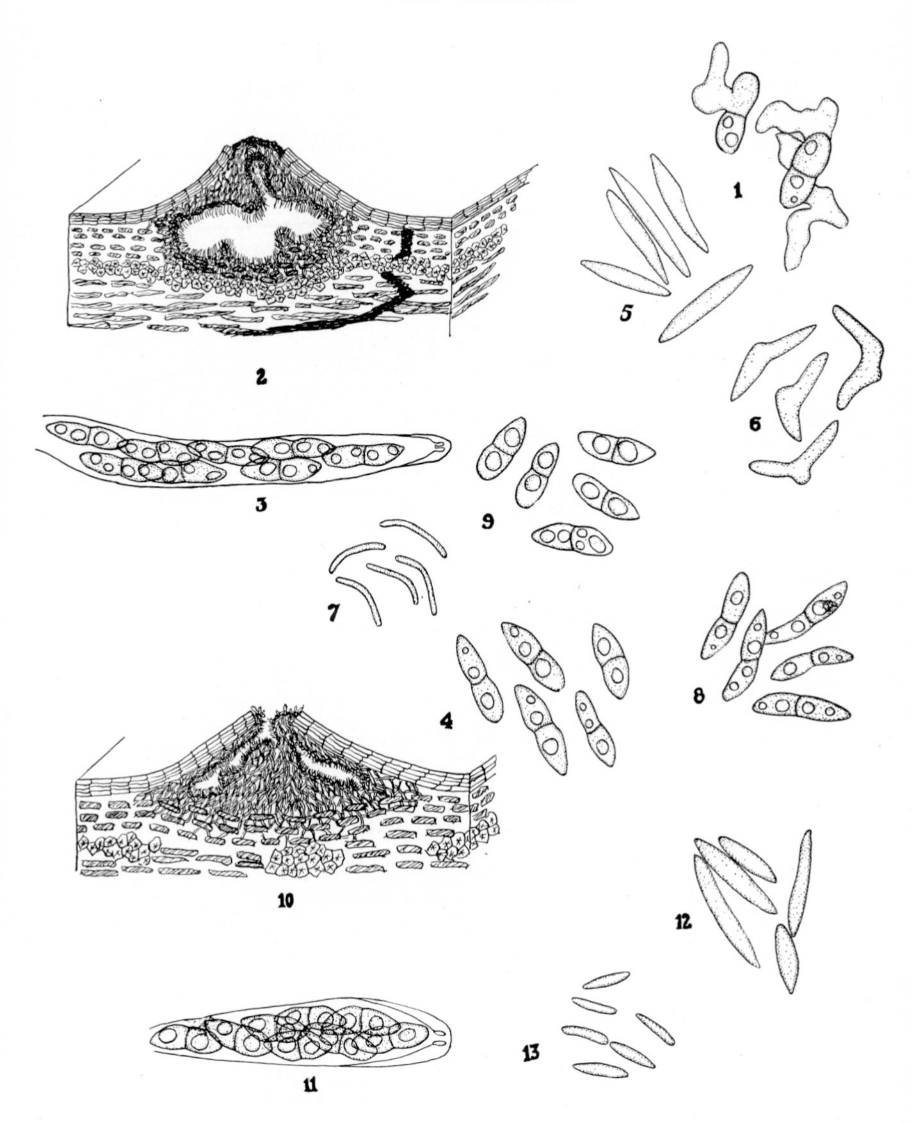

SEED STUDIES IN NYCTAGINACEAE

EDWARD F. WOODCOCK

THOSE plants which have in their mature seed a curved embryo more or less surrounded by a nourishing tissue are included by Engler and Prantl in the Order Centrospermae or Caryophyllales. The close relationship existing between the families in this order has also been established by Malligson (5) in his serum diagnosis investigations.

The predominance of the curved embryo has also been pointed out in several of the families in the order by recent investigators. Artschwager (1) in a careful study of the seed development in *Beta vulgaris* L. has found the curved embryo to be a character of the mature seed. He observed the storage region to consist of a starchy perisperm, the only evidence of endosperm being a cap of densely granular cells over the radicle of the embryo.

The writer has carried on investigations of the seed development in the Polygonaceae (7, 8) Phytolaccaceae (9), Portulacaceae (10), and Caryophyllaceae (11, 12) finding the curved embryo to be a prominent character in each family. Some interesting facts were observed concerning the storage tissue outside the embryo. In the Polygonaceae the storage tissue is entirely endosperm, the nucellar tissue being entirely absorbed by the developing endosperm and embryo. The endosperm surrounding the radicle of the embryo is modified into a tissue containing protein material; the remainder of the endosperm is starchy. An earlier investigator, Stevens (6), has also pointed out the endosperm nature of the storage region in *Fagopyrum esculentum* Moench, one of the species of the Polygonaceae. In the Phytolaccaceae and Portulacaceae the storage tissue is entirely perisperm; the only evidence of endosperm in the mature seed is crushed cell remains. In the former family these remains appear as a cap of distorted cells about the radicle of the embryo, while in the latter family the crushed endosperm cells entirely surround the mature embryo. In the Caryophyllaceae the storage tissue consists almost entirely of starchy perisperm; the only evidence of endosperm is a cap of cells whose contents consists of dense protoplasmic material.

The object of the investigations by the writer has been to determine not only the structure of the mature seed, but also the method of development, so that a proper interpretation might be obtained of the term "albumen" as used in this order by Britton and Brown (3), and the term "endosperm" as used by Bentham and Hooker (2) and Harz (4).

The present paper deals with the morphology of the seed in *Mirabilis jalapa* Linn., a representative of the Nyctaginaceae.

DESCRIPTION AND DISCUSSION OF THE MORPHOLOGY OF THE SEED

The interpretation of the conditions found during seed development were made from microtome sections of the seed at various stages of development and stained in Delafield's haematoxylin.

The single ovary of the flower contains one ovule which, during the entire development of the fruit, completely fills the locule of the ovary (Pl. XC, Fig. 1). The ovary is slightly elongated, ellipsoidal, and somewhat flattened on one side. The main axis of the slender style is not in direct line with the axis of the ovule, but instead is at an angle, appearing to be turned toward the flattened side of the ovary. In longitudinal section (Fig. 2) there is evident a stylar canal extending upward from the locule of the ovary a distance less than the diameter of the style. The parenchyma cells lining this canal are much larger than the other cells of the style in that region. The portion of the torus above the point of attachment of the stamens is broader and longer than the ovary which it supports. The cortical portion of this enlarged region is made up of large parenchyma cells which are almost completely filled with closely placed slender raphids, whose length almost equals that of the parenchyma cell in which they are located. These raphids persist during fruit development and appear in the mature fruit.

The ovule conforms with the shape of the ovary, being ellipsoidal and somewhat compressed on one side. It is of the campylotropous type; the microphylar portion of the nucellus extends almost parallel with the funiculus; the micropyle itself is turned toward the placental region of the ovary. The embryo sac occupies a central position in the nucellus, but does not extend around to the chalazal region in the early stages of development. A layer of nucellar tissue, several cells in thickness, separates the embryo sac from the inner integument. The curved embryo sac partially encircles a columnar region of nucellar tissue. The outer integument is not differentiated into two distinct layers as is the usual condition in most Angiosperms, but instead is a non-layered structure four to six cells in thickness, with cells irregularly arranged. The portion of the outer integument surrounding the micropyle consists of rather long cells which have dense protoplasmic contents, and that part of the integument opposite the stylar canal is somewhat thicker than the rest of the integument. The inner integument is made up of two distinct layers of flattened cells, the inner layer being somewhat the thicker. In the stage shown in Figure 1 each cell of the nucellus, which is partially encircled by the embryo sac, contains a few small simple spherical starch grains clustered about the large centrally placed nucleus (Fig. 3).

The cellular detail of the micropylar portion of Figure 2 is shown in Figure 1. The young spherical embryo shows no sign of cotyledon development and is furnished with a suspensor consisting of a short slender portion next to the embryo and a broader portion toward the micropyle. This suspensor, instead of having the filament of cells observed by the writer for certain families of the Centrospermae, consists of many cells irregularly arranged. In this stage of development the embryo sac is lined with endosperm in the free nuclear condition, except in the micropylar region where cell walls are present. In some cases two nuclei were observed in some of these endosperm cells. The raphids in the cortical cells of the torus just below the ovary are very evident in the stage of development shown in Figure 2.

As development proceeds the embryo sac becomes broader and

extends farther around through the nucellus toward the chalazal region (Fig. 5). The free nuclear endosperm is gradually being disorganized and the cellular portion about the radicle of the embryo and the suspensor is losing its dense protoplasmic contents. The suspensor is still attached to the embryo and retains its normal cell structure. In the stage shown in Figure 5 the embryo has become somewhat cylindrical and the two cotyledons are well developed; the one toward the central axis of the ovule is slightly shorter than the other one. There is no evidence of a plumule at the base of the cotyledons. The number and size of the starch grains in the cells of the nucellus have increased to some extent (Fig. 4).

In the further growth of the seed the embryo sac increases in length until it reaches the chalazal region and almost completely encircles the centrally placed nucellus (Pl. XCI, Fig. 9). The free nuclear endosperm has completely disappeared, leaving a cap of vacuolated cells surrounding the radicle of the embryo and the persistent suspensor. The radicle and hypocotyl constitute the major portion of the embryo and extend almost the entire length of the fruit, completely filling the embryo sac. The two cotyledons, which are now well developed, do not occupy the entire space in the rest of the embryo sac. The outer cotyledon is broader, thinner and longer than the inner cotyledon and extends to the bottom of the embryo sac. Each of the two cotyledons is much thickened at its base. There is evident a well-developed plumule at the base of the cotyledons. At this stage the procambium tissue which will later develop the vascular tissue is evident in the radicle and hypocotyl and for some distance in the cotyledons. There is also evidence of a similar tissue extending from the former tissue to the plumule. The embryo at this stage shows a very well marked root cap. The nucellus between the embryo and integuments has become completely crushed and the integuments and ovary wall have become much thinner than in the young ovary. The style appears as a shrunken structure. Each cell of the nucellus has now become packed with the small simple starch grains to such an extent that the large nucleus often appears somewhat distorted because of the pressure of the starch grains (Fig. 6). The protective wall of the mature fruit (Figs. 7 and 8) is not pericarp, but is the lower portion of the tube of the calyx which has become modified into a thick, tough, brownish-black covering which surrounds the mature ovary with its contained seed. The ovary wall and integuments are compressed into a thin layer which is brown. The curved embryo almost completely surrounds the nucellus, and the radicle and hypocotyl appear as a much thickened portion of the embryo, completely filling the embryo sac as in the earlier stage shown in Figure 9. In cross-section the hypocotyl is nearly spherical in outline, being flattened to a slight extent on the side nearest to the fruit wall. In this view the procambium tissue of the hypocotyl appears as a continuous ring centrally placed. The unequal cotyledons do not completely fill that portion of the embryo sac occupied by them. The difference in size of the cotyledons is very evident when one studies both the longitudinal and cross-section of the fruit. The outer cotyledon in contact with the fruit wall is longer and broader than the inner cotyledon. The starchy perisperm is almost completely surrounded by the hypocotyl and cotyledons. The micropylar portion of the embryo projects beyond the level of the cotyledon tips and is in almost direct contact with the fruit wall. The suspensor and the cap of vacuolated endosperm cells over the radicle of the embryo persist in the mature fruit. The root cap and procambium tissue appear as distinct structures.

The terminal portion of the fruit is blunt-pointed, and contains a cavity in this region between the ovary wall and fruit wall. The basal portion of the seed is slightly constricted and flattened on the end. The torus tissue, earlier mentioned in this paper, is somewhat disorganized, leaving the raphids in scattered bunches in the constricted basal portion of the fruit.

SUMMARY AND CONCLUSIONS

The ovule of *Mirabilis jalapa* Linn. is campylotropous, slightly elongated and ellipsoidal. The ovary is supported on a short columnar extension of the torus beyond the point of attachment of the stamens. In this region raphids are deposited which persist during the entire seed development. The radicle of the embryo is capped by vacuolated cellular endosperm early in the seed development; the remainder of the embryo sac loses its endosperm soon after the free nuclear condition. The embryo is curved and almost completely surrounds the starchy perisperm. The cotyledons equal the hypocotyl and radicle in length and the outer cotyledon is longer and broader than the inner cotyledon. The fruit wall is thick and cork-like, arising from the lower portion of the calyx tube which invests the ovary and its contained seed.

The morphological studies in this family prove that the storage tissue surrounded by the curved embryo is perisperm; and the similarity of conditions in the Nyctaginaceae to the other families of the Centrospermae investigated by the writer and others helps to establish, on a morphological basis, the close relationship existing between the families in this order.

Michigan State College
East Lansing, Michigan

LITERATURE CITED

1. Artschwager, Ernest. 1927. Development of Flowers and Seed in the Sugar Beet. Journ. Agr. Res., 34:1–25.

2. Bentham, G., and Hooker, J. D. 1883. Genera Plantarum. Vol. III. London.

3. Britton, N. L., and Brown, A. 1913. An Illustrated Flora of the Northern United States, Canada, and the British Possessions. Second edition. New York.

4. Harz, C. O. 1885. Landwirthschaftliche Samenkunde. Berlin.

5. Malligson, F. 1922. Sero-diagnostische Untersuchungen über die Verwandtschaften innerhalb des Centrospermenastes des Pflanzenreichs. Botanisches Archiv, 1:2–20.

6. Stevens, Neil E. 1912. The Morphology of the Seed in Buckwheat. Bot. Gaz., 53:59–66.

7. Woodcock, E. F. 1914. Observations on the Development and Germination of the Seed in Certain Polygonaceae. Am. Journ. Bot., 1:454–476.

8. —— 1918. Structure of the Mature Seed of *Eriogonum microthecum*. Twentieth Annual Report of the Michigan Academy of Science.

9. —— 1924. Observations on the Morphology of the Seed in Phytolacca. Papers of the Michigan Academy of Science, Arts and Letters, 4 (Part 1):413–417.

10. —— 1925. Morphology of the Seed in *Claytonia virginica*. Papers of the Michigan Academy of Science, Arts and Letters, 5:195–200.

11. —— 1926. Morphological Studies of the Seed of *Alsine media*. Papers of the Michigan Academy of Science, Arts and Letters, 6:397–402.

12. ——1927. Observations on the Morphology of the Seed of *Cerastium vulgatum*. Papers of the Michigan Academy of Science, Arts and Letters, 8:233–238.

DESCRIPTION OF PLATES

Seed of *Mirabilis jalapa* L.

All figures drawn with aid of camera lucida from median longitudinal sections except Figure 8, which is a cross-section. The following abbreviations are used: E, embryo; ES, embryo sac; S, suspensor; P, perisperm; M, micropyle; N, nucellus; EN, endosperm; OI, outer integument; II, inner integument; PL, plumule; C, cotyledons; R, raphids; SC, stylar canal; T, torus; VS, vascular strand; O, ovary wall; FW, fruit wall; H, hypocotyl; RC, root cap; PC, procambium.

PLATE XC

Fig. 1. Micropylar portion of ovule under high magnification, showing detail of the various regions and the embryo in a young stage (× 105)

Fig. 2. Young ovary, showing campylotropous ovule, embryo sac, young embryo and endosperm in the free nuclear condition throughout most of the embryo sac (× 27)

Fig. 3. Single cell from nucellus of ovule shown in Figure 2. Small spherical starch grains appearing around the nucleus (× 487)

Fig. 4. Single cell from nucellus of ovule reproduced in Figure 5, showing starch grains larger and more numerous than in Figure 3 (× 487)

Fig. 5. Ovule slightly older than that shown in Figure 2. Cotyledons evident in the embryo (× 21)

PLATE XCI

Fig. 6. Single cell from perisperm of mature seed, showing the cell lumen filled with closely packed simple starch grains, the nucleus being somewhat distorted (× 487)

Fig. 7. Mature fruit showing the thick fruit wall, raphids, embryo with the unequal cotyledons, and central perisperm (× 11)

Fig. 8. Cross-section of mature fruit, showing how the perisperm is almost completely surrounded by the embryo (× 11)

Fig. 9. Ovary containing almost mature embryo. Fruit wall not shown (× 11)

PLATE XC

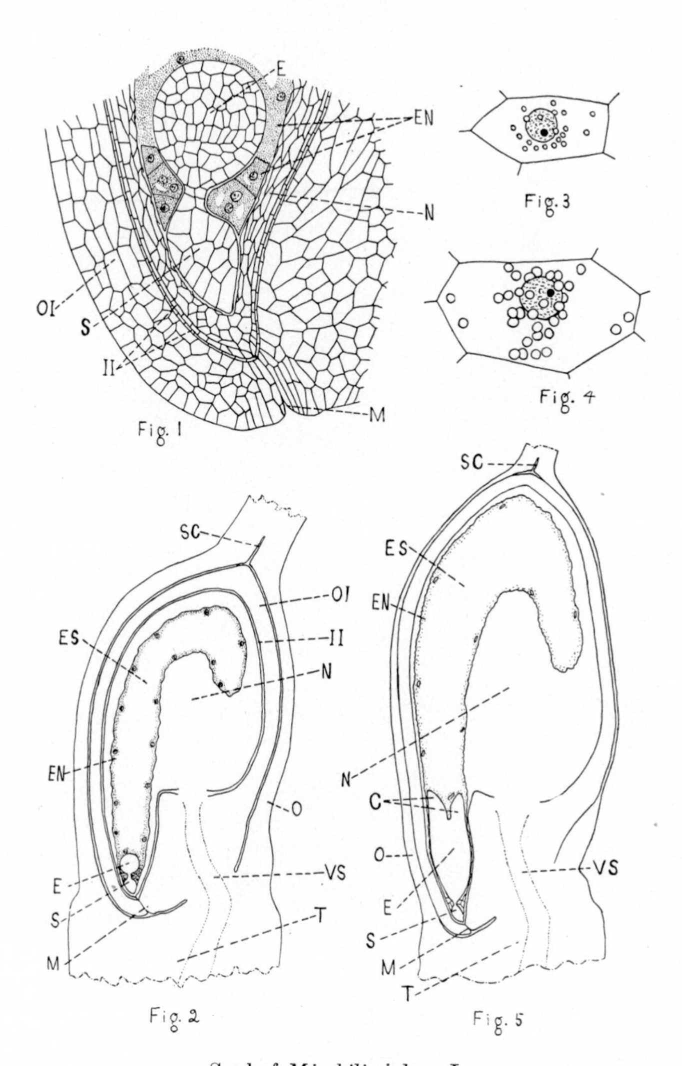

Seed of *Mirabilis jalapa* L.

PLATE XCI

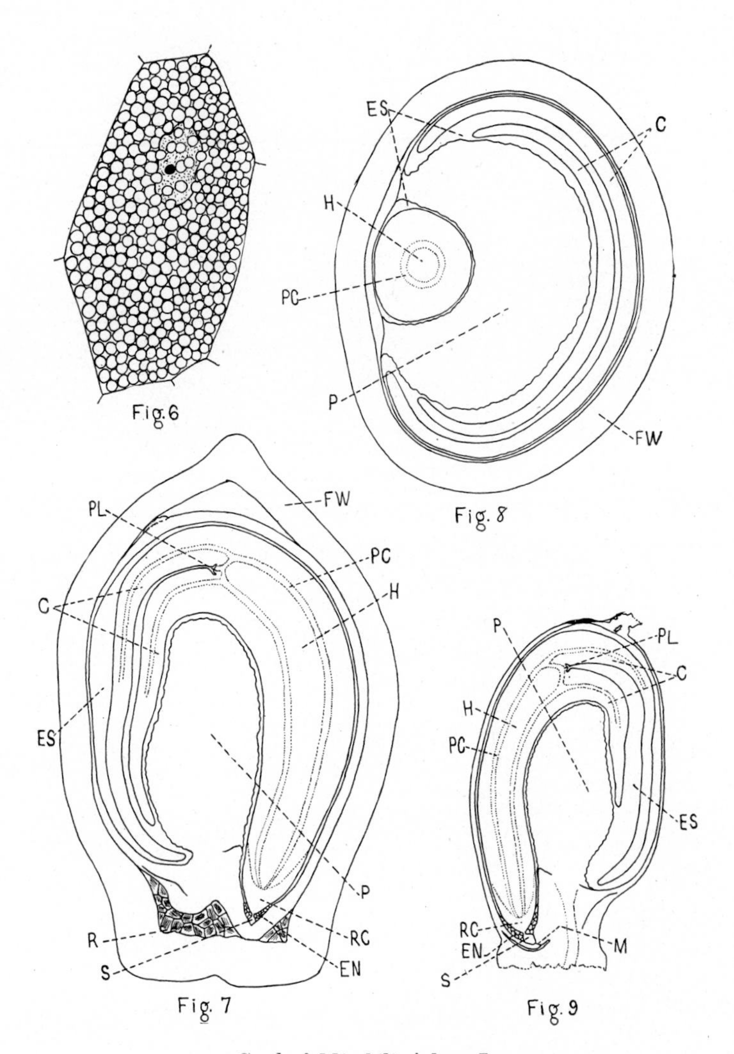

Seed of *Mirabilis jalapa* L.

FOREST FIRE RESEARCH PROBLEMS FOR MICHIGAN

HORACE J. ANDREWS

THE subject "Fundamental Problems in Forest Fire Research" does not accurately describe what I should like to present. I would rather have the title read "Some Questions on the Forest Fire Problem in Michigan in Need of an Answer." Whether some of these problems deserve real research or a mere layman's investigation depends, of course, on just how far the scientific method can and should be used in their solution.

A large number of investigators have felt that only a few aspects of the forest fire problem allowed of true research. I feel that any of the problems later mentioned in this paper are entitled to true research if we will admit that, in their solution, it will be possible to control various factors, evaluate variables and, in general, apply the scientific method.

I have not completely reviewed all the forest research that is being carried on in the United States and in other countries and am aware of the fact that certain of the problems hereafter mentioned are being worked on by investigators in several other localities. However, to the best of my knowledge, the problems I shall mention are receiving no attention, or at least very little, in Michigan.

It is doubtful if a large part of the information on fire so far obtained by research applies to more than local areas. To date more work has been done on the weather phase of the fire problem than on any other phase and, although certain general theories as to the relation between risk, spread of fire and relative humidity have apparently been proved for certain limited localities, no one has as yet cared to state over how much territory these "laws" might hold true.

I shall, therefore, as stated before, confine myself to the fire problem in Michigan and to those particular problems of immediate interest to the Forest Fire Division of the Department of Conservation, the complete or even partial solution of which could and would affect both the administrative and statistical procedure of that division. These problems will not all be fundamental. I am not certain whether or not I am able to recognize and segregate all the fundamental from the non-fundamental problems in forest fire research.

Until more progress has been made I am not at all certain whether or not a large number of the phases of the forest fire problem can be reduced to an exact science. Many investigators have shied from certain aspects of the forest fire problem because of the idea that none or very few of the many variables involved could be evaluated or controlled. They seemed to think that fires must be studied when and as they occurred, with no opportunity for control of many of the factors involved. I see no reason why, in the solution of forest fire questions, laboratory conditions could not be set up in the field. It would seem reasonable that 1000 or 2000 acres of low-grade, state-owned land, with no very valuable cover, might be set aside as a laboratory for fire research. This area might be in the form of one large solid block or might consist of several scattered forty-acre plots covering different conditions. If the area were in one large block it could be divided into 5-, 10- or 20-acre parcels with adequate fire lines around each subdivision and various types of burning could be done under whatever conditions the investigator might desire.

Some of the Michigan problems or questions needing attention are as follows. In all cases I am assuming that the variables involved can be either controlled or evaluated.

1. DAMAGE

(*a*) For various species, the relation between fire damage to tree growth and weather conditions as affected by the season of the year.

For example, casual observation indicates that in the so-called "scrub oak" in the Southern Peninsula sand country, spring fires occur, when the ground is bare of snow and the ground-cover dry enough to burn, with a relatively small amount of damage to the oak as long as the ground is still frozen.

I am acquainted with certain areas in Mason county which burned over early in the spring of 1927 and on which, in the fall of 1927, evidence of fire damage, as far as the oak was concerned, was very hard to find. Apparently none of the trees were killed and the examination in the fall showed but few scars, catfaces and the like. Adjacent to these areas were other small tracts which had burned in August, on which the trees were either completely or partially killed. Our damage statistics will be very weak until we know much more about this subject. We also need more information on the matter of how long after a fire we should wait until damages are assessed.

(*b*) The relation of fires to the humus condition of the soil.

This type of damage not only effects the Department's fire statistics, but also has a bearing on future planting programs. Damage studies must not only result in evaluating losses on the basis of present values but must also consider the future of the burned area.

2. TYPE CHANGES

(*a*) What cover type changes occur after different kinds and degrees of fire?

(*b*) What is the effect of both single and repeated burnings on the sprouting ability of deciduous trees?

(*c*) Does the repeated burning of blueberry areas improve the blueberry crop or what is the relation between the amount and quality of blueberries produced per acre per year and the presence or absence of fires?

(*d*) If certain amounts of fire do improve the quality and quantity of blueberries raised per acre per year, when and how should such burning be done?

(*e*) How many blueberries per acre per year can be raised on the various types of our so-called "blueberry plains"?

These last three problems may appear, offhand, to be out of place here, but answers to them would give the Department of Conservation the information it needs to combat one of the important types of incendiary fires.

3. WEATHER

The weather and its relation to fires have received the lion's share of attention in forest fire research to date. The experiment stations of the Forest Service in conjunction with the U. S. Weather Bureau are well into this subject and possibly all that is needed in Michigan at this time is to have the work which is being done in other states duplicated here for our own local conditions. For example:

(*a*) Do the factors which bring about hazardous conditions in other localities bring about hazardous conditions in Michigan, and is the sequence of these factors the same here as in other localities?
(*b*) Will the forecasting procedure developed in other communities apply in Michigan?
(*c*) Will the critical point in relative humidity vary for different parts of the state?
(*d*) For large areas in Michigan (sandy plains) we have no duff. Will the soil moisture in the upper six inches of the soil be an index of the inflammability of the fuel?
(*e*) How can field men such as are employed by the average protective organization forecast humidity?

Can we furnish them a concrete procedure to follow? We are getting general fire weather forecasts from the Weather Bureau, but these are only rather general as yet and we need some system whereby the average field man can take the data of the day before, add to it the weather data as he can get it in the morning and be able to forecast the relative humidity for the afternoon with reasonable accuracy. Work of this nature has been done in other localities and we need it for Michigan conditions.

(*f*) What is the relation between rate of spread of fires and relative humidity, topography, wind velocity and cover density (shade)?

4. RESULTS OF PUBLICITY AND PROPAGANDA

(*a*) What are the positive results of the different types of fire prevention propaganda and publicity as used?

We use posters, motion pictures, pamphlets, newspaper publicity and direct contact. Possibly all these means are necessary and of value; we have, however, no precise knowledge of the relative value of these different types of prevention propaganda. We might well follow the Massachusetts experiment.

5. SUPPRESSION METHODS

In this connection, we might well turn to the physicists and chemists and ask them to apply their knowledge of the fundamental theories of combustion to our problem.

(*a*) Can we use gases effectively and at reasonable cost in fighting forest fires?

Liquid carbon dioxide might be just as effective as water, or even more so, if put in small knapsack tanks and sprayed out as a gas under pressure. It might be particularly effective for underground peat and muck fires.

(*b*) How far can explosives be used in stopping, checking or breaking up both ground and crown fires?

Dynamite can and has been used as a trench digger. Aërial bombs might be used to snuff out crown fires.

(*c*) Can compressed air be used in fire suppression?

(*d*) What is the relation of wind velocity to size and weight of inflammable particles which the wind can carry? Also, what is the relation of wind velocity to the distance inflammable material can be carried?

(*e*) In fighting muck and peat fires how does water which may be put on the surface by power pumps seep into the dry muck and at what rate?
(*f*) Why, at certain times, do muck fires travel underground instead of burning completely from the surface down?

6. MISCELLANEOUS

(*a*) What kinds of typical Michigan cover can be ignited by live soft coal cinders of a diameter not to exceed one quarter of an inch (ground cover assumed to be as dry as it ever gets under natural conditions)?
(*b*) How long will a live soft coal cinder one quarter of an inch in diameter remain hot enough to ignite ordinary ground cover (ground cover to be as dry as it ordinarily gets under natural conditions)?

Only a few of the problems in forest fire research have been mentioned. Every one mentioned ought to suggest added problems along the same line. Can and will anything be done about them?

DEPARTMENT OF CONSERVATION
LANSING, MICHIGAN

MYCORRHIZA AND SCOTCH PINE IN THE UNIVERSITY OF MICHIGAN FOREST NURSERY *

DOW V. BAXTER

Previous Work on Mycorrhiza of Scotch Pine

THE significance of soil fungi to growth of forest trees has been the subject of much research since the appearance of Frank's classical paper in 1885 on mycorrhiza. Frank (1, 2) later stated his belief that *Pinus sylvestris* did not reach maturity on good pine soils if the appropriate fungus was not present in the soil for mycorrhizal formation. Möller (6, 7) observed the coralloid mycorrhiza of this species, but failed in his attempts to determine the relation of mycorrhiza to nitrogen fixation. This investigator's observations on Scotch pine led him to believe that this tree could develop well in soils lacking humus and in the absence of the mycorrhizal fungus.

The association of mycorrhizas with the fruiting-bodies of the higher fungi has been observed by many investigators, but Melin's work (4, 5) in proving their identity by synthesis is perhaps the most outstanding of the modern studies in this field. Melin has described three types of mycorrhiza on Scotch pine, namely: forked, tuber and simple. (*a*) Forked mycorrhiza is best developed in woodland soils and in the presence of an abundant layer of raw humus. It is usually golden brown to black. (*b*) In tuber mycorrhiza, the tubers are frequently grown together. The color of this type is said to be pale at first but becomes gray to brownish-gray with age. The surface of the tubers is rough. (*c*) Simple mycorrhiza is the unbranched form characteristically found on pine in both woodland and pine-heath soils. It is said that this

* Contribution No. 4 from the School of Forestry and Conservation, University of Michigan.

form may be simply young stages of the tuber or forked types, or that conditions may be unfavorable for optimum growth for the fungus. It has been ascertained by Melin that under artificial conditions the same fungus might give rise to these various types of mycorrhiza. He has formed these types of mycorrhiza by synthesis in artificial cultures. *Boletus luteus, B. variegatus, B. granulatus,* and *B. badius, Amanita muscaria, cortinarius muscosus, Lactarius deliciosus* and *Russula fragilis* have all been identified experimentally as mycorrhiza formers in pine by Melin.

The present paper represents work which has been carried on at the University of Michigan Forest Nursery in connection with certain difficulties which were encountered in the growing of coniferous seedlings.

FIELD OBSERVATIONS ON SCOTCH PINE

The one-year-old Scotch pine seedlings, as well as the Norway, Austrian, Mugho, white pine, and Douglas fir in the nursery all showed unusual growth characteristics during the late summer of 1926. White cedar and Arizona cypress were the only important species which could not be classed with the other conifers relative to this condition.

Although seed germination was excellent in most of the conifers sown, the beds contained many sizes of trees. As a result of this peculiar growth, the beds appeared very ragged and uneven. Many of the plants stagnated and apparently ceased to elongate in the second year. In the same beds there were brown or yellowish plants mixed with small "islands" of dead trees. Other Scotch pine seedlings, however, had made an unusual growth during the season; their tops were much larger, the leaves longer and greener than were those of the other trees in the beds (see Plates XCII and XCIII).

The loss of seedlings in some of the beds was great enough in some species to warrant the complete destruction of the beds. The healthy seedlings of other beds were removed to transplant beds and the remaining plants destroyed. It was estimated that 95 per cent of the white pine, 95 per cent of the Douglas fir, 90 per cent of the Norway spruce, and 75 per cent of the Austrian pine were not suitable for transplanting. As these seed beds were destroyed early in the spring of 1927, it was impossible to make later observations on the development of this condition in these species similar to those made for Scotch pine. It should be emphasized, therefore, that the statements made later for Scotch pine in this paper do not apply to the other conifers just mentioned.

It is of interest to note that this or a similar puzzling condition appeared in the seedlings grown in the heavy soil at the Chillicothe nursery in Ohio this same season (1926) and in other years. So great was the loss there that the entire nursery was moved to Marietta, Ohio.

The writer examined the plants in the Chillicothe nursery in October, 1926, and although the cause for this unusual condition in this nursery is unknown, the plants exhibited the same external growth characteristics as those just reported in the Ann Arbor nursery. The state forester, Mr. Edmund Secrest, has informed the writer of his observations made on the various species there and his records generally correspond to the conditions recorded in the Michigan nursery. He found that the "disease" at Chillicothe always seemingly appeared in the second year after seeding. In the white pine, the "disease" was observed to a minor degree the first year. "In every case where we seeded white pine we encountered the trouble at least during the second year. Scotch pine was the only other species affected to any degree at Chillicothe, although the trouble also occurred slightly in the red pine." Austrian and western yellow pines were not affected, according to Mr. Secrest. The season of sowing cannot be accepted as an explanation for these results obtained at Chillicothe since this condition was observed in the plants regardless of the time of sowing in either spring or fall.

As it was impossible to account satisfactorily for the difficulties encountered in raising the pines in the University of Michigan Forest nursery, two Scotch pine beds (4 by 12) were left undisturbed in order to carry out further observation on the growth of the seedlings. The Scotch pine in these beds continued this irregular rate of growth during the growing season of 1927 (see Plate XCIV).

There was a marked difference not only in the length of the tops and needles (see Table I), as was observed in the seedlings the previous fall, but a difference in root to top ratios and also in dry weights was recorded.

TABLE I

SCOTCH PINE PLANTS, OCTOBER, 1927

Stock	Average top length (terminal bud) in inches	Average needle length in inches	Average root length in inches	Average no. roots 1 inch long or more	Dry weight tops, in grams	Dry weight root, in grams
100 small plants......	3.6	2.3	7.7	12.3	63	20
100 large plants......	8.1	3.7	11.04	18.4	142	67

A difference in the number of lateral roots and in the quantity of mycorrhizal mantles was also observed. While the white mycorrhizal mantles occurred on both the large and small trees, there were a greater abundance and a greater degree of distribution on the smaller and more branched and fibrous-rooted plants. The mycorrhizal roots forked dichotomously and repeatedly in both types of plants and on both the lateral and the tap roots. Whether the fungus mycelium was the cause for a more finely branched root-system or not remains to be determined from culture experiments.

It was found difficult to suggest a reason for this difference in growth-rate of Scotch pine. It was not possible to account for this irregular type of growth on the basis of seed quality. If there had been a marked difference in the seed, it would seem that the tall and short plants would be scattered over the bed instead of occurring in clumps as shown in Plates XCII and XCIII. As all parts of the bed received approximately the same amount of water over this extended period, it was not possible to associate these clumps of trees with areas more moist than others. Similarly, it was not possible to associate such an irregular type of growth with any particular soil condition. As mycorrhizal fungi were found associated abundantly with the roots upon a first examination of the seedlings in 1926, during the fall of 1927 an effort was made to produce mycorrhizal formation synthetically from pure cultures of the fungus found on the Scotch pine roots in the nursery and Scotch pine seedlings. Scotch pine seed were washed in mercuric bichloride (1–1000) and were planted under aseptic conditions in sterilized quartz sand in one liter Erhlenmeyer flasks. After seed germination, certain flasks were inoculated with the fungus cultures. As such cultures have been set up for only a short time, no conclusive evidence relative to the production of synthetic mycorrhiza and the effect of the fungus upon the growth of the seedlings can be presented at this time. Although the physiological reactions of mycorrhiza to the development of seedlings in the nursery are imperfectly understood, it seems desirable to report the identity of such a mycorrhizal fungus in hopes that further investigations concerning growth effects on nursery trees might be stimulated.

THE ASSOCIATION OF SCOTCH PINE AND *RHIZOPOGON RUBESCENS*, TULASNE

In October, 1927, three hundred and seventy fruiting-bodies of *Rhizopogon rubescens* Tulasne [1] were found in the two Scotch pine seed beds. Many of the fruiting-bodies arose from delicate wefts of mycelium in the soil surrounding and in the immediate vicinity of the roots. On examination, some of the fruiting-bodies were found connected by short rhizomorphic strands which made definite connections between the roots of the Scotch pine and the fungus (see Plate XCV).

It is believed that the association of this fungus to coniferous nursery stock is reported here for the first time. It is of interest, however, to note that *Rhizopogon luteolus* has been identified as the fungus generally associated with a mycelium on pine growing in nurseries and in older trees in Australia. It is of additional interest to note that Kessell (3) further reports growth conditions

[1] Plants identified by Dr. S. M. Zeller, Oregon Agricultural College.

of the pine in Australia similar to those recorded in this paper. Kessell states: "In the case of the nurseries referred to and particularly with *Pinus insignis*, odd patches of ground of irregular size and shape were noticed, on which the pines developed comparatively satisfactorily. It was not possible to associate these small patches of a few square feet or less with any particular chemical or physical condition of the soil, and gradually it was realized that the only explanation likely to satisfy the innumerable apparently contradictory results was the dependence of the young pines for healthy and vigorous growth on some soil organism not generally present in local soils. . . . Healthy pine seedlings from older nurseries were known to show a peculiar coral-like development of masses of root hairs, which apparently become thickened, branch and are translucent. In Western Australian nurseries particularly this root condition appears to be associated generally with a network of fungus mycelium extending throughout the top layers of the soil. . . . Fruiting-bodies found in nurseries . . . have been identified by the Government Botanist (Mr. W. N. Carne) as *Rhizopogon luteolus*, which is possibly the mycorrhizal fungus concerned, although this has not yet been proved by direct infection of new nursery sites with the spores of this fungus."

It should be added that in the United States another species of Rhizopogon, *Rhizopogon parasiticus* Coker and Totten, has been reported on the roots of *Pinus echinata* and *Pinus taeda* (8). This fungus is said to form a compound ectotrophic mycorrhiza; but the mycorrhizal character is short-lived and the mass of inclosed rootlets is completely absorbed.

While it was evident, as has been previously stated, that a greater abundance of mycorrhizal mantles appeared on the smaller, but live trees in the Michigan nursery, the number of fruiting-bodies showed no such correlation to the smaller trees. In the first bed there were 601 large trees and 63 fruiting-bodies collected under them. There were 1027 small Scotch pine in this bed under which 108 fruiting-bodies were found. While the proportion of fruiting-bodies to small plants in the second bed was somewhat different, the difference is negligible. The following figures show that there were 189 fruiting-bodies found in this second bed:

No. large Scotch pine plants	No. small trees	No. fruiting-bodies, large plants	No. fruiting-bodies, small plants
1063	1897	85	104

It should be pointed out that no fruiting-bodies were found in the nursery soil outside the areas of either bed. It might be added also that this large collection of fruiting-bodies is the first collection that has been reported from the state of Michigan. Zeller and Dodge (9) report this cosmopolitan species "in sand under pines." They have examined specimens of this plant collected in the United States from Massachusetts, New York, New Jersey, District of Columbia, Tennessee, North Carolina, Florida, Alabama, Texas, Iowa, Washington, and California. Because of the wide distribution of this fungus and its apparently constant association with pine, it is believed that *Rhizopogon rubescens* may prove to be an important soil organism in forest nursery soils.

SUMMARY

1. *Rhizopogon rubescens* Tulasne is reported on the roots of *Pinus sylvestris* for the first time in the United States.

2. The possible mycorrhizal relationships of this fungus and Scotch pine are discussed with reference to the irregular growth conditions of pine which have existed in the University of Michigan nursery, in the Chillicothe Forest nursery, and elsewhere.

UNIVERSITY OF MICHIGAN

LITERATURE CITED

1. FRANK, A. B. 1892. Die Ernährung der Kiefer durch ihre Mykorrhiza-Pilze. Ber. d.d. bot. Gesell., 10 : 577–583.

2. —— 1894. Die Bedeutung der Mykorrhizapilze für die gemeine Kiefer. Forstwiss. Centralbl., 16 : 185–190.

3. KESSELL, S. L. 1927. Soil Organisms. The Dependence of Certain Pine Species on a Biological Soil Factor. Empire Forestry Journal, 6 : 70–74. No. 1.

4. MELIN, ELIAS. 1922. Boletus Arten als Mykorrhizenpilze der Waldbäume. Ber. d.d. bot. Gesell., 40 : 94–97.

5. Melin, Elias. 1924. Zur Kenntnis der Mykorrhizapilze von *Pinus montana.* Bot. Notiser., 69–92.

6. Möller, A. 1903. Untersuchungen über ein- und zweijährige Kiefern in märkischen Sandboden. Zeitschrift f. Forst- und Jagdwesen, 35 : 257–272.

7. —— 1906. Mykorrhizen und Stickstoffernährung. Ber. d.d. bot. Gesell., 24 : 230–233.

8. Totten, H. R. 1923. Development of the Fruit-Body of a New Parasitic Rhizopogon. Journal of the Elisha Mitchell Scientific Society, 39 : 101–109. Nos. 1 and 2.

9. Zeller, S. M., and Dodge, C. W. 1918. Rhizopogon in North America. Annals of the Missouri Botanical Garden, 5 : 1–36. No. 1.

PLATE XCII

Scotch pine in seed beds in the University of Michigan Forest Nursery, October, 1927. Note the irregular appearance exhibited by these plants after the third season of growth. See also the next plate

PLATE XCIII

Scotch pine in seed beds in the University of Michigan
Forest Nursery, October, 1927

Fig. 1 Fig. 2

Representative large and small Scotch pine seedlings found in the seed beds at the Forest Nursery, University of Michigan. The large plants were selected from the groups characterized by large plants; the small plants, from the "islands" containing small plants

Fig. 1. Scotch pine seedlings as they appeared during the fall of 1927 and after the third season of growth

Fig. 2. 2–0 Scotch pine seedlings as they appeared in the seed beds in the spring of 1927

PLATE XCV

Rhizopogon rubescens Tulasne on Scotch pine seedlings, fall of 1927. Note the mycorrhiza on the rootlets

HOST SELECTION BY THE SPRUCE BUDWORM *

SAMUEL A. GRAHAM

THE success of an insect species depends to a very great degree upon the ease with which the developmental stages can find suitable food. If the young on hatching from the egg find an abundance of food close at hand, the chance of their reaching maturity is much greater than if, after hatching, it is necessary for them to face the risks attendant upon a search for food. Almost without exception in the most successful species the adult carefully places her eggs where food for the young is certain to be abundant. This habit is so common among insects that it seldom causes much comment. We take it as a matter of course. Nevertheless we must admit that the instinct is remarkable which prompts such monophagous species as the larch sawfly to deposit her eggs unfailingly upon the one host that can provide food for her larvae. This is host selection in its highest development.

Some insects, however, are not confined to a single host. The spruce budworm, *Archips fumiferana*, is one of these more or less polyphagous species. It is able to feed upon almost every species of fir, spruce, or pine occurring in its range. At first glance it would appear that host selection with such an insect would be of much less significance than with monophagous species. There is evidence, however, that some of these so-called general feeders actually exhibit a high degree of host selection.

It has been shown that certain polyphagous wood-boring beetles have a decided tendency to select for oviposition the same species as the one in which they themselves were reared. For instance, Hopkins (1910) maintains that the mountain pine

* Contribution No. 11 from the School of Forestry and Conservation, University of Michigan.

beetle, *Dendroctonus monticolae*, when bred in lodgepole pine, has a decided tendency to continue generation after generation to attack that tree, whereas the beetles of the same species bred in yellow pine have an equally strong tendency to confine their activities to that host. This tendency of insects to attack generation after generation the same tree species is known as *Hopkins Host Selection Principle.*

Craighead (1921) has shown that this principle is not limited to the barkbeetles, but also holds true with a number of polyphagous Cerambycidae. He states that the longer a strain of beetles is confined to the same host the stronger becomes the tendency to select that host for oviposition. In fact his evidence goes even further. He has demonstrated that after several generations of breeding in one host a high mortality occurs among the young larvae of certain cerambycids when they are forced to feed on a new host. How generally this principle applies is not now known, but in the light of the evidence at hand it seems quite possible that it has a rather wide application, at least among the Coleoptera.

From the economic viewpoint this kind of host selection is very important. For instance, it is possible to treat the mountain pine beetle on lodgepole pine and on yellow pine as two distinct economic species. This is because the beetles that emerge from lodgepole will not readily attack yellow pine, and it is, therefore, possible to concentrate control measures in the valuable yellow pine stands without fear of serious infestation from adjacent infested forests of lodgepole pine.

Although little is known of the operation of the host selection principle among polyphagous Lepidoptera, it is evident that, if a tendency for successive generations to select the same host does exist, it must be taken into consideration when we endeavor to develop forests that will be resistant to these insects. One of the very few evidences of host selection among the Lepidoptera was presented by Pictet (1905), who states that the host preferences of the gipsy moth, *Porthetria dispar*, may be changed by rearing several generations of larvae on one of the less desirable hosts. This is an important phase of the gipsy moth investigations that has received very little attention.

During the study of the spruce budworm in northern Minnesota, evidence has been obtained to indicate that the host selection principle also applies to that species, and that in its control by forest management host selection must be taken into consideration. This evidence will be herein set forth.

General observation in the field gave us the first hint that the host selection principle might apply to the spruce budworm. This evidence was later supplemented by experiments. Unfortunately the series of experiments as originally planned could not be completed because of lack of material, owing to the rather sudden decline of the budworm infestation that occurred during the season of 1927. Inasmuch as material for the completion of these experiments may not be obtainable for many years, it seems desirable to publish at this time the results as far as we have gone. Although they are incomplete they are decidedly significant.

OBSERVATIONAL EVIDENCE

First let us examine the evidence of host selection based on general observations. In Minnesota the spruce budworm has attacked and killed, since 1913, a vast area of balsam fir and spruce in the northern tier of counties. During the period between 1913 and 1925 it is estimated that a volume of balsam fir equal to ten million cords was killed. In addition to this a large volume of white spruce was also killed. Adjacent to this area of spruce and balsam fir forests that were devastated by the budworm, are extensive areas of very poor rocky soil covered with a growth of jack pine, a tree that is also susceptible to attack by the spruce budworm. Although there was no barrier of any sort between these stands of jack pine and the infested balsam fir and spruce, no defoliation of jack pine occurred in that region. The epidemic finally died out in the balsam fir and spruce when the destruction of these species brought about a shortage of food for the insects. Starvation conditions for the budworm larvae existed during the last year of active defoliation, but in spite of this situation the adjacent and readily available jack pine was not attacked.

While the budworm was still active in the spruce and balsam forests of the northern counties, it was also very abundant in jack pine forests on the sandy lands to the south. This jack pine infestation was separated by many miles from the spruce balsam fir infestation, so that in all probability there was no direct connection between these two outbreaks of the budworm. The budworm-infested jack pine forests are interspersed with stands of balsam fir and spruce. But in this region where the budworm was feeding on jack pine, it was almost never to be found on either balsam fir or spruce.

In the jack pine region, during the season of flight, moths of the budworm were seldom observed on trees other than jack pine, and in the region to the north where balsam fir and spruce were attacked the moths were never observed on jack pine. In view of the conditions just described, it appeared that we were dealing either with two indistinguishable species, or with two forms of the same species, one of which exhibited a decided preference for balsam fir and spruce, whereas the other preferred jack pine. Inasmuch as there appear to be no taxonomic differences between the two forms, they are here regarded as ecological varieties of the same species.

EXPERIMENTAL EVIDENCE

One of the first questions of habit that naturally arose was whether or not the larvae are able to change their food from balsam fir to pine and vice versa. Experiments to test this point were, therefore, conducted. Larvae were transferred from one host to another with little or no loss that could be ascribed to food. Table I summarizes the results of these experiments. Unfortunately it was impossible to obtain larvae for transfer younger than the third stage. It may be that larvae of the second instar, which is the first feeding stage, might not have been so easily able to adapt themselves to a change of food as were the older larvae. We can say with certainty, however, that at least from the third stage on to full growth the larvae are able to change from one host to another without much difficulty.

TABLE I

RESULTS OF TRANSFERRING LARVAE FROM ONE HOST TO ANOTHER

Original host	*Transferred to*	*Percentage surviving change*
jack pine	jack pine	69 (check)
jack pine	black spruce	47
jack pine	white spruce	75
jack pine	balsam fir	67
balsam fir	balsam fir	80 (check)
balsam fir	white spruce	63
balsam fir	jack pine	67
balsam fir	Norway pine	63

The concentration on either jack pine or balsam fir and spruce in the different localities is probably not due to specific food limitations, but must be the result of specific host selection on the part of either the adult moths or the second stage larvae, which is, as previously mentioned, the first feeding stage. The decline of the outbreak unfortunately prevented a test of the reactions to food of the second instar larvae, and limited the number of host selection experiments in which the moths were used. The preliminary tests of host selection by the moths, although they cannot be regarded as conclusive, were, however, very definite. They will therefore be presented here.

Several methods were used without much success in an attempt to test the responses of the moths to food plants, but finally an apparatus was perfected that gave satisfactory results. This consisted of a T-tube, one-half inch in diameter, the stem of which could be connected with a larger straight tube containing the moths. At either end of the cross-arm of the T-tube was an enlarged chamber into which fresh tips from the trees to be tested were placed. The outer ends of these chambers were closed with cheese cloth to prevent the escape of the moths. An aspirator was connected by a small tube to the outer end of the tube containing the moths, and air was drawn slowly through the apparatus. This air passed over the tips contained in the opposite ends of the cross-arm and thence down the stem and through the moth tube.

Eighteen seconds were required for the air to pass through the apparatus from one end to the other. Table II summarizes the results of this series of experiments.

TABLE II

HOST SELECTION BY SPRUCE BUDWORM MOTHS

Moths reared on balsam fir

No. moths	To jack pine	To balsam fir	Indefinite response
5	0	4	1
5	0	3	2
12	1	10	1
13	0	11	2
35	1	28	6

Moths reared on jack pine

No. moths	To jack pine	To balsam fir	Indefinite response
4	3	0	1
9	8	1	0
13	11	1	1

From these tests it appears that the moths of the spruce budworm exhibit a decided preference for the host species on which they were reared. This explains to a certain degree at least why jack pine adjacent to budworm-infested jack pine remain uninfested.

CONCLUSIONS

Apparently, then, in these forms of the spruce budworm we have two species in the making. At present they are taxonomically the same but ecologically they are different. If Craighead (1921) is correct in his conclusion that the tendency to select the same host becomes stronger as generation after generation of a race feeds upon that host, then it is possible that in the course of time a monophagous form of budworm that cannot change from one host to the others may be developed.

From the economic viewpoint this host selection of the spruce budworm is of especial importance because its control depends primarily upon methods of forest management that will reduce the proportion of favorite hosts in a forest. If the insect were in the habit of transferring with ease from one host to another, then a change of host preference might result in the upsetting of our management plan. But with the great stability in host selection exhibited by this insect under natural conditions, that prevents a transfer from balsam fir to jack pine even under conditions of starvation, we are justified in treating the two forms in forest management as if they were two distinct species.

University of Michigan

LITERATURE CITED

Craighead, F. C. 1910. Hopkins Host-selection Principle as Related to Certain Cerambycid Beetles. Journ. Agric. Res., 22 (No. 3): 180–220.

Hopkins, A. D. 1910. Letter in files of Bureau of Entomology, U. S. D. A. See Craighead, 1910.

Pictet, Arnold. 1905. Influence de l'alimentation et de l'humidité sur la variation des Papillons. Mem. Soc. Phys. et Hist. Nat. Genève, 35: 45–127.

THE CUBAN FOREST PROBLEM*

DONALD M. MATTHEWS

THE existence of a "forest problem" is a fact which generally escapes attention until it is far beyond the point of easy solution. Some countries, which are only political divisions of continents and whose soils are all definitely agricultural, may never have to meet it. In Europe it has long been definitely recognized that at least 25 per cent of the land area should be under forest. Sweden has over 60 per cent of her area under forest growth, but countries such as Holland and Belgium have but small areas of forest, which are almost integral parts of their agricultural industry. No island country can thus successfully avoid the consideration of forests as a major part of her national economy. Geographical unity and isolation have their advantages, but carry with them certain obligations of economic independence. Timber products can, it is true, be imported from other countries, but never at as low a cost as they can be raised at home; and no island is so situated climatically or constructed topographically as to be able to use all its land for agriculture. Especially is an island in the tropics dependent upon its own forested area for the control of the atmospheric humidity so necessary for successful agriculture. Likewise it makes its own soils from the erosion of its areas of high relief and similarly can lose them again if such erosion be not controlled by the presence of forests on its watersheds.

The percentage of area of an island which should be retained under forest cover should be determined primarily by its topography and its location with respect to continental and ocean winds, and secondarily by the economic needs of the population for timber. Unfortunately, wherever population is at all dense, none of these factors have been given any consideration and the pressure of agricultural and industrial development has reduced forest

* Contribution No. 13 from the School of Forestry and Conservation, University of Michigan.

areas to below the point which would either protect the essentials of successful agriculture or meet the needs of the community for timber. The 25 per cent forest area standard as established for continental Europe cannot be taken as applying everywhere else in the world. The correct standard will have to be determined for each continent and island by a consideration of the factors mentioned above. In general, proportionally more forest will be required on islands than on continents because, islands being smaller, a greater percentage of forest cover will be required if its climatic effect is to be retained on the island area. In the tropics, especially in those regions characterized by a seasonal climate, the erosive effect of a large rainfall concentrated in a few months of the year is greater than elsewhere. A larger proportion of forest area is necessary to control this effect and, if the forest area is unwisely reduced, the tendency is for the climate to become more seasonal in character with consequent longer periods of drought and greater damage from concentrated rainfall.

These indirect effects of the forest on the national economy of any country are generally unappreciated, and it is always only an actual shortage of timber products which calls attention to the fact that a forest problem exists. If it is possible to import these products without any unfavorable effect on the balance of trade, then the problem still fails of appreciation. This has been the case with Cuba, as the following figures show:

TABLE I

TIMBER STATISTICS, 1914

Timber	Cut Cubic feet	Exported Cubic feet
Cedar	10,459,000	10,459,000
Mahogany	10,254,000	10,254,000
Other timbers	3,185,000	1,646,000
Total	23,898,000	22,359,000

TIMBER STATISTICS, 1919

Timber	Cubic feet	Cubic feet
Cedar	5,099,000	561,000
Mahogany	4,104,000	161,000
Other timbers	2,641,000	241,000
Total	11,844,000	963,000

Thus in five years the total reported cut has been reduced by half and the exports to only a little over 4 per cent of what they were at the beginning of the period. A study of the Customs Report for 1924 reveals the end of the story. Timber as an export commodity has vanished from the returns, but the records show imports of timber and timber products — boxes, barrels, etc. — to the value of almost ten million dollars. Nearly half of this value is represented by the importation of 152 million feet of pine and fir lumber valued at $4,381,559, brought in tax free, which is sufficient indication of the shortage of timber in the island. In a decade Cuba has reverted from an important exporter of valuable timber to the position where it is necessary for her to import most of her requirements for even ordinary construction purposes. But during this same period the material prosperity of the island has increased enormously with an ever-mounting favorable balance of trade. The loss of the value of the timber exports and the increasing cost of imports have been heavily overbalanced by the rise in the exports of agricultural products, chiefly sugar. Where then is the forest problem? Apparently Cuba is better off without her forests than she was before. Certainly the average individual cannot be blamed for thinking so.

The true situation can only be determined by a consideration of how the total land resource of the island is being utilized. The approximate area is 26,600,000 acres. The census of 1899 estimated about half of this area, or 13,000,000 acres, to be uncleared woodland. Plantations and small farms were estimated at about 8,700,000 acres, of which something less than 900,000 acres were in cultivation, and the remainder of the area was unclassified. Since then, largely owing to the expansion of the sugar industry, there has been an enormous increase in the land actually cultivated and a concurrent decrease of forest area; but there has also been an increase in the area of unproductive land. No data exist which would permit of an accurate land classification for the island. It is known that the area under cultivation to cane is about 3,500,000 acres and a very rough estimate of the forest area indicates that to be about 4,500,000 acres. With these estimates as bases an approximate classification may be considered to be:

	Acres	Percentage
Land under cultivation to cane	3,500,000	15
Other cultivation	500,000	
Forests	4,500,000	17
Pastures, savannas, and unused land	18,100,000	68
Total	26,600,000	100

This classification is admittedly open to question and the prime requisite to an adequate understanding of the true economic condition of Cuba is the acquisition of more accurate data in this respect; in other words, the preparation of a land and forest inventory. But, although undoubtedly inaccurate in detail, the information at present available indicates plainly that the recent agricultural expansion in Cuba has been brought about at the expense of the forests and that the reduction of the forest area has been out of all proportion to the increased utilization of the land for agriculture. The forest asset has been largely destroyed and, although the pockets of the present generation have not felt it, the large areas of idle land represent a very great economic loss which will have to be measured, not only by the cost of imported timber, but also by a gradual reduction in the value of the soil and climatic factors upon which successful agriculture depend.

It is difficult to see that any business, be it directed by an individual, a corporation, or a government, may not be on a sound basis when the turnover is large and on the increase. That is one of the reasons that annual stock-taking and the preparation of balance sheets are necessary in all businesses. Such stock-taking is necessary from time to time with national assets. This consideration of facts is no more than a rough preaudit of certain important items in the Cuban national balance sheet. It indicates that one asset, the forested area of the country, has been reduced far below the 25 per cent safety figure shown to be correct by the experience of older countries. It shows a probable overvaluation of other assets, so far as they are valued by recent prosperity, and points to the necessity of taking a correct inventory of the natural resources of the country as a first step toward placing national business on a sound basis.

Possibly it may be admitted that this review of the situation in Cuba is interesting. Certainly it should be interesting to Cubans, but how far can we expect interest to be awakened elsewhere — in these United States, for instance? At first this is not apparent, but if we stop to consider the fact that Cuba has been more affected by our own rapid economic development than any other part of tropical America, and indicates the trend of development in the other larger countries, we, in common with the rest of the world, and more than any other political unit, may feel some concern. Agricultural and industrial development in the continent to the south of us is following the same course, with respect to the forest resource, that has been pursued with us, and generally in new countries throughout the world. Wherever concentration of population exists, wholesale destruction of forests to make way for agriculture has been the rule with utter disregard for the value of the resource destroyed or the effect that the ill-considered removal of the forests may have on general economic and climatic conditions. Were we economically independent of tropical America and had we wisely used our own forest resource, we might take a selfish viewpoint and congratulate ourselves on our own wisdom while deploring their lack of it. We are not in such a position. We need the southern Americas as an outlet for our own products, and we require in return large amounts of their agricultural and other products and are on the verge of being forced to look to them for material to supplement our waning timber supplies during the decades which must elapse before we can again balance our own timber budget.

We are, by a very long way, the heaviest consumer of timber and timber products in the world, but we have largely disregarded the great potential source of supply existing in the tropics of our own hemisphere. The reason is not obscure; we knew little about it and there seemed to be no reason why we should take the trouble to find out. This attitude is changing. Our hardwood-using industries are keenly feeling the pinch of shortening supplies and beginning to look elsewhere for them. Here in the United States timber supplies are diminishing, prices are rising, and there is a general trend toward the substitution of other materials for wood where their use is possible; while to the south of us a vast timber resource is being gradually destroyed through lack of a market. This is economic waste on a big scale.

Conservation connotes informed utilization and no policy of conservation can be initiated in the absence of adequate markets. Were the various governments of Latin America fully appreciative of the lesson which a review of the Cuban situation affords, their hands would be tied in the absence of coöperation on our part and, in the absence of this, we are the losers as well as they. Owing to lack of definite, accurate information as to the specific qualities of the various timbers, stands per acre, costs of extraction, etc., neither party is able to treat with the other in bringing about that wise utilization of the resource which is true conservation. Here, then, is the reason for interest on the part of the United States in the wasting resources of tropical America. The necessity for additional supplies of hardwoods is imperative and there are sufficient data with respect to the forests to the south of us to indicate that they can meet our needs. The problem is an entirely practical one and should be approached from that standpoint. Along broad lines a general inventory of the forest resources of tropical America should be aimed at. More specifically laboratory investigation of tropical species which are available in quantity should be carried out to determine their definite structure and identification, their mechanical and physical properties, and the correlation of their determined properties with uses in the United States. Also, concise estimates of stands and costs of extraction are essential to any plan of utilization and, without losing sight of the broad field of research underlying the whole problem, definite focal points of forest industry should be developed in the tropics as soon as possible. These by natural development will become the broad channels necessary to the economic utilization of a locked-up or wasting asset and will be adequate to meet our ultimate demands for a continuous supply of high-grade hardwoods.

University of Michigan

A STUDY OF FORM FACTORS IN WESTERN YELLOW PINE PLANTATIONS *

IVAN H. SIMS AND LEONARD I. BARRETT

COMPUTATIONS of volume in forest stands involve the use of either form factors or volume tables. Such form factors or volume tables are not available for young stands, particularly for young stands in the United States. Kraft (1) in Europe has given tables of form factors for trees in meter height classes, but it is not known whether these could be used for western yellow pine.

Although height and diameter measurements have been recorded periodically for western yellow pine plantations of the University of Michigan School of Forestry and Conservation, it was evident that accurate volume determinations were impossible without available form factor data or volume tables for such stands. The present study was undertaken to determine the breast-high form factors for seventeen-year-old western yellow pine in the Saginaw Forest plantations. While the results obtained in these studies may indicate the form factors which may be expected in other localities, because of the restricted area studied they should be checked in other stands before being used elsewhere.

METHODS

The sample taken for this study consisted of alternate rows of a seventeen-year-old western yellow pine plantation, 4.4 acres in extent. Each tree in the row was measured except those which were obviously deformed. The sample thus taken contained 192 trees.

* Contribution No. 6 from the School of Forestry and Conservation, University of Michigan.

The following data were taken for each tree: total height, diameter at breast height ($4\frac{1}{2}$ feet), basal area at two-foot intervals, beginning with the ground, and crown class. Total heights of the trees were recorded to the nearest tenth of a foot. These heights were read from a pole graduated in tenths of a foot, which was placed alongside the trunk of the tree. This pole was also used to locate the two-foot intervals at which basal areas were measured. Basal areas were measured to the nearest tenth of an inch of diameter by the use of calipers, on the beam of which the basal areas, in square feet, corresponding to diameters, had been stamped. By reading basal area directly and so recording it in the field, much tedious office work was avoided, with no loss in accuracy. The diameter at breast height was measured and recorded to the nearest tenth of an inch. All the diameter and basal area measurements were taken outside the bark. The crown class of each tree was recorded as "dominant," "codominant," "intermediate," or "suppressed."

The data were first sorted into one-inch classes based on the breast-high diameters. Each diameter class was further divided into two-foot height classes.

After the preliminary sorting of the field data, the cubic foot volume of each tree was computed, by Smalian's formula, as given below, for the bole of the tree up to the highest basal area measurement and the formula for the volume of a cone for the tip.

SMALIAN'S FORMULA

$$\text{Volume in cu. ft.} = \frac{(a\ 2b\ 2c\ .\ .\ .\ n)}{2} \times L$$

$a, b, c, \ldots n$ = basal area in square feet at the 2-foot intervals

L = length of the section between the basal area measurements

For each diameter and height class, the mean basal area and mean height were computed. Mean diameter, breast high, for each class was derived from the mean basal area.

The breast-high form factor for each class was calculated by dividing the total volume of the trees in the class by the product of the total basal area at breast height and the mean height. For the entire sample, the form factor as computed by this method was 0.735. The mean diameter breast high of the entire sample was 3.6 inches; the mean height was 16.4 feet.

TABLE I

SEVENTEEN-YEAR-OLD WESTERN YELLOW PINE: SUMMARY OF DATA, NOT CURVED

In the boxes the figures in the first line indicate mean diameter breast height (left) and mean height (right); in the second line, class form factor; in the third line, number of trees.

D.B.H. class	Height class						
	10–12	12–14	14–16	16–18	18–20	20–22	22–24
2	1.8 10.8 .998 9	2.1 12.4 .912 20	2.4 14.4 .827 8	2.4 16.1 1.29 2			
3		2.7 12.8 .783 5	2.9 14.6 .786 27	3.3 16.4 .730 23	3.4 18.1 .691 7		
4			3.7 14.8 .696 5	3.9 16.7 .678 20	4.1 18.7 .665 27	4.3 20.2 .651 11	
5				4.7 17.1 .556 1	4.8 18.7 .682 8	5.1 20.7 .591 15	4.9 22.2 .605 4

The data in Table I were plotted with heights as abscissae and form factors as ordinates; the form factor for each class was plotted over the mean height, as shown in Figure 23 A. Such plotting resulted in a separate curve for each D. B. H. class.

A second set of curves, Figure 23 B, having diameters breast high as abscissae and form factors as ordinates, was then constructed. Form factors at the class marks of the height classes were read from the first curves, A, and plotted over the mean diameter breast high for the class. A curve was thus secured for each height class.

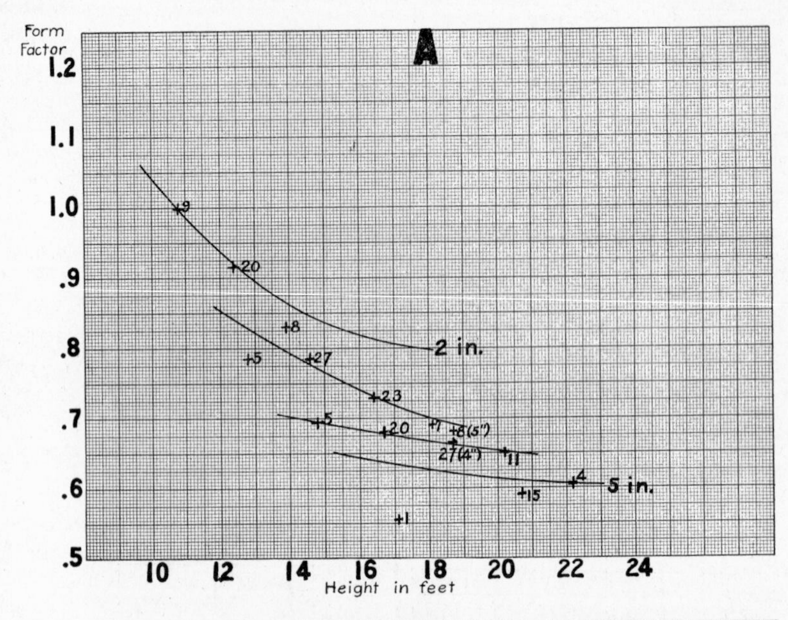
A
Form Factor
1.2
1.1
1.0
.9
.8
.7
.6
.5
10
12
14
16
18
20
22
24
Height in feet
2 in.
5 in.

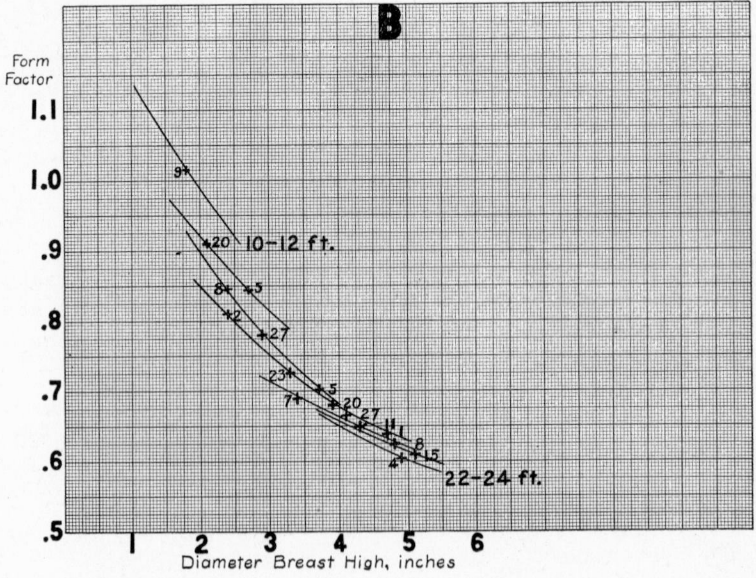
B
Form Factor
1.1
1.0
.9
.8
.7
.6
.5
1
2
3
4
5
6
Diameter Breast High, inches
10-12 ft.
22-24 ft.

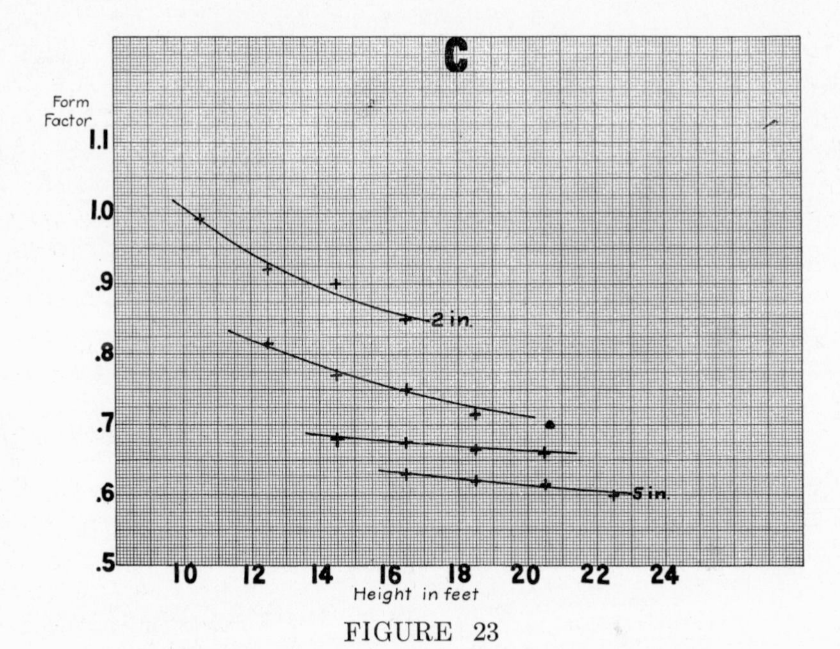

FIGURE 23

A. Curves showing the trend of breast-high form factors within one-inch diameter breast-high classes. Data for the curves were obtained from Table I.

B. Curves showing the breast-high form factors occurring within two-foot height classes as determined by data in Table I and the curves in *A*.

C. Curves showing breast-high form factors for various heights and one-inch diameter breast-high classes. Data for these curves were derived from *B*.

The curves in Figure 23 C were derived by reading the form factor at the class mark of each D. B. H. class and plotting this over the class marks of the height classes. In all curves the points were weighted and the curve balanced in.

The values given in Table II were read from Figure 23 C.

TABLE II

SEVENTEEN-YEAR-OLD WESTERN YELLOW PINE:
FORM FACTORS CURVED

D.B.H. class	Height class						
	10–12	12–14	14–16	16–18	18–20	20–22	22–24
2	.990	.930	.886	.854			
3		.810	.774	.745	.724		
4			.684	.675	.665	.658	
5				.630	.620	.611	.604

The field data were sorted on the basis of crown class and the form factors of the crown classes were derived by the method given previously. These are tabulated in Table III.

TABLE III

SEVENTEEN-YEAR-OLD WESTERN YELLOW PINE:
CROWN CLASS FORM FACTORS

Crown class	Form factor	No. of trees	Mean height in feet
D	.650	47	19.1
CD	.693	87	17.3
I	.836	55	13.5
S	1.42	3	10.2

Table III shows that the breast-high form factors of the lower crown classes are higher than those of the dominant and codominant classes. In the trees studied, however, this is not solely the result of the form of the trees, as will be shown later.

In checking the values given in Table II, the procedure used etermine the class form factor was reversed. The total volume, in cubic feet, of each class is the product of the total basal area at breast height, the mean height, and the class form factor. In each class the volume as computed by the use of the form factor was compared with the sum of the actual volumes of the individual trees of the class.

The maximum error of the class volume obtained by the use of the class form factor as above was 0.8 cubic feet. The net error, or algebraic sum of the individual class errors, was plus 1.0 cubic feet. This was 0.6 per cent of the sum of the actual volumes of the individual trees of the sample, which was 163.1 cubic feet.

The stand form factor and those of the crown classes would, of course, give no error when checked by this method, since the same values would be used in the checks as in their derivation.

DISCUSSION

Kraft (1) gives a table of breast-high form factors for Scotch pine (Kiefer) in height classes comparable to those studied. His values are consistently lower than those given in Table II. This is not surprising, since the leaders and upper part of the boles of the western yellow pines studied are heavier than those of Scotch pines of similar size. This is a large factor when dealing with trees below 20 feet in height.

The higher values of breast-high form factors in small trees is not indicative of greater cylindrical shape, but can be attributed more to the relative position on the trunk at which the breast-high diameter measurement is taken. Thus, on a nine-foot tree the diameter breast high is measured in the middle of the tree, whereas on a fourteen-foot tree it is measured one third of the height from the base.

Table I indicates, in general, that the form factor decreases with increase in height and diameter at breast height. The exceptions are found in the classes having but few trees. These exceptions were corrected in the curves of Figure 23 A, so that the values given in Table II show a more regular reduction than those in Table I.

In taking data in the field the instruments used limited the accuracy of measurement to three significant figures in height as well as basal area. This number is all that was maintained in the computations. Similarly in checking the form factors against the original data only three significant figures resulted.

Although the final results are not as yet available, other studies now in progress indicate that form factors of young trees will vary with species and age, even for trees of the same height and diameter breast high. In order to determine the rate and direction of change of form factors with age, studies similar to the present one should be made at intervals during the life of the stand.

SUMMARY

1. The breast-high form factors of seventeen-year-old western yellow pine decrease with increased height within a given diameter class.

2. The breast-high form factors of seventeen-year-old western yellow pine decrease with increased diameter at breast height within a given height class.

3. The breast-high form factors of the trees studied are influenced more by the relative position on the stem at which the diameter breast high is taken than by the form of the trees.

4. Stamping of basal area on the caliper beam enabled the recording of basal area in the field. This facilitated subsequent computational work.

5. The limitations of measurement confined the computations to three significant figures.

6. Because the study was confined to a small area, 4.4 acres, the form factors should be checked by similar studies on other areas before being applied to other plantations or to natural stands.

7. In checking against the original data the form factors for the height-D. B. H. classes given in Table 2 showed a net error of 0.6 per cent of the actual volume of the entire sample.

8. The use of the stand form factor is more accurate than the use of class form factors for computing the total volume of the stand. This was indicated by the derivation and check of the stand form factor.

9. Breast-high form factors of western yellow pine on the Saginaw Forest are higher than those of Scotch pine trees of the same height as given by Kraft for trees in Europe.

10. The breast-high form factors may be expected to change during the life of the stand and studies similar to the present one should be made at regular intervals.

University of Michigan

REFERENCE CITED

1. Kraft, Gustav. 1885. Beiträge zur förstlichen Zuwachsrechnung. Pp. 1–176. Hanover.

GROWTH AND CULTURAL EXPERIMENTS ON THE SAGINAW FOREST*

LEIGH J. YOUNG †

I. INTRODUCTION

A FOREST school without a forest in which its faculty and students can work and learn would be working under a serious handicap. In the earlier days of forestry in the United States, it was especially important to have actual demonstrations of forestry operations to carry conviction of their practicability to the student mind, though it can hardly be said even now that the need for such demonstrations has passed. To serve its various purposes most fully, a forest of this kind should be under the absolute control of the school and should be near enough to be constantly used without special effort or expense.

History and General Description of Area

It was exceedingly fortunate, therefore, that at the time that the Forestry Department of the University of Michigan was organized,

* Contribution No. 5 from the School of Forestry and Conservation, University of Michigan.

† FOREWORD, by Samuel T. Dana, Dean of the School of Forestry and Conservation, University of Michigan.

It is peculiarly appropriate that the first comprehensive publication of the School of Forestry and Conservation should deal with the Saginaw Forest. Historically, intellectually, and sentimentally the Saginaw Forest has always been inseparably identified with the forestry activities of the University. Not only does it constitute a fitting memorial to Professor Filibert Roth, its creator, guardian, and friend, but for a quarter of a century it has participated in the training of class after class of prospective foresters.

The present publication discloses its value in still another direction — as an outdoor laboratory for scientific research. Such research is of outstanding importance as offering the most effective means of securing the information in 1903, the Honorable Arthur Hill of Saginaw purchased eighty acres of land about three miles west of Ann Arbor and deeded it to the University. Under the terms of the deed, this land was to be used by the Forestry Department as a demonstration and experimental area and was to be known as the "Saginaw Forestry Farm." Later the name was changed by the Regents to that of "Saginaw Forest" as being more appropriate to its real character.

The topography of most of the area varies from level to gentle slopes, though a small percentage lies on very steep slopes. Near the north end of the tract is a lake, covering eleven acres, with about six acres of swamp around the west and south sides. A deep ravine runs southeasterly from the lake to about the middle point of the east boundary.

At the time of purchase practically all the land had been cleared for agriculture. A few small pieces of second-growth oak and hickory had been left on the steeper slopes, and a fairly good growth of elm, aspen, willow, and red and silver maples was present on the wet soils around the lake.

For a number of years prior to the University's ownership the land had been rented for farming. As in the case of most rented farms, the soil had been allowed to deteriorate and was in a generally poor condition. The steeper slopes were badly washed, and a number of deep, actively eroding gullies had been formed.

The soils consist of glacial material approximately two hundred feet in depth and vary from those with a sand content of over

---

necessary for the better handling of our forest lands. The University of Michigan has been fortunate in having in the Saginaw Forest a readily accessible and representative tract on which various experiments can be tried out and the results accurately determined. Professor Young's article analyzes the results so far obtained from the experimental plantings on the tract, for some of which a twenty-year record is now available. The experiments will of course become increasingly valuable as the trees approach maturity and further results will be presented in subsequent reports.

Finally, emphasis should be placed on the value of the Saginaw Forest for demonstration purposes. It is necessary not only to determine experimentally the results of any method of handling the forest, but to demonstrate these results both to forestry students and to timber-land owners. It is hoped, therefore, that an increasing number of forest owners will give the School an opportunity to show them how the forest is being used and what results are being obtained. Visitors are always welcome.

ninety per cent to very compact clays. Nearly all the soils have a considerable admixture of gravel and small boulders. Large boulders occur only occasionally.

After the abandonment of cultivation, a rank growth of weeds took possession of the fields. This, however, was displaced by a grass cover within a few years. On all the heavier soils the grasses formed an exceedingly heavy sod.

Planting of the cleared lands began in 1904, and was completed in 1915, taking first the poorer soils at the north end, since the better ones were still under lease for farming. Since that time, several stands have been clear cut for one reason or another and have been replanted. A total of fifty-five acres has been planted, the remainder of the area being in swamp, natural second growth, roads, and arboretum.

Methods Used for Securing and Recording Data

During the earlier years, annual examinations of the plantations were made by a student assistant to determine the percentage of survival and the average height of the trees. This was done by laying out small plots that presumably represented average conditions and upon which the trees were counted and measured. Since these plots were not permanently marked and were taken in a different location each year, the results were subject to error and were often grossly inconsistent. In 1916 the present system of measuring all the trees in each plantation at five-year intervals was adopted. This is feasible here, because none of the plantations is more than a few acres in extent.

An attempt was made to secure the growth data by having students take the measurements as a part of their class work. This did not give satisfactory results. The present policy is to hire selected students for this kind of work.

Periodic examinations of changes in general conditions, injuries, and the like, have been made and recorded by the author.

Typewritten copies in triplicate are made of the tally sheets of measurements. One copy is used as a work-sheet for checking and computation. A second one is filed in a folder kept in a letter file and the third one is bound in a loose-leaf book for convenience in reference. Each copy is kept in a different place to minimize the chance of loss in case of fire or other accident.

Summaries of each plantation record are kept in a loose-leaf book, having a sheet for each plantation. These sheets are printed forms, with headings and columns as follows:

Lot........ Block.........

Soil:.... Species:.... Ground Cover:.... Spacing:....

Area:.... Slope:.... Planting Method:.... Stock:.... Date of Planting:....

Year	No. Trees Living per acre	Height in Feet			D.B.H. in Inches		
		Average	Maximum	Minimum	Average	Maximum	Minimum

Density of Crown Cover	Forest Floor	Ground Cover	Brush	Average Clear Length	Basal Area per acre sq. ft.	Current Growth	
						cu. ft.	%

Volume per acre cu. ft.	Volume Cut per acre cu. ft.	Injuries	Operations Performed	Remarks

The width of column varies according to the space-requirement of the kind of data to be recorded. The sheets measure twenty inches in width and eight and one-half inches in length and can be used in a long-carriage typewriter, if desired.

For convenience in location and record, the entire area is

divided into five numbered blocks, and the plantations within each block are numbered serially. Each lot is marked at the corners with properly numbered posts, and an accurate map shows the size and position of each lot on the ground.

The written record is supplemented by a photographic one. Pictures are taken of each plantation at five-year intervals with the camera located at the same point and pointed in the same direction each time. Each series of pictures tells the story of the development of the individual stands in a more vivid, striking way than any tables of figures can do.

II. PLANTING AND SEEDING

Methods and Stock Used

Out of a total of fifty-five plantings and seedings, thirty-two were made on soil that had been thoroughly cultivated with the plow and harrow as a preparation for planting. In thirty of these an ordinary spade was used to make a slit in which the trees were set. On the other two slits were made with a grub hoe.

On nineteen of the lots the soil received no cultivation. Squares of sod were stripped off with a grub hoe, and the same tool was used to dig a hole for the tree or seed.

One area was planted by stripping squares of sod with the grub hoe and then making slits with a spade.

In one planting of cottonwood cuttings, slits were made with grub hoes and spade without removing the sod.

Cottonwood cuttings were planted on a site that was rather dry for cottonwood in holes about two feet deep. These holes were dug with a spade as deeply as could be done conveniently and then finished at the bottom with a post-hole augur.

The soil was prepared for a drill-sowing of red oak on another area by plowing narrow strips that were then harrowed lengthwise. Shallow drills were made with the corner of a garden hoe, and the seed covered with a rake.

On all replanted areas the grub hoe method has been used exclusively, because the stumps of the previous stand interfered with cultivation and because it was desirable to avoid the heavy crops of weeds that normally occur on cultivated soils.

A very small percentage of the planting work has been done by students as a part of their instruction. The bulk of it has been done by students in forestry who were paid for it.

The species planted, together with the kinds of stock used for each one, are listed below:

The first figure in the right-hand column gives the number of years in seed-bed, and the second the number of years in transplant area.

Common Name	Scientific Name	Stock
Scotch pine	Pinus sylvestris L.	2–0, 2–2
Austrian pine	Pinus nigra Arnold	2–0
White pine	Pinus strobus L.	2–0, 2–2
Western yellow pine	Pinus ponderosa Laws.	2–0, 2–1
Norway pine	Pinus resinosa Ait.	2–2, 3–1
Japanese red pine	Pinus densiflora Sieb. & Zucc.	2–2
Douglas fir	Pseudotsuga taxifolia (Lam.) Britton	2–0
Norway spruce	Picea excelsa Link	3–0, 2–2
Yellow poplar	Liriodendron tulipifera L.	2–0, 1–0
Hardy catalpa	Catalpa speciosa Warder	1–0
Osage orange	Toxylon pomiferum Sarg.	1–0
Shellbark hickory	Hicoria ovata Britton	seed
Russian mulberry	Morus alba tatarica Loud.	1–0
Box elder	Acer negundo L.	1–0
Black locust	Robinia pseudacacia L.	1–0
Basswood	Tilia americana L.	1–0
White elm	Ulmus americana L.	1–0
Sugar maple	Acer saccharum Marsh.	1–0
White ash	Fraxinus americana L.	1–0
Red oak	Quercus rubra L.	1–0, seed
White oak	Quercus alba L.	1–0, seed
Black walnut	Juglans nigra L.	1–0, seed
Chestnut	Castanea dentata (Marsh.) Burkh.	seed
Cottonwood	Populus deltoides Marsh.	cuttings

Of these species thirteen are indigenous to Michigan, but only eleven are native to this section of the state.

In addition to the species used in regulation plantations, a number of exotics have been grown successfully in small groups in the portion of the area devoted to an arboretum. These species are listed below:

Blue spruce — Picea pungens Engelm.
White spruce — Picea canadensis (Mill.) B.S.P.
Balsam fir — Abies balsamea (L.) Mill.
White fir — Abies concolor (Gord.) Parry

Hemlock — Tsuga canadensis (L.) Carr.
European larch — Larix decidua Mill.
Black alder — Alnus glutinosa Gaertn.
White birch — Betula papyrifera Marsh.
White cedar — Thuja occidentalis L.
Buckeye — Aesculus glabra Willd.
Ailanthus — Ailanthus glandulosa Desf.
Jack pine — Pinus divaricata (Ait.) Du Mont de Cours.
Himalayan pine — Pinus excelsa Wall.

The fact that so many of these have grown vigorously thus far is an indication of the degree to which the native tree flora may be enriched by planting operations.

Plant Survival with the Various Methods and Species

Out of the thirty-two areas on which planting was preceded by a thorough cultivation of the soil, eighteen produced a catch of over ninety per cent at the end of five years after planting, six a catch of between eighty and ninety per cent, six of the remainder a survival of over fifty per cent, and two with less than fifty per cent. On the eight areas showing a survival of less than eighty per cent, the failure in five of them was due to mice and rabbits, in two to soil conditions that were unfavorable to the species planted, and in one to poor condition of stock when received.

On the successful areas (over 80 per cent catch) the species showing the highest rate of survival were Scotch, Austrian, and white pines, catalpa, box elder, black locust, white elm, sugar maple, and white ash. The species that survived less well were Norway spruce, basswood, white oak, and red oak.

All the plantings, except one, on cultivated soil were made with seedling stock. In the one exception 2–1 stock was used, but the survival was so heavily reduced by mice that the results are not comparable with those on areas where seedlings were used.

Where the grub hoe method was used without previous cultivation, the story of survival is very different, as shown in Table I.

TABLE I

Comparison of Planting Method on Basis of Survival

	Slit method preceded by cultivation	Grub hoe method
Survival percentage	Percentage of No. of areas	Percentage of No. of areas
90 and over	56.2	10.5
80 to 90	18.7	26.3
50 to 80	18.7	42.1
less than 50	6.2	21.1

For nine of the plantations established by the grub hoe method, seedling stock was used; on the other ten, seed spots were employed. The use of seed spots was restricted to nut-bearing species. On six areas low survival was due mainly to unsuitability of soil conditions to the species selected, and on two of these the loss was made still greater by damage from mice. On four areas the poor catch was caused primarily by mice.

If the areas upon which partial failures were due to causes other than planting method are eliminated, the results of the two methods were as listed in Table II.

TABLE II

Comparison of Planting Methods on Basis of Survival

	Slit method preceded by cultivation	Grub hoe method
Survival percentage	Percentage of No. of areas	Percentage of No. of areas
90 and over	75.0	22.2
80 to 90	25.0	55.5
50 to 80		22.2
less than 50		

The use of the grub hoe method with transplant stock (mostly 2–2) has given the results shown in Table III. These plantings consisted entirely of coniferous species.

TABLE III

SURVIVAL IN PLANTATIONS ESTABLISHED BY GRUB HOE METHOD AND TRANSPLANT STOCK

Survival percentage	Percentage of No. of areas
90 and over	66.7
80 to 90	
50 to 80	33.3
less than 50	

Comparison of the data in Tables I, II, and III shows definitely that with seedling stock a high degree of survival is more likely to be obtained when planting can be preceded by thorough cultivation. If cultivation is not feasible, the obvious conclusion is that it is better to use transplant stock. The latter statement applies only to plantings with coniferous species and is further supported by experience in planting privately owned lands on which cultivation was not permitted. This statement also applies more to operations on rather heavy soils than to those on light soils. No evidence has been obtained to indicate that there is any gain in using transplant stock of broad-leaved species.

With nut-bearing species direct seeding has given somewhat better survival than was secured by planting seedlings.

Effects of Variations in Spacing

The results of differences in spacing, as they have affected the closing of stands, the rate of cleaning, and the death of trees by suppression, are summarized in Table IV on page 550.

TABLE IV

SOME RESULTS OF DIFFERENCES IN SPACING

Species	Spacing feet	Time required for closing years	Present age years	No. dead trees per acre	Percentage of original trees now dead	Height of cleaning feet
Scotch pine .	4 × 4	6	24	1286	47	21.0
Scotch pine .	3 × 3	4	22			19.5
White pine .	3 × 3	7	24	2285	47	20.0
White pine .	$4\frac{1}{2} \times 4\frac{1}{2}$	9	24	634	29	19.5
Western . . yellow pine	6 × 6	15	20	0	0	7.5
Western. . . yellow pine	3 × 3	8	22			14.0
Box elder . .	6 × 6	14	17	272	22	
Box elder . .	4 × 4	9	17	721	26	
Black locust .	6 × 6	8	19	834	69	22.0
Black locust .	$4\frac{1}{2} \times 4\frac{1}{2}$	6	19	1650	77	22.0
Black locust .	3 × 3	4	19	4246	88	22.0
Sugar maple .	3 × 3	7	21	166	3	12.5
Sugar maple .	4 × 4	10	21	0	0	12.0

"Height of cleaning" means height to which branches have been killed.

All the stands listed above were established by the use of seedling stock, and practically all of them are parallel plantings on the same site. One stand of Scotch pine from transplant stock with 6 × 6 spacing is now six years old and has not yet closed. About two more years will be required for this last stand to establish a complete cover.

The advantages gained by close spacing are an earlier establishment of cover and the killing of lower branches at an earlier age, which means that the branches have a smaller diameter when killed and will presumably drop off in a shorter time than if they were larger.

In view of the relatively small differences shown in Table IV in time required for closing and height of cleaning, it is evident that the additional cost of close spacing is not justified under ordinary conditions. So far as the height of cleaning is concerned, the differences are practically negligible, except in the two stands of western yellow pine. Even in these two stands the difference will be temporary. The reason for the present difference is that the stand with 6 × 6 spacing has been cleaning for only five years, while the other has had fourteen years for the process.

Observation of the various stands has shown that cleaning starts earlier in the more closely spaced stand, but that ultimately the height of cleaning is practically the same in all stands of the same species, of the same age, and on sites of the same quality. In stands that are started with a close spacing, the competition between the crowns of the trees is more severe during the earlier years than in stands that have a wider spacing. As a result, the dominant trees in the former have smaller crowns than the dominant trees in the latter class of stands. Because of this latter fact, the time when the height of cleaning is the same in both cases comes before the age at which the number of trees per acre in the closely spaced stand has become equal to that in the stand started with wider spacing. This means that the gain in cleaning secured by closer spacing is limited to the first fifteen or twenty years and that the final height of cleaning is the same, provided the initial spacing of the various stands varies within ordinary limits.

The amount of wastage due to close spacing is indicated by the figures in Table IV for the numbers of trees that have died from suppression in the more closely spaced stands. The material lost in these is all far too small to have any merchantable value. A close spacing causes a loss in the average diameter of trees of a given age, but produces a gain in a somewhat earlier cleaning of the boles.

In the black locust stands, another element entered the situation, namely, the locust borer. With the 3 × 3 spacing, the growth of the individual trees was slower than in the other stands, so that the mechanical weakening caused by the borers was much more serious and produced a considerably greater loss of trees from breakage near the base. At present, the 3 × 3 stand has a smaller number of trees per acre than the 6 × 6.

The obvious conclusion from the results cited above is that

under average conditions a spacing of 6×6 is sufficiently close. Since no wider spacings were used in these experiments, no data on the results of such spacings are available.

III. THE GROWTH AND DEVELOPMENT OF STANDS

Before it is possible to interest any considerable number of landowners in the business of growing timber, it is necessary to be able to give definite information as to the probable returns. One of the most important factors in determining such returns is the rate of growth that various species will make on different types of soil. The lack of such data at present constitutes one of the serious obstacles to the rapid development of a better forest practice on privately owned lands. Even in the management of public lands, the possession of accurate growth data is both necessary and valuable.

It is with the object of adding to our knowledge of tree-growth that a careful record has been kept of the growth that has actually occurred in the Saginaw Forest plantations. In addition, experiments have been initiated to determine what cultural methods may be employed to stimulate maximum volume production without any material sacrifice in quality.

From the practical standpoint, a timber-grower is interested not only in the total production that may be secured in various periods of time, but also in how long it will take for the bulk of the trees in a stand to reach a merchantable size.

In order to give the growth figures that have been obtained here the greatest degree of usefulness in the way of application to other areas, they should be correlated with definite information on the soil conditions existing in each place. There has been no opportunity as yet for the necessary soil study which would make it possible to do this.

In the earlier years of the development of a young forest, interest is focused primarily upon height growth and the rapidity with which a complete cover is established. Later, the basal area growth per acre and the rate of cleaning become of importance.

The growth attained by the several species is given in detail in Table V on page 553.

TABLE V

SUMMARY OF GROWTH OF SAGINAW FOREST PLANTATIONS

Species	Age years	No. of trees per acre	Average height feet	Average D.B.H. inches	Mean annual height growth feet	Basal area per acre sq. ft.	Volume per acre cu. ft.	Current growth* per acre	
								Cu. ft.	Per-centage
Scotch pine...	22	1436	34.5	4.5	1.6	159.8	2867	196	8.7
Scotch pine...	18	....	28.9	4.2	1.6	.....	....	...	....
Scotch pine...	6	1112	5.1	...	0.8	.....	....	...	....
Scotch pine...	4	....	3.9	...	0.97	.....	....	...	....
Austrian pine.	21	1464	28.8	4.2	1.4	145.5	2430	187	10.2
Austrian pine.	18	....	23.5	3.1	1.3	.....	....	...	....
White pine....	22	2555	27.2	3.5	1.2	178.0	2711	187	8.8
White pine....	22	1517	29.1	4.4	1.3	162.3	2645	197	9.8
White pine....	15	1261	19.5	3.2	1.3	72.1	1125	...	....
White pine....	17	627	19.1	3.6	1.1	43.8	....	...	....
Douglas fir....	19	1143	18.0	2.4	0.9	38.4	....	...	....
Douglas fir....	7	1848	2.4	...	0.3	.....	....	...	....
Yellow poplar.	19	953	21.7	2.1	1.1	23.4	....	...	....
Catalpa......	13	2780	11.6	1.4	0.9	30.6	....	...	....
Catalpa......	24	794	20.9	3.3	0.9	46.9	....	...	....
Catalpa......	15	2216	10.5	1.3	0.7	21.1	....	...	....
Western yellow pine .	15	1427	14.7	2.1	1.0	34.9	....	...	....
Western yellow pine..	16	770	14.8	3.0	0.9	38.1	....	...	....
Western yellow pine..	18	....	18.1	2.8	1.0	.....	....	...	....
Western yellow pine..	17	1192	17.6	3.7	1.0	90.1	....	...	....
Western yellow pine..	12	802	10.6	...	0.9	.....	....	...	....
Western yellow pine..	17	850	15.2	3.4	0.9	54.4	629	...	....
Western yellow pine..	15	832	13.5	2.9	0.9	38.0	395	...	....
Norway spruce	20	3094	11.6	...	0.6	.....	....	...	....
Norway spruce	13	1138	6.5	...	0.5	.....	....	...	....
Norway spruce	14	1430	10.1	...	0.7	.....	....	...	....
Norway pine..	5	1566	2.6	...	0.5	....	....	...	....
Norway pine..	7	1449	6.8	...	0.97	....	....	...	....
Norway pine..	8	1567	6.7	...	0.8	....	....	...	....
Osage orange..	15	2205	6.3	...	0.4	....	....	...	....
Hickory......	21	....	8.7	...	0.4	....	....	...	....
Russian mulberry...	18	1853	8.6	...	0.5	....	....	...	....
Box elder.....	17	938	12.9	1.5	0.8	12.6	....	...	....
Box elder.....	17	2001	16.8	1.9	1.0	39.0	....	...	....
Black locust...	14	496	28.6	3.6	2.0	35.4	....	...	....
Black locust...	14	1016	29.1	3.3	2.1	62.6	....	...	....
Black locust...	14	618	28.8	3.1	2.1	32.6	....	...	....
Basswood.....	18	1609	11.9	1.5	0.7	21.4	....	...	....
White elm....	22	2139	17.3	2.3	0.8	62.9	....	...	....
Sugar maple...	21	2584	23.2	2.1	1.1	62.5	....	...	....

* "Current growth" in all tables is actually mean periodic growth.

TABLE V (*Continued*)

SUMMARY OF GROWTH OF SAGINAW FOREST PLANTATIONS

Species	Age years	No. of trees per acre	Average height feet	Average D.B H. inches	Mean annual height growth feet	Basal area per acre sq. ft.	Volume per acre cu. ft.	Current growth per acre	
								cu. ft.	Per-centage
Sugar maple..	21	1678	25.0	2.5	1.2	59.5	....	...	....
White ash....	12	1253	7.1	...	0.6	....	....	...	....
White ash....	14	2500	11.8	1.2	0.8	20.0	....	...	....
White ash....	13	1100	11.5	1.2	0.9	9.0	....	...	....
Red oak......	18	756	18.0	2.1	1.0	18.9	....	...	....
Red oak......	17	786	14.5	...	0.8	....	....	...	....
Red oak......	17	312	12.5	...	0.7	....	....	...	....
Red oak......	17	1104	16.5	1.7	1.0	17.1	....	...	....
Red oak......	17	1359	17.9	1.8	1.0	25.2	....	...	....
Red oak......	17	1196	16.7	1.7	1.0	20.7	....	...	....
Red oak......	18	865	15.4	1.7	0.8	14.2	....	...	....
Red oak......	18	779	14.6	1.7	0.8	12.6	....	...	....
Red oak......	17	491	17.9	1.9	1.0	10.4	....	...	....
White oak....	18	1566	13.8	1.8	0.8	27.9	....	...	....
White oak....	21	852	11.4	...	0.5	....	....	...	....
White oak....	19	638	8.3	...	0.4	....	....	...	....
Chestnut.....	19	146	8.3	...	0.4	....	....	...	....
Black walnut..	19	531	6.7	...	0.3	....	....	...	....
Black walnut..	19	1069	5.8	...	0.3	....	....	...	....
Black walnut..	17	567	7.9	...	0.5	....	....	...	....
Cottonwood...	15	209	33.1	4.8	2.2	26.1	....	...	....

All diameter measurements have been taken at a point four and one-half feet above the ground, but are not made until the average diameter in any given stand is over one inch. This means that stands for which no average diameter figure is given in Table V had not reached this size at the time the last measurement was made. "Average D. B. H." means average diameter breast high.

In computing mean annual height growth, the figures have been rounded off to the nearest tenth of a foot.

Reference to Table V shows that of all the species planted only cottonwood and black locust have exceeded a mean annual height growth of two feet. Scotch pine ranks second with a mean of 1.6 feet. Some stands of white and Austrian pine have made 1.3 feet per year. White pine in mixture with yellow poplar has made a more rapid height growth than in any of the pure stands. One Norway pine stand only seven years old has reached a mean of

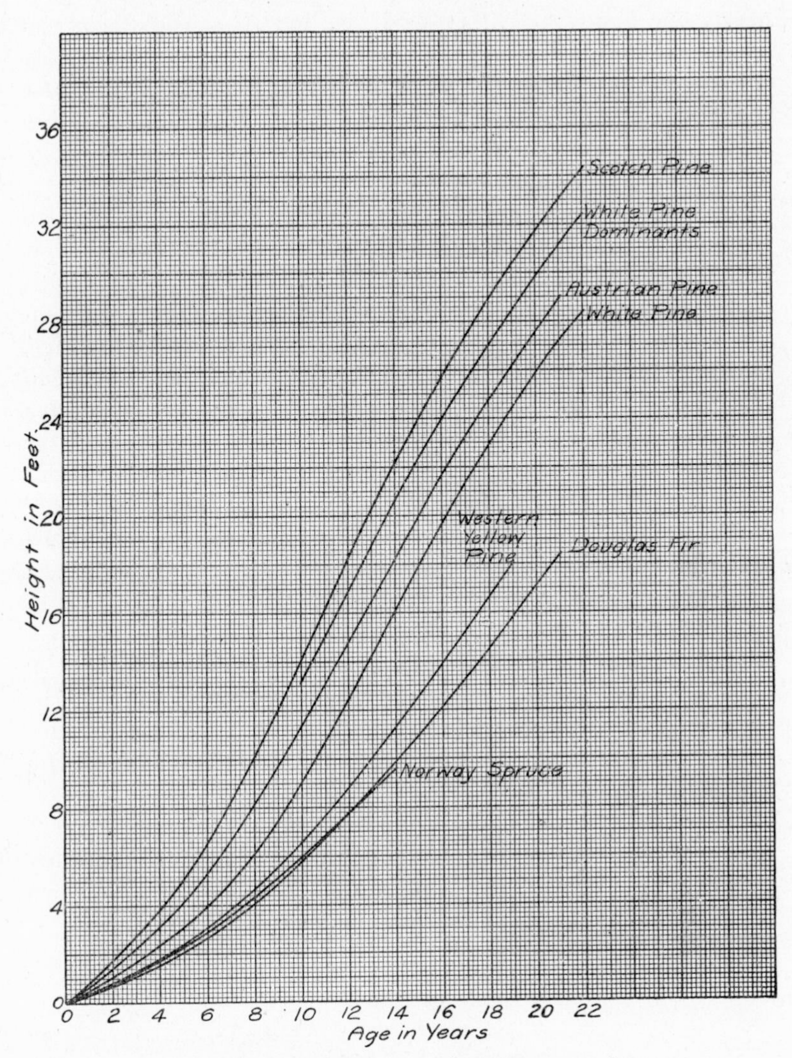

FIG. 24. Age-height curves of coniferous species

nearly one foot. Since this stand has barely passed the period of slowest height growth, this indicates that it will probably surpass the growth of the white and Austrian pines and nearly equal that of Scotch pine. The best growth reached by Norway spruce is 0.7 foot, the poorest is 0.5 foot. The mean growth of Douglas fir has been 0.9 foot.

Among the broad-leaved species, sugar maple ranks next to cottonwood and black locust with a mean of 1.2 feet. Yellow poplar comes close to sugar maple with a growth of 1.1 feet. Most of the stands of red oak show a growth of approximately one foot. The species that show a mean of less than 0.5 foot are osage orange, hickory, Russian mulberry, chestnut, black walnut, and one stand of white oak. The failure of these species to make a better showing is unquestionably due to the fact that the soil conditions of the areas on which they are growing are unfavorable. In the case of chestnut, some of the climatic factors of this locality are probably partly responsible. That black walnut is capable of very much better growth than the average given in Table V is demonstrated by the fact that a portion of one stand, located upon soil of excellent quality and with high moisture content, has maintained a mean growth of 1.3 feet during a period of nineteen years.

A graphical comparison of the height growth of some of the coniferous species is given in Figure 24 in the form of age-height curves. These curves are based upon the growth of a number of stands of each species.

While the variations in the height growth of the different species at different periods in the development of the stands are shown by the curves, they are brought out more clearly when expressed in figures, as in Table VI on page 557.

TABLE VI

MEAN PERIODIC HEIGHT GROWTH OF CONIFEROUS SPECIES

Species	Periods in Years			
	0–5	5–10	10–15	15–20
	feet	feet	feet	feet
Scotch pine	1.0	1.8	2.0	1.5
Austrian pine	0.8	1.5	1.8	1.5
White pine.	0.6	1.2	1.8	1.5
Western yellow pine . . .	0.5	0.9	1.2	1.3
Norway spruce	0.4	0.8	0.9	
Douglas fir	0.4	0.7	1.0	1.2
White pine — dominants .			1.86	1.5

Even a casual examination of Table VI brings out a number of important and interesting facts. The three species (Scotch, Austrian, and white pine) that started most rapidly reached the maximum mean periodic growth at the same time, and in the succeeding period this growth became exactly the same for them all. The period of maximum mean periodic growth is the one immediately following the time of establishment of a complete crown cover in each of these stands. (See Plates XCVI and XCVII.)

Apparently, none of the three species that started more slowly has reached the maximum as yet, though this cannot be accepted as a fact until another period has elapsed. The figures indicate, however, that the maximum is at least nearly reached, since in both Douglas fir and western yellow pine the difference between the growth of the third and fourth periods is less than that between the second and third. The figures for Norway spruce show the same sort of slowing down.

The items in the last line of Table VI are taken from the curve for "white pine — dominants" in Figure 24. The data for this curve were obtained from a single, thinned stand. The *rate* of height growth for the dominants and codominants alone in this stand is

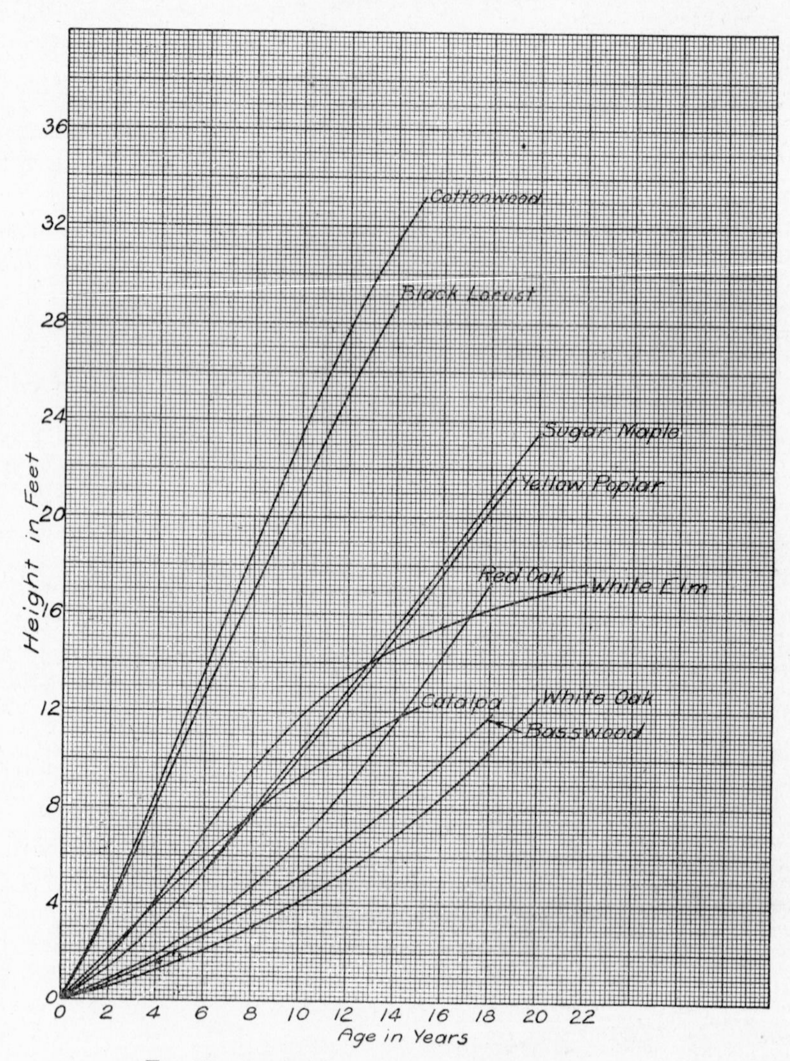

FIG. 25. Age-height curves of broad-leaved species

practically identical with that of the average for all trees in the several stands for which the figures are given in line 3 of Table VI.

The figures for Norway spruce hardly do the species justice. The apparently poor showing made by this species is due to the fact that plantations of it have all been made on sites that are of distinctly low quality for spruce, mainly because of deficiency in available moisture. A number of group plantings on heavier soils with higher water-content have made very satisfactory growth. With one exception, all spruce plantations have shown subnormal color and development for at least two years after planting. After the trees have become established, the color has improved decidedly. The one exception was a case of under-planting black locust. The trees in this planting have maintained a rich color from the start and show a high degree of vigor. One stand, planted on a site that shows a wide variation in conditions, was not included in the data upon which the curves in Figure 24 are based.

Age-height curves for a number of the broad-leaved species and similar to those in Figure 24 are given in Figure 25. These curves are based upon coördinates having the same scales as those in Figure 24, so that they are directly comparable. No curves are given for a number of species that are decided misfits in relation to the soils they occupy.

The curves in Figure 25, together with the figures in Table VII, afford a basis for a ready comparison of the development of the species given. (See Plate XCVIII for growth of red oak at different ages.)

TABLE VII

MEAN PERIODIC HEIGHT GROWTH OF BROAD-LEAVED SPECIES

Species	Periods in Years			
	0–5	5–10	10–15	15–20
	feet	feet	feet	feet
Cottonwood	2.2	2.5	1.9	
Black locust	2.1	2.2	1.9	
Sugar maple	0.8	1.2	1.3	1.3
Yellow poplar	0.8	1.1	1.3	1.3
White elm	1.1	1.2	0.7	0.3
Red oak	0.5	0.8	1.2	1.5
Catalpa	1.0	0.8	0.6	
Basswood	0.4	0.6	0.8	1.0
White oak	0.3	0.5	0.7	0.9

As was true of the conifers, the species showing most rapid growth at the start have reached the maximum early, though in the species named above the maximum has come five years earlier than in the most rapidly growing conifers. The growth of sugar maple and yellow poplar is striking in that it is practically identical for the two species. This is partially due to the fact that the yellow poplar is on soil poorer than that on which the sugar maple is growing. These two species are the only ones, so far as the figures obtained to date show, that have maintained their maximum growth for more than one period. Catalpa is the only species to reach its maximum rate in the first period.

The behavior of the species that started slowly also resembles that of the same group of the conifers in that there has been a steady increase in the periodic rate for twenty years, with the maximum apparently not yet reached. The precise regularity with which the rates of basswood and white oak have increased is particularly noteworthy. (See Plate XCIX for further illustrations of growth.)

The curve for white elm indicates clearly that this species, in spite of its good start, is losing ground rapidly. So pronounced has been the loss of vigor that it is apparent to even a casual observer of the stands themselves. The species has been planted on a heavy clay soil and on high ground, where during the summer it is subject to rather extreme drying out. The density of the stands has shown a marked decrease during the past five years. At no time has the density been great enough to shade out the ground cover and lead to the establishment of anything approaching a forest floor.

In marked contrast to the lack of normal development shown by the majority of the elms, excellent growth has been made by the trees in a few rows along the edges of the stands, where elm adjoins stands of other species. In one place a stand of sugar maple protects the elm on the west and causes a heavy accumulation of leaf litter that is blown into the elm stand from the maple. The combined effect of shading from the maple and mulching has been a pronounced increase in the size of the elms on the edge over that of trees just a few feet distant. A stand of black locust to the north of the elm has caused a similar stimulation of the elm, due undoubtedly to improvement of the nitrogen content of the soil by the locust. Improved growth of elm adjacent to a stand of basswood on the east is apparently due solely to better moisture conditions produced by the shading effect of the basswood during a portion of each day. That there is an appreciable shading effect here is demonstrated by the sparseness of ground cover under the elm near the basswood.

Since it is one of the three factors (height, basal area, form) needed to obtain the total cubic volume production of a stand, basal area growth is just as important as height growth. Basal area per acre is the total obtained by adding the cross-section areas of all the individual trees on an acre, based upon the measurement of their diameters at breast-height. For purposes of comparison, the basal area figures are particularly useful, since they give the combined effect of diameter growth and density of stocking.

The basal area figures for all the individual stands for which they are available are given in Table V. Examination of this table shows the marked superiority of the conifers as a class in this item of growth. The maximum is 178.0 square feet per acre at the age of 22 years. This growth has been made by a stand of white pine, planted with a spacing of 3 × 3 and consequently having a very high density. Other fully stocked stands of white pine started with wider spacings are rapidly approaching this figure and will probably equal the basal area of the 3 × 3 stand or possibly surpass it, when the densities have become more nearly equal. Austrian pine follows rather closely with 145.5 square feet at the age of 21 years, in spite of a thinning five years previously that removed 29 square feet. Next in order are Scotch pine with 159.8 square feet at 22 years and western yellow pine with 90.1 square feet at 17 years. A mixture of nineteen-year-old yellow poplar and fifteen-year-old white pine has reached 95.5 square feet, of which the white pine has made 75 per cent. Another mixture of nineteen-year-old Douglas fir and fifteen-year-old western yellow pine has a basal area of 73.3 square feet, of which 52 per cent has been made by Douglas fir. The figures quoted above are all for fully stocked stands. Wherever Table V shows appreciably lower figures for any of the species named above, reference to the column giving number of trees per acre will show that the stand in question is understocked.

The ranking of the better stands of broad-leaved species is as follows: black locust with 62.6 square feet at 14 years, sugar maple with 62.5 at 21 years, white elm with 62.9 at 22 years, catalpa with 30.6 at 13 years, box elder with 39.0 in 17 years, white oak with 27.9 in 18 years, red oak with 25.2 in 17 years, and basswood with 21.4 in 18 years.

Stands of black walnut, chestnut, Russian mulberry, and osage orange have made such poor diameter growth that it has not seemed worth while to measure diameters of these species.

Since curves of basal area growth are valuable for purposes of comparison only when based upon fully stocked stands and upon those that have been measured enough times to give adequate data, it is possible to draw curves for only six species. These curves are given in Figure 26 on page 563.

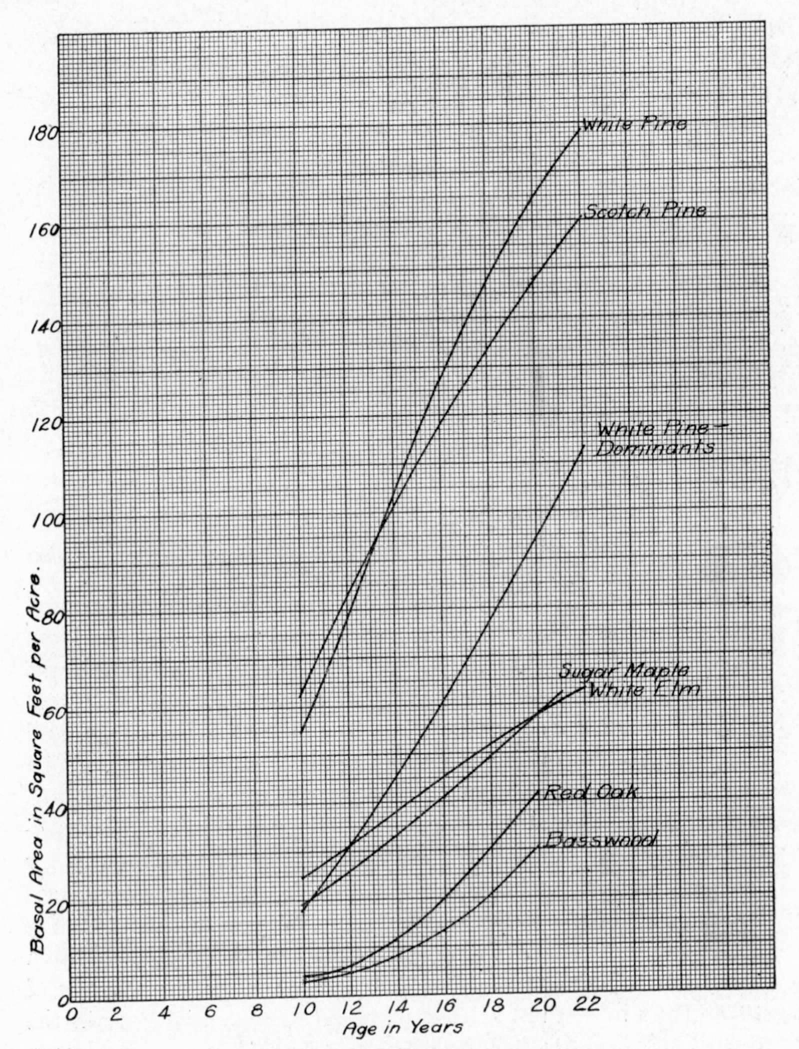

FIG. 26. Age-basal area curves

The mean periodic basal area growth for the species named above is given in Table VIII.

TABLE VIII

MEAN PERIODIC GROWTH IN BASAL AREA

SPECIES	PERIODS IN YEARS	
	10–15	15–20
	sq. feet	sq. feet
White pine	12.0	9.8
Scotch pine	9.4	7.6
Sugar maple	3.7	4.1
White elm	3.4	3.3
Red oak	2.2	5.3
Basswood	1.4	4.2
White pine — dominants	6.9	8.3

It is of interest to note from Table VIII that the maximum rate of basal area growth in the Scotch and white pines occurred during the same period in which these two species reached the maximum rate of height growth. With the exception of white elm, the broad-leaved species are still increasing their rate, and this increase is surprisingly large in red oak and basswood.

For comparison of the difference between the average growth of all the trees in a stand and that of the dominants and codominants alone, the last line of Table VIII contains the figures for the mean periodic growth in basal area of the dominant and codominant trees in the same stand of white pine used for this purpose in Table VI. It appears that the trend of basal area growth in the dominants is different from that of the average of all the trees in a stand in that it shows a decided increase in the 15–20-year period rather than a decrease. The mean basal area growth during the last period of the dominants and codominants amounts to 84.7 per cent of that made by the total stand.

A study of the breast-height form factors of white and western yellow pines was made by I. H. Sims and L. I. Barrett (2) in

1926. This was done in twenty-two-year white pine and in eleven-year and seventeen-year western yellow pine. In this study form factors were found for the various height and diameter classes represented, as well as for the stand as a whole. At twenty-two years the white pine had a form factor of 0.56. At thirteen years the study indicated a form factor of approximately 0.80 for white pine. Western yellow pine seventeen years old showed a form factor of 0.76, and at the age of eleven years the form factor of the same species was 1.36. By using these form factors, volumes were obtained for these two species as given in Table IX.

TABLE IX

VOLUMES OF WHITE AND WESTERN YELLOW PINES

SPECIES	Age years	Form factor	Volume per acre (wood and bark) cubic feet
White pine	13	0.80 (estimated)	1149
White pine	17	0.60 (estimated)	1776
White pine	22	0.56	2711
Western yellow pine . . .	17	0.76	1205

Since the material in these young stands is essentially unmerchantable, the figures given are useful only for purposes of comparison and for indicating the really considerable amount of material that has been produced in what is after all a relatively short time. Taking the weight of a cubic foot of dry white pine wood as 24 pounds, the average annual production of stem wood in the white pine stand has been 2957 pounds per acre. This figure needs some correction, since the volumes in Table IX include the bark.

Kraft (1) gives a form-factor table for Scotch pine that starts with trees as small as three meters in height. Applying this table to Scotch pine stands on the Saginaw Forest gives volumes, in cubic feet per acre, as follows:

At 13 years, 1197
At 17 years, 1923
At 22 years, 3005

While these are perhaps not strictly accurate, they undoubtedly represent close approximations of the volumes actually present and at least indicate the relative changes in volume at the different periods of development.

Another important item in the development of a young stand of timber is the degree to which a given species is able to eliminate ground cover and form a real forest floor by the accumulation of various forms of litter. In all the coniferous stands, ground cover has disappeared and a forest floor has replaced it as soon as a complete crown cover has been formed. This same thing has occurred in stands of sugar maple and box elder. A number of species, including catalpa, Russian mulberry, white elm, white ash, and cottonwood, have failed to shade out ground cover and have formed practically no forest floor at any stage of their development thus far. For about three years after the establishment of a complete cover, there was no ground cover under the black locust stands, and a thin forest litter accumulated. As the locust crowns began to rise, this litter soon disappeared and a heavy growth of weeds developed in which golden-rod predominated for a number of years. Wherever the red and white oak stands have completely closed, ground cover is lacking, but no permanent forest floor has yet been formed. Stands of other species have not closed sufficiently to show what will happen when they do. In some of the coniferous stands that have been thinned, a scanty growth of herbaceous plants has followed the thinnings and has persisted for two or three years and then has disappeared again, as the stand has recovered from the thinning. Such a growth has always consisted of only one or two species.

IV. THINNING EXPERIMENTS

Thinnings have been made in stands of Scotch, Austrian, white and western yellow pine, black locust, sugar maple, and white elm, and in the following mixtures — Douglas fir and western yellow pine, yellow poplar and white pine, catalpa and Scotch pine. Because of the size and shape of some of these plantations, it has been possible to establish definite experiments with unthinned control plots and isolation strips only in Scotch pine, white pine, black locust, sugar maple, and white elm. Results of thinning black locust have been disturbed considerably by the damage caused by the locust borer.

All thinnings, except in one stand of white pine, have followed the Danish method of selecting the best trees (principals) in the stand and then favoring these by removing all subordinate trees that are interfering with the development of the principals. All neutral trees (those that are neither interfering with principals or helping to clean them) have been cut at each thinning. In the one exception cited above, Kraft's crown classification was used as a basis, and a "Grade C" thinning was made which removed all trees in the oppressed and suppressed classes. All badly deformed trees that could be cut without causing too large an opening in the cover were taken out, even though on the basis of size alone they would have fallen in a higher crown class. The interval between thinnings has been five years. In some of the stands this interval will soon need to be lengthened, if excessively light thinnings are to be avoided.

A total of three thinnings has been made in the Scotch pine, beginning with a rather light cut in the fall of 1915 at the age of twelve years. Prior to the thinning, the thinned plot had 2444 trees per acre and the control 2164. The plots were not measured until the fall of 1916. At that time the basal areas were 70.55 square feet per acre for the thinned and 92.345 for the control. The thinning removed 514 trees per acre with a basal area of 13.04 square feet. If these trees had remained in the stand, the basal area of the thinned plot would have been slightly over 83.59 in 1916, so that at the beginning of the experiment the thinned plot had 90.5 per cent of the basal area of the control. With the use of a form factor of 0.60 (approximate), the volumes before thinning were: thinned plot, 1023 cubic feet per acre; control, 1046 cubic feet. The thinning removed 126 cubic feet. The average diameter breast high of trees cut was 2.1 inches. Of trees having a diameter of 3.0 inches and over, a total of 97 per acre was cut.

Prior to the second thinning in 1920, the two plots compared as follows:

TABLE X

Plot	No. trees per acre	Basal area per acre sq. ft.	Volume per acre cu. ft.	Current growth	
				Cu. ft.	Percentage
Thinned. . .	1708	101.33	1610	178	15.7
Control . . .	1800	127.13	1888	210	15.9

The death of 222 trees per acre on the thinned plot during the interval between thinnings shows that the first thinning was altogether too light. In 1920 the basal area of the thinned plot had dropped to 79.7 per cent of that of the control. The volumes for both plots were computed with a form factor of 0.58. The current volume growth in cubic feet of the thinned plot has been only 84.7 per cent of that of the control, but expressed in percentage it is nearly equal on the two plots.

A comparison of the height and diameter development of the two plots before the 1920 thinning is given below:

TABLE XI

Plot	Height in Feet			Diameter in Inches		
	Average	Maximum	Minimum	Average	Maximum	Minimum
Thinned	27.4	41.5	14.0	3.3	7.7	1.2
Control	25.6	34.5	9.0	3.6	6.2	1.4

These figures show that in spite of the thinning the average and minimum diameters of the thinned plot are smaller than those of the control.

The thinning in 1920 removed 708 trees per acre (41.4 per cent of the total), 15.849 square feet of basal area, and 209 cubic feet of volume. The average diameter of cut trees was 2.0 inches with a total of only 28 trees per acre having a diameter of 3.0 inches and over.

The effects of the thinning in 1920 were much more pronounced than those of the light thinning of 1915, as shown by the relation of the plots in 1925 before thinning, given below:

TABLE XII

PLOT	No. trees per acre	Basal area per acre sq. ft.	Volume per acre cu. ft.	Current growth		Height in feet		Diameter in inches	
				Cu. ft.	Per-centage	Aver-age	Mini-mum	Aver-age	Mini-mum
Thinned	944	116.68	2263	172	10.1	37.3	24.0	4.8	1.7
Control	1436	159.82	2867	196	8.7	34.5	21.0	4.5	1.3

The difference in number of trees per acre has now become a decided one. The basal area of the thinned plot has grown still smaller in relation to that of the control than it was in 1920, since in 1925 it amounted to only 73.0 per cent. The current growth in volume in cubic feet has decreased on both plots, but the decrease has been greater on the control. The difference is most striking if given in percentages. Decrease in thinned plot was 3.4 per cent; in control, 6.7 per cent. Current growth percentage for the thinned exceeded that of the control for the first time. The same thing is true of the average and minimum diameters of the thinned plot, which reverses the relation existing in 1920.

If the distance factor, the ratio between average diameter and average distance between trees, is computed for the two plots at the time of thinnings, another basis for comparison is afforded.

TABLE XIII

Plot	Distance Factors			
	1916	1920	1925	1925 (after thinning)
Thinned . . .	20.2	18.2	17.0	19.5
Control . . .	19.3	16.3	14.7	14.7

A decrease in the distance factor indicates a greater degree of crowding in the stand in relation to the size of the trees. The figures given above show that the thinnings have served to lessen competition on the thinned plot as compared with that on the control. However, thinnings have not been sufficiently severe to prevent the competition on the thinned plot from becoming more severe in 1925 than it was in 1920 before thinning. It is interesting to note that the 1925 thinning resulted in a relatively closer spacing of the trees than existed in 1916. By 1930 the factor of 19.5 will probably be reduced to somewhat below 17.0, the factor before the 1925 thinning. The degree of crowding indicated by these changes in distance factors is evidently necessary, if satisfactory cleaning is to be secured.

The thinning of 1925 removed 416 trees per acre, 26.208 square feet of basal area, and 348 cubic feet of volume. The average diameter of trees cut was 3.4 inches with a total of 236 trees having a diameter of 3.0 inches and over. Ninety-seven of the trees cut had a diameter of 4.0 inches and better. The total number of trees cut in the three thinnings has been 1638. In addition, 278 trees have died on the thinned plot, making the total decrease in number of trees 1916, as against a decrease of 728 on the control plot.

The results of thinnings in the two white pine stands show several differences from those obtained in the Scotch pine. For the stand started with a 3 × 3 spacing, the results are summarized in Table XIV on page 571.

TABLE XIV

RESULTS OF THINNING IN WHITE PINE, SPACING 3 × 3

Plot	Age years	No. trees per acre	Basal area per acre sq. ft.	Volume per acre cu. ft.	Current growth		Height in feet		Diameter in inches	
					Cu. ft.	Per-centage	Average	Minimum	Average	Minimum
Thinned	13	4539	105.15	1304			15.5	3.4	2.0	0.0
Control	13	3904	90.89	1149			15.8	4.3	2.1	0.0
Thinned	17	3407	142.63	1848	162	11.4	21.6	12.2	2.7	0.8
Control	17	3376	138.3	1776	157	11.5	21.4	11.0	2.7	0.7
Thinned	22	2044	173.2	2793	261	13.4	28.8	15.0	3.9	1.5
Control	22	2555	178.0	2711	187	8.8	27.2	15.0	3.5	1.5

In these plots, growing conditions are evidently somewhat better on the area occupied by the thinned plot, since at the beginning of the experiment the basal area per acre of the thinned plot was 115.7 per cent of that of the control, though the greater number of trees per acre on the thinned plot contributed to this superiority to a certain extent. Prior to the 1920 thinning this percentage had decreased to 103.1, and by 1925 it had dropped to 97.3. On the other hand, a comparison of the actual increase in basal area on the two plots, following the first two thinnings, shows the thinned plot in a more favorable light.

TABLE XV

Plot	Growth in basal area per acre	
	1916–20 sq. ft.	1920–25 sq. ft.
Thinned . .	47.564	62.142
Control . .	47.41	39.700

During the period after the first thinning, both plots increased their basal areas by practically the same amounts, but after the second thinning the thinned plot added 22.44 square feet more than the control, according to the usual method of calculation. But the control plot lost 821 trees through death during the second period, so that the total basal area of the plot was reduced by an amount equal to that of the dead trees, and this serves to reduce the apparent growth of the trees that were alive on the control plot at the end of the period. If only the increase in basal area of the trees still alive in 1925 is computed for both plots, it is found that the growth on the control plot for the period of 1920–25 was 52.3 square feet and on the thinned plot 62.799 square feet, an excess of 10.479 square feet in favor of the thinned, but this is less than half the apparent excess obtained by calculating the difference in the usual way. The difference in the results obtained by the two methods of calculation is also an indication of the loss in unutilized material in unthinned stands, since the current volume growth on the two plots, when computed upon the same basis as above, would show much the same relation as growth in basal area.

It is important to note that, in stands of Scotch and white pine of the same age, while the current growth in cubic feet of the Scotch pine showed a decrease during the period 1920–25, that of the white pine showed a very marked increase and reached a figure considerably in excess of the maximum of the Scotch pine. This increase in the volume growth of white pine is particularly striking on the thinned area, where it amounted to 99 cubic feet as compared to 30 cubic feet on the control.

Additional data as to the white pine thinning are given in the table below.

TABLE XVI

Plot	No. of trees that died during period		No. of trees cut			Volume cut, cu. ft.			Average D.B.H. of cut trees		
	1916–20	1920–25	1916	1920	1925	1916	1920	1925	1916	1920	1925
Thinned	539	0	593	1363	779	105	362	510	1.7	2.1	2.9
Control	528	821	...	....	...	...	...	...	...	...	...

According to these figures, 1349 trees had died on the control plot prior to 1925, and a total of 2495 trees had been removed from the thinned plot by cutting and death during the same period. The large number of trees that died on the thinned plot after the first thinning indicates that this thinning, as in the case of the Scotch pine, was far too light.

The effects of the thinnings in white pine upon the distance factors are given below.

TABLE XVII

Plot	Distance Factors			
	1916	1920	1925	1925 (after thinning)
Thinned . . .	18.5	15.9	14.2	15.8
Control . . .	19.1	15.9	14.2	14.2

The distance factors show that about all that the first two thinnings accomplished was to remove the excess density that the thinned plot had at the beginning. It has been thought advisable to maintain a higher density in the white pine than in the less tolerant Scotch pine to secure better cleaning. It should be noted that the factor for the control in white pine is only slightly less than for the control in Scotch pine and also that the difference between the factors of the two control plots has increased from 0.2 to 0.5.

In the white pine stand started with a spacing of $4\frac{1}{2} \times 4\frac{1}{2}$, thinning was not needed until 1920 at the age of seventeen years. The following tables give the outstanding facts in connection with the two thinnings made and furnish a basis for a comparison with the results in the 3×3 stand. The 3×3 stand has been thinned according to the Danish method and the $4\frac{1}{2} \times 4\frac{1}{2}$ stand according to Kraft, "Grade C."

TABLE XVIII

RESULTS OF THINNING IN WHITE PINE, SPACING $4\frac{1}{2} \times 4\frac{1}{2}$

Plot	Age years	No. trees per acre	Basal area per acre sq. ft.	Volume per acre cu. ft.	Current growth		Height in feet		Diameter in inches	
					Cu. ft.	Percentage	Average	Minimum	Average	Minimum
Thinned	17	1952	117.4	1500	136	11.9	21.3	6.0	3.3	0.3
Control	17	1924	120.3	1660	176	14.8	23.0	5.9	3.4	0.3
Thinned	22	1382	153.462	2724	270	14.7	31.7	14.0	4.5	1.0
Control	22	1517	162.314	2645	197	9.8	29.1	17.5	4.4	1.7

TABLE XIX

Plot	No. of trees that died during period	No. of trees cut		Volume cut, cu. ft.		Average D.B.H. of cut trees	
	1920–25	1920	1925	1920	1925	1920	1925
Thinned	19	551	396	127	314	2.0	3.2
Control	407						

TABLE XX

Plot	Distance Factors		
	1920	1925	1925 (after thinning)
Thinned . .	17.2	14.9	15.9
Control . .	16.8	14.6	14.6

The basal area growth on the control during the period following the first thinning was 42.014 square feet per acre; that on the thinned plot was 48.651 square feet. The figure for the control does not make any allowance for the loss in basal area resulting from the death of part of the trees. Growth on the control during the period of 1920–25 was slightly greater than on the control of the 3 × 3 stand, but on the thinned plot it was considerably less than in the thinned portion of the 3 × 3 stand.

Growing conditions on the two plots of the $4\frac{1}{2} \times 4\frac{1}{2}$ stand are very similar, as evidenced by the close correspondence in number of trees and basal areas per acre at the beginning of the experiment.

In spite of the great difference in the initial densities of the 3 × 3 and $4\frac{1}{2} \times 4\frac{1}{2}$ stands and between the methods of thinning employed, the relative densities after the 1925 thinning are practically identical.

More than twice as many trees have been removed from the thinned plot in the stand with $4\frac{1}{2}$-foot spacing as have died on the control, but the difference between the distance factors of the two plots just prior to the 1925 thinning remains practically the same.

A number of advantages have been derived from these early thinnings in pine. First, an increase in the average diameter of the trees on the thinned plots over that of the controls. Second, the early removal of badly formed trees. Third, a reduction in fire hazard, due to the removal of trees that would have died otherwise. Fourth, the saving of material in the 1925 thinning, of which the bulk was large enough to be merchantable for pulpwood and firewood. The amount of saved material in Scotch pine amounted to three and one-half standard cords, in the 3 × 3 white pine to five cords, and in the $4\frac{1}{2} \times 4\frac{1}{2}$ white pine to three cords.

Since the value of the results of thinning in white elm have been largely nullified by the generally decadent condition of the stand, the experiment in sugar maple is the only one in a broad-leaved species that can be used for comparison with those in the pine stands.

TABLE XXI

Results of Thinning in Sugar Maple, Spacing 3 × 3

Plot	Age years	No. trees per acre	Basal area per acre sq. ft.	Current growth in basal area		Height in feet		Diameter in inches	
				sq. ft.	Percentage	Average	Minimum	Average	Minimum
Thinned	16	2577	40.223			19.1	6.0	1.7	0.3
Control	16	2896	41.65			17.5	5.0	1.6	0.1
Thinned	21	1564	55.552	4.256	10.0	27.3	6.6	2.5	0.7
Control	21	2584	62.506	4.171	8.4	23.2	5.0	2.1	0.3

Volumes can not be computed for sugar maple at present, because of lack of form factors.

Data on the number of trees that have died and have been cut and the changes in distance factors are given below:

TABLE XXII

Plot	No. of trees that died during period	No. of trees cut		Average D.B.H. of cut trees	
	1921–26	1921	1926	1921	1926
Thinned . .	0	1013	619	1.0	2.0
Control. . .	312				

Plot	Distance Factors		
	1921	1926	1926 (after thinning)
Thinned	28.9	25.3	29.1
Control	29.1	23.4	23.4

Although over a thousand trees were cut in the first thinning, and only three hundred trees died on the control, there was a sharp decrease in the distance factor of the thinned plot at the end of five years. That the thinning had an appreciable effect is shown by the fact that the decrease on the thinned plot was only 63 per cent of that on the control. The distance factors and basal areas indicate that the relative densities of the two plots were not materially different at the beginning of the experiment. The most striking thing about the distance factors is that they are so much larger than for the pine stands at practically the same ages. The pine stands were one year older than the maple at the time measurements were taken. The maple plots, however, are not too open to permit of good cleaning.

As a further illustration of the difference between conifers and hardwoods in the matter of space requirements, the distance factors for a fully stocked stand of red oak, started with a spacing of 5 × 5, are cited as follows: at 12 years, 74.7; at 17 years, 37.7. The factor at 12 years was large, because the stand had not yet closed thoroughly. At 17 years the stand was completely closed, yet the distance factor is decidedly larger than for sugar maple at 16 years. This difference in factors is at least a general indication of the relative amounts of growing space needed by intolerant and tolerant hardwoods.

Since none of the trees cut was merchantable, the entire trees, after being lopped, have been left under the thinned stands.

The current growth in basal area of the maple following the first thinning was less than half of that of the white pine stands.

An adjoining stand of sugar maple, started with a spacing of 4 × 4, has been thinned at the same time as the 3 × 3. The results of these thinnings are given in Table XXIII.

TABLE XXIII

Results of Thinning in Sugar Maple, Spacing 4 × 4

Plot	Age years	No. trees per acre	Basal area per acre sq. ft.	Current growth in basal area		Height in feet		Diameter in inches	
				Sq. ft.	Percentage	Average	Minimum	Average	Minimum
Thinned	16	1455	29.40			18.4	6.1	1.9	0.2
Control	16	1678	37.43			18.8	7.2	2.0	0.4
Thinned	21	1122	47.126	4.113	12.1	26.7	9.3	2.8	0.5
Control	21	1678	59.514	4.417	9.7	25.0	10.1	2.5	0.6

One fail spot in the original planting fell within the boundaries of the thinned plot, and this was largely the cause of the smaller number of trees and smaller basal area on that plot at the beginning of the experiment. In general, the growth of the two plots in this stand is similar to that in the 3 × 3 stand, but the total basal areas are slightly lower, the average diameters are higher in all cases, the current growth of the control in square feet and the current growth in per cent is greater on both plots.

The additional data are given in the following tables.

TABLE XXIV

Plot	No. of trees that died during period	No. of trees cut		Average D.B.H. of cut trees		Distance factors		
		1921	1926	1921	1926	1921	1926	1926 (after thinning)
Thinned	0	333	358	1.2	2.0	34.6	26.7	30.2
Control	0					30.5	24.5	24.5

The smaller numbers of trees cut in the two thinnings as compared to those in the 3 × 3 stand show the saving in labor in making early thinnings in the stand with wider spacing. This is especially important, since the cut trees are unmerchantable.

The distance factors in all cases are larger than those for the corresponding years in the 3 × 3 stand. The factors for the two plots in 1921 show again the difference in density of the two plots

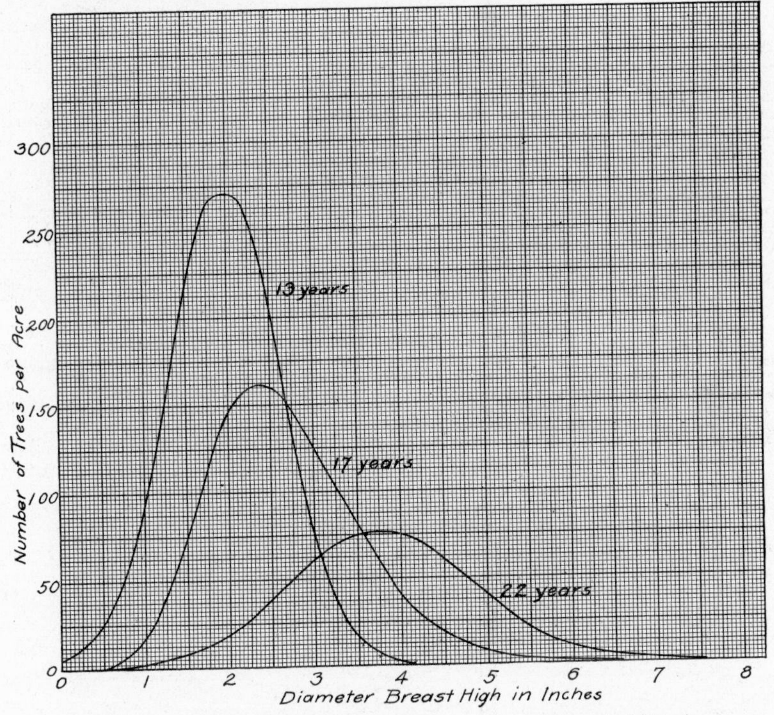

Fig. 27. Distribution curves for diameter of unthinned white pine

that existed at the start of the experiment. In spite of the first thinning, the distance factors of the two plots in 1926 were closer together than at the beginning.

All distance factors for all plots have been computed, except where stated otherwise, for the stands at the time just prior to each thinning.

The differences between thinned and unthinned stands as regards the distribution of the trees among the various diameter classes in each case at different periods can be shown by constructing "distribution curves." As an illustration, such distribution curves for white pine are given in Figures 27 and 28. These curves are based upon the mean standard deviations and skewnesses of the diameter class distributions at the ages indicated.

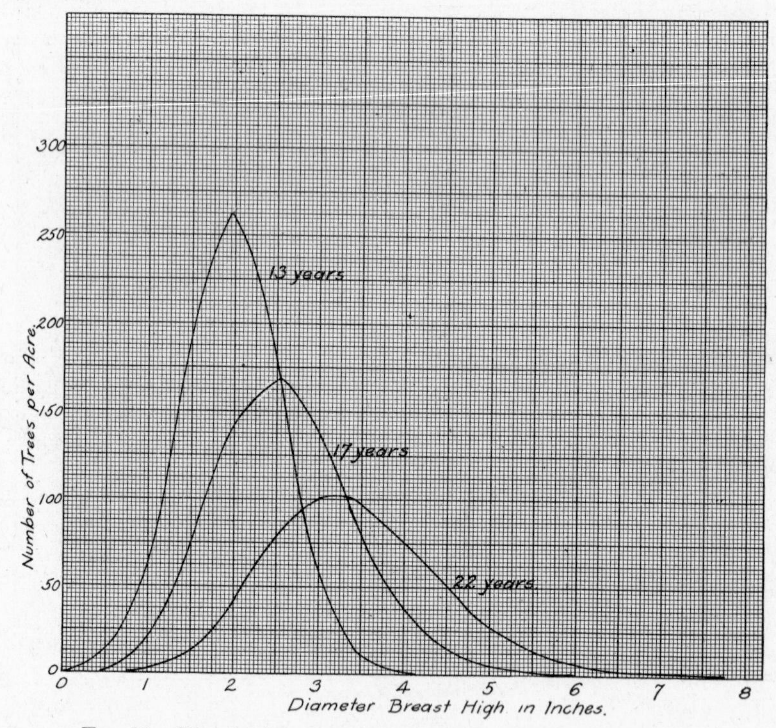

FIG. 28. Distribution curves for diameter of thinned white pine

The peak of each curve corresponds closely to the average diameter of the stand at that age. A comparison of the number of trees in the two stands above or below any given diameter limit at the different periods can be made by comparing the areas included between each curve and the ordinates corresponding to the diameters selected. For example, such a comparison of areas shows that the thinned stand at an age of 22 years has a larger number of trees above four inches in diameter than the unthinned, but when all trees above three inches are taken, the unthinned stand has a larger number than the thinned. It is also interesting to note that the skewness of the curves for the unthinned stand increases with age much more than in those for the thinned stand. The curves show the difference in average diameter between the stands and the greater rapidity with which the number of trees decreases in the thinned stand.

V. SOURCES OF DAMAGE

The list of sources of damage is rather long, including mice, rabbits, red squirrels, insects, wind, frost, winter-killing, ice, hail, fire, and canker. The groups of insects present are defoliators, borers, scales, aphids, and root-eating grubs.

On the basis of aggregate damage, mice have been the most destructive. Wherever a heavy sod formed during the early years after planting, the areas became densely populated with field mice that fed on the bark of the young trees during the winter and early spring. Many of the young trees were girdled and died. Other trees were only partially girdled, which gave decay-producing fungi a chance to become established in some of them. Where young hardwood trees were girdled as much as two or three years after planting, clumps of sprouts resulted, which necessitated early thinnings to secure the development of one good tree in a place. Most of the damage has occurred during the first five to eight years of a plantation's life. The species that have suffered most severely from mice are Douglas fir, yellow poplar, hickory, basswood, red oak, white oak, chestnut, sugar maple, white cedar, and Norway spruce. Those that have been injured only slightly are catalpa, Russian mulberry, western yellow pine, black walnut, osage orange, and white ash. White pine, white elm, black locust, and cottonwood have been free from this form of injury.

The bulk of the area has been poisoned twice with wheat coated with a mixture of strychnine, saccharin, and tallow and with the grain so placed that it was impossible for birds to get it. Poisoning proved to be very effective in reducing the number of mice for a period of several years. If the area had been thoroughly poisoned before planting or soon after planting, mice would have been eliminated as a source of injury.

During the first few years unrestricted hunting was permitted and damage from rabbits was negligible. Later it was necessary to prohibit hunting, and within two years the rabbits had increased to a point where they were decidedly destructive to the younger stands. The older stands were not touched. Then a system of regulated hunting was adopted, which reduced the damage considerably but was not used intensively enough to remove it entirely. Damage by rabbits has been heavy in red oak, Scotch pine, Norway spruce, and black locust. Other species would probably have suffered to an equal extent, if the stands of those species had not passed the susceptible age by the time the rabbits became numerous.

Two forms of injury occur from rabbits. Larger trees are either partially or completely girdled, and small ones usually have their tops bitten off.

That rabbits have certain food-preferences, just as mice do, was demonstrated during the winter of 1927–28 in a mixed planting of Scotch and Japanese red pines. The rabbits chewed off the tops of most of the Scotch pine, but left the Japanese red absolutely untouched.

Damage from red squirrels has never been appreciable until the past winter. In this instance, the squirrels cut a great many terminal shoots from Norway spruce and western yellow pine. In the spruce the terminal of the stem seemed to be preferred, whereas in the pine practically all the cutting was on branches. No easy method of control has been developed. At present, shooting seems to be the most effective but is slow, tedious work.

Among the insects, the locust borer (*Cyllene robiniae*) has been one of the most destructive. When young, many of the trees were so weakened near the ground that they were broken off completely by the wind. Later breakage has been confined mostly to branches, though a small percentage of the trees have had their entire crowns broken off. The quality of the wood of all the surviving trees has been seriously lowered by the burrows of the larvae, so that it is useful for nothing better than posts. There is no method of control that is feasible in the forest, unless it is found that growing locust in mixture with other species will secure at least partial immunity.

The oyster-shell scale (*Lepidosaphes ulmi*) developed to such a point in pure stands of white ash that it killed a large number and was spreading to adjoining stands of black walnut and sugar maple. In order to prevent its further spread to other species, the white ash was all cut and burned. Since the removal of the ash, there has been no appreciable spread on the other species. This scale has also contributed to the death of aspen and Balm of Gilead. The only method of control seems to be to avoid the planting of very susceptible species.

Small infestations of the white pine sawfly (*Neodiprion sp.*) have occurred at intervals for about ten years. As soon as detected, the infested trees have been sprayed with a solution of lead arsenate. This is feasible only while the trees are small. No attacks of this insect have been detected during the past three years.

Three small groups of European larch have been heavily attacked by the larch sawfly every year. These trees are sprayed with lead arsenate as soon as the larvae appear, and damage is prevented.

From 1919 to 1921, there was a rather heavy infestation of a woolly aphid (*Eriosoma sp.*) on the bark of white pine. No appreciable damage was done, and the aphid was apparently reduced in numbers by the action of its natural enemies.

Within the last four years a large percentage of the trees in Norway spruce stands has become infested with the spruce cone-gall (*Adelges abietis*). No pronounced damage has resulted, though there is undoubtedly some lowering of the general vigor of the trees that are heavily attacked. No practicable method of control for this insect has been developed.

Most of the broad-leaved species have suffered moderate amounts of damage from various kinds of defoliating insects nearly every year. In only a few has such defoliation been pronounced enough to be serious. In 1921 an unidentified insect completely stripped the tops of a considerable number of black locusts, and these tops died as a result. The foliage of basswood has been badly riddled by defoliators toward the end of the summer for the past thirteen years. During 1917 and 1918 box elder suffered heavy defoliation. This was not especially serious in portions of the stands where the trees were vigorous, but where trees were already low in vitality, many of them died after the defoliation. An infestation of unusual severity on white elm started in 1917, became very heavy in 1918, and decreased during 1919 to practically normal. No other cases of extreme defoliation have occurred. As the development of the plantations has progressed, the number of birds on the area has increased greatly. It is more than probable that the birds have been an important factor in keeping certain types of insects under control.

Two types of borers (*Prionoxystus robiniae* and a cerambycid beetle) have attacked a large percentage of the red oaks. In addition to lowering the quality of the wood of such trees, the burrows of these insects have been so concentrated in some trees that the tops have been broken off by the wind, just as in the case of black locust. Woodpeckers get some of the larvae, but not soon enough to prevent considerable damage.

It has just been discovered this spring that a number of aspen in the swamp have been killed by the bronze birch borer (*Agrilus anxius*).

The only notable loss in plantations from the larvae of the June bug (*Lachnosterna sp.*) occurred in a freshly planted area of Norway pine in 1919. Fully one third of the trees were killed during the first summer by having their roots eaten off just below the ground level. No subsequent attack of such severity has occurred.

Only one disease has proved at all destructive. This is a poplar canker on aspen and Balm of Gilead. A good many tops of these trees have been killed. Since these trees are also heavily infested with oyster-shell scale, the canker can be considered as only a contributing factor in their death.

Ice storms of varying severity are rather frequent throughout southern Michigan. The heaviest one that has occurred during the life of these experiments was in 1922. Fortunately, it was accompanied by very little wind. Otherwise, the damage would have been enormous. As it was, the only serious injury was to Scotch and Austrian pines. In stands of these species many of the trees on the open sides, and consequently having heavy crowns, had the entire crown broken out. Trees in the interior of the stands were merely bent over and subsequently recovered. Trees of several other species were badly bent by the burden of ice, but were not permanently deformed.

Many terminals of white pine in one exposed stand have been deformed and broken on three different occasions by ice storms of considerably less severity than that of 1922, but which were accompanied by heavy wind.

Hail storms, occurring in June just when the new shoots were in a tender condition, have twice broken many terminals from white pine, Norway spruce, Douglas fir, and western yellow pine.

Late frosts, generally about May 15, have occurred at intervals of about six years with enough severity to kill the new shoots on Douglas fir, Norway spruce, Russian mulberry, black locust, red oak, white oak, and black walnut. The trees have always recovered, however, with no permanent evidence of injury.

Moderate winterkilling of the ends of terminal shoots has occurred rather frequently on catalpa, osage orange, Russian mulberry, black walnut, and chestnut. During the winter of 1917–18 an entire stand of catalpa, fourteen years old, was killed back to the ground.

Fire has been of no importance as a source of damage. Five fires have started on the area, of which three were in plantations and two on open grass land. None of those in plantations burned as much as a square rod before suppression, and most of the trees were old enough to escape damage. The area is kept patrolled during dry weather and posters are maintained to warn the public of the danger of starting fires. The building of camp fires is not permitted, except under supervision of a representative of the School.

In November, 1919, a period of heavy rainfall, which softened the ground, was followed by a severe wind. This wind tipped a large number of Scotch and Austrian pines through an angle of 15 to 20 degrees. Later growth of these trees has developed a wide sweep in the boles and injured their quality as potential logs. All damage was limited to trees on the windward edge of the stands.

VI. MISCELLANEOUS

In 1915 three species of pine, white, Scotch, and western yellow, were planted in a stand of Norway spruce on areas where the spruce had made very poor growth. This was done to test the differences between the four species in their reaction to soil conditions that had proved distinctly unfavorable to one of them. A preliminary report of the results of this experiment has been published (3).

This report was based upon measurements made in March, 1919. At that time, after four growing seasons for the pine and fifteen for the spruce, the total heights for the four species were as follows:

TABLE XXV

Species	Total Height in Feet		
	Maximum	Minimum	Average
Norway spruce	7.0	0.9	2.9
White pine	3.1	0.4	1.3
Scotch pine	5.1	2.2	3.8
Western yellow pine	2.0	0.5	1.1

At the close of the growing season in 1925, after eleven seasons for the pines and twenty-two for the spruce, the total heights were as in Table XXVI on page 587.

TABLE XXVI

Species	Total Height in Feet		
	Maximum	Minimum	Average
Norway spruce	20.6	1.2	8.2
White pine	14.2	1.0	7.8
Scotch pine	21.3	13.3	17.5
Western yellow pine . .	11.6	2.9	7.6

Upon the basis of average height, the ranking of the species was the same in 1925 as it was in 1919. In 1925, however, with just half as much growing time following planting, the average height of Scotch pine was more than twice that of spruce, and the average heights of white and western yellow pine were nearly equal to that of spruce, instead of being less than half the spruce average, as they were in 1919. It is notable that the minimum height of Scotch pine is far ahead of the average height of spruce.

Because of differences in the age of planting stock used, it is better to compare the species by calculating the mean annual growth of each one from the time of germination of the seed. These figures are given below for 1919 and 1925:

TABLE XXVII

Species	Mean Annual Height Growth in Feet	
	1919	1925
Norway spruce	0.17	0.34
White pine	0.16	0.52
Western yellow pine . .	0.18	0.58
Scotch pine	0.54	1.25

The species still occupied the same relative positions on the basis of rate of growth in 1925 that they did in 1919, but there was a most decided increase in the rate for all species. This has been a surprise in the case of spruce, since it appeared in 1919 that exactly the opposite would occur. It seems evident that a steady improvement in soil conditions has taken place as a result of the formation of a protective cover with a decrease in surface erosion and an increase in organic matter content. Merely a casual inspection of the areas from time to time during the past few years would have shown that the spruce was recovering from its period of stunted growth. In the case of the pines, the increase was normally to be expected, since no stunting was involved.

Calculation of the mean annual height growth for the period 1919–25 reveals the recovery of the spruce even more clearly. During that period the rate in feet was 0.76 for Norway spruce, 0.93 for both white and western yellow pine, and 1.96 for Scotch pine. If any of the pines, and particularly Scotch pine, had been planted on these areas at the outset, much more satisfactory growth would have been obtained.

Wherever stands of other species adjoin stands or strips of black locust, there has been a marked stimulation of growth of the other species throughout a considerable zone. Such stimulation has been observed in Norway spruce, white elm, white ash, white oak, Russian mulberry, and box elder. The stimulation was most pronounced in box elder, because of the marked contrast between the trees influenced by the locust and those outside the zone of influence. The effect was shown not only by greater height and diameter growth, but just as strikingly by depth and richness of color.

In 1925, at the age of twenty years, the height and diameter of the box elder were measured and tallied by rows, beginning with the row next to the locust and extending to a point that was manifestly beyond the zone of influence of the locust. The average height and diameter of the trees in each row and the distance of each row from the locust are given in the table on page 589.

TABLE XXVIII

	Number of Row									
	1	2	3	4	5	6	7	8	9	10
Average height in feet......	31.3	31.1	30.0	26.9	23.4	21.3	23.6	19.6	19.7	16.7
Average diameter in inches..	4.8	4.0	3.7	2.8	2.6	2.3	2.5	2.1	2.0	1.5
Distance from locust in feet.	5.6	9.8	14.0	17.0	21.5	26.0	29.5	34.5	39.0	43.5

	Number of Row									
	11	12	13	14	15	16	17	18	19	20
Average height in feet......	16.2	15.9	14.9	14.8	15.2	13.9	13.7	12.8	13.7	13.7
Average diameter in inches..	1.8	1.6	1.7	1.6	1.7	1.4	1.5	1.3	1.4	1.5
Distance from locust in feet.	47.5	51.0	56.0	60.0	64.0	68.0	72.0	76.0	80.0	85.0

If the average heights are plotted as in Figure 29 (p. 590), an irregular curve is obtained, which shows more vividly the steady decline in growth of the box elder as the distance from the locust increased, until growth finally reached a level between 12 and 13 feet. Further inspection of the curve shows that the maximum effect of the locust was produced to a distance of only 13½ feet. From that point on the decrease in effect was rapid to a distance of 43½ feet, except for the seventh row, where other factors were evidently present to counteract the lack of stimulation from locust-produced nitrogen. The line of demarcation between the rich green of the trees near the locust and the light yellowish green of those farther away was at a distance of about 35 feet from the locust. It may be that the growth of a few rows of box elder beyond the direct influence of the locust was aided by the abundant leaf litter and shade produced by the larger box elders adjacent to them.

In order to make a definite test of the stimulating effect of black locust, an experiment with black walnut was initiated. The stand of black walnut selected was twelve years old and showed an average height of 5.1 feet. The current annual height growth of most of the trees was about three inches or less, and the diameter of the terminal shoots of such trees was less than one fourth of an inch. Many of the trees were gradually dying. In one half of this stand black locust seedlings were planted between the

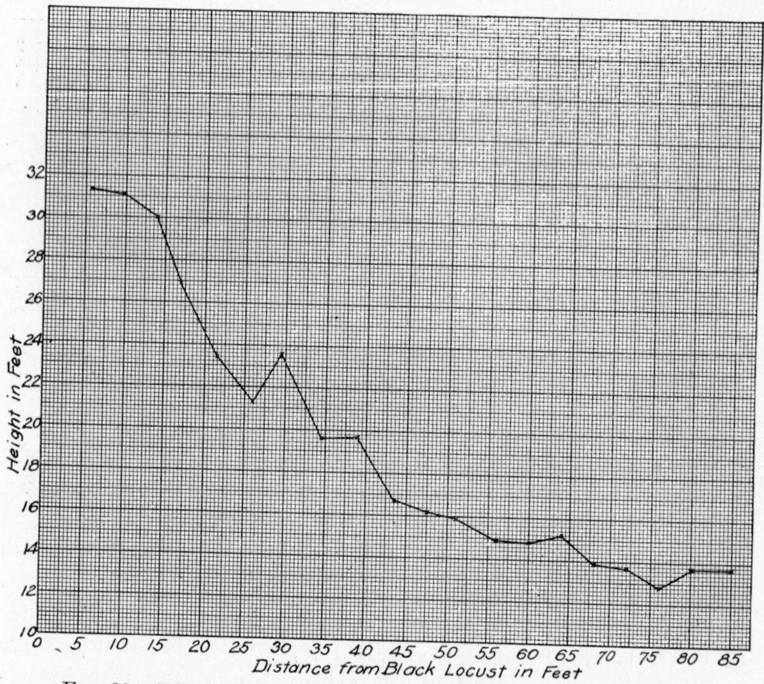

FIG. 29. Effect of black locust upon height growth of box elder

rows of walnut in the spring of 1918. During the following winter most of the locust was killed by rabbits. The locust was replanted in 1919 and again killed by rabbits. The third planting of locust in 1920 was more successful, though a complete catch was not secured. The other half of the walnut stand was left without locust as a control.

In 1924 a sudden increase in the growth of walnuts that were in close proximity to locust was observed. Measurements were made at the close of the growing season of the current height growth for 1924 and of the total height of the trees at the beginning of 1924. The latter figure represented the growth made in 17 years. These measurements were made on both plots. Measurements of the current height growth in 1925 were also made. When these measurements were taken, it was found that the terminal shoots of the year before had been winterkilled from the tips downward for a distance equal to about one half of the previous season's growth. Calculation of averages from the measurements gave the following results:

TABLE XXIX

Plot	Average current height growth in feet		Total average height prior to 1924 in feet	Mean annual height growth prior to 1924 in feet
	1924	1925		
With locust.....	1.20	0.70	5.20	0.30
Without locust...	0.35	0.28	4.80	0.28

These figures show that prior to 1924 there was no marked difference in the mean annual height growth of trees on the two plots. But in 1924 the current growth on the locust plot was over three times that of the control and in 1925 considerably over twice as great. Because of the fact that the locust plot was not uniformly stocked with locust, the averages for that plot are not so large as they would otherwise have been. The growth made by some of the individuals on this plot brings out the effect of the locust still more strikingly. A few instances of these individuals follow on page 592.

TABLE XXX

Total height prior to 1924	Current height growth	
	1924	1925
6.0	4.2	0.9
4.2	2.5	1.3
4.3	3.5	1.3
6.5	2.0	1.5

It will be noted that there was a sharp decrease in the growth of all of them in 1925. This was not true of all the trees, since many of them showed more growth in 1925 than in 1924, though they were usually trees that had made a more moderate growth in 1924 than those cited above. Some trees added more height in the two years, 1924 and 1925, than they had made during the preceding seventeen years. No trees on the control plot showed any marked increase during those years over the growth that had occurred in previous years. In addition to the marked increase in height growth, the diameter of the current terminal shoots more than doubled. Another indication of increased vigor was a heavy coating of hairs, so characteristic of young, healthy walnut shoots, that occurred on the growth of 1924 and 1925, whereas the shoots of previous years had been practically smooth. Since the severe winterkilling of the 1924 shoots, due to over-succulence, this form of injury has been much more moderate and was practically negligible during the winter of 1927–28. It is still too early to judge of the ultimate results, but the indications are that black locust may be used to advantage in some cases at least to correct a nitrogen deficiency in soils.

That the locust has not been affected by any toxic action of the walnut, as noted by many observers in relation to other species, is also important. On the contrary, the locust has grown so rapidly that it has been necessary to cut it back severely to prevent undue interference with the crowns of the walnut.

VII. CONCLUSIONS

If seedling stock of coniferous species is used on heavy soils, a better catch is secured when planting is preceded by thorough cultivation. When the grub hoe method is employed without previous cultivation, transplant stock gives better results than seedlings.

In the case of nut-bearing species, direct seeding is better than planting and costs less.

Under conditions similar to those on the Saginaw Forest, spacings closer than 6 × 6 are not justified.

In general the coniferous species have surpassed the broad-leaved species in growth in height, diameter, and volume.

It is a waste of money and land to plant catalpa, osage orange, Russian mulberry, box elder, chestnut, and black walnut on lands of poor to medium quality under climatic conditions as they exist here.

While a number of exotic species have made satisfactory growth thus far, it is by no means certain that they will continue to do so. Figures obtained here should not be used as a basis for prophecy.

Pure stands of white elm, white ash, and basswood have not been satisfactory. Mixture with a more tolerant species would probably have led to better results on the particular sites planted with these species.

Thinnings have resulted in most cases in an increase in volume growth and in average diameter of stand, resulting in earlier merchantability. The bulk of the material cut in thinnings of twenty-two-year-old pine stands has been large enough for use. That cut from stands below twenty years has been mostly too small.

No rodent-infested areas should be planted with susceptible species until after rodents are practically eliminated.

Frequent inspections should be made to locate incipient attacks of dangerous insects and diseases.

The greatest possible care should be used in selecting the

species for planting a given site, if costly mistakes are to be avoided.

Black locust produces a decidedly beneficial effect upon the growth of adjacent trees of other species on soils that are deficient in nitrogen.

UNIVERSITY OF MICHIGAN

LITERATURE CITED

KRAFT, GUSTAV. 1885. Beiträge zur forstlichen Zuwachsrechnung und zur Lehre vom Weiserprocente, p. 176. Hannover.

SIMS, I. H., AND BARRETT, L. I. 1928. A Study of Form Factors in Western Yellow Pine Plantations. Papers Mich. Acad. Sci., Arts and Letters, 9:531–539.

YOUNG, L. J. 1919. A Study of the Difference in Soil Requirements of Pine and Spruce. Report Mich. Acad. Sci., 21:219–221.

PLATE XCVI

Fig. 1

Fig. 2

Fig. 3

THE EARLY GROWTH OF A SCOTCH PINE PLANTATION

Fig. 1. At the age of eleven and before thinning
Fig. 2. At the age of sixteen after one thinning
Fig. 3. At the age of twenty-one after two thinnings

PLATE XCVII

Fig. 1

Fig. 2

Fig. 3

THREE STAGES IN THE DEVELOPMENT OF A WHITE PINE PLANTATION

Fig. 1. At the age of eleven
Fig. 2. At the age of sixteen
Fig. 3. At the age of twenty-one

PLATE XCVIII

Fig. 1

Fig. 2

Fig. 3

THE EARLY GROWTH OF A RED OAK PLANTATION

Fig. 1. At the age of eight

Fig. 2. At the age of thirteen

Fig. 3. At the age of eighteen

PLATE XCIX

Fig. 1

Fig. 2

Fig. 3

SOME EXAMPLES OF GOOD AND POOR GROWTH OF PLANTATIONS

Fig. 1. Poor growth and form of Russian mulberry at age of nineteen

Fig. 2. Good growth of western yellow pine at age of seventeen

Fig. 3. Norway pine at age of four in foreground; sugar maple at age of nineteen in background

INDEX OF AUTHORS AND SUBJECTS

UNIVERSITY OF MICHIGAN STUDIES

HUMANISTIC SERIES

General Editors: JOHN G. WINTER AND EUGENE S. McCARTNEY

Size, 22.7 × 15.2 cm. 8°. Bound in Cloth.

VOL. I. ROMAN HISTORICAL SOURCES AND INSTITUTIONS. Edited by Henry A. Sanders, University of Michigan. Pp. vii + 402. (*Out of print.*)

VOL. II. WORD FORMATION IN PROVENÇAL. By Edward L. Adams, University of Michigan. Pp. xvii + 607. $4.00. Postage extra.

VOL. III. LATIN PHILOLOGY. Edited by Clarence Linton Meader, University of Michigan. Pp. vii + 290. (*Out of print.*)

Parts Sold Separately in Paper Covers:

Part I. THE USE OF IDEM, IPSE, AND WORDS OF RELATED MEANING. By Clarence L. Meader. Pp. 1–112. $0.75.

Part II. A STUDY IN LATIN ABSTRACT SUBSTANTIVES. By Manson A. Stewart. Pp. 113–178. $0.40.

Part III. THE USE OF THE ADJECTIVE AS A SUBSTANTIVE IN THE DE RERUM NATURA OF LUCRETIUS. By Frederick T. Swan. Pp. 179–214. $0.40.

Part IV. AUTOBIOGRAPHIC ELEMENTS IN LATIN INSCRIPTIONS. By Henry H. Armstrong. Pp. 215–286. $0.40.

VOL. IV. ROMAN HISTORY AND MYTHOLOGY. Edited by Henry A. Sanders. Pp. viii + 427. (*Out of print.*)

Parts Sold Separately in Paper Covers:

Part I. STUDIES IN THE LIFE OF HELIOGABALUS. By Orma Fitch Butler, University of Michigan. Pp. 1–169. $1.25 net.

Part II. THE MYTH OF HERCULES AT ROME. By John G. Winter, University of Michigan. Pp. 171–273. $0.50 net.

Part III. ROMAN LAW STUDIES IN LIVY. By Alvin E. Evans. Pp. 275–354. $0.40 net.

Part IV. REMINISCENCES OF ENNIUS IN SILIUS ITALICUS. By Loura B. Woodruff. Pp. 355–424. $0.40 net.

VOL. V. SOURCES OF THE SYNOPTIC GOSPELS. By Rev. Dr. Carl S. Patton, First Congregational Church, Los Angeles, California. Pp. xiii + 263. $1.30. Postage extra.

Size, 28 × 18.5 cm. 4to.

VOL. VI. ATHENIAN LEKYTHOI WITH OUTLINE DRAWING IN GLAZE VARNISH ON A WHITE GROUND. By Arthur Fairbanks, Director of the Museum of Fine Arts, Boston. With 15 plates, and 57 illustrations in the text. Pp. viii + 371. $4.00. Postage extra.

Orders should be addressed to The Librarian, University of Michigan, Ann Arbor, Michigan. Postage extra.

VOL. VII. ATHENIAN LEKYTHOI WITH OUTLINE DRAWING IN MATT COLOR ON A WHITE GROUND, AND AN APPENDIX: ADDITIONAL LEKYTHOI WITH OUTLINE DRAWING IN GLAZE VARNISH ON A WHITE GROUND. By Arthur Fairbanks. With 41 plates. Pp. x + 275. $3.50. Postage extra.

VOL. VIII. THE OLD TESTAMENT MANUSCRIPTS IN THE FREER COLLECTION. By Henry A. Sanders, University of Michigan. With 9 plates showing pages of the Manuscripts in facsimile. Pp. viii + 357. $3.50. Postage extra.

Parts Sold Separately in Paper Covers:

Part I. THE WASHINGTON MANUSCRIPT OF DEUTERONOMY AND JOSHUA. With 3 folding plates. Pp. vi + 104. $1.25. Postage extra.

Part II. THE WASHINGTON MANUSCRIPT OF THE PSALMS. With 1 single plate and 5 folding plates. Pp. viii + 105–349. $2.00. Postage extra.

VOL. IX. THE NEW TESTAMENT MANUSCRIPTS IN THE FREER COLLECTION. By Henry A. Sanders, University of Michigan. With 8 plates showing pages of the Manuscripts in facsimile. Pp. x + 323. $3.50. Postage extra.

Parts Sold Separately in Paper Covers:

Part I. THE WASHINGTON MANUSCRIPT OF THE FOUR GOSPELS. With 5 plates. Pp. vii + 247. $2.00. Postage extra.

Part II. THE WASHINGTON MANUSCRIPT OF THE EPISTLES OF PAUL. With 3 plates. Pp. ix + 251–315. $1.25. Postage extra.

VOL. X. THE COPTIC MANUSCRIPTS IN THE FREER COLLECTION. By William H. Worrell, Hartford Seminary Foundation. With 12 plates. Pp. xxvi+ 396. $4.75. Postage extra.

Parts Sold Separately in Paper Covers:

Part I. THE COPTIC PSALTER. The Coptic text in the Sahidic Dialect, with an Introduction, and with 6 plates showing pages of the Manuscript and Fragments in facsimile. Pp. xxvi + 112. $2.00. Postage extra.

Part II. A HOMILY ON THE ARCHANGEL GABRIEL BY CELESTINUS, BISHOP OF ROME, AND A HOMILY ON THE VIRGIN BY THEOPHILUS, ARCHBISHOP OF ALEXANDRIA, FROM MANUSCRIPT FRAGMENTS IN THE FREER COLLECTION AND THE BRITISH MUSEUM. The Coptic Text with an Introduction and Translation, and with 6 plates showing pages of the Manuscripts in facsimile. Pp. 113–396. $2.50. Postage extra.

VOL. XI. CONTRIBUTIONS TO THE HISTORY OF SCIENCE.

Part I. ROBERT OF CHESTER'S LATIN TRANSLATION OF THE ALGEBRA OF AL-KHOWARIZMI. With an Introduction, Critical Notes, and an English Version. By Louis C. Karpinski, University of Michigan. With 4 plates showing pages of manuscripts in facsimile, and 25 diagrams in the text. Pp. vii + 164. $2.00. Postage extra.

Part II. THE PRODROMUS OF NICOLAUS STENO'S LATIN DISSERTATION CONCERNING A SOLID BODY ENCLOSED BY PROCESS OF NATURE

Orders should be addressed to The Librarian, University of Michigan, Ann Arbor, Michigan. Postage extra.

WITHIN A SOLID. Translated into English by John G. Winter, University of Michigan, with a Foreword by Professor William H. Hobbs. With 7 plates. Pp. vii + 169–283. $1.30. Postage extra.

VOL. XII. STUDIES IN EAST CHRISTIAN AND ROMAN ART. By Charles R. Morey, Princeton University, and Walter Dennison. With 67 plates (10 colored) and 91 illustrations in the text. Pp. xiii + 175. $4.75. Postage extra.

Parts Sold Separately:

Part I. EAST CHRISTIAN PAINTINGS IN THE FREER COLLECTION. By Charles R. Morey. With 13 plates (10 colored) and 34 illustrations in the text. Pp. xiii + 86. Bound in cloth. $2.50. Postage extra.

Part II. A GOLD TREASURE OF THE LATE ROMAN PERIOD. By Walter Dennison. With 54 plates and 57 illustrations in the text. Pp. 89–175. Bound in cloth. $2.50. Postage extra.

VOL. XIII. FRAGMENTS FROM THE CAIRO GENIZAH IN THE FREER COLLECTION. By Richard Gottheil, Columbia University, and William H. Worrell, University of Michigan. Text, with Translation and an Introduction. With 52 plates showing the different styles of writing in facsimile. Pp. xxxi + 273. Bound in cloth. $4.00. Postage extra.

VOL. XIV. TWO STUDIES IN LATER ROMAN AND BYZANTINE ADMINISTRATION. By Arthur E. R. Boak and James E. Dunlap, University of Michigan. Pp. x + 324. Bound in cloth. $2.25. Postage extra.

Parts Sold Separately in Paper Covers:

Part I. THE MASTER OF THE OFFICES IN THE LATER ROMAN AND BYZANTINE EMPIRES. By Arthur E. R. Boak. Pp. x + 160. $1.00. Postage extra.

Part II. THE OFFICE OF THE GRAND CHAMBERLAIN IN THE LATER ROMAN AND BYZANTINE EMPIRES. By James E. Dunlap. Pp. 164–324. $1.00. Postage extra.

VOL. XV. GREEK THEMES IN MODERN MUSICAL SETTINGS. By Albert A. Stanley, University of Michigan. With 10 plates. Pp. xxii + 385. $4.00. Postage extra.

Parts Sold Separately in Paper Covers:

Part I. INCIDENTAL MUSIC TO PERCY MACKAYE'S DRAMA OF SAPPHO AND PHAON. Pp. 1–68. $0.90 net.

Part II. MUSIC TO THE ALCESTIS OF EURIPIDES WITH ENGLISH TEXT Pp. 71–120. $0.80 net.

Part III. MUSIC FOR THE IPHIGENIA AMONG THE TAURIANS BY EURIPIDES WITH GREEK TEXT. Pp. 123–214. $0.75 net.

Part IV. TWO FRAGMENTS OF ANCIENT GREEK MUSIC. Pp. 217–225. $0.30 net.

Part V. MUSIC TO CANTICA OF THE MENAECHMI OF PLAUTUS. Pp. 229–263. $0.60 net.

Part VI. ATTIS: A SYMPHONIC POEM. Pp. 265–384. $1.00 net.

VOL. XVI. NICOMACHUS OF GERASA: INTRODUCTION TO ARITHMETIC. Translated into English by Martin Luther D'Ooge, with Studies in

Greek Arithmetic by Frank Egleston Robbins and Louis C. Karpinski. Pp. vii + 318. $3.50. Postage extra.

VOLS. XVII, XVIII, XIX, XX. ROYAL CORRESPONDENCE OF THE ASSYRIAN EMPIRE. Translated into English, with a transliteration of the text and a Commentary. By Leroy Waterman, University of Michigan. (*In press.*)

VOL. XXI. THE MINOR PROPHETS IN THE FREER COLLECTION AND THE BERLIN FRAGMENT OF GENESIS. By Henry A. Sanders, University of Michigan, and Carl Schmidt, University of Berlin. With 7 plates. Pp. xiii + 436. $3.50. Postage extra.

VOL. XXII. A PAPYRUS CODEX OF THE SHEPHERD OF HERMAS. By Campbell Bonner, University of Michigan. (*In press.*)

VOL. XXIII. THE COMPLETE COMMENTARY OF OECUMENIUS ON THE APOCALYPSE: Now printed for the first time from Manuscripts at Messina, Rome, Salonika and Athos. By H. C. Hoskier. (*In press.*)

FACSIMILES OF MANUSCRIPTS

Size, 40.5 × 35 cm.

FACSIMILE OF THE WASHINGTON MANUSCRIPT OF DEUTERONOMY AND JOSHUA IN THE FREER COLLECTION. With an Introduction by Henry A. Sanders. Pp. x; 201 heliotype plates. The University of Michigan. Ann Arbor, Michigan, 1910.

Limited edition, distributed only to Libraries, under certain conditions. A list of Libraries containing this Facsimile is printed in *University of Michigan Studies, Humanistic Series*, Volume VIII, pp. 351–353.

Size, 34 × 26 cm.

FACSIMILE OF THE WASHINGTON MANUSCRIPT OF THE FOUR GOSPELS IN THE FREER COLLECTION. With an Introduction by Henry A. Sanders. Pp. x; 372 heliotype plates and 2 colored plates. The University of Michigan. Ann Arbor, Michigan, 1912.

Limited edition, distributed only to Libraries, under certain conditions. A list of Libraries containing this Facsimile is printed in *University of Michigan Studies, Humanistic Series*, Volume IX, pp. 317–320.

Size, 30.5 × 40.6 cm.

FACSIMILE OF THE WASHINGTON MANUSCRIPT OF THE MINOR PROPHETS IN THE FREER COLLECTION AND THE BERLIN FRAGMENT OF GENESIS, with an Introduction by Henry A. Sanders. With 130 plates. The University of Michigan. Ann Arbor, Michigan, 1927.

Limited edition, distributed only to Libraries, under certain conditions. A list of Libraries containing this Facsimile is printed in *University of Michigan Studies, Humanistic Series*, Volume XXI, pp. 431–434.

SCIENTIFIC SERIES

Size, 28 × 18.5 cm. 4°. Bound in Cloth.

VOL. I. THE CIRCULATION AND SLEEP. By John F. Shepard, University of Michigan. Pp. ix + 83, with an Atlas of 63 plates, bound separately Text and Atlas, $2.50. Postage extra.

Orders should be addressed to The Librarian, University of Michigan, Ann Arbor, Michigan. Postage extra.

VOL. II. STUDIES ON DIVERGENT SERIES AND SUMMABILITY. By Walter B. Ford, University of Michigan. Pp. xi + 194. $2.50. Postage extra.

Size, 16 × 23.6 cm.

VOL. III. THE GEOLOGY OF THE NETHERLANDS EAST INDIES. By H. A. Brouwer. With 18 plates and 17 text figures. Pp. xii + 160. $3.00. Postage extra.

VOL. IV. THE GLACIAL ANTICYCLONES: THE POLES OF THE ATMOSPHERIC CIRCULATION. By William Herbert Hobbs. With 3 plates and 53 figures. Pp. xxiv + 198. $2.75. Postage extra.

MEMOIRS OF THE UNIVERSITY OF MICHIGAN MUSEUMS

Size, 26 × 17 cm. 4°. Bound in Cloth.

VOL. I. THE WHIP SNAKES AND RACERS: GENERA MASTICOPHIS AND COLUBER. By A. I. Ortenburger, University of Oklahoma. With 36 plates and 64 text figures. Pp. xviii. + 247. $6.00. Postage extra.

UNIVERSITY OF MICHIGAN PUBLICATIONS

HUMANISTIC PAPERS

General Editor: EUGENE S. McCARTNEY

Size, 22.7 × 15.2 cm. 8°. Bound in Cloth.

THE LIFE AND WORK OF GEORGE SYLVESTER MORRIS. A CHAPTER IN THE HISTORY OF AMERICAN THOUGHT IN THE NINETEENTH CENTURY. By ROBERT M. WENLEY, University of Michigan. Pp. xv + 332. $1.50. Postage extra.

LATIN AND GREEK IN AMERICAN EDUCATION, WITH SYMPOSIA ON THE VALUE OF HUMANISTIC STUDIES, Revised Edition. Edited by FRANCIS W. KELSEY. Pp. xiii + 360. $2.00. Postage extra.

THE MENAECHMI OF PLAUTUS. The Latin Text, with a Translation by JOSEPH H. DRAKE, University of Michigan. Pp. xi + 130. Paper covers. $0.60. Postage extra.

LANGUAGE AND LITERATURE

VOL. I. STUDIES IN SHAKESPEARE, MILTON AND DONNE. By Members of the English Department of the University of Michigan. Pp. viii + 232. $2.50. Postage extra.

VOL. II. ELIZABETHAN PROVERB LORE IN LYLY'S 'EUPHUES' AND IN PETTIE'S 'PETITE PALLACE,' WITH PARALLELS FROM SHAKESPEARE. By Morris P. Tilley. Pp. x + 461. $3.50. Postage extra.

VOL. III. THE SOCIAL MODE OF RESTORATION COMEDY. By Kathleen M. Lynch. Pp. x + 242. $2.50. Postage extra.

VOL. IV. STUART POLITICS IN CHAPMAN'S 'TRAGEDY OF CHABOT.' By Norma D. Solve. Pp. x + 176. Cloth. $2.50. Postage extra.

VOL. V. EL LIBRO DEL CAUALLERO ZIFAR. By C. P. Wagner, University of Michigan. (*In press.*)

Orders should be addressed to The Librarian, University of Michigan, Ann Arbor, Michigan. Postage extra.

HISTORY AND POLITICAL SCIENCE

(*The first three volumes of this series were published as "Historical Studies," under the direction of the Department of History. Volumes IV and V were published without numbers.*)

VOL. I. A HISTORY OF THE PRESIDENT'S CABINET. By Mary Louise Hinsdale. Pp. ix + 355. Cloth. $2.00. Postage extra.

VOL. II. ENGLISH RULE IN GASCONY, 1199–1259, WITH SPECIAL REFERENCE TO THE TOWNS. By Frank Burr Marsh. Pp. xi + 178. Cloth. $1.25. Postage extra.

VOL. III. THE COLOR LINE IN OHIO: A HISTORY OF RACE PREJUDICE IN A TYPICAL NORTHERN STATE. By Frank Uriah Quillan. Pp. xvi + 178. Cloth. $1.50. Postage extra.

VOL. IV. THE SENATE AND TREATIES, 1789–1817. THE DEVELOPMENT OF THE TREATY-MAKING FUNCTIONS OF THE UNITED STATES SENATE DURING THEIR FORMATIVE PERIOD. By Ralston Hayden, University of Michigan. Pp. xvi + 237. Cloth. $1.50. Postage extra.

VOL. V. WILLIAM PLUMER'S MEMORANDUM OF PROCEEDINGS IN THE UNITED STATES SENATE, 1803–1807. Edited by Everett Somerville Brown, University of Michigan. Pp. xi + 673. Cloth. $3.50. Postage extra.

VOL. VI. THE GRAIN SUPPLY OF ENGLAND DURING THE NAPOLEONIC PERIOD. By W. F. Galpin, Syracuse University. Pp. xi + 305. Cloth. $3.00. Postage extra.

VOL. VII. EIGHTEENTH CENTURY DOCUMENTS RELATING TO THE ROYAL FORESTS, THE SHERIFFS AND SMUGGLING: SELECTED FROM THE SHELBURNE MANUSCRIPTS IN THE WILLIAM L. CLEMENTS LIBRARY. By Arthur Lyon Cross, University of Michigan. With 4 plates. Pp. xviii + 328. $3.00. Postage extra.

VOL. VIII. THE LOW COUNTRIES AND THE HUNDRED YEARS' WAR, 1326–1347. By Henry L. Lucas, University of Washington. (*In press.*)

CONTRIBUTIONS FROM THE MUSEUM OF PALEONTOLOGY

VOL. I. THE STRATIGRAPHY AND FAUNA OF THE HACKBERRY STAGE OF THE UPPER DEVONIAN. By Carroll Lane Fenton and Mildred Adams Fenton. With 45 plates, 9 text figures and 1 map. Pp. xi + 260. Cloth. $2.75. Postage extra.

VOL. II. Consisting of 14 miscellaneous papers, published between July 10, 1924, and August 3, 1927. With 41 plates, 39 text figures and 1 map. Pp. ix + 240. Cloth. $3.00. Postage extra.

Parts Sold Separately in Paper Covers:

No. 1. A Possible Explanation of Fenestration in the Primitive Reptilian Skull, with Notes on the Temporal Region of the Genus Dimetrodon, by E. C. Case. Pp. 1–12, with five illustrations. $0.30.

No. 2. Occurrence of the Collingwood Formation in Michigan, by R. Ruedemann and G. M. Ehlers. Pp. 13–18. $0.15.

No. 3. Silurian Cephalopods of Northern Michigan, by Aug. F. Foerste. Pp. 19–86, with 17 plates. $1.00.

No. 4. A Specimen of *Stylemys nebrascensis* Leidy, with the Skull Preserved, by E. C. Case. Pages 87–91, with 7 text figures. Price, $0.20.

Orders should be addressed to The Librarian, University of Michigan, Ann Arbor, Michigan. Postage extra.